The Riverside Literature Series

ESSAYS

BY

RALPH WALDO EMERSON

SELECTED AND EDITED

BY

MARY A. JORDAN, M. A.

Professor of English Language and Literature
Smith College

HOUGHTON, MIFFLIN AND COMPANY
Boston: 4 Park Street; New York: 85 Fifth Avenue
Chicago: 378-388 Wabash Avenue
The Riverside Press, Cambridge

CONTENTS

PREFACE

THE editor of a selection from Ralph Waldo Emerson's Essays has less difficulty in justifying his choice than in explaining his omissions. There is hardly a piece of Emerson's that is not somebody's favorite, and while there is a consensus of opinion about the main features of his teaching, there is great variety of judgment about the relative importance of its partial presentations.

Three considerations have governed the present editor: first, to make the study of the rest that Emerson has written seem delightfully a matter of course; second, to offer a timely reënforcement of the motives for noble living in school boys and girls; and third, to interest them in thinking rather than in thought.

Thanks are due to Dr. Edward W. Emerson for permission to use the notes in his invaluable Centenary Edition of his father's writings.

PREFACE

RALPH WALDO EMERSON

DOCTOR EDWARD GARNETT, in his *Life of Ralph Waldo Emerson*,[1] complains of the severity with which Emerson has dealt with his biographers in leading a life devoid of incident, of nearly untroubled happiness, and of absolute conformity to the moral law. Yet this life was a long one; its years were among the most ominous, crowded, and terrible, as well as hopefully significant, of the world's history. By comparison with the other figures in the struggling human procession of his time, his appears singularly noble; and the serene simplicity of its bearing under all circumstances becomes the beautiful problem of his life, in strong contrast with the eccentricity, deformity, or violence which engages attention without satisfying it.

Ralph Waldo Emerson was born in Boston, May 25, 1803, in the year of the Louisiana Purchase and "within a kite-string of the birthplace of Benjamin Franklin." Dr. O. W. Holmes, in his *Ralph Waldo Emerson*,[2] has called attention to the fact that he was born a descendant of one of the Academic Races of New England. His father, William Emerson, was minister of the First Church in Boston and one of a long line of ministers of varying ability and devotion to Puritan doctrine. His mother was Ruth Haskins of Boston, a woman of "peculiar softness and natural grace and quiet dignity." He was one of five sons. He was nephew to a remarkable woman, Mary Moody Emerson, whose early reading was Milton, Young, Aken-

[1] Walter Scott, London. [2] Houghton, Mifflin & Co.

side, Samuel Clarke, Jonathan Edwards, and always the Bible; later she conned Plato, Plotinus, Marcus Antoninus, Stewart, Coleridge, Herder, Locke, Madame de Staël, Channing, Mackintosh, Byron.

One of Emerson's critics characterizes these conditions and influences into which he was born and bred as being after all those of inexperience. What, then, were the aspects of the greater, more significant world from which these influences secluded him but which was to supply him with experience? In London on the same day as Emerson, Edward Bulwer Lytton was born. Only the year before, Napoleon Bonaparte had had himself elected Consul for life, and in that very year he had declined the offer of Fulton to supply steam to the French ships of war. By the time Emerson was a year old, Napoleon was hereditary Emperor of the French; Emerson was still in knickerbockers when Napoleon rejected, in 1809, Sömmering's invention of the electric telegraph as a " German notion," and when he successfully annexed Holland as the " alluvial deposit of French rivers." When Emerson was nine years old, Napoleon was at war with Russia over his claim to rule the continent of Europe, and we of the United States were at war with England in defence of our commerce. Six years after Emerson's birth, Charles Darwin and Abraham Lincoln were born. Emerson was a boy of twelve when Napoleon was defeated at Waterloo, Paris captured by the allies, and Lorraine, Alsace, and Strasbourg secured to France by the second treaty of Paris. In 1830 the first great railroad for passenger traffic was built between Liverpool and Manchester, but already three years before, cars had been drawn by horses on an iron track in Quincy, Mass. He was a young man still in his twenties when the July Revolution of Paris took place, in his forties when the war of the United States with Mexico vexed the consciences of the idealists, and when the German Empire was constituted. He was entering upon middle life when the Crimean War began, when the Fugitive Slave Law and the Kansas-Nebraska Bill were passed by the Congress of the United States, and when the Jews were admitted to the English Parliament. Serfdom in Russia had been abolished by Alexander II and the Civil War in the United States had been two years in progress when he was sixty. Before his death, in 1882, Napoleon III, Cavour, Garibaldi, Victor Emmanuel, and Lord Beaconsfield had played their parts in the drama of European politics, Abraham Lincoln had been assassinated, the Mexican expedition to regenerate the Latin races had failed, the Austro-Prussian war had closed, Ferdinand de Lesseps had projected and completed the Suez Canal, the dogma of papal infallibility had been proclaimed, the Franco-Prussian war had been fought to the finish in the personal surrender of Napoleon III to William I at Sedan, the third republic of France had been proclaimed, Paris had been besieged and had surrendered, Alsace and German Lorraine had been ceded to Germany and the Turco-Russian War had been begun and ended, Alexander II had been murdered in St. Petersburg, Queen Victoria had been proclaimed Empress of India. Ten years before his death, the claims of the United States against England had been settled at the arbitration of Geneva, to the satisfaction of the United States, and vote by ballot had been introduced in England. His life closed in the midst of renewed Irish agitation, the rise of Jingoism in England, and the growing complexities of the Chinese immigration and of Oriental questions generally in the United States. These mingled colors of human life and opinion his work as poet, lecturer, and essayist reflects and flashes back, like a great jewel of crystal, or as Iceland spar polarizes light.

The story of Emerson's personal interests is easily told. He was a graduate of Harvard College in 1824, entered upon study for the Unitarian ministry in the Divinity School at Cambridge, but was interrupted for more than a year by the failure of his eyes. He tried "the experiment of hard work for the benefit of the health," by teaching school in Chelmsford and in Roxbury. At this time his brother Edward was voyaging for his health in the Mediterranean, and his brother William, who had studied theology in Germany to the destruction of his orthodox Unitarianism, was exchanging theology for law. Ralph Waldo Emerson never completed his course in the Divinity School, but was "approbated to preach" in 1826. In 1829 he was settled in the Second Church of Boston, where he served until 1832, when he resigned because he could not conscientiously administer the rite of the Lord's Supper. In September, 1829, he married Ellen Tucker, who died of consumption in February, 1831. He said of her that she had been to him "a bright revelation of the best nature of woman." In December, 1832, he sailed for Malta in search of change and recuperation after the loss of his wife, his resignation from his church, and the total breakdown of his brother Edward's health.

The intellectual, social, and religious ferment of Europe does not seem to have impressed him. He crossed the Atlantic expecting to find a more stable condition of life and institutions than he had left at home; he was prepared for conservatism, dignity, and even for some charm in graceful inertia, but he was not quick to note signs of revolt that were everywhere in the air. He hardly understood his own disappointment. He was looking for men and he was afraid that the great and interesting ones had somehow eluded him. Walter Savage Landor was the first to meet his needs by being one of the two men on the continent of Europe to whom he had been able to say something in earnest. He met in England John Stuart Mill, Bowring, Sir Henry Taylor, Coleridge, and Wordsworth, all with a sense of more or less well-defined disappointment. In August, 1833, he made his way to Craigenputtock, where Thomas Carlyle and his wife were living in retirement so complete that he had great difficulty in discovering them. At once he felt that he was in the presence of a great, a superior person, whose secret lay "in his commanding sense of justice and incessant demand for sincerity." Carlyle was no less impressed. He said to Lord Houghton, "That man came to see me; I don't know what brought him, and we kept him one night, and then he left us. I saw him go up the hill. I did n't go with him to see him descend. I preferred to watch him mount and vanish like an angel." Thus began one of the most illustrious of literary friendships, whose faith and mutual service were lifelong. The monument of this relation is, of course, the *Correspondence of Carlyle and Emerson*, edited by Charles Eliot Norton.[1] Besides their personal significance, the letters form a considerable part of the literary output of the writers. Emerson in particular wrote with considerate care rather than with familiar abandon.

In October, 1834, Emerson's brother Edward died

[1] Houghton, Mifflin & Co.

in Porto Rico. Another brother, Charles Emerson, became engaged to a young lady in Concord, Mass. Here Dr. Ripley offered Waldo and his mother a home in the Old Manse celebrated by Hawthorne. A little later, April, 1836, Emerson married Lydian Jackson, "the soul of faith," in his phrase, and bought the Coolidge house in Concord, intending to share it with his brother Charles, who died, however, in the first effort that he made to restore his failing health by a southern journey.

Emerson had already learned something of his own power as a lecturer. Besides delivering five biographical lectures in Boston on Michael Angelo, Luther, Milton, George Fox, and Burke, he was slowly writing his "Nature," described by Dr. Garnett as "the most intense and quintessential of his writings, and the first in which he came forward teaching as one having authority." It was published in 1836. On the 31st of August, 1837, Emerson delivered the Phi Beta Kappa Address at Harvard. His theme was "The American Scholar." James Russell Lowell in *My Study Windows*, in the essay on Thoreau, says of it: "An event without any former parallel in our literary annals, a scene to be always treasured in the memory for its picturesqueness and its inspiration. What crowded and breathless aisles! What windows clustering with eager heads, what enthusiasm of approval, what grim silence of foregone dissent!"

In June, 1838, Emerson was invited to deliver the address before the graduating class in the Divinity School of Harvard University. He accepted the invitation and spoke on Sunday evening, July 15. He treated of the state of religion in the community, set forth the causes for the decay of religion in the churches, and suggested radical remedies. Professor George E. Woodberry[1] says: "It is not strange that in such circumstances, Emerson, after the delivery of this address, was commonly regarded as atheistical, anti-Christian, and dangerous. Condemnation was the more unqualified because attention was naturally given at first rather to what he denied than to what he affirmed; what he denied, all men understood; but what he affirmed, few, if any, clearly made out." For upwards of forty years Emerson lectured through the United States, popularizing his own ethical principles and literary culture. He refers repeatedly and in many connections to the debate on fixity of type between Cuvier and Geoffroy Saint-Hilaire. His sympathy with the theory of evolution as presented in the works of Darwin was prompt and outspoken. He was interested at once and practically, in 1831, in the appearance of Carlyle's *Sartor Resartus*, and intellectually in the foundation of the British Association. He read the higher criticism of Strauss and the political optimism of De Tocqueville, and gladly joined a club of a dozen "like-minded seekers" who met at the house of George Ripley in Boston, September 19, 1836. In an account by Bronson Alcott the following persons are said to have been at the first meeting: "George Ripley, R. W. Emerson, F. H. Hedge, Convers Francis, J. F. Clarke, and the present writer. They gave invitations to Dr. Channing, to Jonathan Phillips, to Rev. James Walker, Rev. N. L. Frothingham, Rev. J. S. Dwight, Rev. W. H. Channing, and Rev. C. A. Bartol to join them if they chose to do so. The three last named appeared afterwards, and met the club frequently."

[1] *Ralph Waldo Emerson*, Macmillan, p. 59.

The Fruitlands and Brook Farm communities were attempts to embody the social theories touched upon in Emerson's quaint comment to Carlyle in 1840, "We are a little wild here with numberless projects of social reform. Not a reading man but has his draft of a new community in his waistcoat pocket. I am gently mad myself." To Miss Martineau, who visited him in his home, he did not seem even gently mad. She wrote: "He is a thinker without being solitary, abstracted, and unfitted for the time. He is ready at every call of action. He lectures to the factory people at Lowell when they ask. He preaches when the opportunity is presented. He is known at every house along the road he travels to and from home by the words he has dropped and the deeds he has done."

The *First Series* of Emerson's *Essays* was published in 1841. From 1842 to 1844 he was nominally editor of "The Dial," the organ of the group of persons known as Transcendentalists, among whom were Margaret Fuller, "a true counterpart to the Rahels and Bettinas of Germany," and "the good Alcott, with his long, lean face and figure, with his gray worn temples and mild radiant eyes; all bent on saving the world by a return to acorns and the golden age." In 1844 appeared the *Second Series* of *Essays*, and his *Poems* in 1846, among them the nobly pathetic "Threnody," which expressed his grief at the death of his son Waldo. In 1847 he accepted the invitations of several Mechanics' Institutes to visit England and lecture, and for that purpose sailed October 5. The earlier impressions and friendships which he had made were now renewed and strengthened. His lectures were well received, his acquaintance sought by eminent persons of all classes of society. George Stevenson,

De Quincey, Francis Jeffrey, George Combe, Robert Chambers, Leigh Hunt, Macaulay, Richard Owen, Crabbe Robinson, and George Eliot were among those who repaid him for crossing the Atlantic. He returned refreshed in spirit, and enriched by memories of kindness and appreciation of his efforts to serve his time. Quite characteristically he brought with him also a rocking-horse for the little son, "Edie," whose childish charms made him pitiful to all poor babies. His *Representative Men*, the collected lectures delivered in the winter of 1845–46, appeared in 1850, *Memoir of Margaret Fuller* in 1852, *English Traits* in 1856, *Conduct of Life* in 1860. The edition of this work was exhausted forty-eight hours after its publication, so great had become the demand for Emerson's writing. *May Day and Other Pieces* was the harvest of 1867, *Society and Solitude* of 1870. The results of his wide and catholic reading in poetry he shared with the public in the compilation and editing of *Parnassus* in 1875, " selected from the whole range of English Literature." *Letters and Social Aims* he published in 1876, and a second volume of *Poems* in 1876.

July 24, 1872, his house in Concord was destroyed by fire, but was rebuilt by the liberal kindness of his friends. In October of the same year, accompanied by his daughter Ellen, he sailed for Europe on his way to Egypt.

Much of his charm and power in public address remained with him in his closing years of life. In 1881 he spoke on Carlyle's death before the Massachusetts Historical Society. Walt Whitman described him at about this time as an apparently attentive listener to conversation, " a good color in his face, eyes clear, with the well-known expression of sweetness, and the old

clear-peering aspect quite the same." . . . "A word
or short phrase only when needed, and then almost
always with a smile." He died after a few days' illness
of pneumonia, April 27, 1882. He faced the eternities
in death, as he had faced them in life, reverently but
not unfamiliarly. To the last his eyes lingered affec-
tionately on the portrait of Carlyle on the wall, he
talked tenderly with his wife of their life together, he
desired to see all who came, and passed with the words,
"Oh, the beautiful boy!" on his smiling lips into a
companionship with those he had loved, which death
had interrupted and which he confidently believed
death would now restore.

The same genial critic who found Emerson a disappointment to biographers declares him the despair
of the "natural historian of philosophy." In the first
instance, it was the lack of incident, the absence of
curious suffering, the monotony of spiritual good health
that appalled; in the second, it is the lack of system.
Dr. Garnett says: "If we place him rather upon the
roll of poets, we are still unable to remove him from
the roll of anomalies." The word anomaly has a formidable sound to the tyro in science or in art; it is
almost prohibitive to the formal student of either;
it seems to mark a no-thoroughfare of investigation.
But it must be remembered that in the progress from
one level of intelligence to a higher, the simplest elements of the new order appear anomalous. The
higher mathematics is anomalous from the point of
view of the multiplication table, the action of astro-
nomic force from that of simple addition. System
is a convenient device of contented or of struggling
ignorance; but its value in spiritual and practical
affairs is obviously limited. Here lies the secret of

Emerson's originality, here is the best measure of his service. He was not simply a seer; he was far more than "a voice;" he was quite infinitely more than "a sign of the times." He was one of the small group of human beings who have never lost their sense of their nature and function as forces.

Therefore it is impossible to reduce Emerson to system and unreasonable to require it of him. He was not a scholar any more than Sainte-Beuve; he was not a politician any more than Burke; he was not a philosopher any more than Socrates. He was a Yankee gentleman who read omnivorously, wrote habitually, and so lived that it is quite possible that both Spinoza and Jonathan Edwards would have claimed him as a son after the spirit, though he was imperturbably bent on showing that their systems had had their day. His life is as full of oppositions as his writings of paradox, but he was able to be always perfectly amiable, and the effect of his writing is always tonic. James Russell Lowell's characterization of him in *A Fable for Critics* will always remain the best verdict on the superficial appearance that he presented to the acute and conventional observer, but it is no portrait, — it is a series of snap-shots.

"There comes Emerson first, whose rich words, every one
Are like gold nails in temples to hang trophies on,
Whose prose is grand verse, while his verse, the Lord knows,
Is some of it pr — No, 't is not even prose;
I'm speaking of metres; some poems have welled
From those rare depths of soul that have ne'er been excelled;
They're not epics, but that does n't matter a pin,
In creating, the only hard thing's to begin;
A grass-blade's no easier to make than an oak;
If you've once found the way, you've achieved the grand stroke;
In the worst of his poems are mines of rich matter,
But thrown in a heap with a crash and a clatter;

Now it is not one thing nor another alone
Makes a poem, but rather the general tone,
The something pervading, uniting the whole,
The before unconceived, unconceivable soul,
So that just in removing this trifle or that, you
Take away, as it were, a chief limb of the statue;
Roots, wood, bark, and leaves singly perfect may be,
But, clapt hodge-podge together, they don't make a tree.

"But, to come back to Emerson (whom, by the way,
I believe we left waiting), — his is, we may say,
A Greek head on right Yankee shoulders, whose range
Has Olympus for one pole, for t'other the Exchange;
He seems, to my thinking (although I'm afraid
The comparison must, long ere this, have been made),
A Plotinus-Montaigne, where the Egyptian's gold mist
And the Gascon's shrewd wit cheek-by-jowl coexist;
All admire, and yet scarcely six converts he's got
To I don't (nor they either) exactly know what;
For though he builds glorious temples, 't is odd
He leaves never a doorway to get in a god.
'T is refreshing to old-fashioned people like me
To meet such a primitive Pagan as he,
In whose mind all creation is duly respected
As parts of himself — just a little projected;
And who's willing to worship the stars and the sun,
A convert to — nothing but Emerson.
So perfect a balance there is in his head,
That he talks of things sometimes as if they were dead;
Life, nature, love, God, and affairs of that sort,
He looks at as merely ideas; in short,
As if they were fossils stuck round in a cabinet,
Of such vast extent that our earth's a mere dab in it;
Composed just as he is inclined to conjecture her,
Namely, one part pure earth, ninety-nine parts pure lecturer.
You are filled with delight at his clear demonstration,
Each figure, word, gesture, just fits the occasion,
With the quiet precision of science he'll sort 'em,
But you can't help suspecting the whole a *post mortem*.

"There are persons, mole-blind to the soul's make and style,
Who insist on a likeness 'twixt him and Carlyle;
To compare him with Plato would be vastly fairer,

Carlyle's the more burly, but E. is the rarer;
He sees fewer objects, but clearlier, trulier,
If C.'s as original, E.'s more peculiar;
That he's more of a man you might say of the one,
Of the other he's more of an Emerson;
C.'s the Titan, as shaggy of mind as of limb, —
E. the clear-eyed Olympian, rapid and slim;
The one's two thirds Norseman, the other half Greek,
Where the one's most abounding, the other's to seek;
C.'s generals require to be seen in the mass, —
E.'s specialties gain if enlarged by the glass;
C. gives nature and God his own fits of the blues,
And rims common-sense things with mystical hues, —
E. sits in a mystery calm and intense,
And looks coolly around him with sharp common-sense;
C. shows you how every-day matters unite
With the dim transdiurnal recesses of night, —
While E. in a plain, preternatural way,
Makes mysteries matters of mere everyday;
C. draws all his characters quite à *la* Fuseli, —
Not sketching their bundles of muscles and thews illy,
He paints with a brush so untamed and profuse,
They seem nothing but bundles of muscles and thews;
E. is rather like Flaxman, lines strait and severe,
And a colorless outline, but full, round, and clear;
To the men he thinks worthy he frankly accords
The design of a white marble statue in words.
C. labors to get at the centre, and then
Take a reckoning from there of his actions and men;
E. calmly assumes the said centre as granted,
And, given himself, has whatever is wanted."

The curious discontent of Emerson's biographers
with one aspect after another of his self-expression
is easily explicable when one remembers that he rated
the soul above any expression of it, and valued expression mainly as it led back to its source. As he
said, "There is nothing so wonderful in any particular
landscape as the necessity of being beautiful under
which every landscape lies." His theory and practice
are found defective in respect for formal art, as are his

philosophy and ethics in system. As he erred in the latter with Plato and the Great Teacher of men, so he erred in the former with Michael Angelo, who left part of his statues unfinished as token of his greater ideal.

Emerson's prose serves to remind us of Nature's truth and Emerson's poetry. His essays remind us in their distinctions of the illustrations used in his biographical studies. The best footnote for his essay on "Friendship" is his correspondence with Carlyle. His account of Plato means what it does because the mind of Plato consoled him for the shortcomings of the men Goethe and Napoleon, and it leads inevitably to "Compensation" and "Experience" and "Nature." *English Traits* is a special variety of *The Conduct of Life*, and "The Oversoul" and "Circles" are collections of those "blazing ubiquities" whose signs he discerned in the humblest neighborhoods, whose perfection he denied to the grandest social structures, and for whose best expression he courageously hoped that the United States might prove themselves worthy. Here he bettered the instruction he had from Plato. Father Taylor declared him to be more like Christ than any other man he had known. We are not likely, therefore, either as a nation or as individuals, to outgrow Emerson. From time to time we may forget him or even judge him outworn, but we shall do best to absorb as thoroughly as possible all his writings, that their spirit may not escape us. For more than any other writer Emerson is his own antidote. His shrewd maxims conduct to mystic heights of speculation and his airiest speculation lands the balloon in the market-place.

For years it has been the regret of students that

his journals and correspondence were inaccessible. This lack is now made good by the Centenary Edition of his works, in which his son, Dr. Edward Emerson, has collected everything that can help to make clear his father's meaning or may heighten the sense of human companionship between him and the reader. This edition therefore may be considered the last legacy of Emerson to the public he served so devotedly, by reminding it of the abiding relation between it and the essential virtues of private souls.

The material from journals and note-books, as well as from five essays now published for the first time, bears not only on the history of Emerson's opinions and the working of his mind, but it is of final importance in the study of his style. The facts about him are not quite what popularly they have been supposed. He never changed his attitude toward life, but he did recast sentences. The form of his essays underwent considerable change in different editions and in relation to different audiences. To this end he used literary methods freely, but the freedom he allowed himself appears far less a matter of the moment's convenience or of personal whim, or of indifference to the claims of form, than it has been the fashion to think. By the help of Dr. Emerson's notes, explaining many intimate references and allusions of the text, the "natural history" of his father's opinions is supplied in such a way as to render their organic character more obvious. The man Emerson is seen everywhere in the writer and lecturer. The style which has been traditionally compared to a string of pearls with a like loose arrangement is seen to be much more like cosmic light whose particles are diffused only that changed conditions may make them into particular beams. More than

ever, too, the essential difference between Emerson
and Walt Whitman becomes evident. Emerson's originality in expression was not the result of effort. Walt
Whitman's was. Emerson produced his effects by the
use of all the means at his command. Walt Whitman
deliberately and with recurrent difficulty tried to keep
certain elements of expression out of his work. A study
of their styles in various stages, from journals and note-
books to productions intended for the public, shows
that the democratic aspect of Walt Whitman's work
was the result of self-election, that of Emerson's his
response to the call of nature.

A similar comparison with the work of Emerson's
other companion in originality and in assertion of
individuality, Thomas Carlyle, shows the student the
extraordinary difference between them in directness
of approach to a theme and in ease of expression.
Carlyle's style justifies all that he complained of in his
many accounts of his difficulty in expressing himself.
Emerson writes, "Even in college I was content to be
'screwed' in the recitation room if on my return I
could accurately paint the fact in my journal." In
1837 he wrote of his journal: "This book is my savings
bank. I grow richer because I have somewhere to
deposit my earnings, and fractions are worth more to
me because corresponding fractions are waiting here
that shall be made integers by their addition." It is
impossible to think of Carlyle as anything but a prose-
poet; it is equally impossible to forget that Emerson
is a poet, a writer of prose, and a physician of souls.

There is no royal road to Emerson. To understand
him or any part of his message fully, it is necessary to
study it in as many connections as he uttered it. Emerson was a master of emphasis, and yet his abiding

value is in the relations that he made evident between truths rather than in the force with which he pressed a given truth home. Ten essays from his score of volumes do not exhaust his wealth or serve as small change for the total. Ten essays, however, may serve as an introduction to a thorough study of a genius as elusive as it is impressive. The group chosen undertakes to present with some completeness a simple outline of his work, its central principles, its development, its expression in concrete form, and its organic applications. It is hoped that one unceasing purpose will be found to run through the series, binding it together, but affording also a standard by which independent values in the separate essays may be discriminated. The group may be divided into two related or parallel groups having a similar internal structure: 1. Compensation, Experience, Character, Self-Reliance, and Heroism; 2. History, Politics, Behavior, Manners, and Friendship. The constructive principle of the first group is ultimate or spiritual value. Its development may be traced, the present editor believes, through Experience for the race, Character for the individual, Self-Reliance for the general relations of the individual, and Heroism for a special relation. The constructive principle of the second group is mediate or social value. History, like Compensation, is a process as well as a record. As a process it involves much that is commonly ignored or thought to be contradictory to its function. It is developed through the wide relations of Politics, the concrete expression in Behavior, the permanent coefficient of Manners, and the special relation of Friendship. For this order it is further claimed as an advantage that the duality which Emerson found everywhere is here again presented in a double structure. The simple alternation of his emphasis of dual truth might have been shown by the interpolation of the items of the second group in the first. Compensation then would have found a social or mediate application in History, Experience in Politics, Character in Behavior, Self-Reliance in Manners, and Heroism in Friendship. But for the student of Emerson's mind and process of expression, there can be no doubt that the less obvious and direct order is more useful because more characteristic. Finally, it seems hardly possible that Emerson himself would have been able to find the question of the order of his essays "interesting." It would have seemed to him as superfluous as " an order " for the winds or the waves or the soughing of the pines. And so ultimately it will prove to the student. If he attains to any of his master's spirit, he will see that the order of presentation is as insignificant as time to the soul; the moment of the acceptance of truth, the discovery of spiritual kinship, —these are the important things, and their advent makes a centre in any surroundings, but only for the time being. All the rest must in their turn be centres, subordinating in calm loyalty to the whole truth the most venerable institutions and processes from the centres that they had been to outstanding dependencies that they must take their turn in being. The mind conducting a process of this sort must be active and provided with endurance. The eternal rearrangement of events was what Emerson meant by History of the ultimate sort; the ordinary lineal or superficial or artificial adjustment by dates and prejudices he had a constitutional and really religious aversion to. Experience to him was central and intimate, not superficial nor spectacular. Yet he could not ignore the popular inter-

est in the tale of happenings that made men court travel
and so-called advantages. Politics to him were at
once more and less than the ward heeler found them
or left them. Character could easily swing from a share
of the Oversoul to the poor dignity of a whim, and
Behavior might express either aspect of reality. Self-
Reliance was a misnomer ultimately for anything but
trust in the constitution of the universe, and Manners were good or bad as they were expressive of the
underlying truth or lie. Heroism stood for the moments, frequent or rare, when the soul, conscious of its
high prerogative, lived itself and its claims into the
assertion of crisis. Friendship was a social relation
where the clash between individuals was inevitable;
and heroism, active or latent, a requisite.

Associated with these essays are the mottoes in
verse which serve, in the judgment of some of Emerson's critics, to keep alive the minister within him.
Such does not seem to me to be their office. They are
rather isomeric forms of the elemental stuff he offers
in the essays.

Emerson's message is even more valuable for the
manner than the matter. He leaves with his disciple
the constructive influence of earnest protest. In the
small class of "unsystematic" writers he stands alone.
The Bacon of the *Essays*, the Pascal of the *Pensées*,
the Montaigne of the *Essays* are said to have been
great writers. Was Emerson? It is immaterial. He
was a great man writing.

COMPENSATION

THE wings of Time are black and white,
Pied with morning and with night.
Mountain tall and ocean deep
Trembling balance duly keep.
In changing moon, in tidal wave,
Glows the feud of Want and Have.
Gauge of more and less through space
Electric star and pencil plays.
The lonely Earth amid the balls
That hurry through the eternal halls,
A makeweight flying to the void,
Supplemental asteroid,
Or compensatory spark,
Shoots across the neutral Dark.[1]

MAN's the elm, and Wealth the vine,
Stanch and strong the tendrils twine:
Though the frail ringlets thee deceive,
None from its stock that vine can reave.
Fear not, then, thou child infirm,
There 's no god dare wrong a worm.[2]
Laurel crowns cleave to deserts
And power to him who power exerts;
Hast not thy share? On wingèd feet,
Lo! it rushes thee to meet;
And all that Nature made thy own,
Floating in air or pent in stone,
Will rive the hills and swim the sea
And, like thy shadow, follow thee.

COMPENSATION

EVER since I was a boy I have wished to write a discourse on Compensation; for it seemed to me when very young that on this subject life was ahead of theology and the people knew more than the preachers taught. The documents too from which the doctrine is to be drawn, charmed my fancy by their endless variety, and lay always before me, even in sleep ; for they are the tools in our hands, the bread in our basket, the transactions of the street, the farm and the dwelling-house; greetings, relations, debts and credits, the influence of character, the nature and endowment of all men. It seemed to me also that in it might be shown men a ray of divinity, the present action of the soul of this world, clean from all vestige of tradition; and so the heart of man might be bathed by an inundation of eternal love, conversing with that which he knows was always and always must be, because it really is now. It appeared moreover that if this doctrine could be stated in terms with any resemblance to those bright intuitions in which this truth is sometimes revealed to us, it would be a star in many dark hours and crooked passages in our journey, that would not suffer us to lose our way.

I was lately confirmed in these desires by hearing a sermon at church. The preacher, a man esteemed for his orthodoxy, unfolded in the ordinary manner the doctrine of the Last Judgment. He assumed that judgment is not executed in this world; that the

wicked are successful; that the good are miserable;
and then urged from reason and from Scripture a
compensation to be made to both parties in the next
life. No offence appeared to be taken by the congre-
gation at this doctrine. As far as I could observe
when the meeting broke up they separated without
remark on the sermon.

Yet what was the import of this teaching? What
did the preacher mean by saying that the good are
miserable in the present life? Was it that houses
and lands, offices, wine, horses, dress, luxury, are
had by unprincipled men, whilst the saints are poor
and despised; and that a compensation is to be
made to these last hereafter, by giving them the like
gratifications another day, — bank-stock and doub-
loons, venison and champagne? This must be the
compensation intended; for what else? Is it that
they are to have leave to pray and praise? to love
and serve men? Why, that they can do now. The
legitimate inference the disciple would draw was, —
'We are to have *such* a good time as the sinners have
now;' — or, to push it to its extreme import, — 'You
sin now, we shall sin by and by; we would sin now,
if we could; not being successful we expect our revenge to-morrow.'

The fallacy lay in the immense concession that the
bad are successful; that justice is not done now.[3] The
blindness of the preacher consisted in deferring to
the base estimate of the market of what constitutes
a manly success, instead of confronting and convict-
ing the world from the truth; announcing the presence of the soul; the omnipotence of the will; and
so establishing the standard of good and ill, of success
and falsehood.

I find a similar base tone in the popular religious works of the day and the same doctrines assumed by the literary men when occasionally they treat the related topics. I think that our popular theology has gained in decorum, and not in principle, over the superstitions it has displaced. But men are better than their theology. Their daily life gives it the lie. Every ingenuous and aspiring soul leaves the doctrine behind him in his own experience, and all men feel sometimes the falsehood which they cannot demonstrate. For men are wiser than they know.[4] That which they hear in schools and pulpits without afterthought, if said in conversation would probably be questioned in silence. If a man dogmatize in a mixed company on Providence and the divine laws, he is answered by a silence which conveys well enough to an observer the dissatisfaction of the hearer, but his incapacity to make his own statement.

I shall attempt in this and the following chapter[5] to record some facts that indicate the path of the law of Compensation; happy beyond my expectation if I shall truly draw the smallest arc of this circle.

Polarity, or action and reaction,[6] we meet in every part of nature; in darkness and light; in heat and cold; in the ebb and flow of waters; in male and female; in the inspiration and expiration of plants and animals; in the equation of quantity and quality in the fluids of the animal body; in the systole and diastole of the heart; in the undulations of fluids and of sound; in the centrifugal and centripetal gravity; in electricity, galvanism, and chemical affinity. Superinduce magnetism at one end of a needle, the opposite magnetism takes place at the other end. If the south attracts, the north repels. To empty here, you must condense there. An inevitable dualism bisects nature, so that each thing is a half, and suggests another thing to make it whole; as, spirit, matter; man, woman; odd, even; subjective, objective; in, out; upper, under; motion, rest; yea, nay.

Whilst the world is thus dual, so is every one of its parts. The entire system of things gets represented in every particle. There is somewhat that resembles the ebb and flow of the sea, day and night, man and woman, in a single needle of the pine, in a kernel of corn, in each individual of every animal tribe. The reaction, so grand in the elements, is repeated within these small boundaries. For example, in the animal kingdom the physiologist has observed that no creatures are favorites, but a certain compensation balances every gift and every defect. A surplusage given to one part is paid out of a reduction from another part of the same creature. If the head and neck are enlarged, the trunk and extremities are cut short.

The theory of the mechanic forces is another example. What we gain in power is lost in time, and the converse. The periodic or compensating errors of the planets is another instance. The influences of climate and soil in political history is another. The cold climate invigorates. The barren soil does not breed fevers, crocodiles, tigers or scorpions.

The same dualism underlies the nature and condition of man. Every excess causes a defect; every defect an excess. Every sweet hath its sour; every evil its good. Every faculty which is a receiver of pleasure has an equal penalty put on its abuse. It is to answer for its moderation with its life. For every grain of wit there is a grain of folly. For every thing you have missed, you have gained something else; and for every thing you gain, you lose something. If riches increase, they are increased that use them. If the gatherer gathers too much, Nature takes out of the man what she puts into his chest; swells the estate, but kills the owner. Nature hates monopolies and exceptions. The waves of the sea do not more speedily seek a level from their loftiest tossing than the varieties of condition tend to equalize themselves. There is always some levelling circumstance that puts down the overbearing, the strong, the rich, the fortunate, substantially on the same ground with all others. Is a man too strong and fierce for society and by temper and position a bad citizen, — a morose ruffian, with a dash of the pirate in him? — Nature sends him a troop of pretty sons and daughters who are getting along in the dame's classes at the village school, and love and fear for them smooths his grim scowl to courtesy. Thus she contrives to intenerate the granite and felspar, takes the boar out and puts the lamb in and keeps her balance true.

The farmer imagines power and place are fine things. But the President has paid dear for his White House. It has commonly cost him all his peace, and the best of his manly attributes. To preserve for a short time so conspicuous an appearance before the world, he is content to eat dust before the real masters who stand erect behind the throne. Or do men desire the more substantial and permanent grandeur of genius?[7] Neither has this an immunity. He who by force of will or of thought is great and overlooks thousands, has the charges of that eminence. With every influx of light comes new danger. Has he light? he must bear witness to the light,[8] and always outrun that sympathy

which gives him such keen satisfaction, by his fidelity
to new revelations of the incessant soul.[9] He must
hate father and mother, wife and child. Has he all
that the world loves and admires and covets? — he
must cast behind him their admiration and afflict
them by faithfulness to his truth and become a byword
and a hissing.[10]

This law writes the laws of cities and nations. It is
in vain to build or plot or combine against it. Things
refuse to be mismanaged long. *Res nolunt diu male
administrari.*[11] Though no checks to a new evil appear,
the checks exist, and will appear. If the government
is cruel, the governor's life is not safe. If you tax too
high, the revenue will yield nothing. If you make the
criminal code sanguinary, juries will not convict. If
the law is too mild, private vengeance comes in. If
the government is a terrific democracy, the pressure is
resisted by an over-charge of energy in the citizen, and
life glows with a fiercer flame. The true life and satisfactions of man seem to elude the utmost rigors or
felicities of condition and to establish themselves with
great indifferency under all varieties of circumstances.
Under all governments the influence of character remains the same, — in Turkey and in New England
about alike. Under the primeval despots of Egypt,
history honestly confesses that man must have been
as free as culture could make him.

These appearances indicate the fact that the universe is represented in every one of its particles.[12] Every
thing in nature contains all the powers of nature.
Every thing is made of one hidden stuff; as the naturalist sees one type under every metamorphosis, and
regards a horse as a running man, a fish as a swimming man, a bird as a flying man, a tree as a rooted

man. Each new form repeats not only the main character of the type, but part for part all the details, all
the aims, furtherances, hindrances, energies and whole
system of every other. Every occupation, trade, art,
transaction, is a compend of the world and a correlative of every other. Each one is an entire emblem of
human life; of its good and ill, its trials, its enemies,
its course and its end. And each one must somehow
accommodate the whole man and recite all his destiny.

The world globes itself in a drop of dew. The microscope cannot find the animalcule which is less perfect for being little. Eyes, ears, taste, smell, motion,
resistance, appetite, and organs of reproduction that
take hold on eternity, — all find room to consist in
the small creature. So do we put our life into every
act. The true doctrine of omnipresence is that God
reappears with all his parts in every moss and cobweb.
The value of the universe contrives to throw itself into
every point. If the good is there, so is the evil; if the
affinity, so the repulsion; if the force, so the limitation.

Thus is the universe alive. All things are moral.
That soul which within us is a sentiment, outside of us
is a law. We feel its inspiration; but there in history
we can see its fatal strength. "It is in the world, and
the world was made by it." Justice is not postponed.
A perfect equity adjusts its balance in all parts of life.
Ἀεὶ γὰρ εὖ πίπτουσιν οἱ Διὸς κύβοι,[13] —The dice of God are
always loaded. The world looks like a multiplication-
table, or a mathematical equation, which, turn it how
you will, balances itself. Take what figure you will,
its exact value, nor more nor less, still returns to you.
Every secret is told, every crime is punished, every
virtue rewarded, every wrong redressed, in silence and
certainty. What we call retribution is the universal

necessity by which the whole appears wherever a part appears. If you see smoke, there must be fire. If you see a hand or a limb, you know that the trunk to which it belongs is there behind.

Every act rewards itself, or in other words integrates itself, in a twofold manner; first in the thing, or in real nature; and secondly in the circumstance, or in apparent nature. Men call the circumstance the retribution. The causal retribution is in the thing and is seen by the soul. The retribution in the circumstance is seen by the understanding; it is inseparable from the thing, but is often spread over a long time and so does not become distinct until after many years. The specific stripes may follow late after the offence, but they follow because they accompany it. Crime and punishment grow out of one stem. Punishment is a fruit that unsuspected ripens within the flower of the pleasure which concealed it. Cause and effect, means and ends, seed and fruit, cannot be severed; for the effect already blooms in the cause, the end preexists in the means, the fruit in the seed.

Whilst thus the world will be whole and refuses to be disparted, we seek to act partially, to sunder, to appropriate; for example, — to gratify the senses we sever the pleasure of the senses from the needs of the character. The ingenuity of man has always been dedicated to the solution of one problem, — how to detach the sensual sweet, the sensual strong, the sensual bright, etc., from the moral sweet, the moral deep, the moral fair; that is, again, to contrive to cut clean off this upper surface so thin as to leave it bottomless; to get a *one end*, without an *other end*. The soul says, ' Eat;' the body would feast. The soul says, 'The man and woman shall be one flesh and one soul;' the body would join the flesh only. The soul says, 'Have dominion over all things to the ends of virtue;' the body would have the power over things to its own ends.

The soul strives amain to live and work through all things. It would be the only fact. All things shall be added unto it, — power, pleasure, knowledge, beauty. The particular man aims to be somebody; to set up for himself; to truck and higgle [14] for a private good; and, in particulars, to ride that he may ride; to dress that he may be dressed; to eat that he may eat; and to govern, that he may be seen. Men seek to be great; they would have offices, wealth, power, and fame. They think that to be great is to possess one side of nature, — the sweet, without the other side, the bitter.

This dividing and detaching is steadily counteracted. Up to this day it must be owned no projector has had the smallest success. The parted water reunites behind our hand. Pleasure is taken out of pleasant things, profit out of profitable things, power out of strong things, as soon as we seek to separate them from the whole. We can no more halve things and get the sensual good, by itself, than we can get an inside that shall have no outside, or a light without a shadow. "Drive out Nature with a fork, she comes running back." [15]

Life invests itself with inevitable conditions, which the unwise seek to dodge, which one and another brags [16] that he does not know, that they do not touch him; — but the brag is on his lips, the conditions are in his soul. If he escapes them in one part they attack him in another more vital part. If he has escaped them in form and in the appearance, it is because he has resisted his life and fled from himself, and the retribution is so much death. So signal is the failure of all attempts to make this separation of the good from the tax, that the experiment would not be tried, — since to try it is to be mad, — but for the circumstance that when the disease begins in the will, of rebellion and separation, the intellect is at once infected, so that the man ceases to see God whole in each object, but is able to see the sensual allurement of an object and not see the sensual hurt; he sees the mermaid's head but not the dragon's tail, and thinks he can cut off that which he would have from that which he would not have. "How secret art thou who dwellest in the highest heavens in silence, O thou only great God, sprinkling with an unwearied providence certain penal blindnesses upon such as have unbridled desires!" [17]

The human soul is true to these facts in the painting of fable, of history, of law, of proverbs, of conversation. It finds a tongue in literature unawares. Thus the Greeks called Jupiter, Supreme Mind; but having traditionally ascribed to him many base actions, they involuntarily made amends to reason by tying up the hands of so bad a god. He is made as helpless as a king of England. Prometheus knows one secret which Jove must bargain for; Minerva, another. He cannot get his own thunders; Minerva keeps the key of them: —

> "Of all the gods, I only know the keys
> That ope the solid doors within whose vaults
> His thunders sleep." [18]

A plain confession of the in-working of the All and of its moral aim. The Indian mythology ends in the same ethics; and it would seem impossible for any fable to be invented and get any currency which was not moral. Aurora forgot to ask youth for her lover, and though Tithonus is immortal, he is old. Achilles is not quite invulnerable; the sacred waters did not wash the heel by which Thetis held him. Siegfried, in the Nibelungen, is not quite immortal, for a leaf fell on his back whilst he was bathing in the dragon's blood, and that spot which it covered is mortal. And so it must be. There is a crack in every thing God has made. It would seem there is always this vindictive [19] circumstance stealing in at unawares even into the wild poesy in which the human fancy attempted to make bold holiday and to shake itself free of the old laws, — this back-stroke, this kick of the gun, certifying that the law is fatal; that in nature nothing can be given, all things are sold.

This is that ancient doctrine of Nemesis, who keeps watch in the universe and lets no offence go unchastised. The Furies, they said, are attendants on justice, and if the sun in heaven should trangress his path they would punish him. The poets related that stone walls and iron swords and leathern thongs had an occult sympathy with the wrongs of their owners; that the belt which Ajax gave Hector dragged the Trojan hero over the field at the wheels of the car of Achilles, and the sword which Hector gave Ajax was that on whose point Ajax fell. They recorded that when the Thasians erected a statue to Theagenes, a victor in the games, one of his rivals went to it by night and endeavored to throw it down by repeated blows, until at last he moved it from its pedestal and was crushed to death beneath its fall. [20]

This voice of fable has in it somewhat divine. It came from thought above the will of the writer. That is the best part of each writer which has nothing private in it; that which he does not know; that which flowed out of his constitution and not from his too active invention; that which in the study of a single artist you might not easily find, but in the study of many you would abstract as the spirit of them all. Phidias it is not, but the work of man in that early Hellenic world that I would know. The name and circumstance of Phidias, however convenient for history, embarrass when we come to the highest criticism. We are to see that which man was tending to do in a given period, and was hindered, or, if you will, modified in doing, by the interfering volitions of Phidias, of Dante, of Shakespeare, the organ whereby man at the moment wrought.

Still more striking is the expression of this fact in the proverbs of all nations, which are always the literature of reason, or the statements of an absolute truth without qualification. Proverbs, like the sacred books of each nation, are the sanctuary of the intuitions. That which the droning world, chained to appearances, will not allow the realist to say in his own words, it will suffer him to say in proverbs without contradiction. And his law of laws, which the pulpit, the senate and the college deny, is hourly preached in all markets and workshops by flights of proverbs, whose teaching is as true and as omnipresent as that of birds and flies.

All things are double, one against another. — Tit for tat; an eye for an eye; a tooth for a tooth; blood for blood; measure for measure; love for love. — Give, and it shall be given you. — He that watereth shall be watered himself. — What will you have? quoth God; pay for it and take it. — Nothing venture, nothing have. — Thou shalt be paid exactly for what thou hast done, no more, no less. — Who doth not work shall not eat. — Harm watch, harm catch.

— Curses always recoil on the head of him who imprecates them. — If you put a chain around the neck of a slave, the other end fastens itself around your own. — Bad counsel confounds the adviser. — The Devil is an ass.[21]

It is thus written, because it is thus in life. Our action is overmastered and characterized above our will by the law of nature. We aim at a petty end quite aside from the public good, but our act arranges itself by irresistible magnetism in a line with the poles of the world.

A man cannot speak but he judges himself. With his will or against his will he draws his portrait to the eye of his companions by every word. Every opinion reacts on him who utters it. It is a thread-ball[22] thrown at a mark, but the other end remains in the thrower's bag. Or rather it is a harpoon hurled at the whale, unwinding, as it flies, a coil of cord in the boat, and, if the harpoon is not good, or not well thrown, it will go nigh to cut the steersman in twain or to sink the boat.

You cannot do wrong without suffering wrong. "No man had ever a point of pride that was not injurious to him," said Burke.[23] The exclusive in fashionable life does not see that he excludes himself from enjoyment, in the attempt to appropriate it. The exclusionist in religion does not see that he shuts the door of heaven on himself, in striving to shut out others. Treat men as pawns and ninepins and you shall suffer as well as they. If you leave out their heart, you shall lose your own. The senses would make things of all persons; of women, of children, of the poor. The vulgar proverb, "I will get it from his purse or get it from his skin," is sound philosophy.

All infractions of love and equity in our social relations are speedily punished. They are punished by fear. Whilst I stand in simple relations to my fellow-man, I have no displeasure in meeting him. We meet as water meets water, or as two currents of air mix, with perfect diffusion and interpenetration of nature. But as soon as there is any departure from simplicity and attempt at halfness, or good for me that is not good for him, my neighbor feels the wrong; he shrinks from me as far as I have shrunk from him; his eyes no longer seek mine; there is war between us; there is hate in him and fear in me.

All the old abuses in society, universal and particular, all unjust accumulations of property and power, are avenged in the same manner. Fear is an instructor of great sagacity and the herald of all revolutions. One thing he teaches, that there is rottenness where he appears. He is a carrion crow, and though you see not well what he hovers for, there is death somewhere. Our property is timid, our laws are timid, our cultivated classes are timid. Fear for ages has boded and mowed and gibbered over government and property. That obscene bird is not there for nothing. He indicates great wrongs which must be revised.

Of the like nature is that expectation of change which instantly follows the suspension of our voluntary activity. The terror of cloudless noon, the emerald of Polycrates,[24] the awe of prosperity, the instinct which leads every generous soul to impose on itself tasks of a noble asceticism and vicarious virtue, are the tremblings of the balance of justice through the heart and mind of man.

Experienced men of the world know very well that it is best to pay scot and lot [25] as they go along. and that a man often pays dear for a small frugality.

The borrower runs in his own debt. Has a man gained any thing who has received a hundred favors and rendered none? Has he gained by borrowing, through indolence or cunning, his neighbor's wares, or horses, or money? There arises on the deed the instant acknowledgment of benefit on the one part and of debt on the other; that is, of superiority and inferiority. The transaction remains in the memory of himself and his neighbor; and every new transaction alters according to its nature their relation to each other. He may soon come to see that he had better have broken his own bones than to have ridden in his neighbor's coach, and that "the highest price he can pay for a thing is to ask for it."

A wise man will extend this lesson to all parts of life, and know that it is the part of prudence to face every claimant and pay every just demand on your time, your talents, or your heart. Always pay; for first or last you must pay your entire debt. Persons and events may stand for a time between you and justice, but it is only a postponement. You must pay at last your own debt. If you are wise you will dread a prosperity which only loads you with more. Benefit is the end of nature. But for every benefit which you receive, a tax is levied. He is great who confers the most benefits. He is base, — and that is the one base thing in the universe, — to receive favors and render none. In the order of nature we cannot render benefits to those from whom we receive them, or only seldom. But the benefit we receive must be rendered again, line for line, deed for deed, cent for cent, to somebody. Beware of too much good staying in your hand. It will fast corrupt and worm worms.[26] Pay it away quickly in some sort.

Labor is watched over by the same pitiless laws. Cheapest, say the prudent, is the dearest labor. What we buy in a broom, a mat, a wagon, a knife, is some application of good sense to a common want. It is best to pay in your land a skilful gardener, or to buy good sense applied to gardening; in your sailor, good sense applied to navigation; in the house, good sense applied to cooking, sewing, serving; in your agent, good sense applied to accounts and affairs. So do you multiply your presence, or spread yourself throughout your estate. But because of the dual constitution of things, in labor as in life there can be no cheating. The thief steals from himself. The swindler swindles himself. For the real price of labor is knowledge and virtue, whereof wealth and credit are signs. These signs, like paper money, may be counterfeited or stolen, but that which they represent, namely, knowledge and virtue, cannot be counterfeited or stolen. These ends of labor cannot be answered but by real exertions of the mind, and in obedience to pure motives. The cheat, the defaulter, the gambler, cannot extort the knowledge of material and moral nature which his honest care and pains yield to the operative. The law of nature is, Do the thing, and you shall have the power; but they who do not the thing have not the power.

Human labor, through all its forms, from the sharpening of a stake to the construction of a city or an epic, is one immense illustration of the perfect compensation of the universe. The absolute balance of Give and Take, the doctrine that every thing has its price, — and if that price is not paid, not that thing but something else is obtained, and that it is impossible to get anything without its price, — is not less sublime in the columns of a leger [27] than in the budgets of states, in the laws of light and darkness, in all the action and reaction of nature. I cannot doubt that the high laws which each man sees implicated in those processes with which he is conversant, the stern ethics which sparkle on his chisel-edge, which are measured out by his plumb and foot-rule, which stand as manifest in the footing of the shop-bill as in the history of a state, — do recommend to him his trade, and though seldom named, exalt his business to his imagination.

The league between virtue and nature engages all things to assume a hostile front to vice. The beautiful laws and substances of the world persecute and whip the traitor. He finds that things are arranged for truth and benefit, but there is no den in the wide world to hide a rogue. Commit a crime, and the earth is made of glass. Commit a crime, and it seems as if a coat of snow fell on the ground, such as reveals in the woods the track of every partridge and fox and squirrel and mole. You cannot recall the spoken word, you cannot wipe out the foot-track, you cannot draw up the ladder, so as to leave no inlet or clew. Some damning circumstance always transpires. The laws and substances of nature — water, snow, wind, gravitation — become penalties to the thief.

On the other hand the law holds with equal sureness for all right action. Love, and you shall be loved. All love is mathematically just, as much as the two sides of an algebraic equation. The good man has absolute good, which like fire turns every thing to its own nature, so that you cannot do him any harm; but as the royal armies sent against Napoleon, when he approached cast down their colors and from enemies became friends, so disasters of all kinds, as sickness, offence, poverty, prove benefactors: —

> "Winds blow and waters roll
> Strength to the brave and power and deity,
> Yet in themselves are nothing." [28]

The good are befriended even by weakness and defect. As no man had ever a point of pride that was not injurious to him, so no man had ever a defect that was not somewhere made useful to him. The stag in the fable admired his horns and blamed his feet, but when the hunter came, his feet saved him, and afterwards, caught in the thicket, his horns destroyed him. Every man in his lifetime needs to thank his faults. As no man thoroughly understands a truth until he has contended against it, so no man has a thorough acquaintance with the hindrances or talents of men until he has suffered from the one and seen the triumph of the other over his own want of the same. Has he a defect of temper that unfits him to live in society? Thereby he is driven to entertain himself alone and acquire habits of self-help; and thus, like the wounded oyster, he mends his shell with pearl.

Our strength grows out of our weakness. The indignation which arms itself with secret forces does not awaken until we are pricked and stung and sorely assailed. A great man is always willing to be little. Whilst he sits on the cushion of advantages, he goes to sleep. When he is pushed, tormented, defeated, he has a chance to learn something; he has been put on his wits, on his manhood; he has gained facts; learns his ignorance; is cured of the insanity of conceit; has got moderation and real skill. The wise man throws himself on the side of his assailants. It is more his interest than it is theirs to find his weak point.

The wound cicatrizes and falls off from him like a dead skin, and when they would triumph, lo! he has passed on invulnerable. Blame is safer than praise. I hate to be defended in a newspaper. As long as all that is said is said against me, I feel a certain assurance of success. But as soon as honeyed words of praise are spoken for me I feel as one that lies unprotected before his enemies. In general, every evil to which we do not succumb is a benefactor. As the Sandwich Islander believes that the strength and valor of the enemy he kills passes into himself, so we gain the strength of the temptation we resist.

The same guards which protect us from disaster, defect and enmity, defend us, if we will, from selfishness and fraud. Bolts and bars are not the best of our institutions, nor is shrewdness in trade a mark of wisdom. Men suffer all their life long under the foolish superstition that they can be cheated. But it is as impossible for a man to be cheated by any one but himself, as for a thing to be and not to be at the same time. There is a third silent party to all our bargains. The nature and soul of things takes on itself the guaranty of the fulfilment of every contract, so that honest service cannot come to loss. If you serve an ungrateful master, serve him the more. Put God in your debt. Every stroke shall be repaid. The longer the payment is withholden, the better for you; for compound interest on compound interest is the rate and usage of this exchequer.

The history of persecution is a history of endeavors to cheat nature, to make water run up hill, to twist a rope of sand. It makes no difference whether the actors be many or one, a tyrant or a mob. A mob is a society of bodies voluntarily bereaving themselves of reason and traversing its work.[29] The mob is man voluntarily descending to the nature of the beast. Its fit hour of activity is night. Its actions are insane, like its whole constitution. It persecutes a principle; it would whip a right; it would tar and feather justice, by inflicting fire and outrage upon the houses and persons of those who have these. It resembles the prank of boys, who run with fire-engines to put out the ruddy aurora streaming to the stars. The inviolate spirit turns their spite against the wrongdoers. The martyr cannot be dishonored. Every lash inflicted is a tongue of fame; every prison a more illustrious abode; every burned book or house enlightens the world; every suppressed or expunged word reverberates through the earth from side to side. Hours of sanity and consideration are always arriving to communities, as to individuals, when the truth is seen and the martyrs are justified.

Thus do all things preach the indifferency of circumstances. The man is all. Every thing has two sides, a good and an evil. Every advantage has its tax. I learn to be content. But the doctrine of compensation is not the doctrine of indifferency. The thoughtless say, on hearing these representations, — What boots it to do well? there is one event to good and evil; if I gain any good I must pay for it; if I lose any good I gain some other; all actions are indifferent.

There is a deeper fact in the soul than compensation, to wit, its own nature. The soul is not a compensation, but a life. The soul *is*. Under all this running sea of circumstance, whose waters ebb and flow with perfect balance, lies the aboriginal abyss of real Being. Essence, or God, is not a relation or a part, but the whole. Being is the vast affirmative, excluding negation, self-balanced, and swallowing up all relations, parts and times within itself. Nature, truth, virtue, are the influx from thence. Vice is the absence or departure of the same. Nothing, Falsehood, may indeed stand as the great Night or shade on which as a background the living universe paints itself forth, but no fact is begotten by it; it cannot work, for it is not. It cannot work any good; it cannot work any harm. It is harm inasmuch as it is worse not to be than to be.

We feel defrauded of the retribution due to evil acts, because the criminal adheres to his vice and contumacy and does not come to a crisis or judgment anywhere in visible nature. There is no stunning confutation of his nonsense before men and angels. Has he therefore outwitted the law? Inasmuch as he carries the malignity and the lie with him he so far deceases from nature. In some manner there will be a demonstration of the wrong to the understanding also; but, should we not see it, this deadly deduction makes square the eternal account.

Neither can it be said, on the other hand, that the gain of rectitude must be bought by any loss. There is no penalty to virtue; no penalty to wisdom; they are proper additions of being. In a virtuous action I properly *am*; in a virtuous act I add to the world; I plant into deserts conquered from Chaos and Nothing and see the darkness receding on the limits of the horizon. There can be no excess to love, none to knowledge, none to beauty, when these attributes are considered in the purest sense. The soul refuses limits, and always affirms an Optimism, never a Pessimism.

His life is a progress, and not a station. His instinct

is trust. Our instinct uses "more" and "less" in application to man, of the *presence of the soul*, and not of its absence; the brave man is greater than the coward; the true, the benevolent, the wise, is more a man and not less, than the fool and knave. There is no tax on the good of virtue, for that is the incoming of God himself, or absolute existence, without any comparative. Material good has its tax, and if it came without desert or sweat, has no root in me, and the next wind will blow it away. But all the good of nature is the soul's, and may be had if paid for in nature's lawful coin, that is, by labor which the heart and the head allow. I no longer wish to meet a good I do not earn, for example to find a pot of buried gold, knowing that it brings with it new burdens. I do not wish more external goods, — neither possessions, nor honors, nor powers, nor persons. The gain is apparent; the tax is certain. But there is no tax on the knowledge that the compensation exists and that it is not desirable to dig up treasure.[30] Herein I rejoice with a serene eternal peace. I contract the boundaries of possible mischief. I learn the wisdom of St. Bernard, "Nothing can work me damage except myself; the harm that I sustain I carry about with me, and never am a real sufferer but by my own fault."

In the nature of the soul is the compensation for the inequalities of condition. The radical tragedy of nature seems to be the distinction of More and Less. How can Less not feel the pain; how not feel indignation or malevolence towards More? Look at those who have less faculty, and one feels sad and knows not well what to make of it. He almost shuns their eye; he fears they will upbraid God. What should they do? It seems a great injustice. But see the facts nearly and these mountainous inequalities vanish. Love reduces them as the sun melts the iceberg in the sea. The heart and soul of all men being one, this bitterness of *His* and *Mine* ceases. His is mine. I am my brother and my brother is me. If I feel overshadowed and outdone by great neighbors, I can yet love; I can still receive; and he that loveth maketh his own the grandeur he loves. Thereby I make the discovery that my brother is my guardian,[31] acting for me with the friendliest designs, and the estate I so admired and envied is my own. It is the nature of the soul to appropriate all things. Jesus and Shakspeare are fragments of the soul, and by love I conquer and incorporate them in my own conscious domain. His virtue, — is not that mine? His wit, — if it cannot be made mine, it is not wit.

Such also is the natural history of calamity. The changes which break up at short intervals the prosperity of men are advertisements of a nature whose law is growth. Every soul is by this intrinsic necessity quitting its whole system of things, its friends and home and laws and faith, as the shell-fish crawls out of its beautiful but stony case, because it no longer admits of its growth, and slowly forms a new house.[32] In proportion to the vigor of the individual these revolutions are frequent, until in some happier mind they are incessant and all worldly relations hang very loosely about him, becoming as it were a transparent fluid membrane through which the living form is seen, and not, as in most men, an indurated heterogeneous fabric of many dates and of no settled character, in which the man is imprisoned. Then there can be enlargement, and the man of to-day scarcely recognizes the man of yesterday. And such should be the outward biography of man in time, a putting off of dead circumstances day by day, as he renews his raiment day by day. But to us, in our lapsed estate, resting, not advancing, resisting, not coöperating with the divine expansion, this growth comes by shocks.

We cannot part with our friends. We cannot let our angels go. We do not see that they only go out that archangels may come in.[33] We are idolaters of the old. We do not believe in the riches of the soul, in its proper eternity and omnipresence. We do not believe there is any force in to-day to rival or recreate that beautiful yesterday. We linger in the ruins of the old tent where once we had bread and shelter and organs, nor believe that the spirit can feed, cover, and nerve us again. We cannot again find aught so dear, so sweet, so graceful. But we sit and weep in vain. The voice of the Almighty saith, 'Up and onward for evermore!' We cannot stay amid the ruins. Neither will we rely on the new; and so we walk ever with reverted eyes, like those monsters who look backwards.

And yet the compensations of calamity are made apparent to the understanding also, after long intervals of time. A fever, a mutilation, a cruel disappointment, a loss of wealth, a loss of friends, seems at the moment unpaid loss, and unpayable. But the sure years reveal the deep remedial force that underlies all facts. The death of a dear friend, wife, brother, lover, which seemed nothing but privation, somewhat later assumes the aspect of a guide or genius; for it commonly operates revolutions in our way of life, terminates an epoch of infancy or of youth which was waiting to be closed, breaks up a wonted occupation, or a household, or style of living, and allows the formation of new ones more friendly to the growth of character. It permits or constrains the formation of new acquaintances and the reception of new influences. that prove of the first importance to the next years; and the man or woman who would have remained a sunny garden-flower, with no room for its roots and too much sunshine for its head, by the falling of the walls and the neglect of the gardener is made the banian [34] of the forest, yielding shade and fruit to wide neighborhoods of men.

EXPERIENCE

THE lords of life, the lords of life, —
I saw them pass,
In their own guise,
Like and unlike,
Portly and grim,
Use and Surprise,
Surface and Dream,
Succession swift, and spectral Wrong,
Temperament without a tongue,
And the inventor of the game
Omnipresent without name; —
Some to see, some to be guessed,
They marched from east to west:
Little man, least of all,
Among the legs of his guardians tall,
Walked about with puzzled look: —
Him by the hand dear Nature took;
Dearest Nature, strong and kind,
Whispered, 'Darling, never mind!
To-morrow they will wear another face,
The founder thou! these are thy race!'

EXPERIENCE

WHERE do we find ourselves? In a series of which we do not know the extremes, and believe that it has none. We wake and find ourselves on a stair; there are stairs below us, which we seem to have ascended; there are stairs above us, many a one, which go upward and out of sight. But the Genius which according to the old belief stands at the door by which we enter, and gives us the lethe to drink, that we may tell no tales, mixed the cup too strongly, and we cannot shake off the lethargy now at noonday. Sleep lingers all our lifetime about our eyes, as night hovers all day in the boughs of the fir-tree. All things swim and glitter. Our life is not so much threatened as our perception. Ghostlike we glide through nature, and should not know our place again. Did our birth fall in some fit of indigence and frugality in nature, that she was so sparing of her fire and so liberal of her earth that it appears to us that we lack the affirmative principle, and though we have health and reason, yet we have no superfluity of spirit for new creation? We have enough to live and bring the year about, but not an ounce to impart or to invest. Ah that our Genius were a little more of a genius! We are like millers on the lower levels of a stream, when the factories above them have exhausted the water. We too fancy that the upper people must have raised their dams.

If any of us knew what we were doing, or where we are going, then when we think we best know! We do not know to-day whether we are busy or idle. In times when we thought ourselves indolent, we have afterwards discovered that much was accomplished and much was begun in us. All our days are so unprofitable while they pass, that 't is wonderful where or when we ever got anything of this which we call wisdom, poetry, virtue. We never got it on any dated calendar day. Some heavenly days must have been intercalated somewhere, like those that Hermes [1] won with dice of the Moon, that Osiris might be born. It is said all martyrdoms looked mean when they were suffered. Every ship is a romantic object, except that we sail in. Embark, and the romance quits our vessel and hangs on every other sail in the horizon. Our life looks trivial, and we shun to record it. Men seem to have learned of the horizon the art of perpetual retreating and reference.[2] 'Yonder uplands are rich pasturage, and my neighbor has fertile meadow, but my field,' says the querulous farmer, 'only holds the world together.' I quote another man's saying; unluckily that other withdraws himself in the same way, and quotes me. 'T is the trick of nature thus to degrade to-day; a good deal of buzz, and somewhere a result slipped magically in. Every roof is agreeable to the eye until it is lifted; then we find tragedy and moaning women and hard-eyed husbands and deluges of Lethe, and the men ask, 'What's the news?' as if the old were so bad. How many individuals can we count in society? how many actions? how many opinions? So much of our time is preparation, so much is routine, and so much retrospect, that the pith of each man's genius contracts itself to a very few hours. The history of literature — take the net result of Tiraboschi, Warton, or Schlegel [3] — is a sum of very few ideas and of very few original tales; all the rest being variation of these. So in this great society wide lying around us, a critical analysis would find very few spontaneous actions. It is almost all custom and gross sense. There are even few opinions, and these seem organic in the speakers, and do not disturb the universal necessity.

What opium is instilled into all disaster! It shows formidable as we approach it, but there is at last no rough rasping friction, but the most slippery sliding surfaces; we fall soft on a thought; *Ate Dea*[4] is gentle,

> "Over men's heads walking aloft,
> With tender feet treading so soft." [5]

People grieve and bemoan themselves, but it is not half so bad with them as they say. There are moods in which we court suffering, in the hope that here at least we shall find reality, sharp peaks and edges of truth. But it turns out to be scene-painting and counterfeit. The only thing grief has taught me is to know how shallow it is. That, like all the rest, plays about the surface, and never introduces me into the reality, for contact with which we would even pay the costly price of sons and lovers. Was it Boscovich[6] who found out that bodies never come in contact? Well, souls never touch their objects. An innavigable sea washes with silent waves between us and the things we aim at and converse with. Grief too will make us idealists. In the death of my son,[7] now more than two years ago, I seem to have lost a beautiful estate, — no more. I cannot get it nearer to me. If to-morrow I should be informed of the bankruptcy of my principal debtors, the loss of my property would be a great inconvenience to me, perhaps, for many years; but it would leave me as it found me, — neither better nor worse.

So is it with this calamity; it does not touch me; something which I fancied was a part of me, which could not be torn away without tearing me nor enlarged without enriching me, falls off from me and leaves no scar. It was caducous. I grieve that grief can teach me nothing, nor carry me one step into real nature. The Indian [8] who was laid under a curse that the wind should not blow on him, nor water flow to him, nor fire burn him, is a type of us all. The dearest events are summer rain, and we the Para [9] coats that shed every drop. Nothing is left us now but death. We look to that with a grim satisfaction, saying, There at least is reality that will not dodge us.

I take this evanescence and lubricity of all objects, which lets them slip through our fingers then when we clutch hardest, to be the most unhandsome part of our condition. Nature does not like to be observed, and likes that we should be her fools and playmates. We may have the sphere for our cricket-ball, but not a berry for our philosophy. Direct strokes she never gave us power to make; all our blows glance, all our hits are accidents. Our relations to each other are oblique and casual.

Dream delivers us to dream, and there is no end to illusion. Life is a train of moods [10] like a string of beads, and as we pass through them they prove to be many-colored lenses which paint the world their own hue, and each shows only what lies in its focus. From the mountain you see the mountain. We animate what we can, and we see only what we animate. Nature and books belong to the eyes that see them. It depends on the mood of the man whether he shall see the sunset or the fine poem. There are always sunsets, and

there is always genius; but only a few hours so serene
that we can relish nature or criticism. The more or
less depends on structure or temperament. Temperament is the iron wire on which the beads are strung.
Of what use is fortune or talent to a cold and defective
nature? Who cares what sensibility or discrimination
a man has at some time shown, if he falls asleep in
his chair? or if he laugh and giggle? or if he apologize? or is infected with egotism? or thinks of his
dollar? or cannot go by food? or has gotten a child
in his boyhood? Of what use is genius, if the organ
is too convex or too concave and cannot find a focal
distance within the actual horizon of human life?
Of what use, if the brain is too cold or too hot, and
the man does not care enough for results to stimulate
him to experiment, and hold him up in it? or if the
web is too finely woven, too irritable by pleasure and
pain, so that life stagnates from too much reception
without due outlet? Of what use to make heroic vows
of amendment, if the same old law-breaker is to keep
them? What cheer can the religious sentiment yield,
when that is suspected to be secretly dependent on
the seasons of the year and the state of the blood? I
knew a witty physician [11] who found the creed in the
biliary duct, and used to affirm that if there was disease
in the liver, the man became a Calvinist, and if that
organ was sound, he became a Unitarian. Very mortifying is the reluctant experience that some unfriendly
excess or imbecility neutralizes the promise of genius.
We see young men who owe us a new world, so readily and lavishly they promise, but they never acquit
the debt; they die young and dodge the account; or if
they live they lose themselves in the crowd.

Temperament also enters fully into the system of

illusions and shuts us in a prison of glass which we cannot see. There is an optical illusion about every person we meet. In truth they are all creatures of given temperament, which will appear in a given character, whose boundaries they will never pass; but we look at them, they seem alive, and we presume there is impulse in them. In the moment it seems impulse; in the year, in the lifetime, it turns out to be a certain uniform tune which the revolving barrel of the music-box must play. Men resist the conclusion in the morning, but adopt it as the evening wears on, that temper prevails over everything of time, place and condition, and is inconsumable in the flames of religion. Some modifications the moral sentiment avails to impose, but the individual texture holds its dominion, if not to bias the moral judgments, yet to fix the measure of activity and of enjoyment.

I thus express the law as it is read from the platform of ordinary life, but must not leave it without noticing the capital exception. For temperament is a power which no man willingly hears any one praise but himself. On the platform of physics we cannot resist the contracting influences of so-called science. Temperament puts all divinity to rout. I know the mental proclivity of physicians. I hear the chuckle of the phrenologists. Theoretic kidnappers and slave-drivers, they esteem each man the victim of another, who winds him round his finger by knowing the law of his being; and, by such cheap signboards as the color of his beard or the slope of his occiput, reads the inventory of his fortunes and character. The grossest ignorance does not disgust like this impudent knowingness. The physicians say they are not materialists; but they are: Spirit is matter reduced to an extreme

thinness: O *so* thin! — But the definition of *spiritual*
should be, *that which is its own evidence.*[12] What
notions do they attach to love! what to religion! One
would not willingly pronounce these words in their
hearing, and give them the occasion to profane them.
I saw a gracious gentleman who adapts his conversation to the form of the head of the man he talks with!
I had fancied that the value of life lay in its inscrutable
possibilities; in the fact that I never know, in addressing myself to a new individual, what may befall me.
I carry the keys of my castle in my hand, ready to
throw them at the feet of my lord, whenever and in
what disguise soever he shall appear. I know he is in
the neighborhood, hidden among vagabonds. Shall I
preclude my future by taking a high seat and kindly
adapting my conversation to the shape of heads?
When I come to that, the doctors shall buy me for a
cent. — 'But, sir, medical history; the report to the
Institute; the proven facts!' — I distrust the facts
and the inferences. Temperament is the veto or limi-
tation-power in the constitution, very justly applied
to restrain an opposite excess in the constitution, but
absurdly offered as a bar to original equity. When
virtue is in presence, all subordinate powers sleep.
On its own level, or in view of nature, temperament is
final. I see not, if one be once caught in this trap of
so-called sciences, any escape for the man from the
links of the chain of physical necessity. Given such
an embryo, such a history must follow. On this platform one lives in a sty of sensualism, and would soon
come to suicide.[13] But it is impossible that the creative
power should exclude itself. Into every intelligence
there is a door which is never closed, through which
the creator passes. The intellect, seeker of absolute

truth, or the heart, lover of absolute good, intervenes
for our succor, and at one whisper of these high
powers we awake from ineffectual struggles with this
nightmare. We hurl it into its own hell,[14] and cannot
again contract ourselves to so base a state.

The secret of the illusoriness is in the necessity of
a succession of moods or objects. Gladly we would
anchor, but the anchorage is quicksand. This onward
trick of nature is too strong for us: *Pero si muove*.[15]
When at night I look at the moon and stars, I seem
stationary, and they to hurry. Our love of the real
draws us to permanence, but health of body consists
in circulation, and sanity of mind in variety or facility
of association. We need change of objects. Dedica-
tion to one thought is quickly odious. We house with
the insane, and must humor them; then conversation
dies out. Once I took such delight in Montaigne that
I thought I should not need any other book; before
that, in Shakspeare; then in Plutarch; then in Plotinus;
at one time in Bacon; afterwards in Goethe; even
in Bettine;[16] but now I turn the pages of either of
them languidly, whilst I still cherish their genius.
So with pictures;[17] each will bear an emphasis of
attention once, which it cannot retain, though we fain
would continue to be pleased in that manner. How
strongly I have felt of pictures that when you have
seen one well, you must take your leave of it; you
shall never see it again. I have had good lessons from
pictures which I have since seen without emotion or
remark. A deduction must be made from the opinion
which even the wise express on a new book or occurrence. Their opinion gives me tidings of their mood,
and some vague guess at the new fact, but is nowise

to be trusted as the lasting relation between that intellect and that thing. The child asks, 'Mamma, why don't I like the story as well as when you told it me yesterday?' Alas! child, it is even so with the oldest cherubim of knowledge. But will it answer thy question to say, Because thou wert born to a whole and this story is a particular? The reason of the pain this discovery causes us (and we make it late in respect to works of art and intellect) is the plaint of tragedy which murmurs from it in regard to persons, to friendship and love.[18]

That immobility and absence of elasticity which we find in the arts, we find with more pain in the artist. There is no power of expansion in men.[19] Our friends early appear to us as representatives of certain ideas which they never pass or exceed. They stand on the brink of the ocean of thought and power, but they never take the single step that would bring them there. A man is like a bit of Labrador spar,[20] which has no lustre as you turn it in your hand until you come to a particular angle; then it shows deep and beautiful colors. There is no adaptation or universal applicability in men, but each has his special talent, and the mastery of successful men consists in adroitly keeping themselves where and when that turn shall be oftenest to be practised. We do what we must, and call it by the best names we can, and would fain have the praise of having intended the result which ensues. I cannot recall any form of man who is not superfluous sometimes. But is not this pitiful? Life is not worth the taking, to do tricks in.

Of course it needs the whole society to give the symmetry we seek. The party-colored wheel must revolve very fast to appear white. Something is earned too by conversing with so much folly and defect. In fine, whoever loses, we are always of the gaining party.[21] Divinity is behind our failures and follies also. The plays of children are nonsense, but very educative nonsense. So it is with the largest and solemnest things, with commerce, government, church, marriage, and so with the history of every man's bread, and the ways by which he is to come by it. Like a bird which alights nowhere, but hops perpetually from bough to bough, is the Power which abides in no man and in no woman, but for a moment speaks from this one, and for another moment from that one.

But what help from these fineries or pedantries? What help from thought? Life is not dialectics.[22] We, I think, in these times, have had lessons enough of the futility of criticism. Our young people have thought and written much on labor and reform, and for all that they have written, neither the world nor themselves have got on a step. Intellectual tasting of life will not supersede muscular activity. If a man should consider the nicety of the passage of a piece of bread down his throat, he would starve. At Education Farm[23] the noblest theory of life sat on the noblest figures of young men and maidens, quite powerless and melancholy. It would not rake or pitch a ton of hay; it would not rub down a horse; and the men and maidens it left pale and hungry. A political orator wittily compared our party promises to western roads, which opened stately enough, with planted trees on either side to tempt the traveller, but soon became narrow and narrower and ended in a squirrel-track and ran up a tree. So does culture with us; it ends in headache. Unspeakably sad and barren does life look to those who a few months ago were dazzled with the splendor of the promise of the times. "There is now no longer any right course of action nor any self-devotion left among the Iranis." [24] Objections and criticism we have had our fill of. There are objections to every course of life and action, and the practical wisdom infers an indifferency, from the omnipresence of objection. The whole frame of things preaches indifferency. Do not craze yourself with thinking, but go about your business anywhere. Life is not intellectual or critical, but sturdy. Its chief good is for well-mixed people who can enjoy what they find, without question. Nature hates peeping, and our mothers speak her very sense when they say, "Children, eat your victuals, and say no more of it." To fill the hour, — that is happiness; to fill the hour and leave no crevice for a repentance or an approval. We live amid surfaces, and the true art of life is to skate well on them. Under the oldest mouldiest conventions a man of native force prospers just as well as in the newest world, and that by skill of handling and treatment. [25] He can take hold anywhere. Life itself is a mixture of power and form, and will not bear the least excess of either. [26] To finish the moment, to find the journey's end in every step of the road, to live the greatest number of good hours, is wisdom. [27] It is not the part of men, but of fanatics, or of mathematicians if you will, to say that, the shortness of life considered, it is not worth caring whether for so short a duration we were sprawling in want or sitting high. Since our office is with moments, let us husband them. Five minutes of to-day are worth as much to me as five minutes in the next millennium. Let us be poised, and wise, and our own, to-day. Let us treat the men and women well; treat them as if they were real; perhaps they are. Men live in their fancy, like drunkards whose hands are too soft and tremulous for successful labor. It is a tempest of fancies, and the only ballast I know is a respect to the present hour. Without any shadow of doubt, amidst this vertigo of shows and politics, I settle myself ever the firmer in the creed that we should not postpone and refer [28] and wish, but do broad justice where we are, by whomsoever we deal with, accepting our actual companions and circumstances, however humble or odious, as the mystic officials to whom the universe has delegated its whole pleasure for us. If these are mean and malignant, their contentment, which is the last victory of justice, is a more satisfying echo to the heart than the voice of poets and the casual sympathy of admirable persons. I think that however a thoughtful man may suffer from the defects and absurdities of his company, he cannot without affectation deny to any set of men and women a sensibility to extraordinary merit. The coarse and frivolous have an instinct of superiority, if they have not a sympathy, and honor it in their blind capricious way with sincere homage.

The fine young people despise life, but in me, and in such as with me are free from dyspepsia, and to whom a day is a sound and solid good, it is a great excess of politeness to look scornful and to cry for company. I am grown by sympathy a little eager and sentimental, but leave me alone and I should relish every hour and what it brought me, the potluck [29] of the day, as heartily as the oldest gossip in the bar-room. I am thankful for small mercies. I compared notes with one of my friends who expects everything of the universe and is disappointed when anything is less

than the best, and I found that I begin at the other
extreme, expecting nothing, and am always full of
thanks for moderate goods. I accept the clangor and
jangle of contrary tendencies. I find my account in
sots and bores also. They give a reality to the circum-
jacent picture which such a vanishing meteorous appearance can ill spare. In the morning I awake and
find the old world, wife, babes and mother, Concord
and Boston, the dear old spiritual world and even the
dear old devil not far off. If we will take the good we
find, asking no questions, we shall have heaping measures. The great gifts are not got by analysis. Everything good is on the highway. The middle region of
our being is the temperate zone. We may climb into
the thin and cold realm of pure geometry and lifeless
science, or sink into that of sensation. Between these
extremes is the equator of life, of thought, of spirit,
of poetry, — a narrow belt. Moreover, in popular experience everything good is on the highway. A collector peeps into all the picture-shops of Europe for a
landscape of Poussin,[30] a crayon-sketch of Salvator;[31]
but the Transfiguration, the Last Judgment, the Communion of Saint Jerome,[32] and what are as transcendent as these, are on the walls of the Vatican, the Uffizi,[33]
or the Louvre, where every footman may see them;
to say nothing of Nature's pictures in every street, of
sunsets and sunrises every day, and the sculpture of
the human body never absent. A collector recently
bought at public auction, in London, for one hundred
and fifty-seven guineas, an autograph of Shakspeare;
but for nothing a school-boy can read Hamlet and
can detect secrets of highest concernment yet unpublished therein. I think I will never read any but the
commonest books, — the Bible, Homer, Dante, Shak-

speare and Milton. Then we are impatient of so
public a life and planet, and run hither and thither for
nooks and secrets. The imagination delights in the
woodcraft of Indians, trappers and bee-hunters. We
fancy that we are strangers, and not so intimately
domesticated in the planet as the wild man and the
wild beast and bird. But the exclusion reaches them
also; reaches the climbing, flying, gliding, feathered
and four-footed man. Fox and woodchuck, hawk and
snipe and bittern, when nearly seen, have no more
root in the deep world than man, and are just such
superficial tenants of the globe. Then the new molecular philosophy [34] shows astronomical interspaces
betwixt atom and atom, shows that the world is all
outside; it has no inside.

The mid-world is best. Nature, as we know her,
is no saint. The lights of the church, the ascetics,
Gentoos and corn-eaters, she does not distinguish
by any favor. She comes eating and drinking and
sinning. Her darlings, the great, the strong, the beautiful, are not children of our law; do not come out of
the Sunday School, nor weigh their food, nor punctu-
ally keep the commandments. If we will be strong
with her strength we must not harbor such disconso-
late consciences, borrowed too from the consciences
of other nations. We must set up the strong present
tense [35] against all the rumors of wrath, past or to
come. So many things are unsettled which it is of the
first importance to settle; — and, pending their settlement, we will do as we do. Whilst the debate goes
forward on the equity of commerce, and will not be
closed for a century or two, New and Old England
may keep shop. Law of copyright [36] and international
copyright is to be discussed, and in the interim we

will sell our books for the most we can. Expediency of literature,[37] reason of literature, lawfulness of writing down a thought, is questioned; much is to say on both sides, and, while the fight waxes hot, thou, dearest scholar, stick to thy foolish task, add a line every hour, and between whiles add a line. Right to hold land, right of property, is disputed, and the conventions convene, and before the vote is taken, dig away in your garden, and spend your earnings as a waif or godsend to all serene and beautiful purposes. Life itself is a bubble and a scepticism, and a sleep within a sleep. Grant it, and as much more as they will, — but thou, God's darling! heed thy private dream; thou wilt not be missed in the scorning and scepticism; there are enough of them; stay there in thy closet and toil until the rest are agreed what to do about it. Thy sickness, they say, and thy puny habit require that thou do this or avoid that, but know that thy life is a flitting state, a tent for a night, and do thou, sick or well, finish that stint.[38] Thou art sick, but shalt not be worse, and the universe, which holds thee dear, shall be the better.

Human life is made up of the two elements, power and form, and the proportion must be invariably kept if we would have it sweet and sound. Each of these elements in excess makes a mischief as hurtful as its defect. Everything runs to excess; every good quality is noxious if unmixed, and, to carry the danger to the edge of ruin, nature causes each man's peculiarity to superabound. Here, among the farms, we adduce the scholars as examples of this treachery. They are nature's victims of expression. You who see the artist, the orator, the poet, too near, and find their life no more excellent than that of mechanics or farmers, and themselves victims of partiality, very hollow and haggard, and pronounce them failures, not heroes, but quacks, — conclude very reasonably that these arts are not for man, but are disease. Yet nature will not bear you out. Irresistible nature made men such, and makes legions more of such, every day. You love the boy reading in a book, gazing at a drawing or a cast; yet what are these millions who read and behold, but incipient writers and sculptors? Add a little more of that quality which now reads and sees, and they will seize the pen and chisel. And if one remembers how innocently he began to be an artist, he perceives that nature joined with his enemy. A man is a golden impossibility. The line he must walk is a hair's breadth. The wise through excess of wisdom is made a fool.[39]

How easily, if fate would suffer it, we might keep forever these beautiful limits, and adjust ourselves, once for all, to the perfect calculation of the kingdom of known cause and effect! In the street and in the newspapers, life appears so plain a business that manly resolution and adherence to the multiplication-table through all weathers will insure success. But ah! presently comes a day, or is it only a half-hour, with its angel-whispering, — which discomfits the conclusions of nations and of years! To-morrow again every thing looks real and angular, the habitual standards are reinstated, common-sense is as rare as genius, — is the basis of genius, and experience is hands and feet to every enterprise; — and yet, he who should do his business on this understanding would be quickly bankrupt. Power keeps quite another road than the turnpikes of choice and will; namely the subterranean and invisible tunnels and channels of life. It is ridiculous that we are diplomatists, and doctors, and considerate people; there are no dupes like these. Life is a series of surprises, and would not be worth taking or keeping if it were not. God delights to isolate us every day, and hide from us the past and the future. We would look about us, but with grand politeness he draws down before us an impenetrable screen of purest sky, and another behind us of purest sky. 'You will not remember,' he seems to say, 'and you will not expect.' [40] All good conversation, manners and action come from a spontaneity which forgets usages and makes the moment great. Nature hates calculators; her methods are saltatory and impulsive. Man lives by pulses; our organic movements are such; and the chemical and ethereal agents are undulatory and alternate; and the mind goes antagonizing on, and never prospers but by fits. We thrive by casualties. Our chief experiences have been casual. The most attractive class of people are those who are powerful obliquely and not by the direct stroke; men of genius, but not yet accredited; one gets the cheer of their light without paying too great a tax. Theirs is the beauty of the bird or the morning light, and not of art. In the thought of genius there is always a surprise; and the moral sentiment is well called "the newness," for it is never other; as new to the oldest intelligence as to the young child; — "the kingdom that cometh without observation." In like manner, for practical success, there must not be too much design. A man will not be observed in doing that which he can do best. There is a certain magic about his properest action which stupefies your powers of observation, so that though it is done before you, you wist not of it. The art of life has a pudency, and will not be exposed. Every man is an impossibility until he is born; every thing impossible until we see a success. The ardors of piety agree at last with the coldest scepticism, — that nothing is of us or our works, — that all is of God. Nature will not spare us the smallest leaf of laurel. All writing comes by the grace of God, and all doing and having. I would gladly be moral and keep due metes and bounds, which I dearly love, and allow the most to the will of man; but I have set my heart on honesty in this chapter, and I can see nothing at last, in success or failure, than more or less of vital force supplied from the Eternal. The results of life are uncalculated and uncalculable. The years teach much which the days never know. The persons who compose our company converse, and come and go, and design and execute many things, and somewhat comes of it all, but an unlooked-for result. The individual is always mistaken.[41] He designed many things, and drew in other persons as coadjutors, quarrelled with some or all, blundered much, and something is done; all are a little advanced, but the individual is always mistaken. It turns out somewhat new and very unlike what he promised himself.

The ancients, struck with this irreducibleness of the elements of human life to calculation, exalted Chance into a divinity; but that is to stay too long at the spark, which glitters truly at one point, but the universe is warm with the latency of the same fire. The miracle of life which will not be expounded but will remain a miracle, introduces a new element. In the growth of the embryo, Sir Everard Home,[42] I think, noticed that the evolution was not from one central

point, but coactive from three or more points. Life
has no memory. That which proceeds in succession
might be remembered, but that which is coexistent,
or ejaculated from a deeper cause, as yet far from
being conscious, knows not its own tendency. So is it
with us, now sceptical or without unity, because im-
mersed in forms and effects all seeming to be of equal
yet hostile value, and now religious, whilst in the reception of spiritual law. Bear with these distractions,
with this coetaneous growth of the parts; they will
one day be *members*, and obey one will. On that one
will, on that secret cause, they nail our attention and
hope. Life is hereby melted into an expectation or
a religion. Underneath the inharmonious and trivial
particulars, is a musical perfection; the Ideal journey-
ing always with us, the heaven without rent or seam.
Do but observe the mode of our illumination. When
I converse with a profound mind, or if at any time
being alone I have good thoughts, I do not at once
arrive at satisfactions, as when, being thirsty, I drink
water; or go to the fire, being cold; no! but I am at
first apprised of my vicinity to a new and excellent
region of life. By persisting to read or to think, this
region gives further sign of itself, as it were in flashes
of light, in sudden discoveries of its profound beauty
and repose, as if the clouds that covered it parted at
intervals and showed the approaching traveller the
inland mountains, with the tranquil eternal meadows
spread at their base, whereon flocks graze and shep-
herds pipe and dance. But every insight from this
realm of thought is felt as initial, and promises a sequel.
I do not make it; I arrive there, and behold what was
there already. I make! O no! I clap my hands in
infantine joy and amazement before the first opening

to me of this august magnificence, old with the love and homage of innumerable ages, young with the life of life, the sunbright Mecca of the desert.[43] And what a future it opens! I feel a new heart beating with the love of the new beauty. I am ready to die out of nature and be born again into this new yet unapproachable America I have found in the West: —

> "Since neither now nor yesterday began
> These thoughts, which have been ever, nor yet can
> A man be found who their first entrance knew." [44]

If I have described life as a flux of moods, I must now add that there is that in us which changes not and which ranks all sensations and states of mind. The consciousness in each man is a sliding scale, which identifies him now with the First Cause, and now with the flesh of his body; life above life, in infinite degrees. The sentiment from which it sprung determines the dignity of any deed, and the question ever is, not what you have done or forborne, but at whose command you have done or forborne it.

Fortune, Minerva, Muse, Holy Ghost, — these are quaint names, too narrow to cover this unbounded substance. The baffled intellect must still kneel before this cause, which refuses to be named, — ineffable cause, which every fine genius has essayed to represent by some emphatic symbol, as, Thales by water,[45] Anaximenes by air, Anaxagoras [46] by (Νοῦς) thought, Zoroaster [47] by fire, Jesus and the moderns by love; and the metaphor of each has become a national religion. The Chinese Mencius [48] has not been the least successful in his generalization. "I fully understand language," he said, "and nourish well my vast flowing vigor." — "I beg to ask what you call vast flowing vigor?" said his companion. "The expla-

EXPERIENCE 51

nation," replied Mencius, "is difficult. This vigor is
supremely great, and in the highest degree unbend-
ing. Nourish it correctly and do it no injury, and it will
fill up the vacancy between heaven and earth. This
vigor accords with and assists justice and reason, and
leaves no hunger." — In our more correct writing
we give to this generalization the name of Being, and
thereby confess that we have arrived as far as we can
go. Suffice it for the joy of the universe that we have
not arrived at a wall, but at interminable oceans.
Our life seems not present so much as prospective;
not for the affairs on which it is wasted, but as a hint
of this vast-flowing vigor. Most of life seems to be
mere advertisement of faculty; information is given
us not to sell ourselves cheap; that we are very great.
So, in particulars, our greatness is always in a tendency or direction, not in an action. It is for us to believe
in the rule, not in the exception. The noble are thus
known from the ignoble. So in accepting the leading
of the sentiments, it is not what we believe concerning
the immortality of the soul or the like, but *the universal
impulse to believe*, that is the material circumstance
and is the principal fact in the history of the globe.
Shall we describe this cause as that which works
directly? The spirit is not helpless or needful of
mediate organs. It has plentiful powers and direct
effects. I am explained without explaining, I am felt
without acting, and where I am not. Therefore all
just persons are satisfied with their own praise. They
refuse to explain themselves, and are content that
new actions should do them that office. They believe that we communicate without speech and above
speech, and that no right action of ours is quite un-
affecting to our friends, at whatever distance; for the

influence of action is not to be measured by miles. Why should I fret myself because a circumstance has occurred which hinders my presence where I was expected? If I am not at the meeting, my presence where I am should be as useful to the commonwealth of friendship and wisdom, as would be my presence in that place. I exert the same quality of power in all places. Thus journeys the mighty Ideal before us; it never was known to fall into the rear. No man ever came to an experience which was satiating, but his good is tidings of a better. Onward and onward! In liberated moments we know that a new picture of life and duty is already possible; the elements already exist in many minds around you of a doctrine of life which shall transcend any written record we have. The new statement will comprise the scepticisms as well as the faiths of society, and out of unbeliefs a creed shall be formed. For scepticisms are not gratuitous or lawless, but are limitations of the affirmative statement, and the new philosophy must take them in and make affirmations outside of them, just as much as it must include the oldest beliefs.

It is very unhappy, but too late to be helped, the discovery we have made that we exist. That discovery is called the Fall of Man. Ever afterwards we suspect our instruments. We have learned that we do not see directly, but mediately, and that we have no means of correcting these colored and distorting lenses which we are, or of computing the amount of their errors. Perhaps these subject-lenses have a creative power; perhaps there are no objects. Once we lived in what we saw; now, the rapaciousness of this new power,

which threatens to absorb all things, engages us.
Nature, art, persons, letters, religions, objects, successively tumble in, and God is but one of its ideas.
Nature and literature are subjective phenomena;
every evil and every good thing is a shadow which we
cast. The street is full of humiliations to the proud.
As the fop contrived to dress his bailiffs in his livery
and make them wait on his guests at table, so the
chagrins which the bad heart gives off as bubbles, at
once take form as ladies and gentlemen in the street,
shopmen or bar-keepers in hotels, and threaten or
insult whatever is threatenable and insultable in us.
'T is the same with our idolatries. People forget that
it is the eye which makes the horizon, and the round-
ing mind's eye which makes this or that man a type
or representative of humanity, with the name of hero
or saint. Jesus, the "providential man," is a good
man on whom many people are agreed that these
optical laws shall take effect. By love on one part
and by forbearance to press objection on the other
part, it is for a time settled that we will look at him in
the centre of the horizon, and ascribe to him the properties that will attach to any man so seen. But the
longest love or aversion has a speedy term. The great
and crescive self,[49] rooted in absolute nature, supplants
all relative existence and ruins the kingdom of mortal
friendship and love. Marriage (in what is called the
spiritual world) is impossible, because of the inequality between every subject and every object. The subject is the receiver of Godhead, and at every comparison must feel his being enhanced by that cryptic might.
Though not in energy, yet by presence, this magazine
of substance cannot be otherwise than felt; nor can
any force of intellect attribute to the object the proper

deity which sleeps or wakes forever in every subject. Never can love make consciousness and ascription equal in force. There will be the same gulf between every me and thee as between the original and the picture. The universe is the bride of the soul. All private sympathy is partial. Two human beings are like globes, which can touch only in a point, and whilst they remain in contact all other points of each of the spheres are inert; their turn must also come, and the longer a particular union lasts the more energy of appetency the parts not in union acquire.

Life will be imaged, but cannot be divided nor doubled. Any invasion of its unity would be chaos. The soul is not twin-born but the only begotten, and though revealing itself as child in time, child in appearance, is of a fatal and universal power, admitting no co-life. Every day, every act betrays the ill-concealed deity. We believe in ourselves as we do not believe in others. We permit all things to ourselves, and that which we call sin in others is experiment for us. It is an instance of our faith in ourselves that men never speak of crime as lightly as they think; or every man thinks a latitude safe for himself which is nowise to be indulged to another. The act looks very differently on the inside and on the outside; in its quality and in its consequences. Murder in the murderer is no such ruinous thought as poets and romancers will have it; it does not unsettle him or fright him from his ordinary notice of trifles; it is an act quite easy to be contemplated; but in its sequel it turns out to be a horrible jangle and confounding of all relations. Especially the crimes that spring from love seem right and fair from the actor's point of view, but when acted are found destructive of society. No man at last believes

that he can be lost, or that the crime in him is as black
as in the felon. Because the intellect qualifies in our
own case the moral judgments. For there is no crime
to the intellect. That is antinomian or hypernomian,[50]
and judges law as well as fact. "It is worse than a
crime, it is a blunder," said Napoleon, speaking the
language of the intellect. To it, the world is a problem in mathematics or the science of quantity, and it
leaves out praise and blame and all weak emotions.
All stealing is comparative. If you come to absolutes,
pray who does not steal? Saints are sad, because they
behold sin (even when they speculate) from the point
of view of the conscience, and not of the intellect; a
confusion of thought. Sin, seen from the thought, is
a diminution, or *less ;* seen from the conscience or
will, it is pravity or *bad.* The intellect names it shade,
absence of light, and no essence. The conscience must
feel it as essence, essential evil. This it is not; it has
an objective existence, but no subjective.

Thus inevitably does the universe wear our color,
and every object fall successively into the subject
itself. The subject exists, the subject enlarges; all
things sooner or later fall into place. As I am, so I
see; use what language we will, we can never say
anything but what we are; Hermes, Cadmus, Columbus, Newton, Bonaparte,[51] are the mind's ministers.
Instead of feeling a poverty when we encounter a great
man, let us treat the new-comer like a travelling geologist who passes through our estate and shows us
good slate, or limestone, or anthracite, in our brush
pasture. The partial action of each strong mind in
one direction is a telescope for the objects on which
it is pointed. But every other part of knowledge is to
be pushed to the same extravagance, ere the soul at-

tains her due sphericity. Do you see that kitten chasing so prettily her own tail? If you could look with her eyes you might see her surrounded with hundreds of figures performing complex dramas, with tragic and comic issues, long conversations, many characters, many ups and downs of fate, — and meantime it is only puss and her tail. How long before our masquerade will end its noise of tambourines, laughter and shouting, and we shall find it was a solitary performance? A subject and an object, — it takes so much to make the galvanic circuit complete, but magnitude adds nothing. What imports it whether it is Kepler and the sphere,[52] Columbus and America, a reader and his book, or puss with her tail?

It is true that all the muses and love and religion hate these developments, and will find a way to punish the chemist who publishes in the parlor the secrets of the laboratory. And we cannot say too little of our constitutional necessity of seeing things under private aspects, or saturated with our humors. And yet is the God the native of these bleak rocks. That need makes in morals the capital virtue of self-trust. We must hold hard to this poverty, however scandalous, and by more vigorous self-recoveries, after the sallies of action, possess our axis more firmly. The life of truth is cold and so far mournful; but it is not the slave of tears, contritions and perturbations. It does not attempt another's work, nor adopt another's facts. It is a main lesson of wisdom to know your own from another's. I have learned that I cannot dispose of other people's facts; but I possess such a key to my own as persuades me, against all their denials, that they also have a key to theirs. A sympathetic person is placed in the dilemma of a swimmer among drown-

ing men, who all catch at him, and if he give so much
as a leg or a finger they will drown him. They wish
to be saved from the mischiefs of their vices, but not
from their vices. Charity would be wasted on this
poor waiting on the symptoms. A wise and hardy
physician will say, *Come out of that*, as the first condition of advice.

In this our talking America we are ruined by our
good nature and listening on all sides. This compliance takes away the power of being greatly useful.
A man should not be able to look other than directly
and forthright. A preoccupied attention is the only
answer to the importunate frivolity of other people;
an attention, and to an aim which makes their wants
frivolous. This is a divine answer, and leaves no appeal and no hard thoughts. In Flaxman's drawing [53]
of the Eumenides of Æschylus, Orestes supplicates
Apollo, whilst the Furies sleep on the threshold. The
face of the god expresses a shade of regret and compassion, but is calm with the conviction of the irre-
concilableness of the two spheres. He is born into
other politics, into the eternal and beautiful. The
man at his feet asks for his interest in turmoils of
the earth, into which his nature cannot enter. And
the Eumenides there lying express pictorially this,
disparity. The god is surcharged with his divine destiny.

Illusion, Temperament, Succession, Surface, Surprise, Reality, Subjectiveness,[54] — these are threads
on the loom of time, these are the lords of life. I dare
not assume to give their order, but I name them as I
find them in my way. I know better than to claim
any completeness for my picture. I am a fragment,

and this is a fragment of me. I can very confidently announce one or another law, which throws itself into relief and form, but I am too young yet by some ages to compile a code. I gossip for my hour concerning the eternal politics. I have seen many fair pictures not in vain. A wonderful time I have lived in. I am not the novice I was fourteen, nor yet seven years ago. Let who will ask, Where is the fruit? I find a private fruit sufficient. This is a fruit, — that I should not ask for a rash effect from meditations, counsels and the hiving of truths. I should feel it pitiful to demand a result on this town and county, an overt effect on the instant month and year. The effect is deep and secular as the cause. It works on periods in which mortal lifetime is lost. All I know is reception; I am and I have: but I do not get, and when I have fancied I had gotten anything, I found I did not. I worship with wonder the great Fortune. My reception has been so large, that I am not annoyed by receiving this or that superabundantly. I say to the Genius, if he will pardon the proverb, *In for a mill, in for a million.* When I receive a new gift, I do not macerate my body to make the account square, for if I should die I could not make the account square. The benefit overran the merit the first day, and has overrun the merit ever since. The merit itself, so-called, I reckon part of the receiving.

Also that hankering after an overt or practical effect seems to me an apostasy. In good earnest I am willing to spare this most unnecessary deal of doing. Life wears to me a visionary face. Hardest roughest action is visionary also. It is but a choice between soft and turbulent dreams. People disparage knowing and the intellectual life, and urge doing. I am very content with knowing, if only I could know. That is an august entertainment, and would suffice me a great while. To know a little would be worth the expense of this world. I hear always the law of Adrastia,[55] "that every soul which had acquired any truth, should be safe from harm until another period."

I know that the world I converse with in the city and in the farms, is not the world I *think*. I observe that difference, and shall observe it. One day I shall know the value and law of this discrepance. But I have not found that much was gained by manipular attempts to realize the world of thought. Many eager persons successively make an experiment in this way, and make themselves ridiculous. They acquire democratic manners, they foam at the mouth, they hate and deny. Worse, I observe that in the history of mankind there is never a solitary example of success, —taking their own tests of success. I say this polemically, or in reply to the inquiry, Why not realize your world? But far be from me the despair which prejudges the law by a paltry empiricism; — since there never was a right endeavor but it succeeded. Patience and patience, we shall win at the last. We must be very suspicious of the deceptions of the element of time. It takes a good deal of time to eat or to sleep, or to earn a hundred dollars, and a very little time to entertain a hope and an insight which becomes the light of our life. We dress our garden, eat our dinners, discuss the household with our wives, and these things make no impression, are forgotten next week; but, in the solitude to which every man is always returning, he has a sanity and revelations which in his passage into new worlds he will carry with him. Never mind the ridicule, never mind the defeat; up again, old heart! — it seems to say, — there is victory yet for all justice; and the true romance which the world exists to realize will be the transformation of genius into practical power.

CHARACTER

THE sun set; but set not his hope:
Stars rose; his faith was earlier up:
Fixed on the enormous galaxy,
Deeper and older seemed his eye:
And matched his sufferance sublime
The taciturnity of time.
He spoke, and words more soft than rain
Brought the Age of Gold again:
His action won such reverence sweet,
As hid all measure of the feat.

WORK of his hand
He nor commends nor grieves:
Pleads for itself the fact;
As unrepenting Nature leaves
Her every act.

CHARACTER

I HAVE read that those who listened to Lord Chatham[1] felt that there was something finer in the man than anything which he said. It has been complained of our brilliant English historian[2] of the French Revolution that when he has told all his facts about Mirabeau,[3] they do not justify his estimate of his genius. The Gracchi,[4] Agis,[5] Cleomenes,[6] and others of Plutarch's[7] heroes, do not in the record of facts equal their own fame. Sir Philip Sidney,[8] the Earl of Essex,[9] Sir Walter Raleigh,[10] are men of great figure and of few deeds. We cannot find the smallest part of the personal weight of Washington in the narrative of his exploits. The authority of the name of Schiller[11] is too great for his books. This inequality of the reputation to the works or the anecdotes is not accounted for by saying that the reverberation is longer than the thunder-clap, but somewhat resided in these men which begot an expectation that outran all their performance. The largest part of their power was latent. This is that which we call — Character, a reserved force, which acts directly by presence and without means. It is conceived of as a certain undemonstrable force, a Familiar or Genius,[12] by whose impulses the man is guided, but whose counsels he cannot impart; which is company for him, so that such men are often solitary, or if they chance to be social, do not need society but can entertain themselves very well alone. The purest literary talent appears at one time great, at another time small, but character is of a stellar and undiminishable greatness. What others effect by talent or by eloquence, this man accomplishes by some magnetism. "Half his strength he put not forth." His victories are by demonstration of superiority, and not by crossing of bayonets. He conquers because his arrival alters the face of affairs. "O Iole! how did you know that Hercules was a god?" [13] "Because," answered Iole, "I was content the moment my eyes fell on him. When I beheld Theseus, I desired that I might see him offer battle, or at least guide his horses in the chariot-race; but Hercules did not wait for a contest; he conquered whether he stood, or walked, or sat, or whatever thing he did." Man, ordinarily a pendant to events, only half attached, and that awkwardly, to the world he lives in, in these examples appears to share the life of things, and to be an expression of the same laws which control the tides and the sun, numbers and quantities.

But to use a more modest illustration and nearer home, I observe that in our political elections, where this element, if it appears at all, can only occur in its coarsest form, we sufficiently understand its incomparable rate. The people know that they need in their representative much more than talent, namely the power to make his talent trusted. They cannot come at their ends by sending to Congress a learned, acute and fluent speaker, [14] if he be not one who, before he was appointed by the people to represent them, was appointed by Almighty God to stand for a fact, [15] — invincibly persuaded of that fact in himself, — so that the most confident and the most violent persons learn that here is resistance on which both impudence and terror are wasted, namely faith in a fact. The men who carry their points do not need to inquire of their constituents what they should say, but are themselves

the country which they represent; nowhere are its
emotions or opinions so instant and true as in them;
nowhere so pure from a selfish infusion. The consti-
tuency at home hearkens to their words, watches the
color of their cheek, and therein, as in a glass, dresses
its own. Our public assemblies are pretty good tests
of manly force. Our frank countrymen of the west
and south have a taste for character, and like to know
whether the New Englander is a substantial man, or
whether the hand can pass through him.

The same motive force appears in trade. There are
geniuses in trade, as well as in war, or the State, or
letters; and the reason why this or that man is fortunate is not to be told. It lies in the man; that is all anybody can tell you about it. See him and you will know
as easily why he succeeds, as, if you see Napoleon, you
would comprehend his fortune. In the new objects
we recognize the old game, the habit of fronting the
fact, and not dealing with it at second hand,[16] through
the perceptions of somebody else. Nature seems to
authorize trade, as soon as you see the natural merchant, who appears not so much a private agent as her
factor and Minister of Commerce. His natural probity
combines with his insight into the fabric of society to
put him above tricks, and he communicates to all his
own faith that contracts are of no private interpretation. The habit of his mind is a reference to standards
of natural equity and public advantage; and he inspires respect and the wish to deal with him, both for
the quiet spirit of honor which attends him, and for
the intellectual pastime which the spectacle of so much
ability affords. This immensely stretched trade,[17]
which makes the capes of the Southern Ocean his
wharves and the Atlantic Sea his familiar port, centres

in his brain only; and nobody in the universe can make his place good. In his parlor I see very well that he has been at hard work this morning, with that knitted brow and that settled humor, which all his desire to be courteous cannot shake off. I see plainly how many firm acts have been done; how many valiant *noes* have this day been spoken, when others would have uttered ruinous *yeas*. I see, with the pride of art and skill of masterly arithmetic and power of remote combination, the consciousness of being an agent and playfellow of the original laws of the world. He too believes that none can supply him, and that a man must be born to trade or he cannot learn it.

This virtue draws the mind more when it appears in action to ends not so mixed. It works with most energy in the smallest companies and in private relations. In all cases it is an extraordinary and incomputable agent. The excess of physical strength is paralyzed by it. Higher natures overpower lower ones by affecting them with a certain sleep.[18] The faculties are locked up, and offer no resistance. Perhaps that is the universal law. When the high cannot bring up the low to itself, it benumbs it, as man charms down the resistance of the lower animals. Men exert on each other a similar occult power. How often has the influence of a true master realized all the tales of magic! A river of command seemed to run down from his eyes into all those who beheld him, a torrent of strong sad light, like an Ohio or Danube, which pervaded them with his thoughts and colored all events with the hue of his mind. "What means did you employ?" was the question asked of the wife of Concini,[19] in regard to her treatment of Mary of Medici; and the answer was, "Only that influence which every

strong mind has over a weak one." Cannot Cæsar in
irons shuffle off the irons and transfer them to the
person of Hippo or Thraso[20] the turnkey? Is an iron
handcuff so immutable a bond? Suppose a slaver on
the coast of Guinea should take on board a gang of
negroes which should contain persons of the stamp
of Toussaint L'Ouverture:[21] or, let us fancy, under
these swarthy masks he has a gang of Washingtons
in chains. When they arrive at Cuba, will the relative
order of the ship's company be the same? Is there
nothing but rope and iron? Is there no love, no reverence? Is there never a glimpse of right in a poor
slave-captain's mind; and cannot these be supposed
available to break or elude or in any manner over-
match the tension of an inch or two of iron ring?

This is a natural power, like light and heat, and all
nature coöperates with it. The reason why we feel
one man's presence and do not feel another's is as
simple as gravity. Truth is the summit of being; justice is the application of it to affairs. All individual
natures stand in a scale, according to the purity of
this element in them. The will of the pure runs down
from them into other natures, as water runs down
from a higher into a lower vessel. This natural force
is no more to be withstood than any other natural
force. We can drive a stone upward for a moment
into the air, but it is yet true that all stones will forever
fall; and whatever instances can be quoted of un-
punished theft, or of a lie which somebody credited,
justice must prevail, and it is the privilege of truth to
make itself believed. Character is this moral order
seen through the medium of an individual nature.
An individual is an encloser. Time and space, liberty
and necessity, truth and thought, are left at large no

longer. Now, the universe is a close or pound. All things exist in the man tinged with the manners of his soul. With what quality is in him he infuses all nature that he can reach; nor does he tend to lose himself in vastness, but, at how long a curve soever, all his regards return into his own good at last.[22] He animates all he can, and he sees only what he animates. He encloses the world, as the patriot does his country, as a material basis for his character, and a theatre for action. A healthy soul stands united with the Just and the True, as the magnet arranges itself with the pole; so that he stands to all beholders like a transparent object betwixt them and the sun, and whoso journeys towards the sun, journeys towards that person. He is thus the medium of the highest influence to all who are not on the same level. Thus men of character are the conscience of the society to which they belong.[23]

The natural measure of this power is the resistance of circumstances. Impure men consider life as it is reflected in opinions, events and persons. They cannot see the action until it is done. Yet its moral element preëxisted in the actor, and its quality as right or wrong it was easy to predict. Everything in nature is bipolar, or has a positive and a negative pole. There is a male and a female, a spirit and a fact, a north and a south. Spirit is the positive, the event is the negative. Will is the north, action the south pole. Character may be ranked as having its natural place in the north. It shares the magnetic currents of the system. The feeble souls are drawn to the south or negative pole. They look at the profit or hurt of the action. They never behold a principle until it is lodged in a person. They do not wish to be lovely, but to

be loved. Men of character like to hear of their faults;
the other class do not like to hear of faults; they
worship events; secure to them a fact, a connection,
a certain chain of circumstances, and they will ask
no more. The hero sees that the event is ancillary; [24]
it must follow *him*. A given order of events has no
power to secure to him the satisfaction which the
imagination attaches to it; the soul of goodness escapes from any set of circumstances; whilst prosperity
belongs to a certain mind, and will introduce that
power and victory which is its natural fruit, into any
order of events. No change of circumstances can repair a defect of character. We boast our emancipa-
tion from many superstitions; but if we have broken
any idols it is through a transfer of the idolatry. What
have I gained, that I no longer immolate a bull to Jove
or to Neptune, or a mouse to Hecate; that I do not
tremble before the Eumenides, or the Catholic Pur-
gatory, or the Calvinistic Judgment-day, — if I quake
at opinion, the public opinion as we call it; or at the
threat of assault, or contumely, or bad neighbors, or
poverty, or mutilation, or at the rumor of revolution,
or of murder? If I quake, what matters it what I quake
at? [25] Our proper vice takes form in one or another
shape, according to the sex, age, or temperament of
the person, and, if we are capable of fear, will readily
find terrors. The covetousness or the malignity which
saddens me when I ascribe it to society, is my own. I
am always environed by myself. On the other part,
rectitude is a perpetual victory, celebrated not by cries
of joy but by serenity, which is joy fixed or habitual. It
is disgraceful to fly to events for confirmation of our
truth and worth. The capitalist does not run every
hour to the broker to coin his advantages into current

money of the realm; he is satisfied to read in the quotations of the market that his stocks have risen. The same transport which the occurrence of the best events in the best order would occasion me, I must learn to taste purer in the perception that my position is every hour meliorated, and does already command those events I desire. That exultation is only to be checked by the foresight of an order of things so excellent as to throw all our prosperities into the deepest shade.

The face which character wears to me is self-sufficingness. I revere the person who is riches; so that I cannot think of him as alone, or poor, or exiled, or unhappy, or a client, but as perpetual patron, benefactor and beatified man. Character is centrality, the impossibility of being displaced or overset. A man should give us a sense of mass. Society is frivolous, and shreds its day into scraps, its conversation into ceremonies and escapes. But if I go to see an ingenious man I shall think myself poorly entertained if he give me nimble pieces of benevolence and etiquette; rather he shall stand stoutly in his place and let me apprehend, if it were only his resistance; know that I have encountered a new and positive quality; — great refreshment for both of us. It is much that he does not accept the conventional opinions and practices. That non-conformity will remain a goad and remembrancer, and every inquirer will have to dispose of him, in the first place. There is nothing real or useful that is not a seat of war. Our houses ring with laughter and personal and critical gossip, but it helps little. But the uncivil, unavailable man, who is a problem and a threat to society, whom it cannot let pass in silence but must either worship or hate, — and to whom all parties feel related, both the leaders of

opinion and the obscure and eccentric, — he helps;
he puts America and Europe in the wrong, and destroys the scepticism which says, 'Man is a doll,[26] let
us eat and drink, 't is the best we can do,' by illumi-
nating the untried and unknown. Acquiescence in the
establishment and appeal to the public, indicate infirm
faith, heads which are not clear, and which must see
a house built before they can comprehend the plan of
it. The wise man not only leaves out of his thought
the many, but leaves out the few. Fountains, the
self-moved, the absorbed, the commander because he
is commanded, the assured, the primary, — they are
good; for these announce the instant presence of supreme power.

Our action should rest mathematically on our substance. In nature there are no false valuations. A
pound of water in the ocean-tempest has no more
gravity than in a midsummer pond. All things work
exactly according to their quality and according to
their quantity; attempt nothing they cannot do, except man only. He has pretension; he wishes and
attempts things beyond his force. I read in a book of
English memoirs, "Mr. Fox (afterwards Lord Holland) said, he must have the Treasury; he had served
up to it, and would have it." Xenophon and his Ten
Thousand were quite equal to what they attempted,
and did it; so equal, that it was not suspected to be a
grand and inimitable exploit. Yet there stands that
fact unrepeated, a high-water mark in military history.
Many have attempted it since, and not been equal to
it. It is only on reality that any power of action can
be based. No institution will be better than the insti-
tutor. I knew an amiable and accomplished person[27]
who undertook a practical reform, yet I was never

able to find in him the enterprise of love he took in hand. He adopted it by ear and by the understanding from the books he had been reading. All his action was tentative, a piece of the city carried out into the fields, and was the city still, and no new fact,[28] and could not inspire enthusiasm. Had there been something latent in the man, a terrible undemonstrated genius agitating and embarrassing his demeanor, we had watched for its advent. It is not enough that the intellect should see the evils and their remedy. We shall still postpone our existence, nor take the ground to which we are entitled, whilst it is only a thought and not a spirit that incites us. We have not yet served up to it.

These are properties of life, and another trait is the notice of incessant growth. Men should be intelligent and earnest. They must also make us feel that they have a controlling happy future opening before them, whose early twilights already kindle in the passing hour. The hero is misconceived and misreported;[29] he cannot therefore wait to unravel any man's blunders; he is again on his road, adding new powers and honors to his domain and new claims on your heart, which will bankrupt you if you have loitered about the old things and have not kept your relation to him by adding to your wealth. New actions are the only apologies and explanations of old ones which the noble can bear to offer or to receive. If your friend has displeased you, you shall not sit down to consider it, for he has already lost all memory of the passage, and has doubled his power to serve you, and ere you can rise up again will burden you with blessings.

We have no pleasure in thinking of a benevolence that is only measured by its works. Love is inexhaustible, and if its estate is wasted, its granary emptied, still cheers and enriches, and the man, though he sleep, seems to purify the air and his house to adorn the landscape and strengthen the laws. People always recognize this difference. We know who is benevolent, by quite other means than the amount of subscription to soup-societies. It is only low merits that can be enumerated. Fear, when your friends say to you what you have done well, and say it through; but when they stand with uncertain timid looks of respect and half-dislike, and must suspend their judgment for years to come, you may begin to hope.[30] Those who live to the future must always appear selfish to those who live to the present. Therefore it was droll in the good Riemer, who has written memoirs of Goethe, to make out a list of his donations and good deeds, as, so many hundred thalers given to Stilling, to Hegel, to Tischbein; a lucrative place found for Professor Voss, a post under the Grand Duke for Herder, a pension for Meyer, two professors recommended to foreign universities; etc., etc. The longest list of specifications of benefit would look very short. A man is a poor creature if he is to be measured so. For all these of course are exceptions, and the rule and hodiurnal life of a good man is benefaction. The true charity of Goethe is to be inferred from the account he gave Dr. Eckermann of the way in which he had spent his fortune. "Each *bon mot* of mine has cost a purse of gold. Half a million of my own money, the fortune I inherited, my salary and the large income derived from my writings for fifty years back, have been expended to instruct me in what I now know. I have besides seen," etc.

I own it is but poor chat and gossip to go to enumerate traits of this simple and rapid power, and we are painting the lightning with charcoal; but in these long nights and vacations I like to console myself so. Nothing but itself can copy it. A word warm from the heart enriches me. I surrender at discretion.[31] How death-cold is literary genius before this fire of life! These are the touches that reanimate my heavy soul and give it eyes to pierce the dark of nature. I find, where I thought myself poor, there was I most rich. Thence comes a new intellectual exaltation, to be again rebuked by some new exhibition of character. Strange alternation of attraction and repulsion! Character repudiates intellect, yet excites it; and character passes into thought, is published so, and then is ashamed before new flashes of moral worth.

Character is nature in the highest form. It is of no use to ape it or to contend with it. Somewhat is possible of resistance, and of persistence, and of creation, to this power, which will foil all emulation.

This masterpiece is best where no hands but nature's have been laid on it. Care is taken that the greatly-destined shall slip up into life in the shade, with no thousand-eyed Athens [32] to watch and blazon every new thought, every blushing emotion of young genius. Two persons lately, very young children of the most high God, have given me occasion for thought. When I explored the source of their sanctity and charm for the imagination, it seemed as if each answered, 'From my non-conformity; I never listened to your people's law, or to what they call their gospel, and wasted my time. I was content with the simple rural poverty of my own; hence this sweetness; my work never reminds you of that, — is pure of that.' And nature advertises me in such persons that in demo-

cratic America she will not be democratized. How
cloistered and constitutionally sequestered from the
market and from scandal! It was only this morning
that I sent away some wild flowers of these wood-gods.
They are a relief from literature,—these fresh draughts
from the sources of thought and sentiment; as we
read, in an age of polish and criticism, the first lines
of written prose and verse of a nation. How captivat-
ing is their devotion to their favorite books, whether
Æschylus, Dante, Shakspeare, or Scott, as feeling that
they have a stake in that book; who touches that,
touches them,—and especially the total solitude of the
critic, the Patmos of thought [33] from which he writes,
in unconsciousness of any eyes that shall ever read
this writing. Could they dream on still, as angels, and
not wake to comparisons and to be flattered! Yet some
natures are too good to be spoiled by praise, and wherever the vein of thought reaches down into the profound, there is no danger from vanity. Solemn friends
will warn them of the danger of the head's being turned
by the flourish of trumpets, but they can afford to smile.
I remember the indignation of an eloquent Method-
ist [34] at the kind admonitions of a Doctor of Divinity,
—'My friend, a man can neither be praised nor in-
sulted.' But forgive the counsels; they are very natural. I remember the thought which occurred to me
when some ingenious and spiritual foreigners [35] came
to America, was, Have you been victimized in being
brought hither?—or, prior to that, answer me this,
'Are you victimizable?'

As I have said, Nature keeps these sovereignties
in her own hands, and however pertly our sermons
and disciplines would divide some share of credit, and
teach that the laws fashion the citizen, she goes her

own gait and puts the wisest in the wrong. She makes very light of gospels and prophets, as one who has a great many more to produce and no excess of time to spare on any one. There is a class of men, individuals of which appear at long intervals, so eminently endowed with insight and virtue that they have been unanimously saluted as *divine,* and who seem to be an accumulation of that power we consider. Divine persons are character born, or, to borrow a phrase from Napoleon, they are victory organized. They are usually received with ill-will, because they are new and because they set a bound to the exaggeration that has been made of the personality of the last divine person. Nature never rhymes her children, nor makes two men alike. When we see a great man we fancy a resemblance to some historical person, and predict the sequel of his character and fortune; a result which he is sure to disappoint. None will ever solve the problem of his character according to our prejudice, but only in his own high unprecedented way. Character wants room; must not be crowded on by persons nor be judged from glimpses got in the press of affairs or on few occasions. It needs perspective, as a great building. It may not, probably does not, form relations rapidly; and we should not require rash explanation, either on the popular ethics, or on our own, of its action.

I look on Sculpture as history. I do not think the Apollo and the Jove impossible in flesh and blood. Every trait which the artist recorded in stone he had seen in life, and better than his copy. We have seen many counterfeits, but we are born believers in great men.[36] How easily we read in old books, when men were few, of the smallest action of the patriarchs. We

require that a man should be so large and columnar
in the landscape, that it should deserve to be recorded
that he arose, and girded up his loins, and departed
to such a place. The most credible pictures are those
of majestic men who prevailed at their entrance, and
convinced the senses; as happened to the eastern
magian who was sent to test the merits of Zertusht or
Zoroaster. "When the Yunâni sage arrived at Balkh,
the Persians tell us, Gushtasp appointed a day on
which the Mobeds of every country should assemble,
and a golden chair was placed for the Yunâni sage.
Then the beloved of Yezdam, the prophet Zertusht,
advanced into the midst of the assembly. The Yunâni sage, on seeing that chief, said, 'This form and
this gait cannot lie, and nothing but truth can proceed from them.'" [37] Plato said it was impossible not
to believe in the children of the gods, "though they
should speak without probable or necessary argu-
ments." [38] I should think myself very unhappy in my
associates if I could not credit the best things in history. "John Bradshaw," says Milton,[39] "appears like
a consul, from whom the fasces are not to depart with
the year; so that not on the tribunal only, but throughout his life, you would regard him as sitting in judgment upon kings." I find it more credible, since it is
anterior information, that one man should *know heaven*,
as the Chinese say, than that so many men should
know the world. "The virtuous prince confronts the
gods, without any misgiving. He waits a hundred
ages till a sage comes, and does not doubt. He who
confronts the gods, without any misgiving, knows
heaven; he who waits a hundred ages until a sage
comes, without doubting, knows men. Hence the virtuous prince moves, and for ages shows empire the

way." But there is no need to seek remote examples.
He is a dull observer whose experience has not taught
him the reality and force of magic, as well as of chemistry. The coldest precisian cannot go abroad without
encountering inexplicable influences. One man fastens an eye on him and the graves of the memory render up their dead; the secrets that make him wretched
either to keep or to betray must be yielded; — another,
and he cannot speak, and the bones of his body seem
to lose their cartilages; the entrance of a friend adds
grace, boldness and eloquence to him; and there are
persons he cannot choose but remember, who gave
a transcendent expansion to his thought, and kindled
another life in his bosom.

What is so excellent as strict relations of amity, when
they spring from this deep root? The sufficient reply
to the sceptic who doubts the power and the furniture [40]
of man, is in that possibility of joyful intercourse
with persons, which makes the faith and practice of
all reasonable men. I know nothing which life has to
offer so satisfying as the profound good understanding which can subsist, after much exchange of good
offices, between two virtuous men, each of whom is
sure of himself and sure of his friend. It is a happiness which postpones all other gratifications, and
makes politics, and commerce, and churches, cheap.
For when men shall meet as they ought, each a benefactor, a shower of stars, clothed with thoughts, with
deeds, with accomplishments, it should be the festival
of nature which all things announce. Of such friendship, love in the sexes is the first symbol, as all other
things are symbols of love. Those relations to the best
men, which, at one time, we reckoned the romances
of youth, become, in the progress of the character, the
most solid enjoyment.

If it were possible to live in right relations with men!
— if we could abstain from asking anything of them,
from asking their praise, or help, or pity, and content
us with compelling them through the virtue of the
eldest laws! Could we not deal with a few persons, —
with one person, — after the unwritten statutes, and
make an experiment of their efficacy? Could we not
pay our friend the compliment of truth, of silence, of
forbearing? Need we be so eager to seek him? If we
are related, we shall meet. It was a tradition of the
ancient world that no metamorphosis could hide a
god from a god; and there is a Greek verse which
runs, —

"The gods are to each other not unknown." [41]

Friends also follow the laws of divine necessity; they
gravitate to each other, and cannot otherwise: —

"When each the other shall avoid,
Shall each by each be most enjoyed." [42]

Their relation is not made, but allowed. The gods
must seat themselves without seneschal [43] in our Olympus, and as they can instal themselves by seniority
divine. Society is spoiled if pains are taken, if the
associates are brought a mile to meet. And if it be
not society, it is a mischievous, low, degrading jangle,
though made up of the best. All the greatness of each
is kept back and every foible [44] in painful activity, as
if the Olympians should meet to exchange snuff-boxes.

Life goes headlong. We chase some flying scheme,
or we are hunted by some fear or command behind
us. But if suddenly we encounter a friend, we pause;
our heat and hurry look foolish enough; now pause,
now possession is required, and the power to swell
the moment from the resources of the heart. The moment is all, in all noble relations.

A divine person is the prophecy of the mind; a friend
is the hope of the heart. Our beatitude waits for the
fulfilment of these two in one. The ages are opening
this moral force. All force is the shadow or symbol of
that. Poetry is joyful and strong as it draws its inspiration thence. Men write their names on the world as
they are filled with this. History has been mean; our
nations have been mobs; we have never seen a man;
that divine form we do not yet know, but only the
dream and prophecy of such: we do not know the
majestic manners which belong to him, which appease
and exalt the beholder. We shall one day see that the
most private is the most public energy, that quality
atones for quantity, and grandeur of character acts
in the dark, and succors them who never saw it. What
greatness has yet appeared is beginnings and encour-
agements to us in this direction. The history of those
gods and saints which the world has written and then
worshipped, are documents of character. The ages
have exulted in the manners of a youth [45] who owed
nothing to fortune, and who was hanged at the Tyburn [46] of his nation, who, by the pure quality of his
nature, shed an epic splendor around the facts of his
death which has transfigured every particular into an
universal symbol for the eyes of mankind. This great
defeat is hitherto our highest fact. But the mind requires a victory to the senses; a force of character
which will convert judge, jury, soldier and king; which
will rule animal and mineral virtues, and blend with
the courses of sap, of rivers, of winds, of stars, and of
moral agents.

If we cannot attain at a bound to these grandeurs,
at least let us do them homage. In society, high advantages are set down to the possessor as disadvan-

tages. It requires the more wariness in our private estimates. I do not forgive in my friends the failure to know a fine character and to entertain it with thankful hospitality. When at last that which we have always longed for is arrived and shines on us with glad rays out of that far celestial land, then to be coarse, then to be critical and treat such a visitant with the jabber and suspicion of the streets, argues a vulgarity that seems to shut the doors of heaven. This is confusion, this the right insanity, when the soul no longer knows its own, nor where its allegiance, its religion, are due. Is there any religion but this, to know that wherever in the wide desert of being the holy sentiment we cherish has opened into a flower, it blooms for me? if none sees it, I see it; I am aware, if I alone, of the greatness of the fact. Whilst it blooms, I will keep sabbath or holy time, and suspend my gloom and my folly and jokes. Nature is indulged by the presence of this guest. There are many eyes that can detect and honor the prudent and household virtues; there are many that can discern Genius on his starry track, though the mob is incapable; but when that love which is all-suffering, all-abstaining, all-aspiring, which has vowed to itself that it will be a wretch and also a fool in this world sooner than soil its white hands by any compliances, comes into our streets and houses, — only the pure and aspiring can know its face, and the only compliment they can pay it is to own it.[47]

SELF-RELIANCE

" Ne te quaesiveris extra."

Man is his own star; and the soul that can
Render an honest and a perfect man,
Commands all light, all influence, all fate;
Nothing to him falls early or too late.
Our acts our angels are, or good or ill,
Our fatal shadows that walk by us still.

Epilogue to Beaumont and Fletcher's Honest Man's Fortune.

Cast the bantling on the rocks,
Suckle him with the she-wolf's teat,
Wintered with the hawk and fox,
Power and speed be hands and feet.

SELF-RELIANCE

I READ the other day some verses written by an eminent painter [1] which were original and not conventional. The soul always hears an admonition in such lines, let the subject be what it may. The sentiment they instil is of more value than any thought they may contain. To believe your own thought, to believe that what is true for you in your private heart is true for all men, — that is genius. Speak your latent conviction, and it shall be the universal sense; for the inmost in due time becomes the outmost, and our first thought is rendered back to us by the trumpets of the Last Judgment. Familiar as the voice of the mind is to each, the highest merit we ascribe to Moses, Plato and Milton is that they set at naught books and traditions, and spoke not what men, but what *they* thought. A man should learn to detect and watch that gleam of light which flashes across his mind from within, more than the lustre of the firmament of bards and sages. Yet he dismisses without notice his thought, because it is his. In every work of genius we recognize our own rejected thoughts; they come back to us with a certain alienated majesty.[2] Great works of art have no more affecting lesson for us than this. They teach us to abide by our spontaneous impression with good-humored inflexibility then most when the whole cry of voices is on the other side. Else to-morrow a stranger will say with masterly good sense precisely what we have thought and felt all the time, and we shall be forced to take with shame our own opinion from another.

There is a time in every man's education when he arrives at the conviction that envy is ignorance; that imitation is suicide; that he must take himself for better for worse as his portion; that though the wide universe is full of good, no kernel of nourishing corn can come to him but through his toil bestowed on that plot of ground which is given to him to till. The power which resides in him is new in nature, and none but he knows what that is which he can do, nor does he know until he has tried. Not for nothing one face, one character, one fact, makes much impression on him and another none. This sculpture in the memory is not without preëstablished harmony.[3] The eye was placed where one ray should fall, that it might testify of that particular ray. We but half express ourselves, and are ashamed of that divine idea which each of us represents. It may be safely intrusted as proportionate and of good issues, so it be faithfully imparted, but God will not have his work made manifest by cowards. A man is relieved and gay when he has put his heart into his work and done his best; but what he has said or done otherwise shall give him no peace. It is a deliverance which does not deliver. In the attempt his genius deserts him; no muse befriends; no invention, no hope.

Trust thyself: every heart vibrates to that iron string. Accept the place the divine providence has found for you, the society of your contemporaries, the connection of events. Great men have always done so, and confided themselves childlike to the genius of their age, betraying their perception that the absolutely trustworthy was seated at their heart, working through their hands, predominating in all their being. And we are now men, and must accept in the highest

mind the same transcendent destiny; and not minors
and invalids in a protected corner, not cowards flee-
ing before a revolution, but guides, redeemers and
benefactors, obeying the Almighty effort and advancing on Chaos and the Dark.

What pretty oracles nature yields us on this text in
the face and behavior of children, babes, and even
brutes! That divided and rebel mind, that distrust
of a sentiment because our arithmetic has computed
the strength and means opposed to our purpose, these
have not. Their mind being whole, their eye is as yet
unconquered, and when we look in their faces we are
disconcerted. Infancy conforms to nobody; all conform to it; so that one babe commonly makes four or
five out of the adults who prattle and play to it. So
God has armed youth and puberty and manhood no
less with its own piquancy and charm, and made it
enviable and gracious and its claims not to be put by,
if it will stand by itself. Do not think the youth has no
force, because he cannot speak to you and me. Hark!
in the next room his voice is sufficiently clear and emphatic. It seems he knows how to speak to his contemporaries. Bashful or bold then, he will know how
to make us seniors very unnecessary.[4]

The nonchalance of boys who are sure of a dinner,
and would disdain as much as a lord to do or say aught
to conciliate one, is the healthy attitude of human nature. A boy is in the parlor what the pit is in the play-
house; independent, irresponsible, looking out from
his corner on such people and facts as pass by, he tries
and sentences them on their merits, in the swift, sum-
mary way of boys, as good, bad, interesting, silly, eloquent, troublesome. He cumbers himself never about
consequences, about interests; he gives an indepen-

dent, genuine verdict. You must court him; he does not court you. But the man is as it were clapped into jail by his consciousness. As soon as he has once acted or spoken with *éclat* he is a committed person, watched by the sympathy or the hatred of hundreds, whose affections must now enter into his account. There is no Lethe for this. Ah, that he could pass again into his neutrality! Who can thus avoid all pledges and, having observed, observe again from the same unaffected, unbiased, unbribable, unaffrighted innocence, — must always be formidable. He would utter opinions on all passing affairs, which being seen to be not private but necessary, would sink like darts into the ear of men and put them in fear.

These are the voices which we hear in solitude, but they grow faint and inaudible as we enter into the world. Society everywhere is in conspiracy against the manhood of every one of its members. Society is a joint-stock company, in which the members agree, for the better securing of his bread to each shareholder, to surrender the liberty and culture of the eater. The virtue in most request is conformity. Self-reliance is its aversion. It loves not realities and creators, but names and customs.

Whoso would be a man, must be a nonconformist. He who would gather immortal palms must not be hindered by the name of goodness, but must explore if it be goodness. Nothing is at last sacred but the integrity of your own mind. Absolve you to yourself, and you shall have the suffrage of the world. I remember an answer which when quite young I was prompted to make to a valued adviser who was wont to importune me with the dear old doctrines of the church. On my saying, "What have I to do with the sacred-

ness of traditions, if I live wholly from within?" my
friend suggested, — "But these impulses may be from
below, not from above." I replied, "They do not
seem to me to be such; but if I am the Devil's child,
I will live then from the Devil." No law can be sacred
to me but that of my nature. Good and bad are but
names very readily transferable to that or this; the
only right is what is after my constitution; the only
wrong what is against it. A man is to carry himself
in the presence of all opposition as if every thing were
titular and ephemeral but he.[5] I am ashamed to think
how easily we capitulate to badges and names, to large
societies and dead institutions. Every decent and well-
spoken individual affects and sways me more than is
right. I ought to go upright and vital, and speak the
rude truth in all ways. If malice and vanity wear the
coat of philanthropy, shall that pass? If an angry
bigot assumes this bountiful cause of Abolition, and
comes to me with his last news from Barbadoes,[6] why
should I not say to him, 'Go love thy infant; love thy
wood-chopper; be good-natured and modest; have
that grace; and never varnish your hard, unchari-
table ambition with this incredible tenderness for black
folk a thousand miles off. Thy love afar is spite at
home.' Rough and graceless would be such greeting,
but truth is handsomer than the affectation of love.
Your goodness must have some edge to it, — else it
is none. The doctrine of hatred must be preached, as
the counteraction of the doctrine of love, when that
pules and whines. I shun father and mother and wife
and brother when my genius calls me. I would write
on the lintels of the door-post, *Whim*. I hope it is
somewhat better than whim at last, but we cannot
spend the day in explanation. Expect me not to show

cause why I seek or why I exclude company. Then again, do not tell me, as a good man did to-day, of my obligation to put all poor men in good situations. Are they *my* poor? I tell thee, thou foolish philanthropist, that I grudge the dollar, the dime, the cent I give to such men as do not belong to me and to whom I do not belong. There is a class of persons to whom by all spiritual affinity I am bought and sold; for them I will go to prison if need be; but your miscellaneous popular charities; the education at college of fools; the building of meeting-houses to the vain end to which many now stand; alms to sots, and the thousand-fold Relief Societies; — though I confess with shame I sometimes succumb and give the dollar, it is a wicked dollar, which by and by I shall have the manhood to withhold.

Virtues are, in the popular estimate, rather the exception than the rule. There is the man *and* his virtues. Men do what is called a good action, as some piece of courage or charity, much as they would pay a fine in expiation of daily non-appearance on parade. Their works are done as an apology or extenuation of their living in the world, — as invalids and the insane pay a high board. Their virtues are penances. I do not wish to expiate, but to live. My life is for itself and not for a spectacle. I much prefer that it should be of a lower strain, so it be genuine and equal, than that it should be glittering and unsteady. I wish it to be sound and sweet, and not to need diet and bleeding. I ask primary evidence that you are a man, and refuse this appeal from the man to his actions.[7] I know that for myself it makes no difference whether I do or forbear those actions which are reckoned excellent. I cannot consent to pay for a privilege where I have intrinsic right. Few and mean as my gifts may be, I actually am, and do not need for my own assurance or the assurance of my fellows any secondary testimony.

What I must do is all that concerns me, not what the people think. This rule, equally arduous in actual and in intellectual life, may serve for the whole distinction between greatness and meanness. It is the harder because you will always find those who think they know what is your duty better than you know it. It is easy in the world to live after the world's opinion; it is easy in solitude to live after our own; but the great man is he who in the midst of the crowd keeps with perfect sweetness the independence of solitude.

The objection to conforming to usages that have become dead to you is that it scatters your force. It loses your time and blurs the impression of your character. If you maintain a dead church, contribute to a dead Bible-society, vote with a great party either for the government or against it, spread your table like base housekeepers, — under all these screens I have difficulty to detect the precise man you are: and of course so much force is withdrawn from all your proper life. But do your work, and I shall know you. Do your work, and you shall reinforce yourself. A man must consider what a blind-man's-buff is this game of conformity. If I know your sect I anticipate your argument. I hear a preacher announce for his text and topic the expediency of one of the institutions of his church. Do I not know beforehand that not possibly can he say a new and spontaneous word? Do I not know that with all this ostentation of examining the grounds of the institution he will do no such thing? Do I not know that he is pledged to himself not to look but at one side, the permitted side,

not as a man, but as a parish minister? He is a re-
tained attorney, and these airs of the bench are the
emptiest affectation. Well, most men have bound
their eyes with one or another handkerchief, and attached themselves to some one of these communities
of opinion. This conformity makes them not false in
a few particulars, authors of a few lies, but false in
all particulars. Their every truth is not quite true.
Their two is not the real two, their four not the real
four; so that every word they say chagrins [8] us and we
know not where to begin to set them right. Meantime
nature is not slow to equip us in the prison-uniform of
the party to which we adhere. We come to wear one
cut of face and figure, and acquire by degrees the
gentlest asinine expression. There is a mortifying experience in particular, which does not fail to wreak
itself also in the general history; I mean the "foolish
face of praise," the forced smile which we put on in
company where we do not feel at ease, in answer to
conversation which does not interest us. The muscles,
not spontaneously moved but moved by a low usurping wilfulness, grow tight about the outline of the face,
with the most disagreeable sensation.

For nonconformity the world whips you with its
displeasure. And therefore a man must know how to
estimate a sour face. The by-standers look askance on
him in the public street or in the friend's parlor. If
this aversion had its origin in contempt and resistance
like his own he might well go home with a sad countenance; but the sour faces of the multitude, like their
sweet faces, have no deep cause, but are put on and
off as the wind blows and a newspaper directs. Yet is
the discontent of the multitude more formidable than
that of the senate and the college. It is easy enough

for a firm man who knows the world to brook the rage
of the cultivated classes. Their rage is decorous and
prudent, for they are timid, as being very vulnerable
themselves. But when to their feminine rage the indignation of the people is added, when the ignorant and
the poor are aroused, when the unintelligent brute
force that lies at the bottom of society is made to growl
and mow,[9] it needs the habit of magnanimity and religion to treat it godlike as a trifle of no concernment.

The other terror that scares us from self-trust is our
consistency; a reverence for our past act or word because the eyes of others have no other data for computing our orbit than our past acts, and we are loth to
disappoint them.

But why should you keep your head over your shoulder?[10] Why drag about this corpse of your memory,
lest you contradict somewhat you have stated in this or
that public place? Suppose you should contradict yourself; what then? It seems to be a rule of wisdom never
to rely on your memory alone, scarcely even in acts of
pure memory, but to bring the past for judgment into
the thousand-eyed present, and live ever in a new day.
In your metaphysics you have denied personality to the
Deity, yet when the devout motions of the soul come,
yield to them heart and life, though they should clothe
God with shape and color. Leave your theory, as Joseph his coat in the hand of the harlot, and flee.

A foolish consistency is the hobgoblin of little minds,
adored by little statesmen and philosophers and divines. With consistency a great soul has simply nothing to do. He may as well concern himself with his
shadow on the wall. Speak what you think now in
hard words and to-morrow speak what to-morrow
thinks in hard words again, though it contradict every

thing you said to-day. — 'Ah, so you shall be sure to be misunderstood.' — Is it so bad then to be misunderstood? Pythagoras was misunderstood, and Socrates, and Jesus, and Luther, and Copernicus, and Galileo, and Newton, and every pure and wise spirit that ever took flesh. To be great is to be misunderstood.[11]

I suppose no man can violate his nature. All the sallies of his will are rounded in by the law of his being, as the inequalities of Andes and Himmaleh are insignificant in the curve of the sphere. Nor does it matter how you gauge and try him. A character is like an acrostic or Alexandrian stanza;[12] — read it forward, backward, or across, it still spells the same thing. In this pleasing contrite wood-life which God allows me, let me record day by day my honest thought without prospect or retrospect, and, I cannot doubt, it will be found symmetrical, though I mean it not and see it not. My book should smell of pines and resound with the hum of insects.[13] The swallow over my window should interweave that thread or straw he carries in his bill into my web also. We pass for what we are. Character teaches above our wills.[14] Men imagine that they communicate their virtue or vice only by overt actions, and do not see that virtue or vice emit a breath every moment.

There will be an agreement in whatever variety of actions, so they be each honest and natural in their hour. For of one will, the actions will be harmonious, however unlike they seem. These varieties are lost sight of at a little distance, at a little height of thought. One tendency unites them all. The voyage of the best ship is a zigzag line of a hundred tacks. See the line from a sufficient distance, and it straightens itself to the average tendency. Your genuine action will explain itself and will explain your other genuine actions. Your conformity explains nothing. Act singly, and what you have already done singly will justify you now. Greatness appeals to the future. If I can be firm enough to-day to do right and scorn eyes, I must have done so much right before as to defend me now. Be it how it will, do right now. Always scorn appearances and you always may. The force of character is cumulative. All the foregone days of virtue work their health into this. What makes the majesty of the heroes of the senate and the field, which so fills the imagination? The consciousness of a train of great days and victories behind. They shed a united light on the advancing actor. He is attended as by a visible escort of angels. That is it which throws thunder into Chatham's voice, and dignity into Washington's port, and America into Adams's eye. Honor is venerable to us because it is no ephemera. It is always ancient virtue. We worship it to-day because it is not of to-day. We love it and pay it homage because it is not a trap for our love and homage, but is self-dependent, self-derived, and therefore of an old immaculate pedigree, even if shown in a young person.

I hope in these days we have heard the last of conformity and consistency. Let the words be gazetted and ridiculous henceforward. Instead of the gong for dinner, let us hear a whistle from the Spartan fife. Let us never bow and apologize more. A great man is coming to eat at my house. I do not wish to please him; I wish that he would wish to please me. I will stand here for humanity, and though I would make it kind, I would make it true. Let us affront and reprimand the smooth mediocrity and squalid contentment of the times, and hurl in the face of custom and trade and

office, the fact which is the upshot of all history, that
there is a great responsible Thinker and Actor working wherever a man works; that a true man belongs
to no other time or place, but is the centre of things.
Where he is there is nature. He measures you and
all men and all events. Ordinarily, every body in society reminds us of somewhat else, or of some other
person. Character, reality, reminds you of nothing
else; it takes place of [15] the whole creation. The
man must be so much that he must make all circumstances indifferent. Every true man is a cause, a country, and an age; requires infinite spaces and numbers
and time fully to accomplish his design; — and posterity seem to follow his steps as a train of clients. A
man Cæsar is born, and for ages after we have a Roman Empire. Christ is born, and millions of minds so
grow and cleave to his genius that he is confounded
with virtue and the possible of man. An institution is
the lengthened shadow of one man; as, Monachism,
of the Hermit Antony; the Reformation, of Luther;
Quakerism, of Fox; Methodism, of Wesley; Abolition,
of Clarkson. Scipio, Milton called "the height of
Rome;" and all history resolves itself very easily into
the biography of a few stout and earnest persons.

Let a man then know his worth, and keep things
under his feet. Let him not peep or steal, or skulk up
and down with the air of a charity-boy, a bastard, or
an interloper in the world which exists for him. But
the man in the street, finding no worth in himself
which corresponds to the force which built a tower or
sculptured a marble god, feels poor when he looks on
these. To him a palace, a statue, or a costly book have
an alien and forbidding air, much like a gay equipage,
and seem to say like that, 'Who are you, Sir?' Yet

they all are his, suitors for his notice, petitioners to his faculties that they will come out and take possession. The picture waits for my verdict; it is not to command me, but I am to settle its claims to praise. That popular fable of the sot who was picked up dead-drunk in the street, carried to the duke's house, washed and dressed and laid in the duke's bed, and, on his waking, treated with all obsequious ceremony like the duke, and assured that he had been insane, owes its popularity to the fact that it symbolizes so well the state of man, who is in the world a sort of sot, but now and then wakes up, exercises his reason and finds himself a true prince.[16]

Our reading is mendicant and sycophantic. In history our imagination plays us false. Kingdom and lordship, power and estate, are a gaudier vocabulary than private John and Edward in a small house and common day's work; but the things of life are the same to both; the sum total of both is the same. Why all this deference to Alfred and Scanderbeg [17] and Gustavus? Suppose they were virtuous;[18] did they wear out virtue? As great a stake depends on your private act to-day as followed their public and renowned steps. When private men shall act with original views, the lustre will be transferred from the actions of kings to those of gentlemen.

The world has been instructed by its kings, who have so magnetized the eyes of nations. It has been taught by this colossal symbol the mutual reverence that is due from man to man. The joyful loyalty with which men have everywhere suffered the king, the noble, or the great proprietor to walk among them by a law of his own, make his own scale of men and things and reverse theirs, pay for benefits not with money but with honor, and represent the law in his person, was the hieroglyphic by which they obscurely signified their consciousness of their own right and comeliness, the right of every man.

The magnetism which all original action exerts is explained when we inquire the reason of self-trust. Who is the Trustee? What is the aboriginal Self, on which a universal reliance may be grounded? What is the nature and power of that science-baffling star, without parallax, without calculable elements, which shoots a ray of beauty even into trivial and impure actions, if the least mark of independence appear? The inquiry leads us to that source, at once the essence of genius, of virtue, and of life, which we call Spontaneity or Instinct. We denote this primary wisdom as Intuition, whilst all later teachings are tuitions. In that deep force, the last fact behind which analysis cannot go, all things find their common origin. For the sense of being which in calm hours rises, we know not how, in the soul, is not diverse from things, from space, from light, from time, from man, but one with them and proceeds obviously from the same source whence their life and being also proceed.[19] We first share the life by which things exist and afterwards see them as appearances in nature and forget that we have shared their cause. Here is the fountain of action and of thought. Here are the lungs of that inspiration which giveth man wisdom and which cannot be denied without impiety and atheism. We lie in the lap of immense intelligence, which makes us receivers of its truth and organs of its activity. When we discern justice, when we discern truth, we do nothing of ourselves, but allow a passage to its beams. If we ask whence this comes, if we seek to pry into the soul that causes, all philosophy is at fault. Its presence or its absence is all we can affirm. Every man discriminates between the voluntary acts of his mind and his involuntary perceptions, and knows that to his involuntary perceptions a perfect faith is due. He may err in the expression of them, but he knows that these things are so, like day and night, not to be disputed. My wilful actions and acquisitions are but roving; — the idlest reverie, the faintest native emotion, command my curiosity and respect. Thoughtless people contradict as readily the statement of perceptions as of opinions, or rather much more readily; for they do not distinguish between perception and notion. They fancy that I choose to see this or that thing. But perception is not whimsical, but fatal. If I see a trait, my children will see it after me, and in course of time all mankind, — although it may chance that no one has seen it before me. For my perception of it is as much a fact as the sun.

The relations of the soul to the divine spirit are so pure that it is profane to seek to interpose helps. It must be that when God speaketh he should communicate, not one thing, but all things; should fill the world with his voice; should scatter forth light, nature, time, souls, from the centre of the present thought; and new date and new create the whole. Whenever a mind is simple and receives a divine wisdom, old things pass away, — means, teachers, texts, temples fall; it lives now, and absorbs past and future into the present hour. All things are made sacred by relation to it, — one as much as another. All things are dissolved to their centre by their cause, and in the universal miracle petty and particular miracles disappear. If therefore a man claims to know and speak of God and carries you backward to the phraseology of some old

mouldered nation in another country, in another world,
believe him not. Is the acorn better than the oak which
is its fulness and completion? Is the parent better than
the child into whom he has cast his ripened being?
Whence then this worship of the past? The centuries
are conspirators against the sanity and authority of
the soul. Time and space are but physiological colors
which the eye makes, but the soul is light: where it is,
is day; where it was, is night; and history is an im-
pertinence and an injury if it be any thing more than
a cheerful apologue or parable of my being and becoming.

Man is timid and apologetic; he is no longer upright;
he dares not say 'I think,' 'I am,' but quotes some
saint or sage.[20] He is ashamed before the blade of grass
or the blowing rose. These roses under my window
make no reference to former roses or to better ones;
they are for what they are; they exist with God to-
day. There is no time to them. There is simply the
rose; it is perfect in every moment of its existence.
Before a leaf-bud has burst, its whole life acts; in the
full-blown flower there is no more; in the leafless root
there is no less. Its nature is satisfied and it satisfies
nature in all moments alike. But man postpones or
remembers; he does not live in the present, but with
reverted eye laments the past, or, heedless of the riches
that surround him, stands on tiptoe to foresee the
future. He cannot be happy and strong until he too
lives with nature in the present, above time.

This should be plain enough. Yet see what strong
intellects dare not yet hear God himself unless he speak
the phraseology of I know not what David, or Jere-
miah, or Paul. We shall not always set so great a price
on a few texts, on a few lives. We are like children

who repeat by rote the sentences of grandames and tutors, and, as they grow older, of the men of talents and character they chance to see, — painfully recollecting the exact words they spoke; afterwards, when they come into the point of view which those had who uttered these sayings, they understand them and are willing to let the words go; for at any time they can use words as good when occasion comes. If we live truly, we shall see truly. It is as easy for the strong man to be strong, as it is for the weak to be weak. When we have new perception, we shall gladly disburden the memory of its hoarded treasures as old rubbish. When a man lives with God, his voice shall be as sweet as the murmur of the brook and the rustle of the corn.

And now at last the highest truth on this subject remains unsaid; probably cannot be said; for all that we say is the far-off remembering of the intuition. That thought by what I can now nearest approach to say it, is this. When good is near you, when you have life in yourself, it is not by any known or accustomed way; you shall not discern the footprints of any other; you shall not see the face of man; you shall not hear any name; — the way, the thought, the good, shall be wholly strange and new. It shall exclude example and experience. You take the way from man, not to man. All persons that ever existed are its forgotten ministers. Fear and hope are alike beneath it. There is somewhat low even in hope. In the hour of vision there is nothing that can be called gratitude, nor properly joy. The soul raised over passion beholds identity and eternal causation, perceives the self-existence of Truth and Right, and calms itself with knowing that all things go well. Vast spaces of nature, the Atlantic Ocean, the South Sea; long intervals of time, years, centuries, are of no account. This which I think and feel underlay every former state of life and circumstances, as it does underlie my present, and what is called life and what is called death.

Life only avails, not the having lived. Power ceases in the instant of repose; it resides in the moment of transition from a past to a new state, in the shooting of the gulf, in the darting to an aim. This one fact the world hates; that the soul *becomes;* for that forever degrades the past, turns all riches to poverty, all reputation to a shame, confounds the saint with the rogue, shoves Jesus and Judas equally aside. Why then do we prate of self-reliance? Inasmuch as the soul is present there will be power not confident but agent.[21] To talk of reliance is a poor external way of speaking. Speak rather of that which relies because it works and is. Who has more obedience than I masters me, though he should not raise his finger. Round him I must revolve by the gravitation of spirits. We fancy it rhetoric when we speak of eminent virtue. We do not yet see that virtue is Height, and that a man or a company of men, plastic and permeable to principles, by the law of nature must overpower and ride all cities, nations, kings, rich men, poets, who are not.

This is the ultimate fact which we so quickly reach on this, as on every topic, the resolution of all into the ever-blessed ONE. Self-existence is the attribute of the Supreme Cause, and it constitutes the measure of good by the degree in which it enters into all lower forms. All things real are so by so much virtue as they contain. Commerce, husbandry, hunting, whaling, war, eloquence, personal weight, are somewhat, and engage my respect as examples of its presence and impure action. I see the same law working in nature for conservation and growth. Power is, in nature, the essential measure of right. Nature suffers nothing to remain in her kingdoms which cannot help itself. The genesis and maturation of a planet, its poise and orbit, the bended tree recovering itself from the strong wind, the vital resources of every animal and vegetable, are demonstrations of the self-sufficing and therefore self-relying soul.

Thus all concentrates: let us not rove; let us sit at home with the cause. Let us stun and astonish the intruding rabble of men and books and institutions by a simple declaration of the divine fact. Bid the invaders take the shoes from off their feet, for God is here within. Let our simplicity judge them, and our docility to our own law demonstrate the poverty of nature and fortune beside our native riches.

But now we are a mob. Man does not stand in awe of man, nor is his genius admonished to stay at home, to put itself in communication with the internal ocean, but it goes abroad to beg a cup of water of the urns of other men. We must go alone. I like the silent church before the service begins, better than any preaching. How far off, how cool, how chaste the persons look, begirt each one with a precinct or sanctuary! [22] So let us always sit. Why should we assume the faults of our friend, or wife, or father, or child, because they sit around our hearth, or are said to have the same blood? All men have my blood and I all men's. Not for that will I adopt their petulance or folly, even to the extent of being ashamed of it. But your isolation must not be mechanical, but spiritual, that is, must be elevation. At times the whole world seems to be in conspiracy to importune you with emphatic trifles. Friend, climate, child, sickness, fear, want, charity, all knock at once at thy closet door, and say,—'Come out unto us.' But keep thy state; come not into their confusion. The power men possess to annoy me I give them by a weak curiosity. No man can come near me but through my act. "What we love that we have, but by desire we bereave ourselves of the love."

If we cannot at once rise to the sanctities of obedience and faith, let us at least resist our temptations; let us enter into the state of war and wake Thor and Woden, courage and constancy, in our Saxon breasts. This is to be done in our smooth times by speaking the truth. Check this lying hospitality and lying affection. Live no longer to the expectation of these deceived and deceiving people with whom we converse. Say to them, 'O father, O mother, O wife, O brother, O friend, I have lived with you after appearances hitherto. Henceforward I am the truth's. Be it known unto you that henceforward I obey no law less than the eternal law. I will have no covenants but proximities. I shall endeavor to nourish my parents, to support my family, to be the chaste husband of one wife,— but these relations I must fill after a new and unprecedented way. I appeal from your customs. I must be myself. I cannot break myself any longer for you, or you. If you can love me for what I am, we shall be the happier. If you cannot, I will still seek to deserve that you should. I will not hide my tastes or aversions. I will so trust that what is deep is holy, that I will do strongly before the sun and moon whatever inly rejoices me and the heart appoints. If you are noble, I will love you; if you are not, I will not hurt you and myself by hypocritical attentions. If you are true, but not in the same truth with me, cleave to your companions; I will seek my own. I do this not selfishly but humbly and truly. It is alike your interest, and mine, and all men's, however long we have dwelt in lies, to live in truth. Does this sound harsh to-day? You will soon love what is dictated by your nature as well as mine, and if we follow the truth it will bring us out safe at last. — But so may you give these friends pain. Yes, but I cannot sell my liberty and my power, to save their sensibility. Besides, all persons have their moments of reason, when they look out into the region of absolute truth; then will they justify me and do the same thing.

The populace think that your rejection of popular standards is a rejection of all standard, and mere antinomianism; and the bold sensualist will use the name of philosophy to gild his crimes. But the law of consciousness abides. There are two confessionals, in one or the other of which we must be shriven. You may fulfil your round of duties by clearing yourself in the *direct* or in the *reflex* way. Consider whether you have satisfied your relations to father, mother, cousin, neighbor, town, cat and dog — whether any of these can upbraid you. But I may also neglect this reflex standard and absolve me to myself. I have my own stern claims and perfect circle. It denies the name of duty to many offices that are called duties. But if I can discharge its debts it enables me to dispense with the popular code. If any one imagines that this law is lax, let him keep its commandment one day.

And truly it demands something godlike in him who has cast off the common motives of humanity and has ventured to trust himself for a taskmaster. High be his heart, faithful his will, clear his sight, that he may in good earnest be doctrine, society, law, to himself, that a simple purpose may be to him as strong as iron necessity is to others!

If any man consider the present aspects of what is called by distinction *society*, he will see the need of these ethics. The sinew and heart of man seem to be drawn out, and we are become timorous, desponding whimperers. We are afraid of truth, afraid of fortune, afraid of death, and afraid of each other. Our age yields no great and perfect persons.[23] We want men and women who shall renovate life and our social state, but we see that most natures are insolvent, cannot satisfy their own wants, have an ambition out of all proportion to their practical force and do lean and beg day and night continually. Our housekeeping is mendicant,[24] our arts, our occupations, our marriages, our religion we have not chosen, but society has chosen for us. We are parlor soldiers. We shun the rugged battle of fate, where strength is born.

If our young men miscarry in their first enterprises they lose all heart. If the young merchant fails, men say he is *ruined*. If the finest genius studies at one of our colleges and is not installed in an office within one year afterwards in the cities or suburbs of Boston or New York, it seems to his friends and to himself that he is right in being disheartened and in complaining the rest of his life. A sturdy lad from New Hampshire or Vermont, who in turn tries all the professions, who *teams it, farms it, peddles*, keeps a school, preaches, edits a newspaper, goes to Congress, buys a township, and so forth, in successive years, and always like a cat falls on his feet, is worth a hundred of these city dolls. He walks abreast with his days and feels no shame in not 'studying a profession,' for he does not postpone his life, but lives already. He has not one chance, but a hundred chances.. Let a Stoic open the resources of man and tell men they are not leaning willows, but can and must detach themselves; that with the exercise of self-trust, new powers shall appear; that a man is the word made flesh, born to shed healing to the nations; that he should be ashamed of our compassion, and that the moment he acts from himself, tossing the laws, the books, idolatries and customs out of the window, we pity him no more but thank and revere him; —and that teacher shall restore the life of man to splendor and make his name dear to all history.

It is easy to see that a greater self-reliance must work a revolution in all the offices and relations of men; in their religion; in their education; in their pursuits; their modes of living; their association; in their property; in their speculative views.

1. In what prayers do men allow themselves![25] That which they call a holy office is not so much as brave and manly. Prayer looks abroad and asks for some foreign addition to come through some foreign virtue, and loses itself in endless mazes of natural and supernatural, and mediatorial and miraculous. Prayer that craves a particular commodity, anything less than all good, is vicious. Prayer is the contemplation of the facts of life from the highest point of view. It is the soliloquy of a beholding and jubilant soul. It is the spirit of God pronouncing his works good. But prayer as a means to effect a private end is meanness and theft. It supposes dualism and not unity in nature and consciousness. As soon as the man is at one with God, he will not beg. He will then see prayer in all action. The prayer of the farmer kneeling in his field to weed it, the prayer of the rower kneeling with the stroke of his oar, are true prayers heard throughout

nature, though for cheap ends. Caratach, in Fletcher's
"Bonduca," [26] when admonished to inquire the mind
of the god Audate, replies, —

> "His hidden meaning lies in our endeavors;
> Our valors are our best gods."

Another sort of false prayers are our regrets. Discontent is the want of self-reliance: it is infirmity of
will. Regret calamities if you can thereby help the
sufferer; if not, attend your own work and already the
evil begins to be repaired. Our sympathy is just as
base. We come to them who weep foolishly and sit
down and cry for company, instead of imparting to
them truth and health in rough electric shocks, putting them once more in communication with their
own reason. The secret of fortune is joy in our hands.
Welcome evermore to gods and men is the self-help-
ing man. For him all doors are flung wide; him all
tongues greet, all honors crown, all eyes follow with
desire. Our love goes out to him and embraces him
because he did not need it. We solicitously and apolo-
getically caress and celebrate him because he held on
his way and scorned our disapprobation. The gods
love him because men hated him. "To the persevering mortal," said Zoroaster, "the blessed Immortals
are swift."

As men's prayers are a disease of the will, so are
their creeds a disease of the intellect. They say with
those foolish Israelites, 'Let not God speak to us, lest
we die. Speak thou, speak any man with us, and we
will obey.' Everywhere I am hindered of meeting God
in my brother,[27] because he has shut his own temple
doors and recites fables merely of his brother's, or his
brother's brother's God. Every new mind is a new

classification. If it prove a mind of uncommon activity and power, a Locke, a Lavoisier, a Hutton, a Bentham, a Fourier,[28] it imposes its classification on other men, and lo! a new system! In proportion to the depth of the thought, and so to the number of the objects it touches and brings within reach of the pupil, is his complacency. But chiefly is this apparent in creeds and churches, which are also classifications of some powerful mind acting on the elemental thought of duty and man's relation to the Highest. Such is Calvinism, Quakerism, Swedenborgism. The pupil takes the same delight in subordinating every thing to the new terminology as a girl who has just learned botany in seeing a new earth and new seasons thereby. It will happen for a time that the pupil will find his intellectual power has grown by the study of his master's mind. But in all unbalanced minds the classification is idolized, passes for the end and not for a speedily exhaustible means, so that the walls of the system blend to their eye in the remote horizon with the walls of the universe; the luminaries of heaven seem to them hung on the arch their master built. They cannot imagine how you aliens have any right to see, — how you can see; 'It must be somehow that you stole the light from us.' They do not yet perceive that light, unsystematic, indomitable,[29] will break into any cabin, even into theirs. Let them chirp awhile and call it their own.[30] If they are honest and do well, presently their neat new pinfold will be too strait and low, will crack, will lean, will rot and vanish, and the immortal light, all young and joyful, million-orbed, million-colored, will beam over the universe as on the first morning.

2. It is for want of self-culture that the superstition of Travelling, whose idols are Italy, England, Egypt,

retains its fascination for all educated Americans. They who made England, Italy, or Greece venerable in the imagination, did so by sticking fast where they were, like an axis of the earth. In manly hours we feel that duty is our place. The soul is no traveller; the wise man stays at home, and when his necessities, his duties, on any occasion call him from his house, or into foreign lands, he is at home still and shall make men sensible by the expression of his countenance that he goes, the missionary of wisdom and virtue, and visits cities and men like a sovereign and not like an interloper or a valet.

I have no churlish objection to the circumnavigation of the globe for the purposes of art, of study, and benevolence, so that the man is first domesticated, or does not go abroad with the hope of finding somewhat greater than he knows. He who travels to be amused, or to get somewhat which he does not carry, travels away from himself, and grows old even in youth among old things. In Thebes, in Palmyra, his will and mind have become old and dilapidated as they. He carries ruins to ruins.

Travelling is a fool's paradise. Our first journeys discover to us the indifference of places. At home I dream that at Naples, at Rome, I can be intoxicated with beauty and lose my sadness. I pack my trunk, embrace my friends, embark on the sea and at last wake up in Naples, and there beside me is the stern fact, the sad self, unrelenting, identical, that I fled from. I seek the Vatican and the palaces. I affect to be intoxicated with sights and suggestions, but I am not intoxicated. My giant goes with me wherever I go.[31]

3. But the rage of travelling is a symptom of a deeper unsoundness affecting the whole intellectual action.

The intellect is vagabond, and our system of education fosters restlessness. Our minds travel when our bodies are forced to stay at home. We imitate; and what is imitation but the travelling of the mind? Our houses are built with foreign taste; our shelves are garnished with foreign ornaments; our opinions, our tastes, our faculties lean, and follow the Past and the Distant. The soul created the arts wherever they have flourished. It was in his own mind that the artist sought his model. It was an application of his own thought to the thing to be done and the conditions to be observed. And why need we copy the Doric or the Gothic model? Beauty, convenience, grandeur of thought and quaint expression [32] are as near to us as to any, and if the American artist will study with hope and love the precise thing to be done by him, considering the climate, the soil, the length of the day, the wants of the people, the habit and form of the government, he will create a house in which all these will find themselves fitted, and taste and sentiment will be satisfied also.

Insist on yourself; never imitate. Your own gift you can present every moment with the cumulative force of a whole life's cultivation; but of the adopted talent of another you have only an extemporaneous half possession. That which each can do best, none but his Maker can teach him. No man yet knows what it is, nor can, till that person has exhibited it. Where is the master who could have taught Shakespeare? Where is the master who could have instructed Franklin, or Washington, or Bacon, or Newton? Every great man is a unique. [33] The Scipionism of Scipio is precisely that part he could not borrow. Shakespeare will never be made by the study of Shakespeare. Do that which is assigned you, and you cannot hope too much or dare too much.

There is at this moment for you an utterance brave and grand as that of the colossal [34] chisel of Phidias, or trowel of the Egyptians, or the pen of Moses or Dante, but different from all these. Not possibly will the soul, all rich, all eloquent, with thousand-cloven tongue, deign to repeat itself; but if you can hear what these patriarchs say, surely you can reply to them in the same pitch of voice; for the ear and the tongue are two organs of one nature. Abide in the simple and noble regions of thy life, obey thy heart, and thou shalt reproduce the Foreworld again.

4. As our Religion, our Education, our Art look abroad, so does our spirit of society. All men plume themselves on the improvement of society, and no man improves.

Society never advances. [35] It recedes as fast on one side as it gains on the other. It undergoes continual changes; it is barbarous, it is civilized, it is christianized, it is rich, it is scientific; but this change is not amelioration. For every thing that is given something is taken. Society acquires new arts and loses old instincts. What a contrast between the well-clad, reading, writing, thinking American, with a watch, a pencil and a bill of exchange in his pocket, and the naked New Zealander, whose property is a club, a spear, a mat and an undivided twentieth of a shed to sleep under! But compare the health of the two men and you shall see that the white man has lost his aboriginal strength. If the traveller tell us truly, strike the savage with a broad-axe and in a day or two the flesh shall unite and heal as if you struck the blow into soft pitch, and the same blow shall send the white to his grave.

The civilized man has built a coach, but has lost the use of his feet. He is supported on crutches, but lacks so much support of muscle. He has a fine Geneva watch, but he fails of the skill to tell the hour by the sun. A Greenwich nautical almanac he has, and so being sure of the information when he wants it, the man in the street does not know a star in the sky. The solstice he does not observe; the equinox he knows as little; and the whole bright calendar of the year is without a dial in his mind. His note-books impair his memory; his libraries overload his wit; the insurance-office increases the number of accidents; and it may be a question whether machinery does not encumber; whether we have not lost by refinement some energy, by a Christianity, entrenched in establishments and forms, some vigor of wild virtue. For every Stoic was a Stoic; but in Christendom where is the Christian?

There is no more deviation in the moral standard than in the standard of height or bulk. No greater men are now than ever were. A singular equality may be observed between the great men of the first and of the last ages; nor can all the science, art, religion, and philosophy of the nineteenth century avail to educate greater men than Plutarch's heroes, three or four and twenty centuries ago. Not in time is the race progressive. Phocion,[36] Socrates, Anaxagoras, Diogenes,[37] are great men, but they leave no class. He who is really of their class will not be called by their name, but will be his own man, and in his turn the founder of a sect. The arts and inventions of each period are only its costume and do not invigorate men. The harm of the improved machinery may compensate its good. Hudson and Behring accomplished so much in their fishing-boats as to astonish Parry[38] and Franklin,[39] whose equipment exhausted the resources of science and art. Galileo, with an opera-glass, discovered a more splendid series of celestial phenomena than any one since. Columbus found the New World in an undecked boat. It is curious to see the periodical disuse and perishing of means and machinery which were introduced with loud laudation a few years or centuries before. The great genius returns to essential man. We reckoned the improvements of the art of war among the triumphs of science, and yet Napoleon conquered Europe by the bivouac, which consisted of falling back on naked valor and disencumbering it of all aids. The Emperor held it impossible to make a perfect army, says Las Casas, "without abolishing our arms, magazines, commissaries and carriages, until, in imitation of the Roman custom, the soldier should receive his supply of corn, grind it in his hand-mill and bake his bread himself."

Society is a wave. The wave moves onward, but the water of which it is composed does not. The same particle does not rise from the valley to the ridge. Its unity is only phenomenal. The persons who make up a nation to-day, next year die, and their experience dies with them.

And so the reliance on Property, including the reliance on governments which protect it, is the want of self-reliance. Men have looked away from themselves and at things so long that they have come to esteem the religious, learned and civil institutions as guards of property, and they deprecate assaults on these, because they feel them to be assaults on property. They measure their esteem of each other by what each has, and not by what each is. But a cultivated man becomes ashamed of his property, out of new respect for his nature. Especially he hates what he has if he see that it is accidental, — came to him by inheritance, or gift,

or crime; then he feels that it is not having; it does not
belong to him, has no root in him and merely lies there
because no revolution or no robber takes it away. But
that which a man is, does always by necessity acquire;
and what the man acquires, is living property, which
does not wait the beck of rulers, or mobs, or revolutions, or fire, or storm, or bankruptcies, but perpetually renews itself wherever the man breathes. "Thy
lot or portion of life," said the Caliph Ali, "is seeking
after thee; therefore be at rest from seeking after it." [40]
Our dependence on these foreign goods leads us to our
slavish respect for numbers. The political parties meet
in numerous conventions; the greater the concourse
and with each new uproar of announcement, The de-
legation from Essex! The Democrats from New Hampshire! The Whigs of Maine! the young patriot feels
himself stronger than before by a new thousand of
eyes and arms. In like manner the reformers summon
conventions and vote and resolve in multitude. Not
so, O friends! will the God deign to enter and inhabit
you, but by a method precisely the reverse. It is only
as a man puts off all foreign support and stands alone
that I see him to be strong and to prevail. He is weaker
by every recruit to his banner. Is not a man better
than a town? Ask nothing of men, and, in the endless
mutation, thou only firm column must presently appear
the upholder of all that surrounds thee. He who knows
that power is inborn, that he is weak because he has
looked for good out of him and elsewhere, and, so per-
ceiving, throws himself unhesitatingly on his thought,
instantly rights himself, stands in the erect position,
commands his limbs, works miracles; just as a man
who stands on his feet is stronger than a man who
stands on his head.

So use all that is called Fortune. Most men gamble with her, and gain all, and lose all, as her wheel rolls. But do thou leave as unlawful these winnings, and deal with Cause and Effect, the chancellors of God. In the Will work and acquire, and thou hast chained the wheel of Chance, and shall sit hereafter out of fear from her rotations. A political victory, a rise of rents, the recovery of your sick or the return of your absent friend, or some other favorable event raises your spirits, and you think good days are preparing for you. Do not believe it. Nothing can bring you peace but yourself. Nothing can bring you peace but the triumph of principles. [41]

HEROISM

Paradise is under the shadow of swords. — *Mahomet.*

RUBY wine is drunk by knaves,
Sugar spends to fatten slaves,
Rose and vine-leaf deck buffoons;
Thunderclouds are Jove's festoons,
Drooping oft in wreaths of dread
Lightning-knotted round his head:
The hero is not fed on sweets,
Daily his own heart he eats;
Chambers of the great are jails,
And head-winds right for royal sails.

HEROISM

In the elder English dramatists, and mainly in the plays of Beaumont and Fletcher, there is a constant recognition of gentility, as if a noble behavior were as easily marked in the society of their age as color is in our American population. When any Rodrigo, Pedro or Valerio [1] enters, though he be a stranger, the duke or governor exclaims, 'This is a gentleman,' — and proffers civilities without end; but all the rest are slag and refuse. In harmony with this delight in personal advantages there is in their plays a certain heroic cast of character and dialogue, — as in Bonduca, Sophocles,[2] the Mad Lover, the Double Marriage, — wherein the speaker is so earnest and cordial and on such deep grounds of character, that the dialogue, on the slightest additional incident in the plot, rises naturally into poetry. Among many texts take the following. The Roman Martius has conquered Athens, — all but the invincible spirits of Sophocles, the duke of Athens, and Dorigen, his wife. The beauty of the latter inflames Martius, and he seeks to save her husband; but Sophocles will not ask his life, although assured that a word will save him, and the execution of both proceeds: —

> *Valerius.*   Bid thy wife farewell.
> *Soph.* No, I will take no leave. My Dorigen,
> Yonder, above, 'bout Ariadne's crown,
> My spirit shall hover for thee. Prithee, haste.
> *Dor.* Stay, Sophocles, — with this tie up my sight;
> Let not soft nature so transformèd be,

And lose her gentler sexed humanity,
To make me see my lord bleed. So, 't is well;
Never one object underneath the sun
Will I behold before my Sophocles:
Farewell; now teach the Romans how to die.
    Mar. Dost know what 't is to die?
    Soph.   Thou dost not, Martius,
And, therefore, not what 't is to live; to die
Is to begin to live. It is to end
An old, stale, weary work and to commence
A newer and a better. 'T is to leave
Deceitful knaves for the society
Of gods and goodness. Thou thyself must part
At last from all thy garlands, pleasures, triumphs,
And prove thy fortitude what then 't will do.
    Val. But art not grieved nor vexed to leave thy life thus?
    Soph. Why should I grieve or vex for being sent
To them I ever loved best? Now I'll kneel,
But with my back toward thee: 't is the last duty
This trunk can do the gods.
    Mar.   Strike, strike, Valerius,
Or Martius' heart will leap out at his mouth.
This is a man, a woman. Kiss thy lord,
And live with all the freedom you were wont.
O love! thou doubly hast afflicted me
With virtue and with beauty. Treacherous heart,
My hand shall cast thee quick into my urn,
Ere thou transgress this knot of piety.
    Val. What ails my brother?
    Soph.   Martius, O Martius,
Thou now hast found a way to conquer me.
    Dor. O star of Rome! what gratitude can speak
Fit words to follow such a deed as this?
    Mar. This admirable duke, Valerius,
With his disdain of fortune and of death,
Captived himself, has captivated me,
And though my arm hath ta'en his body here,
His soul hath subjugated Martius' soul.
By Romulus, he is all soul, I think;
He hath no flesh, and spirit cannot be gyved,
Then we have vanquished nothing; he is free,
And Martius walks now in captivity."

I do not readily remember any poem, play, sermon, novel or oration that our press vents in the last few years, which goes to the same tune. We have a great many flutes and flageolets, but not often the sound of any fife. Yet Wordsworth's "Laodamia," and the ode of "Dion," and some sonnets, have a certain noble music; and Scott will sometimes draw a stroke like the portrait of Lord Evandale given by Balfour of Burley.[3] Thomas Carlyle, with his natural taste for what is manly and daring in character, has suffered no heroic trait in his favorites to drop from his biographical and historical pictures. Earlier, Robert Burns has given us a song or two. In the Harleian Miscellanies [4] there is an account of the battle of Lutzen [5] which deserves to be read. And Simon Ockley's [6] History of the Saracens recounts the prodigies of individual valor, with admiration all the more evident on the part of the narrator that he seems to think that his place in Christian Oxford requires of him some proper protestations of abhorrence. But if we explore the literature of Heroism we shall quickly come to Plutarch, who is its doctor and historian. To him we owe the Brasidas, the Dion, the Epaminondas, the Scipio of old, and I must think we are more deeply indebted to him than to all the ancient writers. Each of his "Lives" is a refutation to the despondency and cowardice of our religious and political theorists. A wild courage, a Stoicism not of the schools but of the blood, shines in every anecdote, and has given that book its immense fame.[7]

We need books of this tart cathartic virtue more than books of political science or of private economy. Life is a festival only to the wise. Seen from the nook and chimney-side of prudence, it wears a ragged and dangerous front. The violations of the laws of nature by our predecessors and our contemporaries are punished in us also. The disease and deformity around us certify the infraction of natural, intellectual and moral laws, and often violation on violation to breed such compound misery. A lock-jaw that bends a man's head back to his heels; hydrophobia that makes him bark at his wife and babes; insanity that makes him eat grass; war, plague, cholera, famine, indicate a certain ferocity in nature, which, as it had its inlet by human crime, must have its outlet by human suffering. Unhappily no man exists who has not in his own person become to some amount a stockholder in the sin, and so made himself liable to a share in the expiation.

Our culture therefore must not omit the arming of the man. Let him hear in season that he is born into the state of war, and that the commonwealth and his own well-being require that he should not go dancing in the weeds of peace, but warned, self-collected and neither defying nor dreading the thunder, let him take both reputation and life in his hand, and with perfect urbanity dare the gibbet and the mob by the absolute truth of his speech and the rectitude of his behavior.

Towards all this external evil the man within the breast assumes a warlike attitude, and affirms his ability to cope single-handed with the infinite army of enemies. To this military attitude of the soul we give the name of Heroism. Its rudest form is the contempt for safety and ease, which makes the attractiveness of war. It is a self-trust which slights the restraints of prudence, in the plenitude of its energy and power to repair the harms it may suffer. The hero is a mind [8] of such balance that no disturbances can shake his will, but pleasantly and as it were merrily he advances to his own music, alike in frightful alarms and in the tipsy mirth of universal dissoluteness. There is somewhat not philosophical in heroism; there is somewhat not holy in it; it seems not to know that other souls are of one texture with it; it has pride; it is the extreme of individual nature. Nevertheless we must profoundly revere it. There is somewhat in great actions which does not allow us to go behind them. Heroism feels and never reasons, and therefore is always right; and although a different breeding, different religion and greater intellectual activity would have modified or even reversed the particular action, yet for the hero that thing he does is the highest deed, and is not open to the censure of philosophers or divines. It is the avowal of the unschooled man that he finds a quality in him that is negligent of expense, of health, of life, of danger, of hatred, of reproach, and knows that his will is higher and more excellent than all actual and all possible antagonists.

Heroism works in contradiction to the voice of mankind and in contradiction, for a time, to the voice of the great and good. Heroism is an obedience to a secret impulse of an individual's character. Now to no other man can its wisdom appear as it does to him, for every man must be supposed to see a little farther on his own proper path than any one else. Therefore just and wise men take umbrage at his act, until after some little time be past; then they see it to be in unison with their acts. All prudent men [9] see that the action is clean contrary to a sensual prosperity; for every heroic act measures itself by its contempt of some external good. But it finds its own success at last, and then the prudent also extol.

Self-trust is the essence of heroism. It is the state of

the soul at war, and its ultimate objects are the last defiance of falsehood and wrong, and the power to bear all that can be inflicted by evil agents. It speaks the truth and it is just, generous, hospitable, temperate, scornful of petty calculations and scornful of being scorned. It persists; it is of an undaunted boldness and of a fortitude not to be wearied out. Its jest is the littleness of common life. That false prudence which dotes on health and wealth is the butt and merriment of heroism. Heroism, like Plotinus, is almost ashamed of its body. What shall it say then to the sugar-plums and cats'-cradles, to the toilet, compliments, quarrels, cards and custard, which rack the wit of all society? What joys has kind nature provided for us dear creatures! There seems to be no interval between greatness and meanness.[10] When the spirit is not master of the world, then it is its dupe. Yet the little man takes the great hoax so innocently, works in it so headlong and believing, is born red, and dies gray, arranging his toilet, attending on his own health, laying traps for sweet food and strong wine, setting his heart on a horse or a rifle, made happy with a little gossip or a little praise, that the great soul cannot choose but laugh at such earnest nonsense.[11] "Indeed, these humble considerations make me out of love with greatness. What a disgrace it is to me to take note how many pairs of silk stockings thou hast, namely, these and those that were the peach-colored ones; or to bear the inventory of thy shirts, as one for superfluity, and one other for use!"[12]

Citizens, thinking after the laws of arithmetic, consider the inconvenience of receiving strangers at their fireside, reckon narrowly the loss of time and the unusual display; the soul of a better quality thrusts back

the unseasonable economy into the vaults of life, and
says, I will obey the God, and the sacrifice and the fire
he will provide. Ibn Haukal,[13] the Arabian geographer,
describes a heroic extreme in the hospitality of Sogd,
in Bukharia. "When I was in Sogd I saw a great
building, like a palace, the gates of which were open and
fixed back to the wall with large nails. I asked the reason, and was told that the house had not been shut,
night or day, for a hundred years. Strangers may present themselves at any hour and in whatever number;
the master has amply provided for the reception of the
men and their animals, and is never happier than when
they tarry for some time. Nothing of the kind have I
seen in any other country." The magnanimous know
very well that they who give time, or money, or shelter, to the stranger, — so it be done for love and not
for ostentation, — do, as it were, put God under obligation to them,[14] so perfect are the compensations of
the universe. In some way the time they seem to lose
is redeemed and the pains they seem to take remuner-
ate themselves. These men fan the flame of human
love and raise the standard of civil virtue among mankind. But hospitality must be for service and not for
show, or it pulls down the host. The brave soul rates
itself too high to value itself by the splendor of its table
and draperies. It gives what it hath, and all it hath, but
its own majesty can lend a better grace to bannocks
and fair water than belong to city feasts.

The temperance of the hero proceeds from the same
wish to do no dishonor to the worthiness he has. But he
loves it for its elegancy, not for its austerity. It seems
not worth his while to be solemn and denounce with
bitterness flesh-eating or wine-drinking, the use of tobacco, or opium, or tea, or silk, or gold. A great man

scarcely knows how he dines, how he dresses; but without railing or precision his living is natural and poetic. John Eliot,[15] the Indian Apostle, drank water, and said of wine, — "It is a noble, generous liquor and we should be humbly thankful for it, but, as I remember, water was made before it." Better still is the temperance of King David,[16] who poured out on the ground unto the Lord the water which three of his warriors had brought him to drink at the peril of their lives.

It is told of Brutus, that when he fell on his sword after the battle of Philippi, he quoted a line of Euripides, — "O Virtue! I have followed thee through life, and I find thee at last but a shade." I doubt not the hero is slandered by this report. The heroic soul does not sell its justice and its nobleness. It does not ask to dine nicely and to sleep warm. The essence of greatness is the perception that virtue is enough. Poverty is its ornament. It does not need plenty, and can very well abide its loss.

But that which takes my fancy most in the heroic class, is the good-humor and hilarity they exhibit.[17] It is a height to which common duty can very well attain, to suffer and to dare with solemnity. But these rare souls set opinion, success, and life at so cheap a rate that they will not soothe their enemies by petitions, or the show of sorrow, but wear their own habitual greatness. Scipio, charged with peculation, refuses to do himself so great a disgrace as to wait for justification, though he had the scroll of his accounts in his hands, but tears it to pieces before the tribunes.[18] Socrates's condemnation of himself [19] to be maintained in all honor in the Prytaneum, during his life, and Sir Thomas More's playfulness [20] at the scaffold, are of the same strain. In Beaumont and Fletcher's "Sea

Voyage," Juletta tells the stout captain and his company, —

> *Jul.* Why, slaves, 't is in our power to hang ye.
> *Master.* Very likely,
> 'T is in our powers, then, to be hanged and scorn ye.

These replies are sound and whole. Sport is the bloom and glow of a perfect health. The great will not condescend to take any thing seriously; all must be as gay as the song of a canary, though it were the building of cities or the eradication of old and foolish churches and nations which have cumbered the earth long thousands of years. Simple hearts put all the history and customs of this world behind them, and play their own game in innocent defiance of the Blue-Laws [21] of the world; and such would appear, could we see the human race assembled in vision, like little children frolicking together, though to the eyes of mankind at large they wear a stately and solemn garb of works and influences.

The interest these fine stories have for us, the power of a romance over the boy who grasps the forbidden book under his bench at school, our delight in the hero, is the main fact to our purpose. All these great and transcendent properties are ours. If we dilate in beholding the Greek energy, the Roman pride, it is that we are already domesticating the same sentiment. Let us find room for this great guest in our small houses. The first step of worthiness will be to disabuse us of our superstitious associations with places and times, with number and size. Why should these words, Athenian, Roman, Asia and England, so tingle in the ear? Where the heart is, there the muses, there the gods sojourn, and not in any geography of fame. Massachusetts, Connecticut River and Boston Bay you think paltry places, and the ear loves names of foreign and classic topography. But here we are; and, if we will tarry a little, we may come to learn that here is best. See to it only that thyself is here, and art and nature, hope and fate, friends, angels and the Supreme Being shall not be absent from the chamber where thou sittest. Epaminondas, brave and affectionate,[22] does not seem to us to need Olympus to die upon, nor the Syrian sunshine. He lies very well where he is. The Jerseys were handsome ground[23] enough for Washington to tread, and London streets for the feet of Milton. A great man makes his climate genial in the imagination of men, and its air the beloved element of all delicate spirits. That country is the fairest which is inhabited by the noblest minds. The pictures which fill the imagination in reading the actions of Pericles, Xenophon, Columbus, Bayard,[24] Sidney,[25] Hampden,[26] teach us how needlessly mean our life is; that we, by the depth of our living, should deck it with more than regal or national splendor, and act on principles that should interest man and nature in the length of our days.[27]

We have seen or heard of many extraordinary young men who never ripened, or whose performance in actual life was not extraordinary. When we see their air and mien, when we hear them speak of society, of books, of religion, we admire their superiority; they seem to throw contempt on our entire polity and social state; theirs is the tone of a youthful giant who is sent to work revolutions. But they enter an active profession and the forming Colossus shrinks to the common size of man. The magic they used was the ideal tendencies, which always make the Actual ridiculous; but the tough world had its revenge the moment they put their horses of the sun to plough in its furrow. They found

no example and no companion, and their heart fainted.
What then? The lesson they gave in their first aspira-
tions is yet true; and a better valor and a purer truth
shall one day organize their belief. Or why should a
woman liken herself to any historical woman, and
think, because Sappho,[28] or Sévigné,[29] or De Staël,[30] or
the cloistered souls who have had genius and cultivation do not satisfy the imagination and the serene The-
mis,[31] none can, — certainly not she? Why not? She
has a new and unattempted problem to solve, perchance that of the happiest nature that ever bloomed.
Let the maiden, with erect soul, walk serenely on her
way, accept the hint of each new experience, search in
turn all the objects that solicit her eye, that she may
learn the power and the charm of her new-born being,
which is the kindling of a new dawn in the recesses
of space. The fair girl who repels interference by a
decided and proud choice of influences, so careless of
pleasing, so wilful and lofty, inspires every beholder
with somewhat of her own nobleness. The silent heart
encourages her; O friend, never strike sail to a fear![32]
Come into port greatly, or sail with God the seas. Not
in vain you live, for every passing eye is cheered and
refined by the vision.

The characteristic of heroism is its persistency. All
men have wandering impulses, fits and starts of generosity. But when you have chosen your part, abide by
it, and do not weakly try to reconcile yourself with the
world. The heroic cannot be the common, nor the common the heroic. Yet we have the weakness to expect
the sympathy of people in those actions whose excellence is that they outrun sympathy and appeal to a
tardy justice. If you would serve your brother, because
it is fit for you to serve him, do not take back your

words when you find that prudent people do not commend you. Adhere to your own act, and congratulate yourself if you have done something strange and extravagant and broken the monotony of a decorous age. It was a high counsel that I once heard given to a young person, — "Always do what you are afraid to do." [33] A simple manly character need never make an apology, but should regard its past action with the calmness of Phocion,[34] when he admitted that the event of the battle was happy, yet did not regret his dissuasion from the battle.

There is no weakness or exposure [35] for which we cannot find consolation in the thought — this is a part of my constitution, part of my relation and office to my fellow-creature. Has nature covenanted with me that I should never appear to disadvantage, never make a ridiculous figure? Let us be generous of our dignity as well as of our money. Greatness once and for ever has done with opinion. We tell our charities, not because we wish to be praised for them, not because we think they have great merit, but for our justification. It is a capital blunder; as you discover when another man recites his charities.

To speak the truth, even with some austerity, to live with some rigor of temperance, or some extremes of generosity, seems to be an asceticism which common good-nature would appoint to those who are at ease and in plenty, in sign that they feel a brotherhood with the great multitude of suffering men. And not only need we breathe and exercise the soul by assuming the penalties of abstinence, of debt, of solitude, of unpopularity, — but it behooves the wise man to look with a bold eye into those rarer dangers which sometimes invade men, and to familiarize himself with disgusting forms of disease, with sounds of execration, and the vision of violent death.

Times of heroism are generally times of terror, but the day never shines in which this element may not work. The circumstances of man, we say, are historically somewhat better in this country and at this hour than perhaps ever before. More freedom exists for culture. It will not now run against an axe at the first step out of the beaten track of opinion. But whoso is heroic will always find crises to try his edge. Human virtue demands her champions and martyrs, and the trial of persecution always proceeds. It is but the other day that the brave Lovejoy [36] gave his breast to the bullets of a mob, for the rights of free speech and opinion, and died when it was better not to live.

I see not any road of perfect peace which a man can walk, but after the counsel of his own bosom. Let him quit too much association, let him go home much, and stablish himself in those courses he approves. [37] The unremitting retention of simple and high sentiments in obscure duties is hardening the character to that temper which will work with honor, if need be in the tumult, or on the scaffold. Whatever outrages have happened to men may befall a man again; and very easily in a republic, if there appear any signs of a decay of religion. Coarse slander, fire, tar and feathers and the gibbet, the youth may freely bring home to his mind and with what sweetness of temper he can, and inquire how fast he can fix his sense of duty, braving such penalties, whenever it may please the next newspaper and a sufficient number of his neighbors to pronounce his opinions incendiary.

It may calm the apprehension of calamity in the most susceptible heart to see how quick a bound Na-

ture has set to the utmost infliction of malice. We
rapidly approach a brink over which no enemy can
follow us: —

> "Let them rave:
> Thou art quiet in thy grave." [38]

In the gloom of our ignorance of what shall be, in the
hour when we are deaf to the higher voices, who does
not envy those who have seen safely to an end their
manful endeavor? Who that sees the meanness of our
politics but inly congratulates Washington that he is
long already wrapped in his shroud, and for ever safe;
that he was laid sweet in his grave, the hope of humanity not yet subjugated in him? Who does not sometimes envy the good and brave who are no more to
suffer from the tumults of the natural world, and await
with curious complacency the speedy term of his own
conversation with finite nature? And yet the love that
will be annihilated sooner than treacherous has already
made death impossible, and affirms itself no mortal but
a native of the deeps of absolute and inextinguishable
being.

HISTORY

THERE is no great and no small [1]
To the Soul that maketh all:
And where it cometh, all things **are;**
And it cometh everywhere.

I AM the owner of the sphere,[2]
Of the seven stars and the solar year,
Of Cæsar's hand, and Plato's brain,
Of Lord Christ's heart, and Shakspeare's strain.

HISTORY

THERE is one mind common to all individual men. Every man is an inlet to the same and to all of the same. He that is once admitted to the right of reason is made a freeman of the whole estate. What Plato has thought, he may think; what a saint has felt, he may feel; what at any time has befallen any man, he can understand. Who hath access to this universal mind is a party to all that is or can be done, for this is the only and sovereign agent.

Of the works of this mind history is the record. Its genius is illustrated by the entire series of days. Man is explicable by nothing less than all his history. Without hurry, without rest, the human spirit goes forth from the beginning to embody every faculty, every thought, every emotion which belongs to it, in appropriate events. But the thought is always prior to the fact; all the facts of history [3] preëxist in the mind as laws. Each law in turn is made by circumstances predominant, and the limits of nature give power to but one at a time. A man is the whole encylopædia of facts. The creation of a thousand forests is in one acorn, and Egypt, Greece, Rome, Gaul, Britain, America, lie folded already in the first man. Epoch after epoch, camp, kingdom, empire, republic, democracy, are merely the application of his manifold spirit to the manifold world.

This human mind wrote history, and this must read it. The Sphinx must solve her own riddle. If the whole

of history is in one man, it is all to be explained from
individual experience. There is a relation between the
hours of our life and the centuries of time. As the air
I breathe is drawn from the great repositories of nature, as the light on my book is yielded by a star a hundred millions of miles distant, as the poise of my body
depends on the equilibrium of centrifugal and centripetal forces, so the hours should be instructed by the
ages and the ages explained by the hours. Of the universal mind each individual man is one more incar-
nation. All its properties consist [4] in him. Each new
fact in his private experience flashes a light on what
great bodies of men have done, and the crises of his
life refer to national crises. Every revolution [5] was
first a thought in one man's mind, and when the same
thought occurs to another man, it is the key to that
era. Every reform was once a private opinion,[6] and
when it shall be a private opinion again it will solve
the problem of the age. The fact narrated must cor-
respond to something in me to be credible or intelligible. We, as we read, must become Greeks, Romans,
Turks, priest and king, martyr and executioner; must
fasten these images to some reality in our secret experience, or we shall learn nothing rightly. What befell [7]
Asdrubal or Cæsar Borgia [8] is as much an illustration
of the mind's powers and depravations as what has
befallen us. Each new law and political movement
has a meaning for you. Stand before each of its tablets
and say, 'Under this mask did my Proteus nature hide
itself.' This remedies the defect of our too great nearness to ourselves. This throws our actions into perspective, — and as crabs, goats, scorpions, the balance
and the waterpot lose their meanness when hung as
signs in the zodiac, so I can see my own vices without

heat in the distant persons of Solomon, Alcibiades, and Catiline.

It is the universal nature which gives worth to particular men and things. Human life, as containing this, is mysterious and inviolable, and we hedge it round with penalties and laws. All laws derive hence their ultimate reason; all express more or less distinctly some command of this supreme, illimitable essence. Property also holds of the soul, covers great spiritual facts, and instinctively we at first hold to it with swords and laws and wide and complex combinations. The obscure consciousness of this fact is the light of all our day,[9] the claim of claims; the plea for education, for justice, for charity; the foundation of friendship and love and of the heroism and grandeur which belong to acts of self-reliance. It is remarkable that involuntarily we always read as superior beings.[10] Universal history, the poets, the romancers, do not in their stateliest pictures, — in the sacerdotal, the imperial palaces, in the triumphs of will or of genius, — anywhere lose our ear, anywhere make us feel that we intrude, that this is for better men; but rather is it true that in their grandest strokes we feel most at home. All that Shakspeare says of the king, yonder slip of a boy that reads in the corner feels to be true of himself. We sympathize in the great moments of history, in the great discoveries, the great resistances, the great prosperities of men; — because there law was enacted, the sea was searched, the land was found, or the blow was struck, *for us*, as we ourselves in that place would have done or applauded.

We have the same interest in condition and character. We honor the rich because they have externally the freedom, power, and grace which we feel to be pro-

per to man, proper to us. So all that is said of the wise
man by Stoic or Oriental or modern essayist, describes
to each reader his own idea, describes his unattained
but attainable self. All literature writes the character of the wise man. Books, monuments, pictures, conversation, are portraits in which he finds the lineaments
he is forming. The silent and the eloquent praise him
and accost him, and he is stimulated wherever he moves,
as by personal allusions. A true aspirant therefore
never needs look for allusions personal and laudatory [11]
in discourse. He hears the commendation, not of himself, but, more sweet, of that character he seeks, in
every word that is said concerning character, yea further in every fact and circumstance, — in the running
river and the rustling corn. Praise is looked, homage
tendered, love flows, from mute nature, from the mountains and the lights of the firmament.

These hints, dropped as it were from sleep and night,
let us use in broad day. The student is to read history
actively and not passively; to esteem his own life the
text, and books the commentary. Thus compelled,
the Muse of history will utter oracles, as never to those
who do not respect themselves. I have no expectation
that any man will read history aright who thinks that
what was done in a remote age, by men whose names
have resounded far, has any deeper sense than what
he is doing to-day.

The world exists for the education of each man.
There is no age or state of society or mode of action in
history to which there is not somewhat corresponding
in his life. Everything tends in a wonderful manner
to abbreviate itself and yield its own virtue to him.
He should see that he can live all history in his own
person. He must sit solidly at home, and not suffer

himself to be bullied by kings or empires, but know that he is greater than all the geography and all the government of the world; he must transfer the point of view from which history is commonly read, from Rome and Athens and London, to himself, and not deny his conviction that he is the court, and if England or Egypt have anything to say to him he will try the case; if not, let them forever be silent. He must attain and maintain that lofty sight where facts yield their secret sense, and poetry and annals are alike. The instinct of the mind, the purpose of nature, betrays itself in the use we make of the signal narrations of history. Time dissipates to shining ether the solid angularity of facts. No anchor, no cable, no fences avail to keep a fact a fact. Babylon, Troy, Tyre, Palestine, and even early Rome are passing already into fiction. The Garden of Eden, the sun standing still in Gibeon,[12] is poetry thenceforward to all nations. Who cares what the fact was, when we have made a constellation of it to hang in heaven an immortal sign? London and Paris and New York must go the same way. "What is history," said Napoleon, "but a fable agreed upon?" This life of ours is stuck round with Egypt, Greece, Gaul, England, War, Colonization, Church, Court and Commerce, as with so many flowers and wild ornaments grave and gay. I will not make more account of them. I believe in Eternity. I can find Greece, Asia, Italy, Spain and the Islands, — the genius and creative principle of each and of all eras, in my own mind.

We are always coming up with the emphatic facts of history in our private experience and verifying them here. All history becomes subjective; in other words there is properly no history, only biography. Every mind must know the whole lesson for itself, — must go over the whole ground. What it does not see, what it does not live, it will not know. What the former age has epitomized into a formula or rule for manipular convenience it will lose all the good of verifying for itself, by means of the wall of that rule. Somewhere, sometime, it will demand and find compensation for that loss, by doing the work itself. Ferguson discovered many things in astronomy which had long been known. The better for him.

History must be this or it is nothing. Every law which the state enacts indicates a fact in human nature; that is all. We must in ourselves see the necessary reason of every fact, — see how it could and must be. So stand before every public and private work; before an oration of Burke, before a victory of Napoleon, before a martyrdom of Sir Thomas More, of Sidney, of Marmaduke Robinson;[13] before a French Reign of Terror, and a Salem hanging of witches; before a fanatic Revival and the Animal Magnetism in Paris, or in Providence. We assume that we under like influence should be alike affected, and should achieve the like; and we aim to master intellectually the steps and reach the same height or the same degradation that our fellow, our proxy has done.

All inquiry into antiquity, all curiosity respecting the Pyramids, the excavated cities, Stonehenge, the Ohio Circles, Mexico, Memphis,[14] — is the desire to do away this wild, savage, and preposterous There or Then, and introduce in its place the Here and the Now. Belzoni[15] digs and measures in the mummy-pits and pyramids of Thebes until he can see the end of the difference between the monstrous work and himself. When he has satisfied himself, in general and in detail, that it was made by such a person as he, so armed and so motived, and to ends to which he himself should also have worked, the problem is solved; his thought lives along the whole line of temples and sphinxes and catacombs, passes through them all with satisfaction, and they live again to the mind, or are *now*.[16]

A Gothic cathedral affirms that it was done by us and not done by us. Surely it was by man, but we find it not in our man. But we apply ourselves to the history of its production. We put ourselves into the place and state of the builder. We remember the forest-dwellers, the first temples, the adherence to the first type, and the decoration of it as the wealth of the nation increased; the value which is given to wood by carving led to the carving over the whole mountain of stone of a cathedral. When we have gone through this process, and added thereto the Catholic Church, its cross, its music, its processions, its Saints' days and image-worship, we have as it were been the man that made the minster; we have seen how it could and must be. We have the sufficient reason.

The difference between men is in their principle of association. Some men classify objects by color and size and other accidents of appearance; others by intrinsic likeness, or by the relation of cause and effect. The progress of the intellect is to the clearer vision of causes, which neglects surface differences. To the poet, to the philosopher, to the saint, all things are friendly and sacred, all events profitable, all days holy, all men divine. For the eye is fastened on the life, and slights the circumstance. Every chemical substance, every plant, every animal in its growth, teaches the unity of cause, the variety of appearance.

Upborne and surrounded as we are by this all-creating nature, soft and fluid as a cloud or the air, why should we be such hard pedants, and magnify a few forms? Why should we make account of time, or of magnitude, or of figure? The soul knows them not, and genius, obeying its law, knows how to play with them as a young child plays with graybeards and in churches. Genius studies the causal thought, and far back in the womb of things sees the rays parting from one orb, that diverge, ere they fall, by infinite diameters. Genius watches the monad [17] through all his masks as he performs the metempsychosis of nature. Genius detects through the fly, through the caterpillar, through the grub, through the egg, the constant individual; through countless individuals the fixed species; through many species the genus; through all genera the steadfast type; through all the kingdoms of organized life the eternal unity. Nature is a mutable cloud which is always and never the same. She casts the same thought into troops of forms, as a poet makes twenty fables with one moral. Through the bruteness [18] and toughness of matter, a subtle spirit bends all things to its own will. The adamant streams into soft but precise form before it, and whilst I look at it its outline and texture are changed again. Nothing is so fleeting as form; yet never does it quite deny itself. In man we still trace the remains or hints of all that we esteem badges of servitude in the lower races; yet in him they enchance his nobleness and grace; as Io, in Æschylus, [19] transformed to a cow, offends the imagination; but how changed when as Isis in Egypt she meets Osiris-Jove, a beautiful woman with nothing of the metamorphosis left but the lunar horns as the splendid ornament of her brows!

The identity of history is equally intrinsic, the diversity equally obvious. There is, at the surface, infinite variety of things; at the centre there is simplicity of cause. How many are the acts of one man in which we recognize the same character! Observe the sources of our information in respect to the Greek genius. We have the *civil history* of that people, as Herodotus, Thucydides, Xenophon, and Plutarch [20] have given it; a very sufficient account of what manner of persons they were and what they did. We have the same national mind expressed for us again in their *literature*,[21] in epic and lyric poems, drama, and philosophy; a very complete form. Then we have it once more in their *architecture*, a beauty as of temperance itself, limited to the straight line and the square, — a builded geometry. Then we have it once again in *sculpture*, the "tongue on the balance of expression," [22] a multitude of forms in the utmost freedom of action and never transgressing the ideal serenity; like votaries performing some religious dance before the gods, and, though in convulsive pain or mortal combat, never daring to break the figure and decorum of their dance. Thus of the genius of one remarkable people we have a fourfold representation: and to the senses what more unlike than an ode of Pindar, a marble centaur, the peristyle of the Parthenon, and the last actions of Phocion?

Every one must have observed faces and forms which, without any resembling feature, make a like impression on the beholder. A particular picture or copy of verses, if it do not awaken the same train of images, will yet superinduce the same sentiment as some wild mountain walk, although the resemblance is nowise obvious to the senses, but is occult and out of the reach of the understanding. Nature is an endless combination and repetition of a very few laws.

She hums the old well-known air through innumerable variations.[23]

Nature is full of a sublime family likeness throughout her works, and delights in startling us with resemblances in the most unexpected quarters. I have seen the head of an old sachem of the forest which at once reminded the eye of a bald mountain summit, and the furrows of the brow suggested the strata of the rock.[24] There are men whose manners have the same essential splendor as the simple and awful sculpture on the friezes of the Parthenon and the remains of the earliest Greek art. And there are compositions of the same strain to be found in the books of all ages. What is Guido's Rospigliosi Aurora [25] but a morning thought, as the horses in it are only a morning cloud? If any one will but take pains to observe the variety of actions to which he is equally inclined in certain moods of mind and those to which he is averse, he will see how deep is the chain of affinity.

A painter told me that nobody could draw a tree without in some sort becoming a tree; or draw a child by studying the outlines of its form merely, — but by watching for a time his motions and plays, the painter enters into his nature and can then draw him at will in every attitude. So Roos [26] "entered into the inmost nature of a sheep." I knew a draughtsman employed in a public survey who found that he could not sketch the rocks until their geological structure was first explained to him.[27] In a certain state of thought is the common origin of very diverse works. It is the spirit and not the fact that is identical. By a deeper apprehension, and not primarily by a painful acquisition of many manual skills, the artist attains the power of awakening other souls to a given activity.

It has been said that "common souls pay with what they do, nobler souls with that which they are."[28] And why? Because a profound nature awakens in us by its actions and words, by its very looks and manners, the same power and beauty that a gallery of sculpture or of pictures addresses.

Civil and natural history, the history of art and of literature, must be explained from individual history, or must remain words. There is nothing but is related to us, nothing that does not interest us, — kingdom, college, tree, horse, or iron shoe, — the roots of all things are in man. Santa Croce and the Dome of St. Peter's are lame copies after a divine model.[29] Strasburg Cathedral is a material counterpart of the soul of Erwin of Steinbach.[30] The true poem is the poet's mind; the true ship is the ship-builder. In the man, could we lay him open, we should see the reason for the last flourish and tendril of his work; as every spine and tint in the sea-shell preëxists in the secreting organs of the fish. The whole of heraldry and of chivalry is in courtesy. A man of fine manners shall pronounce your name with all the ornament that titles of nobility could ever add.

The trivial experience of every day is always verifying some old prediction to us and converting into things the words and signs which we had heard and seen without heed. A lady with whom I was riding in the forest said to me that the woods always seemed to her *to wait*, as if the genii who inhabit them suspended their deeds until the wayfarer had passed onward; a thought which poetry has celebrated in the dance of the fairies, which breaks off on the approach of human feet. The man who has seen the rising moon break out of the clouds at midnight, has been present like an archangel

at the creation of light and of the world. I remember
one summer day in the fields my companion pointed
out to me a broad cloud, which might extend a quarter
of a mile parallel to the horizon, quite accurately in the
form of a cherub as painted over churches, a round
block in the centre, which it was easy to animate with
eyes and mouth, supported on either side by wide-
stretched symmetrical wings.[31] What appears once in
the atmosphere may appear often, and it was undoubtedly the archetype of that familiar ornament. I have
seen in the sky a chain of summer lightning which at
once showed to me that the Greeks drew from nature when they painted the thunderbolt in the hand
of Jove. I have seen a snow-drift [32] along the sides of
the stone wall which obviously gave the idea of the
common architectural scroll to abut a tower.[33]

By surrounding ourselves with the original circumstances we invent anew the orders and the ornaments
of architecture, as we see how each people merely
decorated its primitive abodes. The Doric temple pre-
serves the semblance of the wooden cabin in which the
Dorian dwelt. The Chinese pagoda is plainly a Tartar
tent. The Indian and Egyptian temples still betray the
mounds and subterranean houses of their forefathers.
"The custom of making houses and tombs in the living rock," says Heeren [34] in his Researches on the
Ethopians, "determined very naturally the principal
character of the Nubian Egyptian architecture to the
colossal form which it assumed. In these caverns,
already prepared by nature, the eye was accustomed
to dwell on huge shapes and masses, so that when art
came to the assistance of nature it could not move on
a small scale without degrading itself. What would
statues of the usual size, or neat porches and wings

have been, associated with those gigantic halls before which only Colossi could sit as watchmen or lean on the pillars of the interior?"

The Gothic church plainly originated in a rude adaptation of the forest trees, with all their boughs, to a festal or solemn arcade; as the bands about the cleft pillars still indicate the green withes that tied them. No one can walk in a road cut through pine woods, without being struck with the architectural appearance of the grove, especially in winter, when the barrenness of all other trees shows the low arch of the Saxons. In the woods in a winter afternoon one will see as readily the origin of the stained glass window, with which the Gothic cathedrals are adorned, in the colors of the western sky seen through the bare and crossing branches of the forest. Nor can any lover of nature enter the old piles of Oxford and the English cathedrals, without feeling that the forest overpowered the mind of the builder, and that his chisel, his saw and plane still reproduced its ferns, its spikes of flowers, its locust, elm, oak, pine, fir and spruce.

The Gothic cathedral is a blossoming in stone subdued by the insatiable demand of harmony in man. The mountain of granite blooms into an eternal flower, with the lightness and delicate finish as well as the aerial proportions and perspective of vegetable beauty.

In like manner all public facts are to be individualized, all private facts are to be generalized. Then at once History becomes fluid and true, and Biography deep and sublime. As the Persian imitated in the slender shafts and capitals of his architecture the stem and flower of the lotus and palm, so the Persian court in its magnificent era never gave over the nomadism of its barbarous tribes, but travelled from Ecbatana, where the spring was spent, to Susa in summer and to Babylon for the winter.

In the early history of Asia and Africa, Nomadism and Agriculture are the two antagonist facts. The geography of Asia and of Africa necessitated a nomadic life. But the nomads were the terror of all those whom the soil or the advantages of a market had induced to build towns. Agriculture therefore was a religious injunction, because of the perils of the state from nomadism. And in these late and civil countries of England and America these propensities still fight out the old battle, in the nation and in the individual. The nomads of Africa were constrained to wander, by the attacks of the gad-fly, which drives the cattle mad, and so compels the tribe to emigrate in the rainy season and to drive off the cattle to the higher sandy regions. The nomads of Asia follow the pasturage from month to month. In America and Europe the nomadism is of trade and curiosity; a progress, certainly, from the gad-fly of Astaboras [35] to the Anglo and Italomania of Boston Bay. Sacred cities, to which a periodical religious pilgrimage was enjoined, or stringent laws and customs tending to invigorate the national bond, were the check on the old rovers; and the cumulative values of long residence are the restraints on the itinerancy of the present day. The antagonism of the two tendencies is not less active in individuals, as the love of adventure or the love of repose happens to predominate. A man of rude health and flowing spirits has the faculty of rapid domestication, lives in his wagon and roams through all latitudes as easily as a Calmuc. [36] At sea, or in the forest, or in the snow, he sleeps as warm, dines with as good appetite, and associates as happily as beside his own chimneys. Or perhaps his facility is deeper seated, in the increased range of his faculties of observation, which yield him points of interest wherever fresh objects meet his eyes. The pastoral nations were needy and hungry to desperation; and this intellectual nomadism, in its excess, bankrupts [37] the mind through the dissipation of power on a miscellany of objects. The home-keeping wit, on the other hand, is that continence or content which finds all the elements of life in its own soil; and which has its own perils of monotony and deterioration, if not stimulated by foreign infusions.

Everything the individual sees without him corresponds to his states of mind, and everything is in turn intelligible to him, as his onward thinking leads him into the truth to which that fact or series belongs.

The primeval world, — the Fore-World,[38] as the Germans say, — I can dive to it in myself as well as grope for it with researching fingers in catacombs, libraries, and the broken reliefs and torsos of ruined villas.

What is the foundation of that interest all men feel in Greek history, letters, art and poetry, in all its periods from the Heroic or Homeric age down to the domestic life of the Athenians and Spartans, four or five centuries later? What but this, that every man passes personally through a Grecian period. The Grecian state is the era of the bodily nature, the perfection of the senses, — of the spiritual nature unfolded in strict unity with the body. In it existed those human forms which supplied the sculptor with his models of Hercules, Phœbus and Jove; not like the forms abounding in the streets of modern cities, wherein the face is a confused blur of features, but composed of incorrupt, sharply defined and symmetrical features, whose eye-sockets are so formed that it would be impossible for such eyes to squint and take furtive glances on this side and on that, but they must turn the whole head. The manners of that period are plain and fierce. The reverence exhibited is for personal qualities; courage, address, self-command, justice, strength, swiftness, a loud voice, a broad chest. Luxury and elegance are not known. A sparse population and want make every man his own valet, cook, butcher and soldier, and the habit of supplying his own needs educates the body to wonderful performances. Such are the Agamemnon and Diomed of Homer, and not far different is the picture Xenophon gives of himself and his compatriots in the Retreat of the Ten Thousand. "After the army had crossed the river Teleboas in Armenia, there fell much snow, and the troops lay miserably on the ground covered with it. But Xenophon arose naked, and taking an axe, began to split wood; whereupon others rose and did the like." Throughout his army exists a boundless liberty of speech. They quarrel for plunder, they wrangle with the generals on each new order, and Xenophon is as sharp-tongued as any and sharper-tongued than most, and so gives as good as he gets. Who does not see that this is a gang of great boys, with such a code of honor and such lax discipline as great boys have?

The costly charm [39] of the ancient tragedy, and indeed of all the old literature, is that the persons speak simply, — speak as persons who have great good sense without knowing it, before yet the reflective habit has become the predominant habit of the mind. Our admiration of the antique is not admiration of the old, but of the natural. The Greeks are not reflective, but perfect in their senses and in their health, with the finest physical organization in the world. Adults acted with the simplicity and grace of children. They made vases, tragedies and statues,[40] such as healthy senses should, — that is, in good taste. Such things have continued to be made in all ages, and are now, wherever a healthy physique exists; but, as a class, from their superior organization, they have surpassed all. They combine the energy of manhood with the engaging unconsciousness of childhood. The attraction of these manners is that they belong to man, and are known to every man in virtue of his being once a child; besides that there are always individuals who retain these characteristics. A person of childlike genius and inborn energy is still a Greek, and revives our love of the Muse of Hellas. I admire the love of nature in the Philoctetes.[41] In reading those fine apostrophes to sleep, to the stars, rocks, mountains and waves, I feel time passing away as an ebbing sea. I feel the eternity of man, the identity of his thought. The Greek had, it seems, the same fellow-beings as I. The sun and moon, water and fire, met his heart precisely as they meet mine. Then the vaunted distinction between Greek and English,[42] between Classic and Romantic schools, seems superficial and pedantic.[43] When a thought of Plato becomes a thought to me, — when a truth that fired the soul of Pindar fires mine, time is no more. When I feel that we two meet in a perception, that our two souls are tinged with the same hue, and do as it were run into one, why should I measure degrees of latitude, why should I count Egyptian years?

The student interprets the age of chivalry by his own age of chivalry, and the days of maritime adventure and circumnavigation by quite parallel miniature experiences of his own. To the sacred history of the world he has the same key. When the voice of a prophet out of the deeps of antiquity merely echoes to him a sentiment of his infancy, a prayer of his youth, he then pierces to the truth through all the confusion of tradition and the caricature of institutions.

Rare, extravagant spirits come by us at intervals, who disclose to us new facts in nature. I see that men of God have from time to time walked among men and made their commission felt in the heart and soul of the commonest hearer. Hence evidently the tripod, the priest, the priestess inspired by the divine afflatus.

Jesus astonishes and overpowers sensual people. They cannot unite him to history, or reconcile him with themselves. As they come to revere their intuitions and aspire to live holily,[44] their own piety explains every fact, every word.

How easily these old worships of Moses, of Zoroaster, of Menu,[45] of Socrates, domesticate themselves in the mind. I cannot find any antiquity in them. They are mine as much as theirs.

I have seen the first monks and anchorets, without crossing seas or centuries. More than once some individual has appeared to me with such negligence of labor and such commanding contemplation, a haughty beneficiary begging in the name of God, as made good to the nineteenth century Simeon the Stylite, the Thebais, and the first Capuchins.[46]

The priestcraft of the East and West, of the Magian,[47] Brahmin, Druid, and Inca, is expounded in the individual's private life. The cramping influence of a hard formalist on a young child, in repressing his spirits and courage, paralyzing the understanding, and that without producing indignation, but only fear and obedience, and even much sympathy with the tyranny, — is a

familiar fact, explained to the child when he becomes
a man, only by seeing that the oppressor of his youth
is himself a child tyrannized over by those names and
words and forms of whose influence he was merely the
organ to the youth. The fact teaches him how Belus [48]
was worshipped and how the Pyramids were built,
better than the discovery by Champollion [49] of the
names of all the workmen and the cost of every tile.
He finds Assyria and the Mounds of Cholula [50] at his
door, and himself has laid the courses.

Again, in that protest which each considerate person makes against the superstition of his times, he
repeats step by step the part of old reformers, and in
the search after truth finds, like them, new perils to
virtue. He learns again what moral vigor is needed to
supply the girdle of a superstition. A great licentious-
ness treads on the heels of a reformation. How many
times in the history of the world has the Luther of the
day had to lament the decay of piety in his own household! "Doctor," said his wife to Martin Luther, one
day, "how is it that whilst subject to papacy we prayed
so often and with such fervor, whilst now we pray with
the utmost coldness and very seldom?"

The advancing man discovers how deep a property
he has in literature, — in all fable as well as in all history. He finds that the poet was no odd fellow who
described strange and impossible situations, but that
universal man wrote by his pen a confession true for
one and true for all. His own secret biography he finds
in lines wonderfully intelligible to him, dotted down
before he was born. One after another he comes up in
his private adventures with every fable of Æsop, of
Homer, of Hafiz, of Ariosto, of Chaucer, of Scott, and
verifies them with his own head and hands.

The beautiful fables of the Greeks, being proper creations of the imagination and not of the fancy, are universal verities. What a range of meanings and what perpetual pertinence has the story of Prometheus! Beside its primary value as the first chapter of the history of Europe (the mythology thinly veiling authentic facts, the invention of the mechanic arts and the migration of colonies), it gives the history of religion, with some closeness to the faith of later ages. Prometheus is the Jesus of the old mythology. He is the friend of man; stands between the unjust "justice" of the Eternal Father and the race of mortals, and readily suffers all things on their account. But where it departs from the Calvinistic Christianity and exhibits him as the defier of Jove, it represents a state of mind which readily appears wherever the doctrine of Theism is taught in a crude, objective form, and which seems the self-defence of man against this untruth, namely a discontent with the believed fact that a God exists, and a feeling that the obligation of reverence is onerous. It would steal if it could the fire of the Creator, and live apart from him and independent of him. The Prometheus Vinctus [51] is the romance of skepticism. Not less true to all time are the details of that stately apologue. Apollo kept the flocks of Admetus, said the poets. When the gods come among men, they are not known. Jesus was not; Socrates and Shakspeare were not. Antæus was suffocated by the gripe of Hercules, but every time he touched his mother-earth his strength was renewed. Man is the broken giant, and in all his weakness both his body and his mind are invigorated by habits of conversation with nature. The power of music, the power of poetry, to unfix and as it were clap wings to solid nature, interprets the

riddle of Orpheus.[52] The philosophical perception
of identity through endless mutations of form makes
him know the Proteus. What else am I who laughed
or wept yesterday, who slept last night like a corpse,
and this morning stood and ran? And what see I
on any side but the transmigrations of Proteus? I
can symbolize my thought by using the name of any
creature, of any fact, because every creature is man
agent or patient. Tantalus is but a name for you and
me. Tantalus means the impossibility of drinking
the waters of thought which are always gleaming and
waving within sight of the soul.[53] The transmigration
of souls is no fable. I would it were; but men and
women are only half human. Every animal of the
barn-yard, the field and the forest, of the earth and of
the waters that are under the earth, has contrived to
get a footing and to leave the print of its features and
form in some one or other of these upright, heaven-
facing speakers. Ah! brother, stop the ebb of thy soul,[54]
— ebbing downward into the forms into whose habits
thou hast now for many years slid. As near and proper
to us is also that old fable of the Sphinx, who was said
to sit in the road-side and put riddles to every passenger. If the man could not answer, she swallowed
him alive. If he could solve the riddle, the Sphinx was
slain. What is our life but an endless flight of winged
facts or events? In splendid variety these changes
come, all putting questions to the human spirit. Those
men who cannot answer by a superior wisdom these
facts or questions of time, serve them. Facts encumber
them, tyrannize over them, and make the men of
routine, the men of *sense*, in whom a literal obedience
to facts has extinguished every spark of that light by
which man is truly man. But if the man is true to his

better instincts or sentiments, and refuses the dominion of facts, as one that comes of a higher race; remains fast by the soul and sees the principle, then the facts fall aptly and supple into their places; they know their master, and the meanest of them glorifies him.

See in Goethe's Helena [55] the same desire that every word should be a thing. These figures, he would say, these Chirons,[56] Griffins,[57] Phorkyas,[58] Helen and Leda,[59] are somewhat, and do exert a specific influence on the mind. So far then are they eternal entities, as real to-day as in the first Olympiad. Much revolving them he writes out freely his humor, and gives them body to his own imagination. And although that poem be as vague and fantastic as a dream, yet is it much more attractive than the more regular dramatic pieces of the same author, for the reason that it operates a wonderful relief to the mind from the routine of customary images, — awakens the reader's invention and fancy by the wild freedom of the design, and by the unceasing succession of brisk shocks of surprise.

The universal nature, too strong for the petty nature of the bard, sits on his neck and writes through his hand; so that when he seems to vent a mere caprice and wild romance, the issue is an exact allegory. Hence Plato said that "poets utter great and wise things which they do not themselves understand." All the fictions of the Middle Age explain themselves as a masked or frolic expression of that which in grave earnest the mind of that period toiled to achieve. Magic and all that is ascribed to it is a deep presentiment of the powers of science.[60] The shoes of swiftness, the sword of sharpness, the power of subduing the elements, of using the secret virtues of minerals, of understanding the voices of birds, are the obscure efforts of the mind in a right direction. The preternatural prowess of the hero, the gift of perpetual youth, and the like, are alike the endeavor of the human spirit "to bend the shows of things to the desires of the mind."

In Perceforest and Amadis de Gaul [61] a garland and a rose bloom on the head of her who is faithful, and fade on the brow of the inconstant. In the story of the Boy and the Mantle [62] even a mature reader may be surprised with a glow of virtuous pleasure at the triumph of the gentle Venelas; and indeed all the postulates of elfin annals, — that the fairies do not like to be named; that their gifts are capricious and not to be trusted; that who seeks a treasure must not speak; and the like, — I find true in Concord, however they might be in Cornwall or Bretagne.

Is it otherwise in the newest romance? I read the Bride of Lammermoor. Sir William Ashton is a mask for a vulgar temptation, Ravenswood Castle a fine name for proud poverty, and the foreign mission of state only a Bunyan disguise for honest industry. We may all shoot a wild bull that would toss the good and beautiful, by fighting down the unjust and sensual. Lucy Ashton is another name for fidelity, which is always beautiful and always liable to calamity in this world.

But along with the civil and metaphysical history of man, another history goes daily forward, — that of the external world, — in which he is not less strictly implicated. He is the compend of time; [63] he is also the correlative of nature. His power consists in the multitude of his affinities, in the fact that his life is intertwined with the whole chain of organic and inorganic being. In old Rome the public roads beginning at the Forum proceeded north, south, east, west, to the centre of every province of the empire, making each market-town of Persia, Spain and Britain pervious to the soldiers of the capital: so out of the human heart go as it were highways to the heart of every object in nature, to reduce it under the dominion of man. A man is a bundle of relations, a knot of roots, whose flower and fruitage is the world. His faculties refer to natures out of him and predict the world he is to inhabit, as the fins of the fish foreshow that water exists, or the wings of an eagle in the egg presuppose air. He cannot live without a world.[64] Put Napoleon in an island prison, let his faculties find no men to act on, no Alps to climb, no stake to play for, and he would beat the air, and appear stupid. Transport him to large countries, dense population, complex interests and antagonist power, and you shall see that the man Napoleon, bounded that is by such a profile and outline, is not the virtual Napoleon. This is but Talbot's shadow; —

> "His substance is not here.
> For what you see is but the smallest part
> And least proportion of humanity;
> But were the whole frame here,
> It is of such a spacious, lofty pitch,
> Your roof were not sufficient to contain it." [65]

Columbus needs a planet to shape his course upon. Newton and Laplace [66] need myriads of age and thick-strewn celestial areas. One may say a gravitating solar system is already prophesied [67] in the nature of Newton's mind. Not less does the brain of Davy [68] or of Gay-Lussac,[69] from childhood exploring the affinities and repulsions of particles, anticipate the laws of organization. Does not the eye of the human embryo predict the light? the ear of Handel [70] predict the witchcraft of harmonic sound? Do not the constructive fingers of Watt, Fulton, Whittemore,[71] Arkwright, predict the fusible, hard, and temperable texture of metals, the properties of stone, water, and wood? Do not the lovely attributes of the maiden child predict the refinements and decorations of civil society? Here also we are reminded of the action of man on man. A mind might ponder its thoughts for ages and not gain so much self-knowledge as the passion of love shall teach it in a day. Who knows himself before he has been thrilled with indignation at an outrage, or has heard an eloquent tongue, or has shared the throb of thousands in a national exultation or alarm? No man can antedate his experience, or guess what faculty or feeling a new object shall unlock, any more than he can draw to-day the face of a person whom he shall see to-morrow for the first time.

I will not now go behind the general statement to explore the reason of this correspondency. Let it suffice that in the light of these two facts, namely, that the mind is One, and that nature is its correlative, history is to be read and written.

Thus in all ways does the soul concentrate and reproduce its treasures for each pupil. He too shall pass through the whole cycle of experience. He shall collect into a focus the rays of nature. History no longer shall be a dull book. It shall walk incarnate in every just and wise man. You shall not tell me by languages and titles a catalogue of the volumes you have read.[72] You shall make me feel what periods you have lived. A man shall be the Temple of Fame. He shall walk, as the poets have described that goddess, in a robe painted all over with wonderful events and experiences; — his own form and features by their exalted intelligence shall be that variegated vest. I shall find in him the Foreworld; in his childhood the Age of Gold, the Apples of Knowledge, the Argonautic Expedition, the calling of Abraham, the building of the Temple, the Advent of Christ, Dark Ages, the Revival of Letters, the Reformation, the discovery of new lands, the opening of new sciences and new regions in man. He shall be the priest of Pan, and bring with him into humble cottages the blessing of the morning stars, and all the recorded benefits of heaven and earth.

Is there somewhat overweening in this claim? Then I reject all I have written, for what is the use of pretending to know what we know not? But it is the fault of our rhetoric that we cannot strongly state one fact without seeming to belie some other. I hold our actual knowledge very cheap. Hear the rats in the wall, see the lizard on the fence, the fungus under foot, the lichen on the log. What do I know sympathetically, morally, of either of these worlds of life? As old as the Caucasian man, — perhaps older, — these creatures have kept their counsel beside him, and there is no record of any word or sign that has passed from one to the other. What connection do the books show between the fifty or sixty chemical elements and the historical eras? Nay, what does history yet record of the metaphysical annals of man? What light does it shed on those mysteries which we hide under the names Death and Immortality? Yet every history should be written in a wisdom which divined the range of our affinities and looked at facts as symbols. I am ashamed to see what a shallow village tale our so-called History is. How many times we must say Rome, and Paris, and Constantinople! What does Rome know of rat and lizard?[73] What are Olympiads and Consulates to these neighboring systems of being? Nay, what food or experience or succor have they for the Esquimaux seal-hunter, for the Kanàka[74] in his canoe, for the fisherman, the stevedore, the porter?

Broader and deeper we must write our annals, — from an ethical reformation, from an influx of the ever new, ever sanative conscience, — if we would trulier express our central and wide-related nature, instead of this old chronology of selfishness and pride to which we have too long lent our eyes. Already that day exists for us, shines in on us at unawares, but the path of science and of letters is not the way into nature. The idiot, the Indian, the child and unschooled farmer's boy stand nearer to the light by which nature is to be read, than the dissector or the antiquary.[75]

POLITICS

GOLD and iron are good
To buy iron and gold;
All earth's fleece and food
For their like are sold.
Boded Merlin wise,[1]
Proved Napoleon great, —
Nor kind nor coinage buys
Aught above its rate.
Fear, Craft, and Avarice
Cannot rear a State.
Out of dust to build
What is more than dust, —
Walls Amphion piled
Phœbus stablish must.
When the Muses nine
With the Virtues meet,
Find to their design
An Atlantic seat,
By green orchard boughs
Fended from the heat,
Where the statesman ploughs
Furrow for the wheat;
When the Church is social worth,
When the state-house is the hearth,
Then the perfect State is come,
The republican at home.

POLITICS

In dealing with the State we ought to remember that its institutions are not aboriginal, though they existed before we were born; that they are not superior to the citizen; that every one of them was once the act of a single man; every law and usage was a man's expedient to meet a particular case; that they all are imitable, all alterable; we may make as good, we may make better. Society is an illusion to the young citizen. It lies before him in rigid repose, with certain names, men and institutions rooted like oak-trees to the centre, round which all arrange themselves the best they can. But the old statesman knows that society is fluid; there are no such roots and centres, but any particle may suddenly become the centre of the movement and compel the system to gyrate round it; as every man of strong will, like Pisistratus [2] or Cromwell, [3] does for a time, and every man of truth, like Plato or Paul, does forever. But, politics rest on necessary foundations, and cannot be treated with levity. Republics abound in young civilians who believe that the laws make the city, that grave modifications of the policy and modes of living and employments of the population, that commerce, education and religion may be voted in or out; and that any measure, though it were absurd, may be imposed on a people if only you can get sufficient voices to make it a law. But the wise know that foolish legislation is a rope of sand [4] which perishes in the twisting; [5] that the State must follow and not lead the character and progress of the citizen; the strongest usurper is quickly got rid of; and they only who build on Ideas, build for eternity; and that the form of government which prevails is the expression of what cultivation exists in the population which permits it. The law is only a memorandum. We are superstitious, and esteem the statute somewhat: so much life as it has in the character of living men is its force. The statute stands there to say, Yesterday we agreed so and so, but how feel ye this article to-day? Our statute is a currency which we stamp with our own portrait: it soon becomes unrecognizable, and in process of time will return to the mint. Nature is not democratic, nor limited-monarchical, but despotic, and will not be fooled or abated of any jot of her authority by the pertest of her sons; and as fast as the public mind is opened to more intelligence,[6] the code is seen to be brute and stammering.[7] It speaks not articulately, and must be made to. Meantime the education of the general mind never stops. The reveries of the true and simple are prophetic. What the tender poetic youth dreams, and prays, and paints to-day, but shuns the ridicule of saying aloud, shall presently be the resolutions of public bodies; then shall be carried as grievance and bill of rights through conflict and war, and then shall be triumphant law and establishment for a hundred years, until it gives place in turn to new prayers and pictures. The history of the State sketches in coarse outline the progress of thought, and follows at a distance the delicacy of culture and of aspiration.

The theory of politics which has possessed the mind of men, and which they have expressed the best they could in their laws and in their revolutions, considers persons and property as the two objects for whose protection government exists. Of persons, all have

equal rights, in virtue of being identical in nature.
This interest of course with its whole power demands
a democracy. Whilst the rights of all as persons are
equal, in virtue of their access to reason, their rights
in property are very unequal. One man owns his
clothes, and another owns a county. This accident,
depending primarily on the skill and virtue of the
parties, of which there is every degree, and secondarily
on patrimony, falls unequally, and its rights of course
are unequal. Personal rights, universally the same,
demand a government framed on the ratio of the
census; property demands a government framed on
the ratio of owners and of owning. Laban,[8] who has
flocks and herds, wishes them looked after by an officer
on the frontiers, lest the Midianites shall drive them
off; and pays a tax to that end. Jacob has no flocks or
herds and no fear of the Midianites, and pays no tax
to the officer. It seemed fit that Laban and Jacob
should have equal rights to elect the officer who is to
defend their persons, but that Laban and not Jacob
should elect the officer who is to guard the sheep and
cattle. And if question arise whether additional officers
or watch-towers should be provided, must not Laban
and Isaac, and those who must sell part of their herds
to buy protection for the rest, judge better of this,
and with more right, than Jacob, who, because he is
a youth and a traveller, eats their bread and not his
own ?

In the earliest society the proprietors made their
own wealth, and so long as it comes to the owners in the
direct way, no other opinion would arise in any equi-
table community than that property should make the
law for property, and persons the law for persons.
But property passes through donation or inheritance

to those who do not create it. Gift, in one case, makes it as really the new owner's as labor made it the first owner's: in the other case, of patrimony, the law makes an ownership which will be valid in each man's view according to the estimate which he sets on the public tranquillity.

It was not, however, found easy to embody the readily admitted principle that property should make law for property, and persons for persons; since persons and property mixed themselves in every transaction. At last it seemed settled that the rightful distinction was that the proprietors should have more elective franchise than non-proprietors, on the Spartan principle of "calling that which is just, equal; not that which is equal, just."

That principle no longer looks so self-evident as it appeared in former times, partly because doubts have arisen [9] whether too much weight had not been allowed in the laws to property, and such a structure given to our usages as allowed the rich to encroach on the poor, and to keep them poor; but mainly because there is an instinctive sense, however obscure and yet inarticulate, that the whole constitution of property, on its present tenures, is injurious, and its influence on persons deteriorating and degrading; that truly the only interest for the consideration of the State is persons; that property will always follow persons; that the highest end of government is the culture of men; and that if men can be educated, the institutions will share their improvement and the moral sentiment will write the law of the land.

If it be not easy to settle the equity of this question, the peril is less when we take note of our natural defences. We are kept by better guards than the vigilance of such magistrates as we commonly elect. Society always consists in greatest part of young and foolish persons. The old, who have seen through the hypocrisy of courts and statesmen, die and leave no wisdom to their sons. They believe their own newspaper, as their fathers did at their age. With such an ignorant and deceivable [10] majority, States would soon run to ruin, but that there are limitations beyond which the folly and ambition of governors cannot go. Things have their laws, as well as men; and things refuse to be trifled with. [11] Property will be protected. Corn will not grow unless it is planted and manured; but the farmer will not plant or hoe it unless the chances are a hundred to one that he will cut and harvest it. [12] Under any forms, persons and property must and will have their just sway. They exert their power, as steadily as matter its attraction. Cover up a pound of earth never so cunningly, divide and subdivide it; melt it to liquid, convert it to gas; it will always weigh a pound; it will always attract and resist other matter by the full virtue of one pound weight: — and the attributes of a person, his wit and his moral energy, will exercise, under any law or extinguishing tyranny, their proper force, — if not overtly, then covertly; if not for the law, then against it; if not wholesomely, then poisonously; with right, or by might.

The boundaries of personal influence it is impossible to fix, as persons are organs of moral or supernatural force. Under the dominion of an idea which possesses the minds of multitudes, as civil freedom, or the religious sentiment, the powers of persons [13] are no longer subjects of calculation. A nation of men unanimously bent on freedom or conquest can easily confound the arithmetic of statists, and achieve extravagant actions, out of all proportions to their means; as the Greeks, the Saracens, the Swiss, the Americans and the French have done.

In like manner to every particle of property belongs its own attraction. A cent is the representative of a certain quantity of corn or other commodity. Its value is in the necessities of the animal man. It is so much warmth, so much bread, so much water, so much land. The law may do what it will with the owner of property; its just power will still attach to the cent. The law may in a mad freak say that all shall have power except the owners of property; they shall have no vote. Nevertheless, by a higher law, the property will, year after year, write every statute that respects property. The non-proprietor will be the scribe of the proprietor. What the owners wish to do, the whole power of property will do, either through the law or else in defiance of it. Of course I speak of all the property, not merely of the great estates. When the rich are outvoted, as frequently happens, it is the joint treasury of the poor which exceeds their accumulations. Every man owns something, if it is only a cow, or a wheelbarrow, or his arms, and so has that property to dispose of.[14]

The same necessity which secures the rights of person and property against the malignity or folly of the magistrate, determines the form and methods of governing, which are proper to each nation and to its habit of thought, and nowise transferable to other states of society. In this country we are very vain of our political institutions, which are singular in this, that they sprung, within the memory of living men, from the character and condition of the people, which they still express with sufficient fidelity, — and we ostentatiously prefer them to any other in history. They are not

better, but only fitter for us. We may be wise in asserting the advantage in modern times of the democratic
form, but to other states of society, in which religion
consecrated the monarchical, that and not this was
expedient. Democracy is better for us, because the
religious sentiment of the present time accords better
with it. Born democrats, we are nowise qualified to
judge of monarchy, which, to our fathers living in the
monarchical idea, was also relatively right. But our
institutions, though in coincidence with the spirit of
the age, have not any exemption from the practical
defects which have discredited other forms. Every
actual State is corrupt. Good men must not obey the
laws too well.[15] What satire on government can equal
the severity of censure conveyed in the word *politic*,
which now for ages has signified *cunning*, intimating
that the State is a trick?

The same benign necessity and the same practical
abuse appear in the parties, into which each State
divides itself, of opponents and defenders of the administration of the government. Parties are also
founded on instincts,[16] and have better guides to their
own humble aims than the sagacity of their leaders.
They have nothing perverse in their origin, but rudely
mark some real and lasting relation. We might as
wisely reprove the east wind or the frost, as a political
party, whose members, for the most part, could give
no account of their position, but stand for the defence
of those interests in which they find themselves. Our
quarrel with them begins when they quit this deep
natural ground at the bidding of some leader, and
obeying personal considerations, throw themselves
into the maintenance and defence of points nowise
belonging to their system. A party is perpetually cor-

rupted by personality. Whilst we absolve the association from dishonesty, we cannot extend the same charity to their leaders. They reap the rewards of the docility and zeal of the masses which they direct. Ordinarily our parties are parties of circumstance, and not of principle; as the planting interest in conflict with the commercial; the party of capitalists and that of operatives: parties which are identical in their moral character, and which can easily change ground with each other in the support of many of their measures. Parties of principle, as, religious sects, or the party of free-trade, of universal suffrage, of abolition of slavery, of abolition of capital punishment, — degenerate into personalities, or would inspire enthusiasm. The vice of our leading parties in this country (which may be cited as a fair specimen of these societies of opinion) is that they do not plant themselves on the deep and necessary grounds to which they are respectively entitled, but lash themselves to fury in the carrying of some local and momentary measure, nowise useful to the commonwealth. Of the two great parties which at this hour almost share the nation between them, I should say that one has the best cause, and the other contains the best men. The philosopher, the poet, or the religious man, will of course wish to cast his vote with the democrat, for free-trade, for wide suffrage, for the abolition of legal cruelties in the penal code, and for facilitating in every manner the access of the young and the poor to the sources of wealth and power. But he can rarely accept the persons whom the so-called popular party propose to him as representatives of these liberalities. They have not at heart the ends which give to the name of democracy what hope and virtue are in it. The spirit of our American radicalism is destructive and aimless: [17] it is not loving; it has no ulterior and divine ends, but is destructive only out of hatred and selfishness. On the other side, the conservative party, composed of the most moderate, able and cultivated part of the population, is timid, and merely defensive of property. It vindicates no right, it aspires to no real good, it brands no crime, it proposes no generous policy; it does not build, nor write, nor cherish the arts, nor foster religion, nor establish schools, nor encourage science, nor emancipate the slave, nor befriend the poor, or the Indian, or the immigrant. From neither party, when in power, has the world any benefit to expect in science, art or humanity, at all commensurate with the resources of the nation.

I do not for these defects despair of our republic. We are not at the mercy of any waves of chance. In the strife of ferocious parties, human nature always finds itself cherished; as the children of the convicts at Botany Bay [18] are found to have as healthy a moral sentiment as other children. Citizens of feudal states are alarmed at our democratic institutions lapsing into anarchy, and the older and more cautious among ourselves are learning from Europeans to look with some terror at our turbulent freedom. It is said that in our license of construing the Constitution, and in the despotism of public opinion, we have no anchor; and one foreign observer thinks he has found the safeguard in the sanctity of Marriage among us; and another thinks he has found it in our Calvinism. Fisher Ames [19] expressed the popular security more wisely, when he compared a monarchy and a republic, saying that a monarchy is a merchantman, which sails well, but will sometimes strike on a rock and go to the bottom; whilst a republic is a raft, which would never sink, but then your feet are always in water. No forms can have any dangerous importance whilst we are befriended by the laws of things. It makes no difference how many tons' weight of atmosphere presses on our heads, so long as the same pressure resists it within the lungs. Augment the mass a thousand-fold, it cannot begin to crush us, as long as reaction is equal to action. The fact of two poles, of two forces, centripetal and centrifugal, is universal, and each force by its own activity develops the other. Wild liberty develops iron conscience.[20] Want of liberty, by strengthening law and decorum, stupefies conscience. 'Lynch-law'[21] prevails only where there is greater hardihood and self-subsistency in the leaders. A mob cannot be a permanency; everybody's interest requires that it should not exist, and only justice satisfies all.

We must trust infinitely to the beneficent necessity which shines through all laws. Human nature expresses itself in them as characteristically as in statues, or songs, or railroads; and an abstract of the codes of nations would be a transcript of the common conscience. Governments have their origin in the moral identity of men. Reason for one is seen to be reason for another, and for every other. There is a middle measure which satisfies all parties, be they never so many or so resolute for their own. Every man finds a sanction for his simplest claims and deeds, in decisions of his own mind, which he calls Truth and Holiness. In these decisions all the citizens find a perfect agreement, and only in these; not in what is good to eat, good to wear, good use of time, or what amount of land or of public aid each is entitled to claim. This truth and justice men presently endeavor to make application of to the measuring of land, the appor-

tionment of service, the protection of life and property.
Their first endeavors, no doubt, are very awkward.
Yet absolute right is the first governor; or, every government is an impure theocracy. The idea after which
each community is aiming to make and mend its law,
is the will of the wise man. The wise man it cannot
find in nature,[22] and it makes awkward but earnest
efforts to secure his government by contrivance; as by
causing the entire people to give their voices on every
measure; or by a double choice to get the representation of the whole; or by a selection of the best citizens;
or to secure the advantages of efficiency and internal
peace by confiding the government to one, who may
himself select his agents. All forms of government
symbolize an immortal government, common to all
dynasties and independent of numbers, perfect where
two men exist, perfect where there is only one man.

Every man's nature is a sufficient advertisement to
him of the character of his fellows. My right and my
wrong is their right and their wrong. Whilst I do what
is fit for me, and abstain from what is unfit, my neighbor and I shall often agree in our means, and work together for a time to one end. But whenever I find my
dominion over myself not sufficient for me, and undertake the direction of him also, I overstep the truth, and
come into false relations to him. I may have so much
more skill or strength than he that he cannot express
adequately his sense of wrong, but it is a lie, and hurts
like a lie both him and me. Love and nature cannot
maintain the assumption; it must be executed by a
practical lie, namely by force. This undertaking for
another is the blunder which stands in colossal ugliness
in the governments of the world. It is the same thing
in numbers, as in a pair, only not quite so intelligible.

I can see well enough a great difference between my setting myself down to a self-control, and my going to make somebody else act after my views; but when a quarter of the human race assume to tell me what I must do, I may be too much disturbed by the circumstances to see so clearly the absurdity of their command. Therefore all public ends look vague and quixotic beside private ones. For any laws but those which men make for themselves are laughable.[23] If I put myself in the place of my child, and we stand in one thought and see that things are thus or thus, that perception is law for him and me. We are both there, both act. But if, without carrying him into the thought, I look over into his plot, and, guessing how it is with him, ordain this or that, he will never obey me. This is the history of governments, — one man does something which is to bind another. A man who cannot be acquainted with me taxes me; looking from afar at me ordains that a part of my labor shall go to this or that whimsical end, — not as I, but as he happens to fancy. Behold the consequence. Of all debts men are least willing to pay the taxes.[24] What a satire is this on government! Everywhere they think they get their money's worth, except for these.

Hence the less government we have the better, — the fewer laws, and the less confided power. The antidote to this abuse of formal government is the influence of private character, the growth of the Individual; the appearance of the principal to supersede the proxy; the appearance of the wise man; of whom the existing government is, it must be owned, but a shabby imitation. That which all things tend to educe; which freedom, cultivation, intercourse, revolutions, go to form and deliver, is character; that is the end of Nature, to

reach unto this coronation of her king. To educate
the wise man the State exists, and with the appearance
of the wise man the State expires. The appearance of
character makes the State unnecessary. The wise man
is the State. He needs no army, fort, or navy, — he
loves men too well; no bribe, or feast, or palace, to
draw friends to him; no vantage ground, no favorable
circumstance. He needs no library, for he has not done
thinking; no church, for he is a prophet; no statute-
book, for he has the lawgiver; no money, for he is value;
no road, for he is at home where he is; no experience,
for the life of the creator shoots through him, and looks
from his eyes. He has no personal friends,[25] for he who
has the spell to draw the prayer and piety of all men
unto him needs not husband and educate a few to
share with him a select and poetic life. His relation
to men is angelic; his memory is myrrh to them; his
presence, frankincense and flowers.

We think our civilization near its meridian, but we
are yet only at the cock-crowing and the morning star.
In our barbarous society the influence of character is
in its infancy. As a political power, as the rightful lord
who is to tumble all rulers from their chairs, its presence is hardly yet suspected. Malthus[26] and Ricardo[27]
quite omit it; the Annual Register[28] is silent; in the
Conversations' Lexicon[29] it is not set down; the President's Message, the Queen's Speech, have not mentioned it; and yet it is never nothing. Every thought
which genius and piety throw into the world, alters
the world.[30] The gladiators in the lists of power feel,
through all their frocks of force[31] and simulation, the
presence of worth. I think the very strife of trade and
ambition is confession of this divinity; and successes in
those fields are the poor amends, the fig-leaf[32] with

which the shamed soul attempts to hide its nakedness.
I find the like unwilling homage in all quarters. It is
because we know how much is due from us that we
are impatient to show some petty talent as a substi-
tute for worth. We are haunted by a conscience [33] of
this right to grandeur of character, and are false to it.
But each of us has some talent, can do somewhat useful, or graceful, or formidable, or amusing, or lucrative. That we do, as an apology to others and to ourselves for not reaching the mark of a good and equal
life. But it does not satisfy *us*, whilst we thrust it on
the notice of our companions. It may throw dust in
their eyes, but does not smooth our own brow, or give
us the tranquillity of the strong when we walk abroad.
We do penance as we go. Our talent is a sort of expiation, and we are constrained to reflect on our splendid moment [34] with a certain humiliation, as somewhat
too fine, and not as one act of many acts, a fair expression of our permanent energy. Most persons of ability
meet in society with a kind of tacit appeal. Each seems
to say, ' I am not all here.' [35] Senators and presidents
have climbed so high with pain enough, not because
they think the place specially agreeable, but as an
apology for real worth, and to vindicate their manhood
in our eyes. This conspicuous chair is their compensation to themselves for being of a poor, cold, hard
nature. They must do what they can. Like one class
of forest animals, they have nothing but a prehensile
tail; climb they must, or crawl. [36] If a man found himself so rich-natured that he could enter into strict relations with the best persons and make life serene
around him by the dignity and sweetness of his behavior, could he afford to circumvent the favor of the
caucus and the press, and covet relations so hollow

and pompous as those of a politician? Surely nobody would be a charlatan who could afford to be sincere.

The tendencies of the times favor the idea of self-government, and leave the individual, for all code,[37] to the rewards and penalties of his own constitution; which work with more energy than we believe whilst we depend on artificial restraints. The movement in this direction has been very marked in modern history. Much has been blind and discreditable, but the nature of the revolution is not affected by the vices of the re-volters; for this is a purely moral force. It was never adopted by any party in history, neither can be. It separates the individual from all party, and unites him at the same time to the race. It promises a recognition of higher rights than those of personal freedom, or the security of property. A man has a right to be employed, to be trusted, to be loved, to be revered. The power of love, as the basis of a State, has never been tried. We must not imagine that all things are lapsing into confusion if every tender protestant be not compelled to bear his part in certain social conventions; nor doubt that roads can be built, letters carried, and the fruit of labor secured, when the government of force is at an end. Are our methods now so excellent that all competition is hopeless?[38] could not a nation of friends even devise better ways? On the other hand, let not the most conservative and timid fear anything from a premature surrender of the bayonet and the system of force. For, according to the order of nature, which is quite superior to our will, it stands thus; there will always be a government of force where men are selfish; and when they are pure enough to abjure the code of force they will be wise enough to see how these public ends of the post-office, of the highway, or commerce and the exchange 'of property, of museums and libraries, of institutions of art and science can be answered.

We live in a very low state of the world, and pay unwilling tribute to governments founded on force. There is not, among the most religious and instructed men of the most religious and civil nations, a reliance on the moral sentiment and a sufficient belief in the unity of things, to persuade them that society can be maintained without artificial restraints, as well as the solar system; or that the private citizen might be reasonable and a good neighbor, without the hint of a jail or a confiscation. What is strange too, there never was in any man sufficient faith in the power of rectitude to inspire him with the broad design of renovating the State on the principle of right and love. All those who have pretended this design [39] have been partial reformers, and have admitted in some manner the supremacy of the bad State. I do not call to mind a single human being who has steadily denied the authority of the laws, on the simple ground of his own moral nature. Such designs, full of genius and full of faith [40] as they are, are not entertained except avowedly as air-pictures.[41] If the individual who exhibits them dare to think them practicable, he disgusts scholars and churchmen; and men of talent and women of superior sentiments cannot hide their contempt. Not the less does nature continue to fill the heart of youth with suggestions of this enthusiasm, and there are now men, — if indeed I can speak in the plural number, — more exactly, I will say, I have just been conversing with one man, to whom no weight of adverse experience will make it for a moment appear impossible that thousands of human beings might exercise towards each other the grandest and simplest sentiments, as well as a knot of friends, or a pair of lovers.

BEHAVIOR

GRACE, Beauty, and Caprice
Build this golden portal,
Graceful women, chosen men
Dazzle every mortal:
Their sweet and lofty countenance
His enchanting food;
He need not go to them, their forms
Beset his solitude.
He looketh seldom in their face,
His eyes explore the ground,
The green grass is a looking-glass
Whereon their traits are found.
Little he says to them,
So dances his heart in his breast,
Their tranquil mien bereaveth him
Of wit, of words, of rest.
Too weak to win, too fond to shun
The tyrants or his doom,
The much deceived Endymion
Slips behind a tomb.

BEHAVIOR

THE soul which animates nature is not less significantly published in the figure, movement and gesture
of animated bodies, than in its last vehicle of articulate
speech. This silent and subtile language is Manners;
not *what*, but *how*. Life expresses. A statue has no
tongue, and needs none. Good tableaux do not need
declamation. Nature tells every secret once. Yes, but
in man she tells it all the time, by form, attitude, gesture, mien, face and parts of the face, and by the whole
action of the machine. The visible carriage or action
of the individual, as resulting from his organization
and his will combined, we call manners. What are
they but thought entering the hands and feet, controlling the movements of the body, the speech and
behavior?

There is always a best way of doing everything, if it
be to boil an egg. Manners are the happy way of doing
things; each, once a stroke of genius or of love, now
repeated and hardened into usage. They form at last
a rich varnish with which the routine of life is washed
and its details adorned. If they are superficial, so are
the dew-drops which give such a depth to the morning meadows. Manners are very communicable; men
catch them from each other. Consuelo,[1] in the romance,
boasts of the lessons she had given the nobles in manners, on the stage; and in real life, Talma [2] taught
Napoleon [3] the arts of behavior. Genius invents fine
manners, which the baron and the baroness copy very
fast, and, by the advantage of a palace, better the

instruction.[4] They stereotype the lesson they have
learned, into a mode.

The power of manners is incessant, — an element
as unconcealable as fire. The nobility cannot in any
country be disguised, and no more in a republic or a
democracy than in a kingdom. No man can resist
their influence. There are certain manners which are
learned in good society, of that force that if a person
have them, he or she must be considered, and is everywhere welcome, though without beauty, or wealth, or
genius. Give a boy address and accomplishments and
you give him the mastery of palaces and fortunes
where he goes. He has not the trouble of earning or
owning them, they solicit him to enter and possess.
We send girls of a timid, retreating disposition to the
boarding-school, to the riding-school, to the ball-room,
or wheresoever they can come into acquaintance and
nearness of leading persons of their own sex; where
they may learn address, and see it near at hand. The
power of a woman of fashion to lead and also to daunt
and repel, derives from their [5] belief that she knows
resources and behaviors not known to them; but when
these have mastered her secret they learn to confront
her, and recover their self-possession.

Every day bears witness to their gentle rule. People
who would obtrude, now do not obtrude. The mediocre
circle learns to demand that which belongs to a high
state of nature or of culture. Your manners are always
under examination, and by committees little suspected, a police in citizens' clothes, who are awarding
or denying you very high prizes when you least think
of it.

We talk much of utilities, but 't is our manners that
associate us. In hours of business we go to him who

knows, or has, or does this or that which we want, and
we do not let our taste or feeling stand in the way. But
this activity over, we return to the indolent state, and
wish for those we can be at ease with; those who will
go where we go, whose manners do not offend us, whose
social tone chimes with ours. When we reflect on their
persuasive and cheering force; [6] how they recommend,
prepare, and draw people together; how, in all clubs,
manners make the members; how manners make the
fortune of the ambitious youth; that, for the most part,
his manners marry him, and, for the most part, he
marries manners; when we think what keys they are,
and to what secrets; what high lessons and inspiring
tokens of character they convey, and what divination
is required in us for the reading of this fine telegraph,
— we see what range the subject has, and what relations to convenience, power and beauty.

Their first service is very low, — when they are the
minor morals; but 't is the beginning of civility, — to
make us, I mean, endurable to each other. We prize
them for their rough-plastic, abstergent force; to get
people out of the quadruped state; to get them washed,
clothed and set up on end; to slough their animal husks
and habits; compel them to be clean; overawe their
spite and meanness; teach them to stifle the base and
choose the generous expression, and make them know
how much happier the generous behaviors are.

Bad behavior the laws cannot reach. Society is infested with rude, cynical, restless and frivolous persons,
who prey upon the rest, and whom a public opinion
concentrated into good manners — forms accepted by
the sense of all — can reach; the contradictors and
railers at public and private tables, who are like ter-
riers, who conceive it the duty of a dog of honor to

growl at any passer-by and do the honors of the house by barking him out of sight. I have seen men who neigh like a horse when you contradict them or say something which they do not understand: — then the overbold, who make their own invitation to your hearth; the persevering talker, who gives you his society in large saturating doses; the pitiers of themselves, a perilous class; the frivolous Asmodeus,[7] who relies on you to find him in ropes of sand to twist; the monotones; in short, every stripe [8] of absurdity; — these are social inflictions which the magistrate cannot cure or defend you from, and which must be entrusted to the restraining force of custom and proverbs and familiar rules of behavior impressed on young people in their school-days.

In the hotels on the banks of the Mississippi they print, or used to print, among the rules of the house, that "No gentleman can be permitted to come to the public table without his coat;" and in the same country, in the pews of the churches little placards plead with the worshipper against the fury of expectoration. Charles Dickens self-sacrificingly undertook the reformation of our American manners in unspeakable particulars. I think the lesson was not quite lost; that it held bad manners up, so that the churls could see the deformity. Unhappily the book had its own deformities. It ought not to need to print in a reading-room a caution to strangers not to speak loud; nor to persons who look over fine engravings that they should be handled like cobwebs and butterflies' wings; nor to persons who look at marble statues that they shall not smite them with canes. But even in the perfect civilization of this city such cautions are not quite needless in the Athenæum [9] and City Library.

Manners are factitious, and grow out of circumstance as well as out of character. If you look at the pictures of patricians and of peasants of different periods and countries, you will see how well they match the same classes in our towns. The modern aristocrat not only is well drawn in Titian's [10] Venetian doges and in Roman coins and statues, but also in the pictures which Commodore Perry brought home of dignitaries in Japan. Broad lands and great interests not only arrive to such heads as can manage them, but form manners of power. A keen eye too will see nice gradations of rank, or see in the manners the degree of homage the party is wont to receive. A prince who is accustomed every day to be courted and deferred to by the highest grandees, acquires a corresponding expectation and a becoming mode of receiving and replying to this homage.

There are always exceptional people and modes. English grandees affect to be farmers. Claverhouse [11] is a fop, and under the finish of dress and levity of behavior hides the terror of his war. But Nature and Destiny are honest, and never fail to leave their mark, to hang out a sign for each and for every quality. It is much to conquer one's face, and perhaps the ambitious youth thinks he has got the whole secret when he has learned that disengaged manners are commanding. Don't be deceived by a facile exterior. Tender men sometimes have strong wills. We had in Massachusetts an old statesman who had sat all his life in courts and in chairs of state without overcoming an extreme irritability of face, voice and bearing; when he spoke, his voice would not serve him; it cracked, it broke, it wheezed, it piped; — little cared he; he knew that it had got to pipe, or wheeze, or screech his argument and his indignation. When he sat down, after speaking, he seemed in a sort of fit, and held on to his chair with both hands: but underneath all this irritability was a puissant will, firm and advancing, and a memory in which lay in order and method like geologic strata every fact of his history, and under the control of his will.[12]

Manners are partly factitious, but mainly there must be capacity for culture in the blood. Else all culture is vain. The obstinate prejudice in favor of blood, which lies at the base of the feudal and monarchical fabrics of the Old World, has some reason in common experience. Every man — mathematician, artist, soldier or merchant — looks with confidence for some traits and talents in his own child which he would not dare to presume in the child of a stranger. The Orientalists are very orthodox on this point. "Take a thorn-bush," said the emir Abdel-Kader,[13] "and sprinkle it for a whole year with rose-water; — it will yield nothing but thorns. Take a date-tree, leave it without water, without culture, and it will always produce dates. Nobility is the date-tree and the Arab populace is a bush of thorns."

A main fact in the history of manners is the wonderful expressiveness of the human body. If it were made of glass, or of air, and the thoughts were written on steel tablets within, it could not publish more truly its meaning than now. Wise men read very sharply all your private history in your look and gait and behavior. The whole economy of nature is bent on expression. The tell-tale body is all tongues. Men are like Geneva watches with crystal faces which expose the whole movement. They carry the liquor of life flowing up and down in these beautiful bottles and announcing

to the curious how it is with them. The face and eyes
reveal what the spirit is doing, how old it is, what aims
it has. The eyes indicate the antiquity of the soul, or
through how many forms it has already ascended. It
almost violates the proprieties if we say above the
breath here what the confessing eyes do not hesitate to
utter to every street passenger.

Man cannot fix his eye on the sun, and so far seems
imperfect. In Siberia a late traveller found men who
could see the satellites of Jupiter with their unarmed
eye. In some respects the animals excel us. The birds
have a longer sight, beside the advantage by their
wings of a higher observatory. A cow can bid her calf,
by secret signal, probably of the eye, to run away or to
lie down and hide itself. The jockeys say of certain
horses that "they look over the whole ground." The
out-door life and hunting and labor give equal vigor
to the human eye. A farmer looks out at you as strong
as the horse; his eye-beam is like the stroke of a staff.
An eye can threaten like a loaded and levelled gun, or
can insult like hissing or kicking; or in its altered mood
by beams of kindness it can make the heart dance with
joy.

The eye obeys exactly the action of the mind. When
a thought strikes us, the eyes fix and remain gazing at
a distance; in enumerating the names of persons or of
countries, as France, Germany, Spain, Turkey, the
eyes wink at each new name. There is no nicety of
learning sought by the mind which the eyes do not vie
in acquiring. "An artist," said Michael Angelo, "must
have his measuring tools not in the hand, but in the
eye;" and there is no end to the catalogue of its performances, whether in indolent vision (that of health and
beauty), or in strained vision (that of art and labor).

Eyes are bold as lions, — roving, running, leaping, here and there, far and near. They speak all languages. They wait for no introduction; they are no Englishmen; ask no leave of age, or rank; they respect neither poverty nor riches, neither learning nor power nor virtue nor sex; but intrude, and come again, and go through and through you in a moment of time. What inundation of life and thought is discharged from one soul into another, through them! The glance is natural magic.[14] The mysterious communication established across a house between two entire strangers, moves all the springs of wonder. The communication by the glance is in the greatest part not subject to the control of the will. It is the bodily symbol of identity of nature. We look into the eyes to know if this other form is another self, and the eyes will not lie, but make a faithful confession what inhabitant is there. The revelations are sometimes terrific. The confession of a low, usurping devil is there made, and the observer shall seem to feel the stirring of owls and bats and horned hoofs, where he looked for innocence and simplicity. 'T is remarkable too that the spirit that appears at the windows of the house does at once invest himself in a new form of his own to the mind of the beholder.

The eyes of men converse as much as their tongues, with the advantage that the ocular dialect needs no dictionary, but is understood all the world over. When the eyes say one thing and the tongue another, a practised man relies on the language of the first. If the man is off his centre, the eyes show it. You can read in the eyes of your companion whether your argument hits him, though his tongue will not confess it. There is a look by which a man shows he is going to say a good thing, and a look when he has said it. Vain and forgotten are all the fine offers and offices of hospitality, if there is no holiday in the eye. How many furtive inclinations avowed by the eye, though dissembled by the lips! One comes away from a company in which, it may easily happen, he has said nothing and no important remark has been addressed to him, and yet, if in sympathy with the society, he shall not have a sense of this fact, such a stream of life has been flowing into him and out from him through the eyes. There are eyes, to be sure, that give no more admission into the man than blueberries.[15] Others are liquid and deep, — wells that a man might fall into; — others are aggressive and devouring, seem to call out the police, take all too much notice, and require crowded Broadways and the security of millions to protect individuals against them. The military eye I meet, now darkly sparkling under clerical, now under rustic brows. 'T is the city of Lacedæmon; 't is a stack of bayonets. There are asking eyes, asserting eyes, prowling eyes; and eyes full of fate, — some of good and some of sinister omen. The alleged power to charm down insanity, or ferocity in beasts, is a power behind the eye. It must be a victory achieved in the will, before it can be signified in the eye. It is very certain that each man carries in his eye the exact indication of his rank in the immense scale of men, and we are always learning to read it. A complete man should need no auxiliaries to his personal presence. Whoever looked on him would consent to his will, being certified that his aims were generous and universal. The reason why men do not obey us is because they see the mud at the bottom of our eye.

If the organ of sight is such a vehicle of power, the other features have their own. A man finds room in the few square inches of the face for the traits of all his ancestors; for the expression of all his history and his wants. The sculptor and Winckelmann [16] and Lavater will tell you how significant a feature is the nose; how its forms express strength or weakness of will, and good or bad temper. The nose of Julius Cæsar, of Dante, and of Pitt, suggest "the terrors of the beak." What refinement and what limitations the teeth betray! "Beware you don't laugh," said the wise mother, "for then you show all your faults."

Balzac left in manuscript a chapter which he called "*Théorie de la démarche*," in which he says, "The look, the voice, the respiration, and the attitude or walk, are identical. But, as it has not been given to man the power to stand guard at once over these four different simultaneous expressions of his thought, watch that one which speaks out the truth, and you will know the whole man."

Palaces interest us mainly in the exhibition of manners, which, in the idle and expensive society dwelling in them, are raised to a high art. The maxim of courts is that manner is power. A calm and resolute bearing, a polished speech, an embellishment of trifles, and the art of hiding all uncomfortable feeling, are essential to the courtier; and Saint Simon [17] and Cardinal de Retz and Rœderer and an encyclopædia of *Mémoires* will instruct you, if you wish, in those potent secrets. Thus it is a point of pride with kings to remember faces and names. It is reported of one prince that his head had the air of leaning downwards, in order not to humble the crowd. There are people who come in ever like a child with a piece of good news. It was said of the late Lord Holland [18] that he always came down to breakfast with the air of a man who had just met with some signal good fortune. In *Notre Dame*,[19] the grandee took his place on the dais with the look of one who is thinking of something else. But we must not peep and eavesdrop at palace doors.

Fine manners need the support of fine manners in others. A scholar may be a well-bred man, or he may not. The enthusiast is introduced to polished scholars in society and is chilled and silenced by finding himself not in their element. They all have somewhat which he has not, and, it seems, ought to have. But if he finds the scholar apart from his companions, it is then the enthusiast's turn, and the scholar has no defence, but must deal on his terms. Now they must fight the battle out on their private strength. What is the talent of that character so common — the successful man of the world — in all marts, senates and drawing-rooms? Manners: manners of power; sense to see his advantage, and manners up to it. See him approach his man. He knows that troops behave as they are handled at first; that is his cheap secret; just what happens to every two persons who meet on any affair, — one instantly perceives that he has the key of the situation, that his will comprehends the other's will, as the cat does the mouse; and he has only to use courtesy and furnish good-natured reasons to his victim to cover up the chain, lest he be shamed into resistance.

The theatre in which this science of manners has a formal importance is not with us a court, but dress-circles, wherein, after the close of the day's business, men and women meet at leisure, for mutual entertainment, in ornamented drawing-rooms. Of course it has every variety of attraction and merit; but to earnest persons, to youths or maidens who have great objects at heart, we cannot extol it highly. A well-dressed

talkative company where each is bent to amuse the
other, — yet the high-born Turk who came hither
fancied that every woman seemed to be suffering for a
chair; that all the talkers were brained and exhausted
by the deoxygenated air; it spoiled the best persons; it
put all on stilts. Yet here are the secret biographies
written and read. The aspect of that man is repulsive;
I do not wish to deal with him. The other is irritable,
shy and on his guard. The youth looks humble and
manly; I choose him. Look on this woman. There is
not beauty, nor brilliant sayings, nor distinguished
power to serve you; but all see her gladly; her whole
air and impression are healthful. Here come the sen-
timentalists, and the invalids. Here is Elise, who
caught cold in coming into the world and has always
increased it since. Here are creep-mouse manners,
and thievish manners. "Look at Northcote,"[20] said
Fuseli;[21] "he looks like a rat that has seen a cat." In
the shallow company, easily excited, easily tired, here
is the columnar Bernard; the Alleghanies do not express more repose than his behavior. Here are the
sweet following eyes of Cecile; it seemed always that
she demanded the heart. Nothing can be more excellent in kind than the Corinthian grace of Gertrude's
manners, and yet Blanche, who has no manners, has
better manners than she; for the movements of Blanche
are the sallies of a spirit which is sufficient for the moment, and she can afford to express every thought by
instant action.

Manners have been somewhat cynically defined to
be a contrivance of wise men to keep fools at a distance.
Fashion is shrewd to detect those who do not belong
to her train, and seldom wastes her attentions. Society
is very swift in its instincts, and, if you do not belong

to it, resists and sneers at you, or quietly drops you. The first weapon enrages the party attacked; the second is still more effective, but is not to be resisted, as the date of the transaction is not easily found. People grow up and grow old under this infliction, and never suspect the truth, ascribing the solitude which acts on them very injuriously to any cause but the right one.

The basis of good manners is self-reliance. Necessity is the law of all who are not self-possessed. Those who are not self-possessed obtrude and pain us. Some men appear to feel that they belong to a Pariah[22] caste. They fear to offend, they bend and apologize, and walk through life with a timid step. As we sometimes dream that we are in a well-dressed company without any coat, so Godfrey acts ever as if he suffered from some mortifying circumstance. The hero should find himself at home, wherever he is; should impart comfort by his own security and good nature to all beholders. The hero is suffered to be himself. A person of strong mind comes to perceive that for him an immunity is secured so long as he renders to society that service which is native and proper to him, — an immunity from all the observances, yea, and duties, which society so tyrannically imposes on the rank and file of its members. "Euripides," says Aspasia,[23] "has not the fine manners of Sophocles; but," she adds good-humoredly," the movers and masters of our souls have surely a right to throw out their limbs as carelessly as they please, on the world that belongs to them, and before the creatures they have animated." [24]

Manners require time, as nothing is more vulgar than haste. Friendship should be surrounded with ceremonies and respects, and not crushed into corners. Friendship requires more time than poor busy men

can usually command. Here comes to me Roland,
with a delicacy of sentiment leading and enwrapping
him like a divine cloud or holy ghost. 'T is a great
destitution to both that this should not be entertained
with large leisures, but contrariwise should be balked
by importunate affairs.

But through this lustrous varnish the reality is ever
shining.[25] 'T is hard to keep the *what* from breaking through this pretty painting of the *how*. The core
will come to the surface. Strong will and keen perception overpower old manners and create new; and the
thought of the present moment has a greater value
than all the past. In persons of character we do not
remark manners, because of their instantaneousness.
We are surprised by the thing done, out of all power
to watch the way of it. Yet nothing is more charming
than to recognize the great style which runs through
the actions of such. People masquerade before us in
their fortunes, titles, offices, and connections, as academic or civil presidents, or senators, or professors,
or great lawyers, and impose on the frivolous, and a
good deal on each other, by these fames. At least it is
a point of prudent good manners to treat these reputations tenderly, as if they were merited. But the
sad realist knows these fellows at a glance, and they
know him; as when in Paris the chief of the police
enters a ball-room, so many diamonded pretenders
shrink and make themselves as inconspicuous as they
can, or give him a supplicating look as they pass. "I
had received," said a sibyl, "I had received at birth
the fatal gift of penetration;" and these Cassandras
are always born.[26]

Manners impress as they indicate real power. A
man who is sure of his point, carries a broad and con-

tented expression, which everybody reads. And you cannot rightly train one to an air and manner, except by making him the kind of man of whom that manner is the natural expression. Nature forever puts a premium on reality. What is done for effect is seen to be done for effect; what is done for love is felt to be done for love. A man inspires affection and honor because he was not lying in wait for these.[27] The things of a man for which we visit him were done in the dark and cold. A little integrity is better than any career. So deep are the sources of this surface-action that even the size of your companion seems to vary with his freedom of thought. Not only is he larger, when at ease and his thoughts generous, but everything around him becomes variable with expression. No carpenter's rule, no rod and chain will measure the dimensions of any house or house-lot; go into the house; if the proprietor is constrained and deferring, 't is of no importance how large his house, how beautiful his grounds,[28] — you quickly come to the end of all: but if the man is self-possessed, happy and at home, his house is deep-founded, indefinitely large and interesting, the roof and dome buoyant as the sky. Under the humblest roof, the commonest person in plain clothes sits there massive, cheerful, yet formidable, like the Egyptian colossi.

Neither Aristotle, nor Leibnitz, nor Junius,[29] nor Champollion[30] has set down the grammar-rules of this dialect, older than Sanscrit; but they who cannot yet read English, can read this. Men take each other's measure, when they meet for the first time, — and every time they meet. How do they get this rapid knowledge, even before they speak, of each other's power and disposition? One would say that the persuasion of their speech is not in what they say, — or that men do not convince by their argument, but by their personality, by who they are, and what they said and did heretofore. A man already strong is listened to, and everything he says is applauded. Another opposes him with sound argument, but the argument is scouted until by and by it gets into the mind of some weighty person; then it begins to tell on the community.

Self-reliance is the basis of behavior, as it is the guaranty that the powers are not squandered in too much demonstration. In this country, where school education is universal, we have a superficial culture, and a profusion of reading and writing and expression. We parade our nobilities in poems and orations, instead of working them up into happiness. There is a whisper out of the ages to him who can understand it, — "Whatever is known to thyself alone, has always very great value." There is some reason to believe that when a man does not write his poetry it escapes by other vents through him, instead of the one vent of writing; clings to his form and manners, whilst poets have often nothing poetical about them except their verses. Jacobi[31] said that "when a man has fully expressed his thought, he has somewhat less possession of it." One would say, the rule is, — What man is irresistibly urged to say, helps him and us. In explaining his thought to others, he explains it to himself, but when he opens it for show, it corrupts him.

Society is the stage on which manners are shown; novels are the literature. Novels are the journal or record of manners, and the new importance of these books derives from the fact that the novelist begins to penetrate the surface and treat this part of life more worthily. The novels used to be all alike, and had a quite vulgar tone. The novels used to lead us on to a foolish interest in the fortunes of the boy and girl they described. The boy was to be raised from a humble to a high position. He was in want of a wife and a castle, and the object of the story was to supply him with one or both. We watched sympathetically, step by step, his climbing, until at last the point is gained, the wedding day is fixed, and we follow the gala procession home to the bannered portal, when the doors are slammed in our face and the poor reader is left outside in the cold, not enriched by so much as an idea or a virtuous impulse.

But the victories of character are instant, and victories for all. Its greatness enlarges all. We are fortified by every heroic anecdote. The novels are as useful as Bibles if they teach you the secret that the best of life is conversation, and the greatest success is confidence, or perfect understanding between sincere people. 'T is a French definition of friendship, *rien que s'entendre*, good understanding. The highest compact we can make with our fellow, is, — 'Let there be truth between us two forevermore.' That is the charm in all good novels, as it is the charm in all good histories, that the heroes mutually understand, from the first, and deal loyally and with a profound trust in each other. It is sublime to feel and say of another, I need never meet or speak or write to him; we need not reinforce ourselves, or send tokens of remembrance; I rely on him as on myself; if he did thus or thus, I know it was right.

In all the superior people I have met I notice directness, truth spoken more truly, as if everything of obstruction, of malformation, had been trained away. What have they to conceal? What have they to exhibit? Between simple and noble persons there is always a quick intelligence; they recognize at sight, and meet on a better ground than the talents and skills they may chance to possess, namely on sincerity and uprightness. For it is not what talents or genius a man has, but how he is to his talents, that constitutes friendship and character. The man that stands by himself, the universe stands by him also. It is related by the monk Basle,[32] that being excommunicated by the Pope, he was, at his death, sent in charge of an angel to find a fit place of suffering in hell; but such was the eloquence and good humor of the monk, that wherever he went he was received gladly and civilly treated even by the most uncivil angels; and when he came to discourse with them, instead of contradicting or forcing him, they took his part, and adopted his manners; and even good angels came from far to see him and take up their abode with him. The angel that was sent to find a place of torment for him attempted to remove him to a worse pit, but with no better success; for such was the contented spirit of the monk that he found something to praise in every place and company, though in hell, and made a kind of heaven of it. At last the escorting angel returned with his prisoner to them that sent him, saying that no phlegethon could be found that would burn him; for that in whatever condition, Basle remained incorrigibly Basle. The legend says his sentence was remitted, and he was allowed to go into heaven and was canonized as a saint.

There is a stroke of magnanimity in the correspondence of Bonaparte with his brother Joseph, when the latter was King of Spain, and complained that he missed in Napoleon's letters the affectionate tone which had marked their childish correspondence. "I am sorry," replies Napoleon, "you think you shall find your brother again only in the Elysian Fields. It is natural that at forty he should not feel toward you as he did at twelve. But his feelings toward you have greater truth and strength. His friendship has the features of his mind."

How much we forgive to those who yield us the rare spectacle of heroic manners! We will pardon them the want of books, of arts, and even of the gentler virtues. How tenaciously we remember them! Here is a lesson which I brought along with me in boyhood from the Latin School, and which ranks with the best of Roman anecdotes. Marcus Scaurus was accused by Quintus Varius Hispanus, that he had excited the allies to take arms against the Republic. But he, full of firmness and gravity, defended himself in this manner: — "Quintus Varius Hispanus alleges that Marcus Scaurus, President of the Senate, excited the allies to arms: Marcus Scaurus, President of the Senate, denies it. There is no witness. Which do you believe, Romans?" *"Utri creditis, Quirites?"* When he had said these words he was absolved by the assembly of the people.

I have seen manners that make a similar impression with personal beauty;[33] that give the like exhilaration, and refine us like that; and in memorable experiences they are suddenly better than beauty, and make that superfluous and ugly. But they must be marked by fine perception, the acquaintance with real beauty. They must always show self-control; you shall not be facile, apologetic, or leaky, but king over your word; and every gesture and action shall indicate power at rest.[34] Then they must be inspired by the good heart. There is no beautifier of complexion, or form, or behavior, like the wish to scatter joy and not pain around

us. It is good to give a stranger a meal, or a night's
lodging. It is better to be hospitable to his good meaning and thought, and give courage to a companion.[35]
We must be as courteous to a man as we are to a picture,[36] which we are willing to give the advantage of a
good light. Special precepts are not to be thought of;
the talent of well-doing contains them all. Every hour
will show a duty as paramount as that of my whim
just now, and yet I will write it, — that there is one
topic peremptorily forbidden to all well-bred, to all
rational mortals, namely, their distempers. If you
have not slept, or if you have slept, or if you have headache, or sciatica, or leprosy, or thunderstroke, I be-
seech you by all angels to hold your peace, and not
pollute the morning, to which all the housemates bring
serene and pleasant thoughts, by corruption and
groans. Come out of the azure. Love the day. Do not
leave the sky out of your landscape. The oldest and
the most deserving person should come very modestly
into any newly awaked company, respecting the divine
communications out of which all must be presumed
to have newly come. An old man who added an ele-
vating culture to a large experience of life, said to me,
"When you come into the room, I think I will study
how to make humanity beautiful to you."' [37]

As respects the delicate question of culture I do not
think that any other than negative rules can be laid
down. For positive rules, for suggestion, nature alone
inspires it. Who dare assume to guide a youth, a maid,
to perfect manners? the golden mean is so delicate,
difficult, — say frankly, unattainable. What finest
hands would not be clumsy to sketch the genial precepts of the young girl's demeanor? The chances
seem infinite against success; and yet success is con-

tinually attained. There must not be secondariness, and 't is a thousand to one that her air and manner will at once betray that she is not primary, but that there is some other one or many of her class to whom she habitually postpones herself. But nature lifts her easily and without knowing it over these impossibilities, and we are continually surprised with graces and felicities not only unteachable but undescribable.[38]

MANNERS

"How near to good is what is fair!
    Which we no sooner see,
But with the lines and outward air
    Our senses taken be."

" Again yourselves compose,
And now put all the aptness on
Of Figure, that Proportion
    Or Color can disclose;
That if those silent arts were lost,
Design and Picture, they might boast
    From you a newer ground,
Instructed by the heightening sense
Of dignity and reverence
    In their true motions found."

BEN JONSON.

MANNERS

HALF the world, it is said, knows not how the other half live. Our Exploring Expedition saw the Feejee islanders getting their dinner off human bones; and they are said to eat their own wives and children. The husbandry of the modern inhabitants of Gournou (west of old Thebes) is philosophical [1] to a fault. To set up their housekeeping nothing is requisite but two or three earthen pots, a stone to grind meal, and a mat which is the bed. The house, namely a tomb, is ready without rent or taxes. No rain can pass through the roof, and there is no door, for there is no want of one, as there is nothing to lose. If the house do not please them, they walk out and enter another, as there are several hundreds at their command. "It is somewhat singular," adds Belzoni,[2] to whom we owe this account, "to talk of happiness among people who live in sepulchres, among the corpses and rags of an ancient nation which they know nothing of." In the deserts of Borgoo[3] the rock-Tibboos [4] still dwell in caves, like cliff-swallows, and the language of these negroes is compared by their neighbors to the shrieking of bats and to the whistling of birds. Again, the Bornoos[5] have no proper names; individuals are called after their height, thickness, or other accidental quality, and have nicknames merely. But the salt, the dates, the ivory, and the gold, for which these horrible regions are visited, find their way into countries where the purchaser and consumer can hardly be ranked in one race with these cannibals

and man-stealers; countries where man serves himself
with metals, wood, stone, glass, gum, cotton, silk and
wool; honors himself with architecture; [6] writes laws,
and contrives to execute his will through the hands of
many nations; and, especially, establishes a select society, running through all the countries of intelligent
men, a self-constituted aristocracy, or fraternity of the
best, which, without written law or exact usage of any
kind, perpetuates itself, colonizes every new-planted
island and adopts and makes its own whatever
personal beauty or extraordinary native endowment
anywhere appears.

What fact more conspicuous in modern history than
the creation of the gentleman? Chivalry is that, and
loyalty is that, and in English literature half the drama,
and all the novels, from Sir Philip Sidney to Sir Walter
Scott, paint this figure. The word *gentleman*, which,
like the word *Christian*, must hereafter characterize
the present and the few preceding centuries by the importance attached to it, is a homage to personal and
incommunicable properties. Frivolous and fantastic
additions have got associated with the name, but the
steady interest of mankind in it must be attributed
to the valuable properties which it designates. An element which unites all the most forcible persons of
every country, makes them intelligible and agreeable
to each other, and is somewhat so precise that it is at
once felt if an individual lack the masonic sign, — cannot be any casual product, but must be an average
result of the character and faculties universally found
in men. It seems a certain permanent average; as the
atmosphere is a permanent composition, whilst so
many gases are combined only to be decompounded.
Comme il faut, is the Frenchman's description of good

society: *as we must be.*[7] It is a spontaneous fruit of
talents and feelings of precisely that class who have
most vigor, who take the lead in the world of this hour,
and though far from pure, far from constituting the
gladdest and highest tone of human feeling, it is as
good as the whole society permits it to be. It is made
of the spirit, more than of the talent of men, and is a
compound result into which every great force enters
as an ingredient, namely virtue, wit, beauty, wealth
and power.

There is something equivocal in all the words in use
to express the excellence of manners and social cultivation, because the quantities are fluxional, and the
last effect is assumed by the senses as the cause. The
word *gentleman* has not any correlative abstract to express the quality. *Gentility* is mean, and *gentilesse* [8] is
obsolete. But we must keep alive in the vernacular
the distinction between *fashion*, a word of narrow and
often sinister meaning, and the heroic character which
the gentleman imports. The usual words, however,
must be respected; they will be found to contain the
root of the matter. The point of distinction in all this
class of names, as courtesy, chivalry, fashion, and the
like, is that the flower and fruit, not the grain of the
tree, are contemplated. It is beauty which is the aim
this time, and not worth.[9] The result is now in question, although our words intimate well enough the
popular feeling that the appearance supposes a substance. The gentleman is a man of truth, lord of his
own actions, and expressing that lordship in his behavior; not in any manner dependent and servile,
either on persons, or opinions, or possessions. Beyond
this fact of truth and real force, the word denotes good-
nature or benevolence: manhood first, and then gentle-

ness. The popular notion certainly adds a condition of ease and fortune; but that is a natural result of personal force and love, that they should possess and dispense the goods of the world. In times of violence, every eminent person must fall in with many opportunities to approve his stoutness and worth; therefore every man's name that emerged at all from the mass in the feudal ages rattles in our ear like a flourish of trumpets. But personal force never goes out of fashion. That is still paramount to-day, and in the moving crowd of good society the men of valor and reality are known and rise to their natural place. The competition is transferred from war to politics and trade, but the personal force appears readily enough in these new arenas.

Power first, or no leading class. In politics and in trade, bruisers and pirates are of better promise than talkers and clerks. God knows that all sorts of gentlemen knock at the door; but whenever used in strictness and with any emphasis, the name will be found to point at original energy. It describes a man standing in his own right and working after untaught methods. In a good lord there must first be a good animal,[10] at least to the extent of yielding the incomparable advantage of animal spirits. The ruling class must have more, but they must have these, giving in every company the sense of power, which makes things easy to be done which daunt the wise. The society of the energetic class, in their friendly and festive meetings, is full of courage and of attempts which intimidate the pale scholar. The courage which girls exhibit is like a battle of Lundy's Lane,[11] or a sea-fight. The intellect relies on memory to make some supplies to face these extemporaneous squadrons. But memory is a base mendicant with basket and badge, in the presence of these sudden masters. The rulers of society must be up to the work of the world, and equal to their versatile office: men of the right Cæsarian pattern, who have great range of affinity. I am far from believing the timid maxim of Lord Falkland [12] ("that for ceremony there must go two to it; since a bold fellow will go through the cunningest forms"), and am of opinion that the gentleman is the bold fellow whose forms are not to be broken through; and only that plenteous nature is rightful master which is the complement of whatever person it converses with. My gentleman gives the law where he is; he will outpray saints in chapel, outgeneral veterans in the field, and outshine all courtesy in the hall. He is good company for pirates and good with academicians; so that it is useless to fortify yourself against him; he has the private entrance to all minds, and I could as easily exclude myself, as him. The famous gentlemen of Asia and Europe have been of this strong type; Saladin, Sapor,[13] the Cid,[14] Julius Cæsar, Scipio, Alexander, Pericles, and the lordliest personages. They sat very carelessly in their chairs, and were too excellent themselves, to value any condition at a high rate.

A plentiful fortune is reckoned necessary, in the popular judgment, to the completion of this man of the world; and it is a material deputy which walks through the dance which the first has led. Money is not essential, but this wide affinity is, which transcends the habits of clique and caste and makes itself felt by men of all classes. If the aristocrat is only valid in fashionable circles and not with truckmen, he will never be a leader in fashion; and if the man of the people cannot speak on equal terms with the gentle-

man, so that the gentleman shall perceive that he is
already really of his own order, he is not to be feared.
Diogenes, Socrates, and Epaminondas, are gentlemen
of the best blood who have chosen the condition of
poverty when that of wealth was equally open to them.
I use these old names, but the men I speak of are my
contemporaries.[15] Fortune will not supply to every
generation one of these well-appointed knights, but
every collection of men furnishes some example of the
class; and the politics of this country, and the trade of
every town, are controlled by these hardy and irresponsible doers, who have invention to take the lead,
and a broad sympathy which puts them in fellowship
with crowds, and makes their action popular.

The manners of this class are observed and caught
with devotion by men of taste. The association of
these masters with each other and with men intelligent
of their merits, is mutually agreeable and stimulating.
The good forms, the happiest expressions of each, are
repeated and adopted. By swift consent everything
superfluous is dropped, everything graceful is renewed.
Fine manners show themselves formidable to the uncul-
tivated man. They are a subtler science of defence to
parry and intimidate; but once matched by the skill
of the other party, they drop the point of the sword, —
points and fences disappear,[16] and the youth finds
himself in a more transparent atmosphere, wherein
life is a less troublesome game, and not a misunder-
standing rises between the players. Manners aim to
facilitate life, to get rid of impediments and bring the
man pure to energize.[17] They aid our dealing and
conversation as a railway aids travelling, by getting
rid of all avoidable obstructions of the road and leaving nothing to be conquered but pure space.[18] These

forms very soon become fixed, and a fine sense of propriety is cultivated with the more heed that it becomes a badge of social and civil distinctions. Thus grows up Fashion, an equivocal semblance, the most puissant, the most fantastic and frivolous, the most feared and followed, and which morals [19] and violence assault in vain.

There exists a strict relation between the class of power and the exclusive and polished circles. The last are always filled or filling from the first. The strong men usually give some allowance even to the petulances of fashion, for that affinity they find in it. Napoleon, child of the revolution, destroyer of the old noblesse, never ceased to court the Faubourg St. Germain; [20] doubtless with the feeling that fashion is a homage to men of his stamp. Fashion, though in a strange way, represents all manly virtue. It is virtue gone to seed: it is a kind of posthumous honor. It does not often caress the great, but the children of the great: it is a hall of the Past. It usually sets its face against the great of this hour. Great men are not commonly in its halls; they are absent in the field: they are working, not triumphing. Fashion is made up of their children; of those who through the value and virtue of somebody, have acquired lustre to their name, marks of distinction, means of cultivation and generosity, and in their physical organization a certain health and excellence which secure to them, if not the highest power to work, yet high power to enjoy. The class of power, the working heroes, the Cortez, the Nelson, the Napoleon, see that this is the festivity and permanent celebration of such as they; that fashion is funded talent; is Mexico, Marengo [21] and Trafalgar [22] beaten out thin; that the brilliant names of fashion run back to just such busy names as their own, fifty or sixty years ago. They are the sowers, their sons shall be the reapers, and *their* sons, in the ordinary course of things, must yield the possession of the harvest to new competitors with keener eyes and stronger frames. The city is recruited from the country. In the year 1805, it is said, every legitimate monarch in Europe was imbecile. The city would have died out, rotted and exploded, long ago, but that it was reinforced from the fields. It is only country which came to town day before yesterday that is city and court to-day.[23]

Aristocracy and fashion are certain inevitable results. These mutual selections are indestructible. If they provoke anger in the least favored class, and the excluded majority revenge themselves on the excluding minority by the strong hand and kill them, at once a new class finds itself at the top, as certainly as cream rises in a bowl of milk: and if the people should destroy class after class, until two men only were left, one of these would be the leader and would be involuntarily served and copied by the other. You may keep this minority out of sight and out of mind, but it is tenacious of life, and is one of the estates of the realm. I am the more struck with this tenacity, when I see its work. It respects the administration of such unimportant matters, that we should not look for any durability in its rule. We sometimes meet men under some strong moral influence, as a patriotic, a literary, a religious movement, and feel that the moral sentiment rules man and nature. We think all other distinctions and ties will be slight and fugitive, this of caste or fashion for example; yet come from year to year and see how permanent that is, in this Boston or New York life of man, where too it has not the least countenance from the law of the land. Not in Egypt or in India a

firmer or more impassable line. Here are associations
whose ties go over and under and through it, a meeting
of merchants, a military corps, a college class, a fire-
club, a professional association, a political, a religious
convention; — the persons seem to draw inseparably
near; yet, that assembly once dispersed, its members
will not in the year meet again. Each returns to his
degree in the scale of good society, porcelain remains
porcelain, and earthen earthen. The objects of fashion
may be frivolous, or fashion may be objectless, but the
nature of this union and selection can be neither frivolous nor accidental. Each man's rank in that perfect
graduation depends on some symmetry in his structure
or some agreement in his structure to the symmetry of
society. Its doors unbar instantaneously to a natural
claim of their own kind. A natural gentleman finds
his way in, and will keep the oldest patrician out who
has lost his intrinsic rank. Fashion understands itself;
good-breeding and personal superiority of whatever
country readily fraternize with those of every other.
The chiefs of savage tribes have distinguished themselves in London and Paris by the purity of their
tournure.[24]

To say what good of fashion we can, it rests on reality, and hates nothing so much as pretenders; to exclude and mystify pretenders and send them into everlasting 'Coventry,'[25] is its delight. We contemn in
turn every other gift of men of the world; but the habit
even in little and the least matters of not appealing to
any but our own sense of propriety, constitutes the
foundation of all chivalry. There is almost no kind of
self-reliance, so it be sane and proportioned, which
fashion does not occasionally adopt and give it the
freedom of its saloons. A sainted soul is always ele-

gant, and, if it will, passes unchallenged into the most guarded ring. But so will Jock the teamster pass, in some crisis that brings him thither, and find favor, as long as his head is not giddy with the new circumstance, and the iron shoes do not wish to dance in waltzes and cotillons. For there is nothing settled in manners, but the laws of behavior yield to the energy of the individual. The maiden at her first ball, the countryman at a city dinner, believes that there is a ritual according to which every act and compliment must be performed, or the failing party must be cast out of this presence. Later they learn that good sense and character make their own forms every moment, and speak or abstain, take wine or refuse it, stay or go, sit in a chair or sprawl with children on the floor, or stand on their head, or what else soever, in a new and aboriginal way; and that strong will is always in fashion, let who will be unfashionable. All that fashion demands is composure and self-content. A circle of men perfectly well-bred would be a company of sensible persons in which every man's native manners and character appeared. If the fashionist [26] have not this quality, he is nothing. We are such lovers of self-reliance that we excuse in a man many sins if he will show us a complete satisfaction in his position, which asks no leave to be, of mine, or any man's good opinion. But any deference to some eminent man or woman of the world, forfeits all privilege of nobility. He is an underling: I have nothing to do with him; I will speak with his master. A man should not go where he cannot carry his whole sphere or society with him, — not bodily, the whole circle of his friends, but atmospherically. He should preserve in a new company the same attitude of mind and reality of relation which his daily associates draw him to, else he is shorn of his best beams, and will be an orphan in the merriest club. "If you could see Vich Ian Vohr[27] with his tail on!—" But Vich Ian Vohr must always carry his belongings in some fashion, if not added as honor, then severed as disgrace.

There will always be in society certain persons who are mercuries of its approbation, and whose glance will at any time determine for the curious their standing in the world. These are the chamberlains of the lesser gods.[28] Accept their coldness as an omen of grace with the loftier deities, and allow them all their privilege. They are clear in their office, nor could they be thus formidable without their own merits. But do not measure the importance of this class by their pretension, or imagine that a fop can be the dispenser of honor and shame. They pass also at their just rate; for how can they otherwise, in circles which exist as a sort of herald's office for the sifting of character?

As the first thing man requires of man is reality, so that appears in all the forms of society. We pointedly, and by name, introduce the parties to each other. Know you before all heaven and earth, that this is Andrew, and this is Gregory, — they look each other in the eye; they grasp each other's hand, to identify and signalize each other. It is a great satisfaction. A gentleman never dodges; his eyes look straight forward, and he assures the other party, first of all, that he has been met. For what is it that we seek, in so many visits and hospitalities? Is it your draperies, pictures and decorations? Or do we not insatiably ask, Was a man in the house? I may easily go into a great household where there is much substance, excellent provision for comfort, luxury and taste, and yet not encounter there any Amphitryon [29] who shall subordinate these appendages. I may go into a cottage, and find a farmer who feels that he is the man I have come to see, and fronts me accordingly. It was therefore a very natural point of old feudal etiquette that a gentleman who received a visit, though it were of his sovereign, should not leave his roof, but should wait his arrival at the door of his house. No house, though it were the Tuileries or the Escurial, is good for anything without a master. And yet we are not often gratified by this hospitality. Everybody we know surrounds himself with a fine house, fine books, conservatory, gardens, equipage and all manner of toys, as screens to interpose between himself and his guest. Does it not seem as if man was of a very sly, elusive nature, and dreaded nothing so much as a full rencontre front to front with his fellow? It were unmerciful, I know, quite to abolish the use of these screens, which are of eminent convenience, whether the guest is too great or too little. We call together many friends who keep each other in play, or by luxuries and ornaments we amuse the young people, and guard our retirement. Or if perchance a searching realist comes to our gate, before whose eye we have no care to stand, then again we run to our curtain, and hide ourselves as Adam at the voice of the Lord God in the garden. Cardinal Caprara, the Pope's legate at Paris, defended himself from the glances of Napoleon by an immense pair of green spectacles. Napoleon remarked them, and speedily managed to rally them off: and yet Napoleon, in his turn, was not great enough, with eight hundred thousand troops at his back, to face a pair of freeborn eyes, but fenced himself with etiquette and within triple barriers of reserve; and, as all the world knows from Madame de

Staël, was wont, when he found himself observed, to
discharge his face of all expression. But emperors and
rich men are by no means the most skilful masters of
good manners. No rent-roll nor army-list can dignify
skulking and dissimulation; and the first point of
courtesy must always be truth, as really all the forms
of good-breeding point that way.

I have just been reading, in Mr. Hazlitt's translation,
Montaigne's account of his journey into Italy, and
am struck with nothing more agreeably than the self-
respecting fashions of the time. His arrival in each
place, the arrival of a gentleman of France, is an event
of some consequence. Wherever he goes he pays a
visit to whatever prince or gentleman of note resides
upon his road, as a duty to himself and to civilization.
When he leaves any house in which he has lodged for
a few weeks, he causes his arms to be painted and
hung up as a perpetual sign to the house, as was the
custom of gentlemen.

The complement of this graceful self-respect, and
that of all the points of good-breeding I most require
and insist upon, is deference. I like that every chair [30]
should be a throne, and hold a king. I prefer a tendency to stateliness to an excess of fellowship. Let the
incommunicable objects of nature and the metaphysical
isolation of man teach us independence. Let us not be
too much acquainted. I would have a man enter his
house through a hall filled with heroic and sacred
sculptures, that he might not want the hint of tranquillity and self-poise. We should meet each morning
as from foreign countries, and, spending the day together, should depart at night, as into foreign countries. In all things I would have the island of a man
inviolate. Let us sit apart as the gods, talking from

peak to peak all round Olympus. No degree of affection need invade this religion. This is myrrh and rosemary to keep the other sweet. Lovers should guard their strangeness.[31] If they forgive too much, all slides into confusion and meanness. It is easy to push this deference to a Chinese etiquette; but coolness and absence of heat and haste indicate fine qualities. A gentleman makes no noise; a lady is serene. Proportionate is our disgust at those invaders who fill a studious house with blast and running, to secure some paltry convenience. Not less I dislike a low sympathy of each with his neighbor's needs. Must we have a good understanding with one another's palates? as foolish people [32] who have lived long together know when each wants salt or sugar. I pray my companion, if he wishes for bread, to ask me for bread, and if he wishes for sassafras or arsenic, to ask me for them, and not to hold out his plate as if I knew already. Every natural function can be dignified by deliberation and privacy. Let us leave hurry to slaves. The compliments and ceremonies of our breeding should recall,[33] however remotely, the grandeur of our destiny.

The flower of courtesy does not very well bide handling, but if we dare to open another leaf and explore what parts go to its conformation, we shall find also an intellectual quality. To the leaders of men, the brain as well as the flesh and the heart must furnish a proportion. Defect in manners is usually the defect of fine perceptions. Men are too coarsely made for the delicacy of beautiful carriage and customs. It is not quite sufficient to good-breeding, a union of kindness and independence. We imperatively require a perception of, and a homage to beauty in our companions. Other virtues are in request in the field and workyard, but a certain degree of taste is not to be spared in those we sit with. I could better eat with one who did not respect the truth or the laws than with a sloven and unpresentable person. Moral qualities rule the world, but at short distances the senses are despotic. The same discrimination of fit and fair runs out, if with less rigor, into all parts of life. The average spirit of the energetic class is good sense, acting under certain limitations and to certain ends. It entertains every natural gift. Social in its nature, it respects everything which tends to unite men. It delights in measure. The love of beauty is mainly the love of measure or proportion. The person who screams, or uses the superlative degree, or converses with heat, puts whole drawing-rooms to flight. If you wish to be loved, love measure. You must have genius or a prodigious usefulness if you will hide the want of measure. This perception comes in to polish and perfect the parts of the social instrument. Society will pardon much to genius and special gifts, but, being in its nature a convention, it loves what is conventional, or what belongs to coming together.[34] That makes the good and bad of manners, namely what helps or hinders fellowship. For fashion is not good sense absolute, but relative; not good sense private, but good sense entertaining company. It hates corners and sharp points of character, hates quarrelsome, egotistical, solitary and gloomy people; hates whatever can interfere with total blending of parties; whilst it values all peculiarities as in the highest degree refreshing, which can consist with good fellowship. And besides the general infusion of wit to heighten civility, the direct splendor of intellectual power is ever welcome in fine society as the costliest addition to its rule and its credit.

The dry light must shine in to adorn our festival, but it must be tempered and shaded, or that will also offend.[35] Accuracy is essential to beauty, and quick perceptions to politeness, but not too quick perceptions. One may be too punctual and too precise. He must leave the omniscience of business at the door, when he comes into the palace of beauty. Society loves creole natures and sleepy languishing manners, so that they cover sense, grace and good-will: the air of drowsy strength, which disarms criticism; perhaps because such a person seems to reserve himself for the best of the game, and not spend himself on surfaces; an ignoring eye, which does not see the annoyances, shifts and inconveniences that cloud the brow and smother the voice of the sensitive.

Therefore besides personal force and so much perception as constitutes unerring taste, society demands in its patrician class another element already intimated, which it significantly terms good-nature, — expressing all degrees of generosity, from the lowest willingness and faculty to oblige, up to the heights of magnanimity and love. Insight we must have,[36] or we shall run against one another and miss the way to our food; but intellect is selfish and barren. The secret of success in society is a certain heartiness and sympathy. A man who is not happy in the company cannot find any word in his memory that will fit the occasion. All his information is a little impertinent.[37] A man who is happy there, finds in every turn of the conversation equally lucky occasions for the introduction of that which he has to say. The favorites of society, and what it calls *whole souls*,[38] are able men and of more spirit than wit, who have no uncomfortable egotism, but who exactly fill the hour and the company; contented and contenting, at a marriage or a funeral, a ball or a jury, a water-party or a shooting-match. England, which is rich in gentlemen, furnished, in the beginning of the present century, a good model of that genius which the world loves, in Mr. Fox, who added to his great abilities the most social disposition and real love of men. Parliamentary history has few better passages than the debate in which Burke and Fox separated in the House of Commons; when Fox urged on his old friend the claims of old friendship with such tenderness that the house was moved to tears. Another anecdote is so close to my matter, that I must hazard the story. A tradesman who had long dunned him for a note of three hundred guineas, found him one day counting gold, and demanded payment. "No," said Fox, " I owe this money to Sheridan; it is a debt of honor; if an accident should happen to me, he has nothing to show." "Then," said the creditor, "I change my debt into a debt of honor," and tore the note in pieces. Fox thanked the man for his confidence and paid him, saying, "his debt was of older standing, and Sheridan must wait." Lover of liberty, friend of the Hindoo, friend of the African slave, he possessed a great personal popularity; and Napoleon said of him on the occasion of his visit to Paris, in 1805, "Mr. Fox will always hold the first place in an assembly at the Tuileries."

We may easily seem ridiculous in our eulogy of courtesy, whenever we insist on benevolence as its foundation. The painted phantasm Fashion rises to cast a species of derision on what we say. But I will neither be driven from some allowance to Fashion as a symbolic institution, nor from the belief that love is the basis of courtesy.[39] We must obtain *that*, if we can; but by all means we must affirm *this*. Life owes much of its spirit to these sharp contrasts. Fashion, which affects to be honor, is often, in all men's experience, only a ballroom code. Yet so long as it is the highest circle in the imagination of the best heads on the planet, there is something necessary and excellent in it; for it is not to be supposed that men have agreed to be the dupes of anything preposterous; and the respect which these mysteries inspire in the most rude and sylvan characters, and the curiosity with which details of high life are read, betray the universality of the love of cultivated manners. I know that a comic disparity would be felt, if we should enter the acknowledged 'first circles' and apply these terrific standards of justice, beauty and benefit to the individuals actually found there. Monarchs and heroes, sages and lovers, these gallants are not. Fashion has many classes and many rules of probation and admission, and not the best alone. There is not only the right of conquest, which genius pretends, — the individual demonstrating his natural aristocracy best of the best; [40] — but less claims will pass for the time; for Fashion loves lions, and points like Circe [41] to her horned company. This gentleman is this afternoon arrived from Denmark; and that is my Lord Ride, who came yesterday from Bagdat; here is Captain Friese, from Cape Turnagain; and Captain Symmes, from the interior of the earth; and Monsieur Jovaire, who came down this morning in a balloon; Mr. Hobnail, the reformer; and Reverend Jul Bat, who has converted the whole torrid zone in his Sunday school; and Signor Torre del Greco, who extinguished Vesuvius by pouring into it the Bay of Naples; Spahi, the Persian ambassador; and Tul Wil Shan, the exiled nabob of Nepaul, whose saddle is the new moon. — But these are monsters of one day,

and to-morrow will be dismissed to their holes and
dens; for in these rooms every chair is waited for. The
artist, the scholar, and, in general, the clerisy,[42] win
their way up into these places and get represented here,
somewhat on this footing of conquest. Another mode
is to pass through all the degrees, spending a year and
a day in St. Michael's Square,[43] being steeped in Cologne water, and perfumed, and dined, and introduced,
and properly grounded in all the biography and politics
and anecdotes of the boudoirs.

Yet these fineries may have grace and wit. Let there
be grotesque sculpture [44] about the gates and offices of
temples. Let the creed and commandments even have
the saucy homage of parody.[45] The forms of politeness
universally express benevolence in superlative degrees.
What if they are in the mouths of selfish men, and
used as means of selfishness? What if the false gentleman almost bows the true out of the world? What if
the false gentleman contrives so to address his companion as civilly to exclude all others from his discourse,
and also to make them feel excluded? Real service
will not lose its nobleness. All generosity is not merely
French and sentimental; nor is it to be concealed that
living blood and a passion of kindness does at last distinguish God's gentleman from Fashion's. The epitaph
of Sir Jenkin Grout is not wholly unintelligible to
the present age: "Here lies Sir Jenkin Grout, who
loved his friend and persuaded his enemy: what his
mouth ate, his hand paid for: what his servants robbed,
he restored: if a woman gave him pleasure, he supported her in pain: he never forgot his children; and
whoso touched his finger, drew after it his whole
body." [46] Even the line of heroes is not utterly extinct.
There is still ever some admirable person in plain

clothes, standing on the wharf, who jumps in to rescue a drowning man; there is still some absurd inventor of charities; some guide and comforter of runaway slaves; some friend of Poland; some Philhellene; some fanatic who plants shade-trees for the second and third generation, and orchards when he is grown old; some well-concealed piety; some just man happy in an ill fame; some youth ashamed of the favors of fortune and impatiently casting them on other shoulders. And these are the centres of society, on which it returns for fresh impulses. These are the creators of Fashion, which is an attempt to organize beauty of behavior. The beautiful and the generous are, in the theory, the doctors and apostles of this church: Scipio, and the Cid, and Sir Philip Sidney, and Washington, and every pure and valiant heart who worshipped Beauty by word and by deed. The persons who constitute the natural aristocracy are not found in the actual aristocracy, or only on its edge; as the chemical energy of the spectrum is found to be greatest just outside of the spectrum. Yet that is the infirmity of the seneschals, who do not know their sovereign when he appears. The theory of society supposes the existence and sovereignty of these. It divines afar off their coming. It says with the elder gods, —

> "As Heaven and Earth are fairer far
> Than Chaos and blank Darkness, though once chiefs;
> And as we show beyond that Heaven and Earth
> In form and shape compact and beautiful; . . .
> So on our heels a fresh perfection treads,
> A power more strong in beauty, born of us
> And fated to excel us, as we pass
> In glory that old Darkness . . . .
> . . . For 't is the eternal law
> That first in beauty shall be first in might." [47]

Therefore, within the ethnical circle [48] of good society there is a narrower and higher circle, concentration of its light, and flower of courtesy, to which there is always a tacit appeal of pride and reference, as to its inner and imperial court; the parliament of love and chivalry. And this is constituted of those persons in whom heroic dispositions are native; with the love of beauty, the delight in society, and the power to embellish the passing day. If the individuals who compose the purest circles of aristocracy in Europe, the guarded blood of centuries, should pass in review, in such manner as that we could at leisure and critically inspect their behavior, we might find no gentleman and no lady; for although excellent specimens of courtesy and high-breeding would gratify us in the assemblage, in the particulars we should detect offence. Because elegance comes of no breeding, but of birth. There must be romance of character, or the most fastidious exclusion of impertinencies will not avail. It must be genius which takes that direction: it must be not courteous, but courtesy. High behavior is as rare in fiction as it is in fact. Scott is praised for the fidelity with which he painted the demeanor and conversation of the superior classes. Certainly, kings and queens, nobles and great ladies, had some right to complain of the absurdity that had been put in their mouths before the days of Waverley; but neither does Scott's dialogue bear criticism. His lords brave each other in smart epigrammatic speeches, but the dialogue is in costume, and does not please on the second reading: it is not warm with life. In Shakspeare alone the speakers do not strut and bridle, the dialogue is easily great, and he adds to so many titles that of being the best-bred man in England and in Christendom. Once or twice in a lifetime we are permitted to enjoy the charm of noble manners, in the presence of a man or woman who have no bar in their nature, but whose character emanates freely in their word and gesture. A beautiful form is better than a beautiful face; a beautiful behavior is better than a beautiful form: it gives a higher pleasure than statues or pictures; it is the finest of the fine arts.[49] A man is but a little thing in the midst of the objects of nature, yet, by the moral quality radiating from his countenance he may abolish all considerations of magnitude, and in his manners equal the majesty of the world. I have seen an individual whose manners, though wholly within the conventions of elegant society, were never learned there, but were original and commanding and held out protection and prosperity; one who did not need the aid of a court-suit, but carried the holiday in his eye; who exhilarated the fancy by flinging wide the doors of new modes of existence; who shook off the captivity of etiquette, with happy, spirited bearing, good-natured and free as Robin Hood; yet with the port of an emperor, if need be, — calm, serious and fit to stand the gaze of millions.

The open air and the fields, the street and public chambers are the places where Man executes his will; let him yield or divide the sceptre at the door of the house. Woman, with her instinct of behavior, instantly detects in man a love of trifles, any coldness or imbecility, or, in short, any want of that large, flowing and magnanimous deportment which is indispensable as an exterior in the hall. Our American institutions have been friendly to her, and at this moment I esteem it a chief felicity of this country, that it excels in women. A certain awkward consciousness of inferiority in the men may give rise to the new chivalry in behalf of

Woman's Rights. Certainly let her be as much better placed in the laws and in social forms as the most zealous reformer can ask, but I confide so entirely in her inspiring and musical nature, that I believe only herself can show us how she shall be served. The wonderful generosity of her sentiments raises her at times into heroical and godlike regions, and verifies the pictures of Minerva, Juno, or Polymnia; and by the firmness with which she treads her upward path, she convinces the coarsest calculators [50] that another road exists than that which their feet know. But besides those who make good in our imagination the place of muses and of Delphic Sibyls, are there not women who fill our vase with wine and roses to the brim, so that the wine runs over and fills the house with perfume; who inspire us with courtesy; who unloose our tongues and we speak; who anoint our eyes and we see? [51] We say things we never thought to have said; for once, our walls of habitual reserve vanished and left us at large; we were children playing with children in a wide field of flowers. Steep us, we cried, in these influences, for days, for weeks, and we shall be sunny poets and will write out in many-colored words the romance that you are. Was it Hafiz or Firdousi [52] that said of his Persian Lilla, She was an elemental force, and astonished me by her amount of life, when I saw her day after day radiating, every instant, redundant joy and grace on all around her? She was a solvent powerful to reconcile all heterogeneous persons into one society: like air or water, an element of such a great range of affinities that it combines readily with a thousand substances. Where she is present all others will be more than they are wont. She was a unit and whole, so that whatsoever she did, became her. She had too much sympathy and desire to please, than that you could say her manners were marked with dignity, yet no princess could surpass her clear and erect demeanor on each occasion. She did not study the Persian grammar, nor the books of the seven poets, but all the poems of the seven seemed to be written upon her. For though the bias of her nature was not to thought, but to sympathy, yet was she so perfect in her own nature as to meet intellectual persons by the fulness of her heart, warming them by her sentiments; believing, as she did, that by dealing nobly with all, all would show themselves noble.

I know that this Byzantine pile [53] of chivalry or Fashion, which seems so fair and picturesque to those who look at the contemporary facts for science or for entertainment, is not equally pleasant to all spectators. The constitution of our society makes it a giant's castle to the ambitious youth who have not found their names enrolled in its Golden Book,[54] and whom it has excluded from its coveted honors and privileges. They have yet to learn that its seeming grandeur is shadowy and relative: it is great by their allowance; its proudest gates will fly open at the approach of their courage and virtue. For the present distress, however, of those who are predisposed to suffer from the tyrannies of this caprice, there are easy remedies. To remove your residence a couple of miles,[55] or at most four, will commonly relieve the most extreme susceptibility. For the advantages which fashion values are plants which thrive in very confined localities, in a few streets namely. Out of this precinct they go for nothing; are of no use in the farm, in the forest, in the market, in war, in the nuptial society, in the literary or scientific circle, at sea, in friendship, in the heaven of thought or virtue.

But we have lingered long enough in these painted courts. The worth of the thing signified must vindicate our taste for the emblem. Everything that is called fashion and courtesy humbles itself before the cause and fountain of honor, creator of titles and dignities, namely the heart of love. This is the royal blood, this the fire, which[56] in all countries and contingencies, will work after its kind and conquer and expand all that approaches it. This gives new meanings to every fact. This impoverishes the rich, suffering no grandeur but its own. What *is* rich? Are you rich enough to help anybody? to succor the unfashionable and the eccentric? rich enough to make the Canadian in his wagon, the itinerant with his consul's paper which commends him "To the charitable," the swarthy Italian with his few broken words of English, the lame pauper hunted by overseers from town to town, even the poor insane or besotted wreck of man or woman, feel the noble exception of your presence and your house from the general bleakness and stoniness; to make such feel that they were greeted with a voice which made them both remember and hope? What is vulgar but to refuse the claim on acute and conclusive reasons?[57] What is gentle, but to allow it, and give their heart and yours one holiday from the national caution? Without the rich heart, wealth is an ugly beggar. The king of Schiraz could not afford to be so bountiful as the poor Osman[58] who dwelt at his gate. Osman had a humanity so broad and deep that although his speech was so bold and free with the Koran as to disgust all the dervishes, yet was there never a poor outcast, eccentric, or insane man, some fool who had cut off his beard, or who had been mutilated under a vow, or had a pet madness in his brain, but fled at once to him;

that great heart lay there so sunny and hospitable in
the centre of the country, that it seemed as if the instinct of all sufferers drew them to his side. And the
madness which he harbored he did not share. Is not
this to be rich? this only to be rightly rich?

But I shall hear without pain that I play the courtier
very ill, and talk of that which I do not well understand. It is easy to see that what is called by distinction society and fashion has good laws as well as bad,
has much that is necessary, and much that is absurd.
Too good for banning,[59] and too bad for blessing, it
reminds us of a tradition of the pagan mythology, in
any attempt to settle its character. 'I overheard Jove,
one day,' said Silenus, 'talking of destroying the earth;
he said it had failed; they were all rogues and vixens,
who went from bad to worse, as fast as the days succeeded each other. Minerva said she hoped not; they
were only ridiculous little creatures, with this odd circumstance, that they had a blur, or indeterminate
aspect, seen far or seen near; if you called them bad,
they would appear so; if you called them good, they
would appear so; and there was no one person or action among them which would not puzzle her owl,
much more all Olympus, to know whether it was fundamentally bad or good.' [60]

FRIENDSHIP

A RUDDY drop of manly blood [1]
The surging sea outweighs;
The world uncertain comes and goes,
The lover rooted stays.
I fancied he was fled,
And, after many a year,
Glowed unexhausted kindliness
Like daily sunrise there.
My careful heart was free again, —
O friend, my bosom said,
Through thee alone the sky is arched,
Through thee the rose is red,
All things through thee take nobler form
And look beyond the earth,
The mill-round of our fate appears [2]
A sun-path in thy worth.
Me too thy nobleness has taught
To master my despair;
The fountains of my hidden life
Are through thy friendship fair.

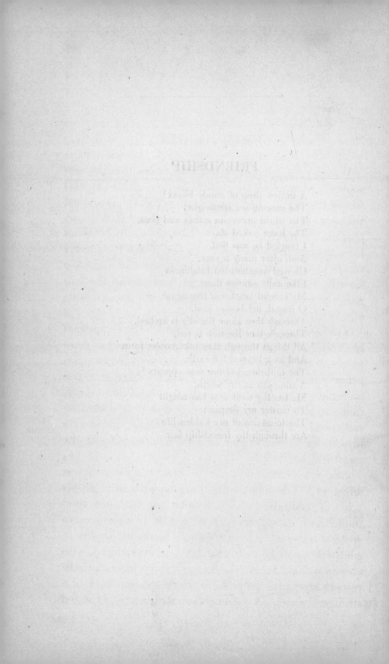

FRIENDSHIP

WE have a great deal more kindness than is ever
spoken. Maugre all the selfishness that chills like east
winds the world, the whole human family is bathed
with an element of love like a fine ether. How many
persons we meet in houses, whom we scarcely speak
to, whom yet we honor, and who honor us! How many
we see in the street, or sit with in church, whom, though
silently, we warmly rejoice to be with! Read the language of these wandering eye-beams. The heart know-
eth.

The effect of the indulgence of this human affection
is a certain cordial exhilaration. In poetry and in common speech the emotions of benevolence and complacency which are felt towards others are likened to the
material effects of fire; so swift, or much more swift,
more active, more cheering, are these fine inward ir-
radiations. From the highest degree of passionate
love to the lowest degree of good-will, they make the
sweetness of life.

Our intellectual and active powers increase with our
affection.[3] The scholar sits down to write, and all his
years of meditation do not furnish him with one good
thought or happy expression; but it is necessary to
write a letter to a friend, — and forthwith troops of
gentle thoughts invest themselves, on every hand, with
chosen words. See, in any house where virtue and self-
respect abide, the palpitation which the approach of a
stranger causes. A commended stranger is expected

and announced, and an uneasiness betwixt pleasure and pain invades all the hearts of a household. His arrival almost brings fear to the good hearts that would welcome him. The house is dusted, all things fly into their places, the old coat is exchanged for the new, and they must get up a dinner if they can. Of a commended stranger, only the good report is told by others, only the good and new is heard by us. He stands to us for humanity. He is what we wish. Having imagined and invested him, we ask how we should stand related in conversation and action with such a man, and are uneasy with fear. The same idea exalts conversation with him. We talk better than we are wont.[4] We have the nimblest fancy, a richer memory, and our dumb devil has taken leave for the time. For long hours we can continue a series of sincere, graceful, rich communications, drawn from the oldest, secretest experience, so that they who sit by, of our own kinsfolk and acquaintance, shall feel a lively surprise at our unusual powers. But as soon as the stranger begins to intrude his partialities, his definitions, his defects into the conversation, it is all over.[5] He has heard the first, the last and best he will ever hear from us. He is no stranger now. Vulgarity, ignorance, misapprehension are old acquaintances. Now, when he comes, he may get the order, the dress and the dinner, — but the throbbing of the heart and the communications of the soul, no more.

What is so pleasant as these jets of affection which make a young world for me again? What so delicious as a just and firm encounter of two, in a thought, in a feeling? How beautiful, on their approach to this beating heart, the steps and forms of the gifted and the true! The moment we indulge our affections, the earth is metamorphosed;[6] there is no winter and no night; all tragedies, all ennuis vanish, — all duties even; nothing fills the proceeding eternity but the forms all radiant of beloved persons. Let the soul be assured that somewhere in the universe it should rejoin its friend, and it would be content and cheerful alone for a thousand years.

I awoke this morning with devout thanksgiving for my friends, the old and the new. Shall I not call God the Beautiful, who daily showeth himself so to me in his gifts? I chide society, I embrace solitude, and yet I am not so ungrateful as not to see the wise, the lovely and the noble-minded, as from time to time they pass my gate. Who hears me, who understands me, becomes mine, — a possession for all time. Nor is Nature so poor but she gives me this joy several times, and thus we weave social threads of our own, a new web of relations; and, as many thoughts in succession substantiate themselves, we shall by and by stand in a new world of our own creation, and no longer strangers and pilgrims in a traditionary globe. My friends have come to me unsought. The great God gave them to me. By oldest right, by the divine affinity of virtue with itself, I find them, or rather not I, but the Deity in me and in them [7] derides and cancels the thick walls of individual character, relation, age, sex, circumstance, at which he usually connives, and now makes many one. High thanks I owe you, excellent lovers, who carry out the world for me to new and noble depths, and enlarge the meaning of all my thoughts. These are new poetry of the first Bard, — poetry without stop, — hymn, ode and epic, poetry still flowing, Apollo and the Muses chanting still. Will these too separate themselves from me again, or some of them? I know not, but I fear it not; for my relation to them is so pure that we hold by simple affinity, and the Genius of my life being thus social, the same affinity will exert its energy on whomsoever is as noble as these men and women, wherever I may be.

I confess to an extreme tenderness of nature on this point. It is almost dangerous to me to "crush the sweet poison of misused wine"[8] of the affections. A new person is to me a great event and hinders me from sleep. I have often had fine fancies about persons which have given me delicious hours; but the joy ends in the day; it yields no fruit. Thought is not born of it; my action is very little modified. I must feel pride in my friend's accomplishments as if they were mine, and a property in his virtues. I feel as warmly when he is praised, as the lover when he hears applause of his engaged maiden. We over-estimate the conscience of our friend. His goodness seems better than our goodness, his nature finer, his temptations less. Everything that is his, — his name, his form, his dress, books and instruments,—fancy enhances. Our own thought sounds new and larger from his mouth.[9]

Yet the systole and diastole [10] of the heart are not without their analogy in the ebb and flow of love. Friendship, like the immortality of the soul, is too good to be believed. The lover, beholding his maiden, half knows that she is not verily that which he worships; and in the golden hour of friendship we are surprised with shades of suspicion and unbelief. We doubt that we bestow on our hero the virtues in which he shines, and afterwards worship the form to which we have ascribed this divine inhabitation. In strictness, the soul does not respect men as it respects itself. In strict science all persons underlie the same condition of an infinite remoteness. Shall we fear to cool our love by min-

ing for the metaphysical foundation of this Elysian
temple? Shall I not be as real as the things I see? If
I am, I shall not fear to know them for what they are.
Their essence is not less beautiful than their appearance, though it needs finer organs for its apprehension. The root of the plant is not unsightly to science,
though for chaplets and festoons we cut the stem
short. And I must hazard the production of the bald
fact amidst these pleasing reveries, though it should
prove an Egyptian skull[11] at our banquet. A man who
stands united with his thought conceives magnifi-
cently of himself. He is conscious of a universal success,[12] even though bought by uniform particular failures. No advantages, no powers, no gold or force,
can be any match for him. I cannot choose but rely
on my own poverty more than on your wealth. I cannot make your consciousness tantamount to mine.
Only the star dazzles; the planet has a faint, moonlike
ray. I hear what you say of the admirable parts and
tried temper of the party you praise, but I see well
that, for all his purple cloaks, I shall not like him, unless he is at least a poor Greek like me. I cannot deny
it, O friend, that the vast shadow of the Phenomenal
includes thee also in its pied and painted immensity,
— thee also, compared with whom all else is shadow.
Thou art not Being, as Truth is, as Justice is, — thou
art not my soul, but a picture and effigy of that. Thou
hast come to me lately, and already thou art seizing
thy hat and cloak.[13] Is it not that the soul puts forth
friends as the tree puts forth leaves, and presently, by
the germination of new buds, extrudes the old leaf?
The law of nature is alternation for evermore. Each
electrical state superinduces the opposite. The soul
environs itself with friends that it may enter into a

grander self-acquaintance or solitude;[14] and it goes alone for a season that it may exalt its conversation or society. This method betrays itself along the whole history of our personal relations. The instinct of affection revives the hope of union with our mates, and the returning sense of insulation recalls us from the chase. Thus every man passes his life in the search after friendship, and if he should record his true sentiment, he might write a letter like this to each new candidate for his love: —

DEAR FRIEND,

If I was sure of thee, sure of thy capacity, sure to match my mood with thine, I should never think again of trifles in relation to thy comings and goings. I am not very wise; my moods are quite attainable, and I respect thy genius; it is to me as yet unfathomed; yet dare I not presume in thee a perfect intelligence of me, and so thou art to me a delicious torment. Thine ever, or never.

Yet these uneasy pleasures and fine pains are for curiosity and not for life.[15] They are not to be indulged. This is to weave cobweb, and not cloth. Our friendships hurry to short and poor conclusions, because we have made them a texture of wine and dreams, instead of the tough fibre of the human heart. The laws of friendship [16] are austere and eternal, of one web with the laws of nature and of morals. But we have aimed at a swift and petty benefit, to suck a sudden sweetness.[17] We snatch at the slowest fruit in the whole garden of God, which many summers and many winters must ripen. We seek our friend not sacredly,[18] but with an adulterate passion which would appropriate

him to ourselves. In vain. We are armed all over with
subtle antagonisms, which, as soon as we meet, begin
to play, and translate all poetry into stale prose. Almost all people descend to meet.[19] All association must
be a compromise, and, what is worst, the very flower
and aroma of the flower of each of the beautiful natures disappears as they approach each other. What
a perpetual disappointment is actual society, even of
the virtuous and gifted! After interviews have been
compassed with long foresight we must be tormented
presently by baffled blows, by sudden, unseasonable
apathies, by epilepsies of wit and of animal spirits, in
the heyday of friendship and thought. Our faculties
do not play us true, and both parties are relieved by
solitude.

I ought to be equal to every relation.[20] It makes no
difference how many friends I have and what content
I can find in conversing with each, if there be one to
whom I am not equal. If I have shrunk unequal from
one contest, the joy I find in all the rest becomes mean
and cowardly. I should hate myself, if then I made
my other friends my asylum: —

> " The valiant warrior famousèd for fight,
> After a hundred victories, once foiled,
> Is from the book of honor razèd quite
> And all the rest forgot for which he toiled." [21]

Our impatience is thus sharply rebuked. Bashful-
ness and apathy are a tough husk in which a delicate
organization is protected from premature ripening.
It would be lost if it knew itself before any of the best
souls were yet ripe enough to know and own it. Respect the *naturlangsamkeit* [22] which hardens the ruby
in a million years, and works in duration in which
Alps and Andes come and go as rainbows. The good

spirit of our life has no heaven which is the price of rashness.[23] Love, which is the essence of God, is not for levity, but for the total worth of man. Let us not have this childish luxury in our regards, but the austerest worth; let us approach our friend with an audacious trust in the truth of his heart, in the breadth, impossible to be overturned, of his foundations.

The attractions of this subject are not to be resisted, and I leave, for the time, all account of subordinate social benefit, to speak of that select and sacred relation which is a kind of absolute, and which even leaves the language of love suspicious and common, so much is this purer, and nothing is so much divine.

I do not wish to treat friendships daintily, but with roughest courage. When they are real, they are not glass threads or frostwork, but the solidest thing we know. For now, after so many ages of experience, what do we know of nature or of ourselves? Not one step has man taken toward the solution of the problem of his destiny. In one condemnation of folly stand the whole universe of men.[24] But the sweet sincerity of joy and peace which I draw from this alliance with my brother's soul is the nut itself [25] whereof all nature and all thought is but the husk and shell. Happy is the house that shelters a friend! It might well be built, like a festal bower or arch, to entertain him a single day. Happier, if he know the solemnity of that relation and honor its law! He who offers himself a candidate for that covenant comes up, like an Olympian, to the great games where the first-born of the world are the competitors. He proposes himself for contests where Time, Want, Danger, are in the lists, and he alone is victor who has truth enough in his constitution to preserve the delicacy of his beauty from the wear and tear of all these. The gifts of fortune may be present or absent, but all the speed in that contest depends on intrinsic nobleness and the contempt of trifles. There are two elements that go to the composition of friendship, each so sovereign that I can detect no superiority in either, no reason why either should be first named. One is truth. A friend is a person with whom I may be sincere. Before him I may think aloud. I am arrived at last in the presence of a man so real and equal that I may drop even those undermost garments [26] of dissimulation, courtesy, and second thought, which men never put off, and may deal with him with the simplicity and wholeness with which one chemical atom meets another. Sincerity is the luxury allowed,[27] like diadems and authority, only to the highest rank; *that* being permitted to speak truth, as having none above it to court or conform unto. Every man alone is sincere.[28] At the entrance of a second person, hypocrisy begins. We parry and fend the approach of our fellow-man by compliments, by gossip, by amusements, by affairs. We cover up our thought from him under a hundred folds. I knew a man who under a certain religious frenzy cast off this drapery, and omitting all compliment and commonplace, spoke to the conscience of every person he encountered, and that with great insight and beauty.[29] At first he was resisted, and all men agreed he was mad. But persisting — as indeed he could not help doing — for some time in this course, he attained to the advantage of bringing every man of his acquaintance into true relations with him. No man would think of speaking falsely with him, or of putting him off with any chat of markets or reading-rooms. But every man was constrained by so much sincerity to the like plaindealing, and what love of nature, what poetry, what symbol of truth he had, he did certainly show him. But to most of us society shows not its face and eye, but its side and its back. To stand in true relations with men in a false age is worth a fit of insanity, is it not?[30] We can seldom go erect. Almost every man we meet requires some civility — requires to be humored; he has some fame, some talent, some whim of religion or philanthropy in his head that is not to be questioned, and which spoils all conversation with him. But a friend is a sane man who exercises not my ingenuity, but me. My friend gives me entertainment without requiring any stipulation on my part. A friend therefore is a sort of paradox in nature. I who alone am, I who see nothing in nature whose existence I can affirm with equal evidence to my own, behold now the semblance of my being, in all its height, variety and curiosity, reiterated in a foreign form; so that a friend may well be reckoned the masterpiece of nature.[31]

The other element of friendship is tenderness. We are holden to men by every sort of tie, by blood, by pride, by fear, by hope, by lucre, by lust, by hate, by admiration, by every circumstance and badge and trifle, — but we can scarce believe that so much character can subsist in another as to draw us by love. Can another be so blessed and we so pure that we can offer him tenderness? When a man becomes dear to me I have touched the goal of fortune. I find very little written directly to the heart of this matter in books. And yet I have one text which I cannot choose but remember. My author[32] says, — "I offer myself faintly and bluntly to those whose I effectually am, and tender myself least to him to whom I am the most devoted." I wish that friendship should have feet, as well as eyes and eloquence. It must plant itself on the ground, before it vaults over the moon. I wish it to be a little of a citizen, before it is quite a cherub. We chide the citizen because he makes love a commodity. It is an exchange of gifts, of useful loans; it is good neighborhood; it watches with the sick; it holds the pall at the funeral; and quite loses sight of the delicacies and nobility of the relation. But though we cannot find the god under this disguise of a sutler, yet on the other hand we cannot forgive the poet if he spins his thread too fine and does not substantiate his romance by the municipal virtues of justice, punctuality, fidelity and pity. I hate the prostitution of the name of friendship to signify modish and worldly alliances. I much prefer the company of ploughboys and tin-peddlers to the silken and perfumed amity [33] which celebrates its days of encounter by a frivolous display, by rides in a curricle and dinners at the best taverns. The end of friendship is a commerce the most strict and homely that can be joined; more strict than any of which we have experience. It is for aid and comfort through all the relations and passages of life and death. It is fit for serene days and graceful gifts and country rambles, but also for rough roads and hard fare, shipwreck, poverty and persecution. It keeps company with the sallies of the wit and the trances of religion. We are to dignify to each other the daily needs and offices of man's life, and embellish it by courage, wisdom and unity. It should never fall into something usual and settled, but should be alert and inventive and add rhyme and reason to what was drudgery. [34]

Friendship may be said to require natures so rare and costly, each so well tempered and so happily adapted, and withal so circumstanced (for even in that particular, a poet says, love demands that the parties be altogether paired), that its satisfaction can very seldom be assured. It cannot subsist in its perfection, say some of those who are learned in this warm lore of the heart, betwixt more than two. I am not quite so strict in my terms, perhaps because I have never known so high a fellowship as others. I please my imagination more with a circle of godlike men and women variously related to each other and between whom subsists a lofty intelligence. But I find this law of *one to one* peremptory for conversation,[35] which is the practice and consummation of friendship. Do not mix waters too much.[36] The best mix as ill as good and bad. You shall have very useful and cheering discourse at several times with two several men, but let all three of you come together and you shall not have one new and hearty word. Two may talk and one may hear, but three cannot take part in a conversation of the most sincere and searching sort. In good company there is never such discourse between two, across the table, as takes place when you leave them alone. In good company the individuals merge their egotism into a social soul exactly co-extensive with the several consciousnesses there present. No partialities of friend to friend, no fondnesses of brother to sister, of wife to husband, are there pertinent, but quite otherwise. Only he may then speak who can sail on the common thought of the party, and not poorly limited to his own. Now this convention, which good sense demands, destroys the high freedom of great conversation, which requires an absolute running of two souls into one.

No two men but being left alone with each other

enter into simpler relations. Yet it is affinity that determines *which* two shall converse. Unrelated men give little joy to each other, will never suspect the latent powers of each. We talk sometimes of a great talent for conversation, as if it were a permanent property in some individuals. Conversation is an evanescent relation, — no more.[37] A man is reputed to have thought and eloquence; he cannot, for all that, say a word to his cousin or his uncle. They accuse his silence with as much reason as they would blame the insignificance of a dial in the shade. In the sun it will mark the hour. Among those who enjoy his thought he will regain his tongue.

Friendship requires that rare mean betwixt likeness and unlikeness that piques each with the presence of power and of consent in the other party. Let me be alone to the end of the world, rather than that my friend should overstep, by a word or a look, his real sympathy. I am equally balked by antagonism and by compliance. Let him not cease an instant to be himself. The only joy I have in his being mine, is that the *not mine* is *mine*. I hate, where I looked for a manly futherance or at least a manly resistance, to find a mush of concession.[38] Better be a nettle in the side of your friend than his echo. The condition which high friendship demands is ability to do without it. That high office requires great and sublime parts. There must be very two, before there can be very one. Let it be an alliance of two large, formidable natures, mutually beheld, mutually feared, before yet they recognize the deep identity which, beneath these disparities, unites them.

He only is fit for this society who is magnanimous; who is sure that greatness and goodness are always economy; who is not swift to intermeddle with his fortunes. Let him not intermeddle with this. Leave to the diamond its ages to grow, nor expect to accelerate the births of the eternal. Friendship demands a religious treatment. We talk of choosing our friends, but friends are self-elected. Reverence is a great part of it. Treat your friend as a spectacle. Of course he has merits that are not yours,[39] and that you cannot honor if you must needs hold him close to your person. Stand aside; give those merits room; let them mount and expand. Are you the friend of your friend's buttons,[40] or of his thought? To a great heart he will still be a stranger in a thousand particulars, that he may come near in the holiest ground. Leave it to girls and boys to regard a friend as property, and to suck a short and all-confounding pleasure, instead of the noblest benefit.[41]

Let us buy our entrance to this guild by a long probation. Why should we desecrate noble and beautiful souls by intruding on them? Why insist on rash personal relations with your friend?[42] Why go to his house, or know his mother and brother and sisters? Why be visited by him at your own? Are these things material to our covenant? Leave this touching and clawing. Let him be to me a spirit. A message, a thought, a sincerity, a glance from him, I want, but not news, nor pottage. I can get politics and chat and neighborly conveniences from cheaper companions. Should not the society of my friend be to me poetic, pure, universal and great as nature itself? Ought I to feel that our tie is profane in comparison with yonder bar of cloud that sleeps on the horizon, or that clump of waving grass that divides the brook? Let us not vilify, but raise it to that standard. That great defying eye, that scornful beauty of his mien and action, do not pique yourself on reducing, but rather fortify and enchance. Worship his superiorities; wish him not less by a thought, but hoard and tell them all. Guard him as thy counterpart. Let him be to thee for ever a sort of beautiful enemy,[43] untamable, devoutly revered, and not a trivial conveniency to be soon outgrown and cast aside. The hues of the opal, the light of the diamond, are not to be seen if the eye is too near. To my friend I write a letter and from him I receive a letter.[44] That seems to you a little. It suffices me. It is a spiritual gift, worthy of him to give and of me to receive. It profanes nobody. In these warm lines the heart will trust itself, as it will not to the tongue, and pour out the prophecy of a godlier existence than all the annals of heroism have yet made good.

Respect so far the holy laws of this fellowship as not to prejudice its perfect flower by your impatience for its opening. We must be our own before we can be another's. There is at least this satisfaction in crime, according to the Latin proverb; — you can speak to your accomplice on even terms. *Crimen quos inquinat, æquat.*[45] To those whom we admire and love, at first we cannot. Yet the least defect of self-possession vitiates, in my judgment, the entire relation. There can never be deep peace between two spirits, never mutual respect, until in their dialogue each stands for the whole world.

What is so great as friendship, let us carry with what grandeur of spirit we can. Let us be silent,[46] — so we may hear the whisper of the gods. Let us not interfere. Who set you to cast about what you should say to the select souls, or how to say anything to such ? No matter how ingenious, no matter how graceful and bland.

There are innumerable degrees of folly and wisdom, and for you to say aught is to be frivolous. Wait, and thy heart shall speak. Wait until the necessary and everlasting overpowers you, until day and night avail themselves of your lips. The only reward of virtue is virtue; the only way to have a friend is to be one. You shall not come nearer a man by getting into his house. If unlike, his soul only flees the faster from you, and you shall never catch a true glance of his eye. We see the noble afar off and they repel us; why should we intrude? Late, — very late, — we perceive that no arrangements,[47] no introductions, no consuetudes or habits of society would be of any avail to establish us in such relations with them as we desire, — but solely the uprise of nature in us to the same degree it is in them; then shall we meet as water with water; and if we should not meet them then, we shall not want them, for we are already they. In the last analysis, love is only the reflection of a man's own worthiness from other men. Men have sometimes exchanged names with their friends, as if they would signify that in their friend each loved his own soul.

The higher the style we demand of friendship, of course the less easy to establish it with flesh and blood. We walk alone in the world. Friends such as we desire are dreams and fables. But a sublime hope cheers ever the faithful heart, that elsewhere, in other regions of the universal power, souls are now acting, enduring and daring, which can love us and which we can love. We may congratulate ourselves that the period of nonage, of follies, of blunders and of shame, is passed in solitude, and when we are finished men we shall grasp heroic hands in heroic hands.[48] Only be admonished by what you already see, not to strike leagues of friendship with cheap persons, where no friendship can be. Our impatience betrays us into rash and foolish alliances which no god attends. By persisting in your path, though you forfeit the little you gain the great. You demonstrate yourself, so as to put yourself out of the reach of false relations, and you draw to you the first-born of the world, — those rare pilgrims whereof only one or two wander in nature at once, and before whom the vulgar great show as spectres and shadows merely.

It is foolish to be afraid of making our ties too spiritual, as if so we could lose any genuine love. Whatever correction of our popular views we make from insight, nature will be sure to bear us out in, and though it seem to rob us of some joy, will repay us with a greater. Let us feel if we will the absolute insulation of man.[49] We are sure that we have all in us. We go to Europe, or we pursue persons, or we read books, in the instinctive faith that these will call it out and reveal us to ourselves. Beggars all. The persons are such as we; the Europe, an old faded garment of dead persons; the books, their ghosts. Let us drop this idolatry. Let us give over this mendicancy. Let us even bid our dearest friends farewell, and defy them, saying, 'Who are you? Unhand me: I will be dependent no more.' Ah! seest thou not, O brother, that thus we part only to meet again on a higher platform, and only be more each other's because we are more our own? A friend is Janus-faced; he looks to the past and the future. He is the child of all my foregoing hours, the prophet of those to come, and the harbinger of a greater friend.

I do then with my friends as I do with my books. I would have them where I can find them, but I seldom use them. We must have society on our own terms and admit or exclude it on the slightest cause. I cannot afford to speak much with my friend.[50] If he is great he makes me so great that I cannot descend to converse. In the great days, presentiments hover before me in the firmament. I ought then to dedicate myself to them. I go in that I may seize them, I go out that I may seize them. I fear only that I may lose them receding into the sky in which now they are only a patch of brighter light. Then, though I prize my friends, I cannot afford to talk with them and study their visions, lest I lose my own. It would indeed give me a certain household joy to quit this lofty seeking, this spiritual astronomy or search of stars, and come down to warm sympathies with you; but then I know well I shall mourn always the vanishing of my mighty gods. It is true, next week I shall have languid moods, when I can well afford to occupy myself with foreign objects; then I shall regret the lost literature of your mind, and wish you were by my side again. But if you come, perhaps you will fill my mind only with new visions; not with yourself but with your lustres, and I shall not be able any more than now to converse with you. So I will owe to my friends this evanescent intercourse. I will receive from them not what they have but what they are. They shall give me that which properly they cannot give, but which emanates from them. But they shall not hold me by any relations less subtile and pure. We will meet as though we met not, and part as though we parted not.

It has seemed to me lately more possible than I knew, to carry a friendship greatly, on one side, without due correspondence on the other. Why should I cumber myself with regrets that the receiver is not capacious? It never troubles the sun that some of his rays fall wide and vain into ungrateful space, and only a small part on the reflecting planet. Let your greatness educate the crude and cold companion. If he is unequal, he will presently pass away; but thou art enlarged by thy own shining, and no longer a mate for frogs and worms, dost soar and burn with the gods of the empyrean. It is thought a disgrace to love unrequited. But the great will see that true love cannot be unrequited.[51] True love transcends the unworthy object and dwells and broods on the eternal, and when the poor interposed mask crumbles, it is not sad, but feels rid of so much earth and feels its independency the surer. Yet these things may hardly be said without a sort of treachery to the relation. The essence of friendship is entireness, a total magnanimity and trust. It must not surmise or provide for infirmity. It treats its object as a god, that it may deify both.

NOTES

COMPENSATION

Doctor Edward Emerson notes that it is not certain that this essay was originally given in lecture form, as were so many others. The Centenary Edition also calls attention to the early date at which this theme is treated in Emerson's *Journal* and in the *Poems* (1834). "During the days of his ministry, he wrote thus in his Journal: —

'CHARDON ST., June 29, 1831.

' Is not the law of Compensation perfect? It holds, as far as we can see, different gifts to different individuals, but with a mortgage of responsibility on every one. "The gods sell all things." — Well, old man, hast got no farther? Why, this was taught thee months and years ago. It was writ on the autumn leaves at Roxbury in keep-school days — it sounded in the blind man's ear at Cambridge. And all the joy and all the sorrow since have added nothing to thy wooden book. I can't help it. Heraclitus, grown old, complains that all resolved itself into identity. . . . And I have nothing charactered in my brain that outlives this word Compensation.'"

NOTE 1. Mr. Emerson loved to place a motto at the head of his chapter. Dr. Holmes suggested that the hereditary use of a text before a discourse survived thus in him. *C. E.* [1]

NOTE 2. The phrase is an example of the startling way in which truth that nobody ought to question can be put by an Emerson. For an equally unconventional treatment of the same idea, the student should compare Robert Browning's *Instans Tyrannus:* —

> " Did I say ' without friend ' ?
> Say rather, from marge to blue marge
> The whole sky grew his targe
> With the sun's self for visible boss,
> While an Arm ran across
> Which the earth heaved beneath like a breast
> Where the wretch was safe prest!
> Do you see? Just my vengeance complete,
> The man sprang to his feet,
> Stood erect, caught at God's skirts, and prayed!
> — So, *I* was afraid ! "

[1] Centenary Edition of Emerson's Works. Houghton, Mifflin and Co., 1904.

NOTE 3. This sentence is illustrative not only of Emerson's philosophy but of his characteristic rhetoric. The reader is likely to overemphasize the first clause at the expense of the second, to forget that if evil seemed ultimately unreal to Emerson, so did time appear to him a human limitation. Eternal justice is now or never. The terms are not badness, success, and justice only, but being, appearing, and time as implied by them. The underlying thought is not only that of the Platonic dialogues, but of the New Testament, John XVII, 3: "And this is life eternal, that they might *know* thee the only true God, and Jesus Christ, whom thou hast sent." To one who knows virtue, the "immense concession" is indeed a fallacy.

NOTE 4. This is a favorite thought with Emerson. Compare the famous sentence from *Pensées de Pascal*, Art. XVI, iii: "Le cœur a ses raisons, que la raison ne connait pas." Pascal was a favorite author with Emerson, who as a young man carried a copy of the *Pensées* in his pocket.

NOTE 5. This is a reference to *Spiritual Laws*.

NOTE 6. The thought of this paragraph is far from simple. It takes into account the things which in nature are undoubtedly dual and also the tendency of the mind to associate things in pairs until finally the duality becomes merely verbal. The same method is used by the Platonic Socrates in conducting his dialectic. His victim does not clearly see that some things may have more than one opposite. Besides upper and under, for example, there is sidelong. The next paragraph is clearly an exaggeration of instances into law.

NOTE 7. The theory that genius is abnormal has been elaborately worked out by the Italian Lombroso in *The Man of Genius*. Dryden, in *Absalom and Achitophel*, Pt. 1, l. 163, has, —

> "Great wits are sure to madness near allied,
> And thin partitions do their bounds divide."

NOTE 8. See John I, 7.

NOTE 9. An instance of Emerson's precise use of words. "Continuous means unbroken, and is passive; incessant means unceasing, and is active." *Cent. Dict.*

NOTE 10. The close of this passage illustrates the way in which Emerson used Bible phrases to round out his thought or to give familiar point to his distinctions.

NOTE 11. This precise combination of words thus far eludes search. The sentiment is found in Cicero, Lucretius, Burke, Blackstone, and others, but as a quotation it refuses to give up its secret.

NOTE 12. This passage is not to be interpreted literally of course. It reflects Emerson's wide reading and independent use of what he had read in science and philosophy. The influence of the monad theory of Leibnitz is evident as well as that of the evolutionary thought at that time in the air. Darwin's *Origin of Species* did not appear until 1850.

NOTE 13. From a lost play of Sophocles.

NOTE 14. The meaning of *to truck* is to barter or exchange; its origin is unknown. It is used in Hakluyt's *Voyages*. *Higgle* is a form of huckster and means to bend over merchandise for the purpose of selling it. The word is used by Crabbe and by Sterne, and Burke has "truck and huckster." Both words occur in the colloquial speech of New England.

NOTE 15. Horace, *Epistles*, I, 10, "Naturam expellas furca, tamen usque recurret."

NOTE 16. This word is seldom used with a negative dependent clause.

> "Brags of his substance, not of ornament."
>> *Romeo and Juliet*, II, vi.

But the brag is on his lips.

> "Beauty is Nature's brag."
>> Milton, *Comus*, I, 745.

NOTE 17. St. Augustine's *Confessions*, Bk. I.

NOTE 18. From the *Prometheus* of Æschylus.

NOTE 19. Punitive; pertaining to or serving as punishment.

NOTE 20. Inhabitants of an island, Thasus, in the Ægean Sea off the coast of Thrace. It is mentioned by Virgil, Livy, Pliny, Statius, and others. This story of Theagenes is found in *Pausanias*, Bk. VI, ii, 11. The rest of the story is that the relatives of the victim brought suit against the statue. This custom of keeping out natural justice by law is treated by E. B. Tylor, *Primitive Culture*, Vol. I, pp. 286–7. The old English law declared forfeit such inanimate objects as had caused the death of any one, and ordered them to be sold for the poor.

NOTE 21. The title of a comedy by Ben Jonson, played in 1616, printed in 1631. The name of the "less devil" is Pug.

NOTE 22. "A clew or cop of thread, twine, or yarn." *Cent. Dict.* In the effort to make his meaning clear, Emerson was casting about among the stores of figure with which his experience, his reading, and his sympathy familiarized him. The thread-ball has taken its place in literature now as one of the quaint devices employed by Henrik Ibsen to present the close of Peer Gynt's career:—

PEER

What is this, like children's weeping?
Weeping, but half-way to song. —
Thread-balls at my feet are rolling! —
(*Kicking at them*)

THE THREAD-BALLS (*on the ground*)

We are thoughts;
thou shouldst have thought us; —
feet to run on
thou shouldst have given us !

PEER (*going roundabout*)

I have given life to *one;* —
't was a bungled, crook-legged thing!

THE THREAD-BALLS

We should have soared up
like clangorous voices, —
and here we must trundle
as grey-yarn thread-balls.

In a letter written about 1845 Emerson says: "It is strange how people act on me. I am not a pith-ball nor raw silk, yet to human electricity is no piece of humanity so sensible."

NOTE 23. The political philosophy of Burke is very congenial to that of Emerson. The essays are full of reminiscence of Burke's wise sayings and magnanimous politics. Yet I fail to find these words in Burke's writings.

NOTE 24. "Herodotus tells that Fortune had so favored Polycrates, the tyrant of Samos, that his friend Amasis, king of Egypt, sent him word that to ward off the fate sure to follow unbroken prosperity, he ought to sacrifice whatever he valued most. Struck by this counsel, Polycrates cast into the sea his emerald ring. Next day it returned to him in the stomach of a fish sent as a present. Amasis at once broke off the alliance, foreseeing in this event the impending doom of Polycrates. Revolt of his subjects, and civil and foreign wars followed, and not long after the tyrant was lured out of his domain by the satrap of Sardis and crucified." *C. E.*

NOTE 25. A rhyming formula from the Latin laws of William the Conqueror (*hlot et scot*). The general meaning is a contribution laid on subjects according to their ability.

"I have paid scot and lot there any time these eighteen years."
        Ben Jonson, *Every Man in His Humor*, III, 3.

NOTE 26. See the account of the manna, Exodus XVI, 20.

NOTE 27. An obsolete form of " ledger."

NOTE 28. See Wordsworth's Sonnet, *Near Dover*, 1802.

NOTE 29. This sentiment expresses Emerson's extreme individualism and is curiously worded into paradox. "Voluntarily bereaving" and "traversing" are used to vindicate cause and effect, or separate stages of the mob's behavior. Traversing is used in the sense of destroying or contradicting, not in its more common one, of passing over.

NOTE 30. "This passage, as written in the Journal, March 19, 1839, is perhaps more fresh and vigorous: —

"'Such is my confidence in the compensations of nature, that I no longer wish to find silver dollars in the road, nor to have the best of the bargain in my dealings with people, nor that my property should be increased, knowing that all such gains are apparent and not real; for they pay their sure tax. But the perception that it is not desirable to find the dollar I enjoy without any alloy. This is an abiding good: this is so much accession of Godhead.'" *C. E.*

NOTE 31. Naturally the suggestion is by contrary to the question of Cain, "Am I my brother's keeper?" Genesis IV, 9.

NOTE 32. This is very characteristic of the spiritual intrepidity of Emerson's habit of mind. The assertion is almost stern in its emphasis. The use of "whole" is one that Carlyle shared with him and that is somewhat misleading. It is employed generally, for all; not particularly or precisely, as an equivalent for perfect or complete. The student should read Holmes's poem, *The Chambered Nautilus*, two stanzas of which are, —

> "Year after year beheld the silent toil
>   That spread his lustrous coil;
>   Still, as the spiral grew,
> He left the past year's dwelling for the new,
> Stole with soft step its shining archway through,
>   Built up its idle door,
> Stretched in his last-found home, and knew the old no more.

> "Build thee more stately mansions, O my soul,
>   As the swift seasons roll !
>   Leave thy low-vaulted past !
> Let each new temple, nobler than the last,
> Shut thee from heaven with a dome more vast,
>   Till thou at length art free,
> Leaving thine outgrown shell by life's unresting sea ! "

A much more commonplace expression of the duty thus described is to be found in Longfellow's *Excelsior*. The influence of repeated choice of the better on the soul is one of the doctrines taught by Plato in dialectic and in myth. See *The Symposium*, and *Phædrus*. The superiority of the soul to the body is taught in the last book of *The Laws*. By far the most interesting parallel for the suggestion of this passage is to be found in Edmund Spenser's *An Hymne In Honour of Beautie*, five stanzas of which Emerson has placed under the title *Beauty* in *Parnassus*. The first stanza of his selection reads: —

> "So every spirit, as it is most pure,
>   And hath in it the more of heavenly light,
>   So it the fairer body doth procure
>   To habit in, and is more fairly dight
>   With cheerful grace and amiable sight;
>   For of the Soul the body form doth take;
>   For Soul is form, and doth the body make."

A careful comparison of the entire poem with this part of the essay will repay the student.

NOTE 33. See *Give All to Love* : —

> " When half-gods go
>   The gods arrive."

NOTE 34. "An East Indian fig-tree, remarkable for the area which individual trees cover through the development of roots from the branches, which descend to the ground and become trunks for the support and nourishment of the extending crown. . . . As in some other tropical species of the genus, the seeds rarely germinate in the ground, but usually in the crown of palms or other trees, where they have been deposited by birds. Roots are sent down to the ground, and they embrace and finally kill the nurse-palm." *Cent. Dict.* This account seems to raise the question whether Emerson was seriously occupied with the natural history of the banian, or whether he did not use the word in the ornamental way so frequent with Milton, with his friend Carlyle, and at present with Kipling. As to the office he assigns to the tree of his imagination, may he not have been influenced by the mustard of the Bible? See Luke XIII, 18–19: "Then said he, Unto what is the kingdom of God like? and whereunto shall I resemble it?

"It is like a grain of mustard seed, which a man took and cast into his garden; and it grew, and waxed a great tree; and the fowls of the air lodged in the branches of it."

EXPERIENCE

This Essay is one of the number published under the title "Second Series." Part of the account given of the series by Doctor Emerson in the Centenary Edition is here presented: —

This second book of Essays followed the first by a three years' interval, allowing time for the rehearsal of the lectures, or rather the trial of them on assemblages of men and women in country villages, and before more cultivated, if not more critical, audiences in the city. During that time the matter was often rearranged and extended, and always severely pruned. The book was published by James Munroe & Co., of Boston, in 1844. The papers of the time show that it was better received than either of its predecessors. The Rev. Dr. Hedge, writing in the *Christian Examiner*, praising the *Essays*, though troubled at some expressions with regard to Jesus, went so far as to say that they "were destined to carry far into coming time their lofty cheer and spirit-stirring notes of courage and hope." Chapman, the English publisher, had written to Mr. Emerson asking him to send some work not yet published, for which he would try to get and maintain copyright, and allow half profits to the author. So the book appeared in America and England about the same time.

Carlyle wrote in November: "Your English volume of *Essays*, as Chapman probably informs you by this Post, was advertised yesterday, 'with a Preface from me.' That is hardly accurate — that latter clause. My 'Preface' consists only of a certificate that the Book is correctly printed, and sent forth by a

Publisher of your appointment, whom therefore all readers of yours ought to regard accordingly. Nothing more. There proves, I believe, no visible real vestige of a copyright obtainable here. . . . I will say already of it, It is a *sermon* to me, as all your other deliberate utterances are; a real *word*, which I feel to be such, — alas, almost or altogether the one such, in a world all full of jargons, hearsays, echoes, and vain noises, which cannot pass with me for *words*. This is a praise far beyond any 'literary' one; literary praises are not worth repeating in comparison. For the rest, I have to object still (what you will call objecting against the Law of Nature) that we find you a Speaker indeed, but as it were a *Soliloquizer* on the eternal mountain-tops only, in vast solitudes where men and their affairs lie all hushed in a very dim remoteness; and only *the man* and the stars and the earth are visible, — whom, so fine a fellow seems he, we could perpetually punch into, and say, 'Why won't you come and help us then? We have terrible need of one man like you down among us! It is cold and vacant up there; nothing paintable but rainbows and emotions; come down, and you shall do life-pictures, passions, facts, — which *transcend* all thought, and leave it stuttering and stammering!' To which he answers that he won't, can't, and does n't want to (as the Cockneys have it); and so I leave him, and say, 'You Western Gymnosophist! Well, we can afford one man for that too. But — !' — By the bye, I ought to say, the sentences are very *brief;* and did not, in my *sheet* reading, always entirely cohere for me. Pure genuine Saxon; strong and simple; of a clearness, of a beauty — But they did not, sometimes, rightly stick to their foregoers and their followers; the paragraph not as a beaten *ingot,* but as a beautiful square *bag of duck-shot* held together by canvas! I will try them again, with the Book deliberately before me. There are also one or two utterances about 'Jesus,' 'immortality,' and so forth, which will produce wide-eyes here and there. I do not say it was wrong to utter them; a man obeys his own Dæmon in these cases as his supreme law."

The characteristic reply of Emerson is as follows:—

December, 1844.

My knowledge of the defects of these things I write is all but sufficient to hinder me from writing at all. I am only a sort of lieutenant here in a deplorable absence of captains, and write the laws ill as thinking it a better homage than universal silence. You Londoners know little of the dignities and duties of country lyceums. But of what you say now and heretofore respecting the remoteness of my writing and thinking from real life, though I hear substantially the same criticism made by my countrymen, I do not know what it means. If I can at any time express the law and the ideal right, that should satisfy me without measuring the divergence from it of the last act of Congress. And though I sometimes accept a popular call, and preach on Temperance or the Abolition of Slavery, as lately on the 1st of August, I am sure to feel, before I have done with it, what an intrusion it is into another sphere, and so much loss of virtue in my own.

A part of Doctor Emerson's account of the essay on *Experience* is:—

"This essay was written at one of the critical epochs of Mr. Emerson's life. 'The Angel troubled the pool.' The old and the new were contending in him. His growth was not without pain. He bore 'the yoke of conscience masterful,' and this inheritance he fortunately could not shake off. But his sudden intellectual growth possibly made the yoke gall at times. He had cut loose from tradition and experienced the difficulties attendant on trying to live only according to each day's oracle. Life became experimental, and manifold experiments were suggested in that period of spiritual and social upheaval. He was severely tried in these years. In many places in his journals he gratefully recognizes his debt to the Puritan tradition of a virtuous ancestry and their inherited impulse. This carried him through the whirlpools or sloughs in which he saw many of the sons of the morning of that day sink. Grief came to him in heavy form — the death of his first-born child, of wonderful promise and charm. In this essay, which presents moods and aspects in an unusual degree of contrast, and of which he says, 'I have set my heart on honesty in this chapter,' he speaks of the speedy healing of this wound and his grieving at the slightness of the scar left. In his desire for utter freedom from hypocrisy, he makes an overstrong statement. But his health and faith and great power of detachment shortened and soothed his suffering.

"He passed through this epoch of unrest bravely, and came soon into that serene strength and happiness which remained for life.

"I find no record of this essay delivered as a lecture. A very small part of it was taken from *Being and Seeming* in the course on 'Human Culture' in 1837–38.

"The motto would seem to have been written after the essay. The 'lords of life' are named a little more fully in a paragraph near its closing portion. This image of a passing of demigods in procession pleased Emerson's fancy, and he often used it. The last lines show him aware of the unrestful character of the piece, and in sure faith of a harmonious solution of the difficulties on a better day.

> 'The dear, dangerous lords that rule our life'

are spoken of in his poem *Musketaquid*."

NOTE 1. "Rhea having accompanied with Saturn by stealth, the Sun found them out, and pronounced a solemn curse against her, containing that she should not be delivered in any month or year; but Hermes afterwards making his court to the goddess, obtained her favor, in requital of which he went and played at dice with the Moon and won of her the seventieth part from each day, and out of all these made five new days, which he added to the three hundred and sixty other days of the year, and these the Egyptians . . . observe as the birthdays of their gods. Upon the first of these, as they say, Osiris was born, and a voice came into the world with him, saying, 'The Lord of all things is now born.'" — Plutarch's *Morals*, "Of Isis and Osiris." *C. E.*

NOTE 2. This use of the word "reference" is unexpected to the conventional reader. Its etymology and suggestion justify the use, however. Possibly Emerson had in mind the circumlocution offices where inquiry is referred from one point to another, as well as the habit of mind which shirks responsibility and refuses to be authoritative or ultimate. His scorn of apology and evasion is characteristic.

NOTE 3. The first, Girolamo Tiraboschi, was a distinguished Italian professor of literature, born at Bergamo, Italy, 1731, died near Modena, 1794: the second, Thomas Warton, 1728–1790, a poet, critic, and historian of English literature; the third, Karl Wilhelm Friedrich von Schlegel, 1772–1829, or more probably, his brother, August Wilhelm von Schlegel, 1767–1845. The works by which they are respectively best known are *Geschichte der alten und neuen Literatur* (Friedrich), and translations from Shakespeare and Calderon (August).

NOTE 4. According to Hesiod, a daughter of Eris; according to Homer, of Zeus. An ancient Greek divinity who led both gods and men to rash and inconsiderate actions and to suffering. By Zeus she was hurled from Olympus and banished forever from the abodes of the gods. In the tragic writers, she appears as the avenger of evil deeds, inflicting just punishments upon offenders and their posterity. Here her character is almost the same as that of Nemesis and Erinnys. She is said by competent critics to be the most prominent in the dramas of Æschylus and least so in those of Euripides, where the idea of justice is more fully developed. In one of his letters to his wife Emerson expresses the thought in a different way: "We fat on our failures and by our dumbness we speak."

NOTE 5. Doctor Emerson says: "The source of these lines cannot be found."

NOTE 6. Boscovich, Ruggiero Giuseppe, 1711–1787. An Italian Jesuit, mathematician, astronomer, and physicist. Two of his works are *Theoria philosophiae naturalis*, and *De maculis solaribus*.

NOTE 7. This event occurred January 27, 1842, and was for the time an overwhelming blow which first seemed to deprive the father of expression and then was the inspiration of the *Threnody*, Emerson's poem that ranks with *Lycidas* and *O Captain! My Captain!* The bereaved Emerson wrote to a friend: "The innocent and beautiful should not be sourly and gloomily lamented, but with music and fragrant thoughts and sportive recollections. Alas! I chiefly grieve that I cannot grieve. Dear boy, too precious and unique a creation to be huddled aside into the waste and prodigality of things; yet his image, so gentle, so rich in hopes, blends easily with every happy moment, every fair remembrance, every cherished friendship, of my life. Calm and wise, calmly and wisely happy, the beautiful Creative Power looked out from him, and spoke of anything but chaos and interruption. What was the moral of sun and moon, of roses and acorns, that was the moral of the sweet boy's life; softened only and humanized by blue eyes and infant eloquence."

In 1844 he wrote in a letter to Miss Fuller: "When last Saturday night, Lidian (Mrs. Emerson) said, 'It is two years to-day,' I only heard the bell-stroke again. I have had no experience, no progress to put me into better intelligence with my calamity than when it was new. . . . But the inarticulateness of the Supreme Power, how can we insensate hearers, perceivers, and thinkers ever reconcile ourselves unto? It deals all too lightly with us low-levelled and weaponed men. Does the Power labor as men do with the impossibility of perfect application, that always the hurt is of one kind and the compensation of another? My divine temple, which all angels seemed to love to rebuild, and which was shattered in a night, I can never rebuild: and is the facility of entertainment from thought, or friendship, or affairs an amends? Rather it seems like a cup of Somnus or of Momus. Yet the nature of things, against all appearances and specialities whatever, assures us of eternal benefit. But these affirmations are tacit and secular; if spoken, they have a hollow and canting sound. And thus all our being, dear friend, is evermore adjourned. Patience, and patience, and patience! I will try, since you ask it, to copy my rude dirges to my darling, and send them to you." From James Elliot Cabot's *A Memoir of Ralph Waldo Emerson*, Vol. II, p. 483.

NOTE 8. See Southey's *The Curse of Kehama*, II, *The Curse*, 14 ff.: —

> " I charm thy life
> From the weapons of strife,
> From stone and from wood,
> From fire and from flood,
> From the serpent's tooth,
> And the beasts of blood :
> From sickness I charm thee ,
> And time shall not harm thee ;
> But Earth which is mine,
> Its fruits shall deny thee ;
> And water shall hear me,
> And know thee and fly thee ;
> And the winds shall not touch thee
> When they pass by thee,
> And the dews shall not wet thee

When they fall nigh thee;
And thou shalt seek Death
To release thee in vain!
Thou shalt live in thy pain,
While Kehama shall reign,
With a fire in thy heart,
And a fire in thy brain;
And Sleep shall obey me
And visit thee never;
And the Curse shall be on thee
For ever and ever."

NOTE 9. In full, Santa Maria de Belem do Grão Pará. The seaport capital of Pará, Brazil, the centre of the river trade of the Amazon system, exporting rubber, cacao, copaiba balsam, hides, nuts, etc. Founded in 1615. An elaborately decorative designation for storm coats. Possibly illustrative of Emerson's stately manners and ceremonious address.

NOTE 10. Shelley's *Adonais*, LII, reads as follows:—

"The one remains, the many change and pass:
Heaven's light forever shines, earth's shadows fly;
Life, like a dome of many-colored glass,
Stains the white radiance of eternity,
Until Death tramples it to fragments. — Die,
If thou wouldst be with that which thou dost seek!
Follow where all is fled! Rome's azure sky,
Flowers, ruins, statues, music, words are weak
The glory they transfuse with fitting truth to speak."

NOTE 11. The reference is to Doctor Gamaliel Bradford. *C. E.*

NOTE 12. "The soul is its own witness." — *Laws of Menu*, printed among the "Ethnical Scriptures" in the *Dial. C. E.*

NOTE 13. The vigorous phrasing in this passage is reminiscent of Milton, *Comus*, l. 77, "To roll with pleasure in a sensual sty." The later reference to the intervention of intellect for the help of the struggler also suggests the sentiments of the Elder Brother in the same poem:—

" Virtue could see to do what Virtue would
By her own radiant light, though sun and moon
Were in the flat sea sunk."

NOTE 14. See Milton, *Paradise Lost*, Bk. IV, 73 ff.:—

"Which way shall I fly
Infinite wrath, and infinite despair?
Which way I fly is hell; myself am hell;
And, in the lowest deep, a lower deep,
Still threatening to devour me, opens wide,
To which the hell I suffer seems a heaven."

NOTE 15. *Nevertheless it moves.* The now famous words of Galileo after his retraction before the Inquisition of the heresy of teaching that the earth was not stationary but moved around the sun.

NOTE 16. The reference is to Elizabeth or Bettina von Arnim, 1785–1850, a German writer principally noted for her correspondence with Goethe. Her acquaintance with him lasted from 1807 to 1811. After Goethe's death she published an extensive correspondence for which, however, she could never produce the originals of the letters. It is said of her that "her vanity, caprice, mendacity, and utter want of principle can only be excused on the supposition of her virtual irresponsibility for her actions. She possessed a brilliant fancy, and her remarks occasionally display great penetration; her conversational powers are described as marvellous." This accounts for Emerson's "even" in connection with her name.

NOTE 17. Sentiments like these have been objected to on the ground that Emerson really did not properly understand or value art, as would appear from the latter part of his essay on *Shakespeare* and from the one on *Art*. Such statements are cited as these: "Shall I now add that the whole extant product of the plastic arts has herein its highest value, as *history;* as a stroke drawn in the portrait of that fate, perfect and beautiful, according to whose ordinations all beings advance to their beatitude?" . . . "There is higher work for Art than the arts. They are abortive births of an imperfect or vitiated instinct." . . . "Would it not be better to begin higher up, — to serve the ideal before they eat and drink; to serve the ideal in eating and drinking, in drawing the breath, and in the functions of life? Beauty must come back to the useful arts, and the distinction between the fine and the useful arts be forgotten." The upholders of art for art's sake and the globe-trotters in search of culture by Baedeker have made short work of these declarations, but time is justifying the homing instinct of Emerson. His doctrine touches Plato and his Greeks in one direction and reaches out to Whistler, in his *Ten O'clock* (London, February 10, 1885), and the art theories of functional psychologists, as represented by Henry Sturt in *Art and Personality* published with other essays under the title *Personal Idealism* (Macmillan Co.). He says in one place: "Primarily the person for whom art is valuable is the artist himself. If any one asked, For whom was Shakespeare's artistic life a good? the answer would be: In the first place, for Shakespeare. And this is not an exceptional rule for exceptional men, but merely the common rule for the valuation of human life. We cannot say of the rank and file of humanity that A's life is valuable because it furthers the lives of B, C, and D, and so on. Nor can we say it of the chiefs."

NOTE 18. Emerson's self-respecting recognition of the exceptional character of his own social relations is touched on here. It appears again in his poem of the *Visit*, and in a letter to Margaret Fuller, he says: "Ice has its uses, when deception is not thought of and we are not looking for bread. Being made by chemistry and not by cooks, its composition is unerring, and it has a universal value, as ice, not as glass or gelatine. . . . Therefore, my friend, treat me always as a mute, not ungrateful though now incommunicable."

Note 19. Henry Sturt in the essay already cited writes: "As causes of ordinary bad taste we may enumerate Fossilism, that is, a stupid adherence to artistic forms that may have been very well in their day, but should now be abandoned for others more adequate; Vuglarity, which leads us to prefer forms conducive to self-glorification; Crankiness, or the undue insistence on some element which has only a subordinate value. None of these kinds of bad taste has any special philosophical significance. Their valuation is at bottom the standard valuation stunted or distorted. They have no strength of conviction, no principle to oppose to us."

Note 20. A lime-soda feldspar (labradorite). It is rarely found crystallized, but usually in masses, and these often show a brilliant change of colors; on this account it is sometimes used as an ornamental stone. The finest specimens come from the coast of Labrador, whence the name. *Cent. Dict.*

Note 21. The same idea is expressed in *Compensation:* "Such also is the natural history of calamity" *et seq.* Compare these passages to get the different points of view.

Note 22. Same as "dialectic." The Century Dictionary says, "Dialectic was limited by Aristotle to logic accommodated to the uses of the rhetorician, appealing only to general belief, but not to first principles."

Note 23. Here is meant Brook Farm at West Roxbury, Mass. The Brook Farm Association in 1841 made an experiment in agriculture and education in the interests of plain living and high thinking. The organization broke up in 1847.

Note 24. The Centenary Edition notes this as probably from some of the sayings ascribed to Zoroaster.

Note 25. This passage presents another aspect of the statement in *Compensation:* "Under the primeval despots of Egypt, history honestly confesses that man must have been as free as culture could make him."

Note 26. Cf. —

> "Life is a jest, and all things show it;
> I thought so once, but now I know it."
> *My Own Epitaph*, John Gay.

> "Our revels now are ended. These our actors,
> As I foretold you, were all spirits, and
> Are melted into air, into thin air:
> And like the baseless fabric of this vision,
> The cloud-capp'd towers, the gorgeous palaces,
> The solemn temples, the great globe itself,
> Yea, all which it inherit, shall dissolve,
> And, like this insubstantial pageant faded,
> Leave not a rack behind. We are such stuff
> As dreams are made on; and our little life
> Is rounded with a sleep."
> *The Tempest*, Act IV, Sc. 1.

NOTE 27. This is clearly one of the phases of experience in which the dualism mentioned in *Compensation* appears.

NOTE 28. Earlier in this essay the phrase "perpetual retreating and reference" occurs. The rhetorical and logical relations are interesting.

NOTE 29. What may happen to be in the pot; a meal where no preparation has been made for guests, hence any chance provision.

NOTE 30. Poussin, Nicolas, 1594–1665. A French historical and landscape painter, decorator of the Grande Galerie in the Louvre, favored by Louis XIII. The Deluge and The Rape of the Sabines are two of his pictures.

NOTE 31. Salvator Rosa, 1615(?)–1673, painter, musician, and satirist. The Conspiracy of Catiline, in the Pitti, is considered his masterpiece.

NOTE 32. The Transfiguration, a famous painting by Raphael in the Vatican; The Last Judgment, a great picture by Michelangelo on the end wall above the high altar in the Sistine Chapel; The Last Communion of Saint Jerome, a picture by Domenichino in the Vatican; or possibly the picture by Agostino Carracci of which Domenichino's has been said to be a plagiarism. Carracci's picture is in Bologna.

NOTE 33. A famous art gallery in Florence, founded in the fifteenth century. It is connected with the galleries in the Pitti palace by a covered gallery over the Ponte Vecchio.

NOTE 34. "Molecular force is a force acting between molecules, but insensible at sensible distances." *Cent. Dict.* The force of the word "new" is to be found in the fact that the underlying conception of force in the atomic theory of matter is opposed to the teaching of the ancients, and is not yet demonstratively established in its details and applications. Buffon, Clerk-Maxwell, Lockyer, and Sir William Thomson have all contributed to this philosophy. The recent investigations of radium are extensions of it.

NOTE 35. This is perhaps an instance of Emerson's alert sense of values and distinctions in lines of study not his own. The grammatical use of "strong" applies to the past tense, but Emerson employs the term out of its setting for his own purposes.

NOTE 36. The right by law to the produce of man's intellectual industry and the protection of it from use by others without adequate compensation. The first copyright was the English statute of 1709. International copyright protects an author residing in one country from trespass in such other countries as are parties to the arrangement.

NOTE 37. Cf. Milton's *Areopagitica*: "What is to be thought in general of reading, whatever sort the books be; . . . I deny not but that it is of greatest concernment in the Church and Commonwealth. I have a vigilant eye how books demean themselves as well as men; and thereafter to confine, imprison, and do sharpest justice on them as malefactors; for books are not absolutely dead things, but do contain a progeny of life in them to be as active as that soul was whose progeny they are; nay, they do preserve as in a vial the purest efficacy and extraction of that living intellect that bred them. I know they are as lively, and as vigorously productive, as those fabulous dragons' teeth; and being sown up and down, they may chance to spring up armed men. And yet on the other hand, unless wariness be used, as good almost kill a man as kill a good book: who kills a man kills a reasonable creature, God's image; but he who destroys a good book, kills reason itself, kills the image of God as it were in the eye. Many a man lives a burden to the earth; but a good book is the precious life-blood of a master spirit, imbalmed and treasured up on purpose to a life beyond life."

NOTE 38. The reader naturally expects to find *thy* stint. The use of the demonstrative instead of the personal pronoun illustrates Emerson's characteristic impersonality. Man shall not appropriate even the duty that lies nearest him. He and it are but aspects of the forces and relations treated in *The Over-Soul* and in *Circles*, illustrated by examples in *Representative Men*. The word "stint" is given as obsolete or dialectic in the dictionaries, but it was a favorite device of Emerson's thus to express the external claim of practical obligation. In his *Miscellanies* is, "In the divided or social state, these functions are parcelled out to individuals, each of whom aims to do his stint of the joint work."

NOTE 39. Cf. —

> "His form had not yet lost
> All her original brightness, nor appeared
> Less than Archangel ruined, and th' excess
> Of glory obscured."
>
> Milton, *Paradise Lost*, Bk. I. 591.

also, —

> ":Dark with excessive bright."
>
> Milton, *Paradise Lost*, Bk. III, 380.

also, —

> "He saw; but, blasted with excess of light,
> Closed his eyes in endless night."
>
> Gray, *The Progress of Poesy*, III, 2, l. 4.

NOTE 40. This is a paraphrase of the idea later given in the quotation from Luke xvii, 20.

NOTE 41. This perhaps seems contradictory of Emerson's doctrine of *Self-Reliance* and destructive of the emphasis which in *Compensation* he puts on decision and individual authority, but the contradiction is only apparent. The individual must err in order to learn, he must suffer calamity if he would succeed. The intrepidity to be wrong while one learns to be greatly right is one of the aspects of Emerson's spiritual courage. A passage from Milton is in point: "This I know, that errours in a good government and in a bad are equally almost incident; for what magistrate may not be misinformed, and much the sooner, if liberty of printing be reduced into the power of a few. But to redress willingly and speedily what hath been erred, and in highest authority to esteem a plain advertisement more than others have done a sumptuous pride, is a virtue . . . whereof none can participate but greatest and wisest men."

NOTE 42. A Scottish surgeon and writer on Comparative Anatomy, supposed to have been mainly indebted for his knowledge to the manuscripts of his brother-in-law, John Hunter, which he burned. *C. E.*

NOTE 43. The capital of Arabia, the birthplace of Mohammed, the site of the Kaaba. It is situated in a sandy valley seventy miles from the Red Sea.

NOTE 44. Antigone, in Sophocles's tragedy, reproached by Creon for burying her outlawed brother's body, says, "Nor did I think thy proclamation, since thou art a mortal, of force to outweigh the unwritten and secure laws of the gods, for these are not matters of now and yesterday, but always were, and nŏ man knows whence they came." *C. E.*

NOTE 45. Thales of Miletus, 640–546 B. C., one of the seven wise men of Greece, the earliest of the Ionian natural philosophers. Discoveries in astronomy and geometry are attributed to him as well as a prediction of an eclipse of the sun, May 28, 585 B. C.

NOTE 46. Anaxagoras, 500–428 B. C., a great Greek philosopher, the friend and teacher of Pericles, Thucydides, and Euripides. He was banished from Athens on a charge of impiety.

NOTE 47. Zoroaster — Zarathushtra, the founder of the Perso-Iranian national religion. It is still represented in Persia, Russian Transcaucasia, and India.

NOTE 48. Latinized form of Meng-tse, d. *c.* 289 B. C., one of the most noted expounders of Confucianism.

NOTE 49. This is high and hard doctrine, but it is the teaching of the New Testament that a man must leave wife and children and houses and lands for the kingdom of heaven's sake. Cf. Tennyson in *In Memoriam*, XLVII : —

> "That each, who seems a separate whole,
>   Should move his rounds, and fusing all
>   The skirts of self again, should fall
> Remerging in the general Soul,
>
> "Is faith as vague as all unsweet:
>   Eternal form shall still divide
>   The eternal soul from all beside;
> And I shall know him when we meet:
>
>   ". . . He seeks at least
>
> "Upon the last and sharpest height,
>   Before the spirits fade away,
>   Some landing-place, to clasp and say,
> 'Farewell! we lose ourselves in light.'"

NOTE 50. Denying the obligation to obey the moral law —
the distinction precisely is, against or above the law.

NOTE 51. Hermes, in Greek mythology, son of Zeus and
Maia, herald and messenger of the gods, protector of herdsmen,
god of science, commerce, invention, and the arts of life, patron
of travelers and rogues. Cadmus, son of Agenor, king of
Phenicia and Telephassa, founder of Thebes in Bœotia, and
inventor of the alphabet. Columbus, 1446(?)–1506, sailor,
discoverer, colonizer, student, statesman, Christian. He never
knew that the land he discovered in 1492 was not part of Asia.
Newton, 1642–1727, English mathematician and natural philosopher, author of the *Principia*, member of Parliament,
Warden of the Mint, author of the theory of universal gravitation. Bonaparte, Napoleon I, 1769(?)–1821, Emperor of the
French, whose brilliant career and whose baffling character
served Emerson as the ideal of a man of the world. This list
may be compared with similar devices in Walt Whitman's
rhetoric, in Milton's or in Sir Thomas Browne's. Emerson's
structure has a central point from which the qualities vary to
either extreme. Cf. Milton: "It is no new thing never heard
of before, for a parochial minister, who has his reward, is at
his Hercules pillars in a warm benefice, to be easily inclinable,
if he have nothing else that may rouse up his studies, to finish
his circuit in an English Concordance and a topic folio, the
gatherings and savings of a sober graduateship, a Harmony
and a Catena treading the constant round of certain common
doctrinal heads, attended with their uses, motives, marks, and
means; out of which, as out of an alphabet or Sol fa, by forming
and transforming, joining and disjoining variously, a little
bookcraft and two hours meditation might furnish him unspeakably to the performance of more than a weekly charge
of sermoning: not to reckon up the infinite helps of interliniaries,
breviaries, synopses, and other loitering gear."
Cf. Whitman: —

"Aware of the fresh free giver the flowing Missouri, aware of the mighty
   Niagara.
Aware of the buffalo herds grazing the plains, the hirsute and strong-
   breasted bull,
Of earth, rocks, Fifth-month flowers experienced, stars, rain, snow, my
   amaze,
Having studied the mocking-bird's tones and the flight of the mountain-
   hawk,
And heard at dawn the unrivall'd one, the hermit-thrush from the swamp-
   cedars,
Solitary, singing in the West, I strike up for a New World."

Cf. Sir Thomas Browne: "But certainly false it is, what is
commonly affirmed and believed, that garlic doth hinder the
attraction of the loadstone; which is, notwithstanding, delivered
by grave and worthy writers, by Pliny, Solinus, Ptolemy,

Plutarch, Albertus, Malthiolus, Rescus, Longius, and many more. An effect as strange as that of Homer's *Moly*, and the garlic that Mercury bestowed upon Ulysses."

NOTE 52. A characteristic suggestion of detail associated in Emerson's mind with Newton's use of Kepler's laws.

NOTE 53. John Flaxman, 1755–1826, a famous English sculptor and draftsman. "For pure conceptive faculty, controlled by unerring sense of beauty, we have to think of Pheidias or Raphael before we find his equal," says Symonds, in *Studies of the Greek Poets*. Henry James, in his *Life of Hawthorne*, calls somewhat contemptuous attention to the pleasures derived by members of the Concord society of Emerson's day from bending over Flaxman's "attenuated outlines."

NOTE 54. This list of abstract terms is a doubtful aid to the reader in interpreting the course of Emerson's treatment of Experience. It is certainly a final challenge to the curiosity and ingenuity of the critic to make out their function or their identity as "the lords of life."

NOTE 55. A name for Nemesis, derived, according to some authorities, from Adrastus, the builder of the first temple to Nemesis, by others from the verb διδράσκειν. In this last connection emphasis is put upon the inevitable power of the goddess who spares none. In the Phædrus of Plato, the myth dealing with the truth about the affections and actions of the soul represents it as of composite nature — a pair of winged horses and a charioteer. "And there is a law of the goddess Retribution, that the soul which attains any vision of truth in company with the god is preserved from harm until the next period, and he who always attains is always unharmed. But when she is unable to follow, and fails to behold the vision of truth, and through some ill-hap sinks beneath the double load of forgetfulness and vice, and her feathers fall from her and she drops to earth, then the law ordains that this soul shall in the first generation pass, not into that of any other animal, but only of man." B. Jowett, Tr., *The Dialogues of Plato*, Vol. I.

CHARACTER

The essay on *Character* is in part a lecture of the same title in the course on *The Times*, delivered in Masonic Temple, Boston, 1841–42.

The first motto is part of an unpublished poem, *The Poet*. — The second motto is part of a poem in memory of Edward Bliss Emerson, who died in Porto Rico in 1834. See Centenary Edition. An essay under this title was the concluding lecture of a course given before the Parker Fraternity by Emerson in Boston, 1864–65.

NOTE 1. William Pitt, first Earl of Chatham, 1708–1778. A great orator and statesman of England. He was a Whig and known as the Great Commoner before his elevation to the peerage. He opposed the policy pursued towards the American colonies, but protested against the acknowledgment of their independence.

NOTE 2. The reference is to Thomas Carlyle.

NOTE 3. Mirabeau, Comte de, Gabriel Honoré Riquetti, 1749–1791, the most eloquent orator of the French Revolution. He was President of the Jacobin Club and of the National Assembly.

NOTE 4. The Gracchi, Caius Sempronius, and Tiberius Sempronius, sons of Cornelia, daughter of Scipio Africanus Major. They interested themselves in the agrarian troubles of their time, *c.* 133 B. C. Both were killed in their efforts to carry out their political measures.

NOTE 5. King of Sparta, B. C. 244. Sentenced to death by the ephors in consequence of his efforts for unpopular military and agrarian reform.

NOTE 6. Two famous kings of Sparta bore this name. One, Cleomenes I, expelled Hippias from Athens in 510. Another, Cleomenes III, abolished the ephorate, fought the Achæan League, and was defeated at Sellasia, 221.

NOTE 7. Plutarch, of Chæronea, b. *c.* 46 A. D., a Greek historian, author of *Parallel Lives* of forty-six Greeks and Romans. He was also a moralist. Emerson refers frequently to his works and admired his Platonist habit of thought.

NOTE 8. Sir Philip Sidney, 1554–1586, an English writer and soldier. A gallant and generous man. His principal works are the *Arcadia*, *Astrophel and Stella*, and the *Defence of Poesie*.

NOTE 9. The Earl of Essex, Robert Devereux, second Earl, 1567–1601. He was a favorite of Queen Elizabeth, fell into disfavor, and was executed on charge of treason.

NOTE 10. Sir Walter Raleigh, 1552–1618. An English courtier, soldier, colonizer, and writer. He was a favorite of Elizabeth. He organized colonizing expeditions to Virginia, Trinidad, and Guiana and the Orinoco. After the failure of his venture to Orinoco, he was condemned and executed.

NOTE 11. Schiller, 1759–1805, a famous German poet and writer of history and drama. He was a friend of Goethe and has exerted an almost equally strong influence upon the culture of our time. The Transcendentalists were all deeply interested in Schiller and the group of his contemporaries to whom they had been emphatically directed by Thomas Carlyle in his essays and criticisms of German literature. This collection of names undoubtedly has significance of many kinds, but the value that it has for its sound must not be overlooked. The names are vaguely eminent, but perhaps none the less impressive to the general reader for all that. Several of them are known to the plain person rather by the company they keep with reputations he does know than for their own deserts. They do not illustrate, they stimulate by requiring explanation.

NOTE 12. Burton's *Anatomy of Melancholy* elaborates a

similar idea. Cf. Pt. 1, Sec. 2, Mem. 1, Subs. 2, and Pt. 1, Sec. 3, Mem. 1, Subs. 4.

NOTE 13. The story of Iole is told in the *Trachiniæ* of Sophocles, but the form given to it here is believed by Doctor Edward Emerson to be of his father's invention. See *Č. E.*

NOTE 14. Probably an allusion to Daniel Webster.

NOTE 15. This reiterated emphasis on fact was almost a mannerism of the group of writers and thinkers led by Emerson and Carlyle. The recurrence of the word "fact" is nearly as significant in their expression as is "sense" in the writing inspired by Alexander Pope. The "eternal veracities" are familiar to the reader of Carlyle. Emerson preferred "fact."

NOTE 16. This is another expression of Emerson's objection to "reference" and "retreating" in *Experience*. In *Education*, he writes: . . . "the day of facts is a rock of diamonds; . . . a fact is an Epiphany of God."

NOTE 17. This entire passage is reminiscent of Burke. Compare the analytical and descriptive parts of the *Speech on Conciliation* dealing with the resources of the American colonies.

NOTE 18. Probably a reference to one of the features of mesmerism, so-called from F. A. Mesmer, a German physician, propounder of the doctrine in 1778. He held that influence could be exerted by one person over the will and nervous system of another by virtue of an emanation called animal magnetism. Most of what was taught or practised by Mesmer has been discredited or reaffirmed on more satisfactory scientific grounds by the students of hypnotism, first brought to public notice in 1880. Emerson's allusion is characteristic. He spiritualized phenomena which, familiar as they may have been to Plato, were in his time, as in Emerson's, put to ignoble uses and vulgarized by sensual accompaniments. This characterization, delivered in 1841, published in 1844, as well as the one on *Demonology*, 1838–39, is naturally associated with the treatment of the same theme by Nathaniel Hawthorne in *The House of the Seven Gables* (1851), chapter xiii, "Alice Pyncheon." Significant extracts are: "Now the wizard's grandson, the young Matthew Maule of our story, was popularly supposed to have inherited some of his ancestor's questionable traits. . . . He was fabled, for example, to have a strange power of getting into people's dreams, and regulating matters there according to his own fancy, pretty much like the stage-manager of a theatre. . . . Some said that he could look into people's minds; others that by the marvellous power of this eye, he could draw people into his own mind, or send them, if he pleased, to do errands to his grandfather, in the spiritual world; others again, that it was what is called an Evil Eye, and possessed the valuable faculty of blighting corn, and drying children into mummies with the heartburn. . . . 'There sits Mistress Alice quietly asleep! Now let Matthew Maule try whether she be as proud as the carpenter found her awhile since.' He spoke, and Alice responded, with a soft, subdued, inward acquiescence, and a bending of her form towards him, like the flame of a torch when it indicates a gentle draught of air. He beckoned with his hand, and rising from her chair, — blindly, but undoubtingly, as tending to her sure and inevitable centre, — the proud Alice approached him. He waved her back, and retreating, Alice sank again into her seat. 'She is mine!' said Matthew Maule. 'Mine, by the right of the strongest spirit!'"

In chapter vi of his biography of Cotton Mather, Barrett Wendell deals with the Salem witchcraft. Bearing on this point he says: "At various periods of history epidemics of superstition have appeared, sometimes in madly tragic forms, sometimes, as in modern spiritualism, in grotesquely comic ones. . . . Oracles, magic, witchcraft, animal magnetism, spiritualism, — call the phenomena what you will, — seem to me a fact. Certain phases of it are beginning to be understood under the name of hypnotism. Other phases, after the best study that has been given them, seem to be little else than deliberate fraud and false-hood; but they are fraud and falsehood, if this be all they are, of a specific kind, unchanged for centuries. . . . And some of them are very like what are related in the trials of the Salem witches. So specific is the fraud, if only fraud it be, that it may well be regarded, I think, as a distinct mental, or perhaps rather moral disorder." His explanation of the conditions on evolu-tionary grounds follows, pp. 95–97.

A recent contribution to the subject is *Dissociated Person-ality*, by Doctor Morton Prince.

NOTE 19. The reference is to Leonora, wife of the Marquis d'Ancre, accused of sorcery in the influence she exerted over the queen of Henry IV.

NOTE 20. Seemingly names used by Emerson to illustrate his point vividly.

NOTE 21. See Wordsworth's fine sonnet to his memory. He lived 1743–1803, was a negro slave of rudimentary educa-tion and natural genius as a statesman and commander of men. In 1798, the British treated with him as the real ruler of Haiti. He was subdued by Napoleon and died in prison.

NOTE 22. In the *Song of Myself*, l. 20, Walt Whitman writes:

"Having pried through the strata, analyzed to a hair, counsel'd with doc-tors and calculated close,
I find no sweeter fat than sticks to my own bones."

NOTE 23. This is the appropriate illustration of the general statement made in *Compensation*. "These appearances indi-cate the fact that the universe is represented in every one of its particles."

NOTE 24. Serving as an aid, adjunct, or accessory; subser-vient, auxiliary; supplementary.

NOTE 25. See James ii, 19: "The devils also believe and tremble."

Note 26. This phrase has new significance since the publication of Ibsen's play known in its English translation as *The Doll's House*. Nora's final revolt is in the general line of Emerson's contention for the non-conformity of the soul.

Note 27. Probably Mr. George Ripley, head of the Brook Farm Association, is alluded to here.

Note 28. The use of "fact" here as antithetical to "city still," should be noted.

Note 29. Compare Robert Browning's elaboration of a similar theme in *Balaustion's Adventure* : —

> " Herakles
> Had flung into the presence, frank and free,
> Out from the labor into the repose,
> Ere out again and over head and ears
> I' the heart of labor, all for love of men:
> Making the most o' the minute, that the soul
> And body, strained to height a minute since,
> Might lie relaxed in joy, this breathing space,
> For man's sake more than ever; till the bow,
> Restrung o' the sudden, at first cry for help,
> Should send some unimaginable shaft
> True to the aim and shatteringly through
> The plate-mail of a monster, save man so.
> He slew the pest o' the marish yesterday:
> To-morrow he would bit the flame-breathed stud
> That fed on man's flesh: and this day between —
> Because he held it natural to die,
> And fruitless to lament a thing past cure,
> So, took his fill of food, wine, song, and flowers,
> Till the new labor claimed him soon enough, —
> 'Hate him and justly !'"

Note 30. The Centenary Edition notes this passage in *Prayer* : —

> "When success exalts thy lot
> God for thy virtue lays a plot."

It must be admitted, however, that this is a "hard saying." Nor does it conform to our present doctrine of diffused social sympathy and personal ease and congeniality as its natural expression.

Note 31. That is, at the mercy of an antagonist or enemy; to surrender at discretion is to surrender without terms. This martial phrase has an odd sound on Emerson's tranquil lips, but it represents well the wide range of his interests and the equanimity of his intelligence.

Note 32. This phrase is an excellent example of Emerson's constructive skill exercised in conditions of great rhetorical danger — most writers would have been reminded of Argus-eyed, as undoubtedly was Emerson, and they would have accepted the suggestion while he repulsed it, but made use of it in this admirable one. In *Self-Reliance* occurs "thousand-fold Relief Societies" and "thousand-eyed present." Thus Emerson's rhetoric illustrates his own "centrality" of thought.

Note 33. Patmos, an island of the Ægean Sea from which the Revelation of St. John the Divine is reported to have come. Here he is supposed to have seen the visions of the Apocalypse. Emerson's phrase is enriched by the suggestion of the conventional antithesis between thought and vision.

Note 34. The Reverend Edward Taylor of the Sailors' Bethel in Boston.

Note 35. Messrs. Lane and Wright, two English visitors interested in the transcendental conception of society and desirous of realizing it in some form of community life.

Note 36. This is one of Emerson's most personal confessions. His faith in possible greatness made him quick to give recognition to claims of originality. The letter he wrote to Walt Whitman after reading *Leaves of Grass* is a good example of his attitude. His lifelong championship of Mr. Alcott is another. So anxious was he lest some expression of genius should escape him that he seemed over-credulous and uncritical to observers of less ardent hope.

CONCORD, MASS., July 21, 1855.

DEAR SIR, — I am not blind to the worth of the wonderful gift of *Leaves of Grass*. I find it the most extraordinary piece of wit and wisdom that America has yet contributed. I am very happy in reading it, as great power makes us happy. It meets the demand I am always making of what seems the sterile and stingy Nature, as if too much handiwork or too much lymph in the temperament were making our Western wits fat and mean. I give you joy of your fine and brave thought. I have great joy in it. I find incomparable things, said incomparably well, as they must be. I find the courage of treatment which so delights us, and which large perception only can inspire.

I greet you at the beginning of a great career, which yet must have had a long foreground, somewhere, for such a start. I rubbed my eyes a little to see if this sunbeam were no illusion; but the solid sense of the book is a sober certainty. It has the best merits, namely, of fortifying and encouraging.

I did not know, until I last night saw the book advertised in a newspaper, that I could trust the name as real and available for a post office.

I wish to see my benefactor, and have felt much like striking my tasks and visiting New York to pay you my respects.

R. W. EMERSON.

Note 37. This passage is quoted from "The Book of Shet the Prophet Zirtûsht," in the second volume of *The Desatir, or Sacred Writings of the Ancient Persian Prophets, together with the Ancient Persian Version and Commentary of the Fifth Sasan,* carefully published by *Mulla Firuz Bin Kaus.* Bombay, 1818.

As the book is exceedingly rare, I give the whole passage: "It is said that when the fame of the excellence of the nature

of Zertûsht had spread all over the world, and when Isfendiar
went around the world, erected fire-temples and raised domes
over the fires, the wise men of Yunân selected a Sage named
Tûtiânûsh, who at that time had the superiority in acquire-
ments over them all, to go to Irân and to enquire of Zertûsht
concerning the real nature of things. If he was puzzled and
unable to answer, he could be no prophet, but if he returned
an answer, he was a speaker of truth." (Here follows the
passage quoted in the text.) "He then asked the day of the
prophet's nativity. The prophet of God told it. He said, 'On
such a day, and under such a fortunate star a deceiver cannot be born.' He next enquired into his diet and mode of life.
The prophet of God explained the whole. The Sage said, 'His
mode of life cannot suit an impostor.' The prophet of Yezdân
then said to him, 'I have answered you the questions which
you have put to me; now in return retain in your mind what
the famed Yunâni Sage directed you to enquire of Zertûsht and
disclose it not, but listen and hear what they ask; for God hath
informed me of it and hath sent his word unto me to unfold it.'
The Sage said, 'Speak.' Thereupon the prophet of Zertûsht
repeated the . . . texts." *C. E.*

NOTE 38. This is found in the *Timœus*.

NOTE 39. This quotation is used again by Emerson in the
eulogy on Samuel Hoar.

NOTE 40. Furniture in the sense of that with which anything
is supplied to fit it for operation or use; equipment. The use of
the word to designate the spiritual powers as opposed to external equipment is characteristic of Emerson and peculiarly
his in this particular combination of words.

NOTE 41. See Homer's *Odyssey*, Bk. V, l. 99.

NOTE 42. See *Initial, Dæmonic and Celestial Love.*

NOTE 43. A household officer of a prince or dignitary, a
steward, a major-domo. This use of the word is by what may be
called attraction. It corresponds to the outward "furniture"
of gods and Olympus as the factors that must be reduced to
the level of man's furniture and homes.

NOTE 44. This active use of "foible," properly a noun of
defect, is characteristic of Emerson's insistence upon the essential, central virtue and strength of human nature, and of
his habit of making evil a temporary falling away into an alien
condition.

NOTE 45. The reference is to Jesus Christ.

NOTE 46. A tributary of the Thames. There was a place of
execution on the Tyburn near what is now the Marble Arch,
Hyde Park. In 1783 the executions were removed to Newgate.
This is an example of attracted diction. The change of pitch
from Calvary to Tyburn is fully appreciated by Emerson.
Some readers are hardly furnished with the needed rhetorical
fortitude.

NOTE 47. The close of this essay is one of the most perfectly "concerted" treatments of a rhetorical *motif*. All the implications of *Compensation*, *Experience*, and *Character* are here gathered up into a single chord. In the word "compliment" may be found an element to reappear in *Behavior* and *Manners*.

SELF–RELIANCE

The introduction to this essay in the Centenary Edition is in part the following: —

Thus it appears that the writings of Landor (*Imaginary Conversations*), read the year before Mr. Emerson sought him out in Rome, may have given the original push towards the writing of this essay on "Self-Reliance." A small portion of the essay came from the lecture "Individualism," the last in the course on "The Philosophy of History" in 1836–37, and other passages from the lectures "School," "Genius," and "Duty," in the course on "Human Life," 1838–39.

In reading this essay, it is well to call to mind,1st, Mr. Emerson's fear of weakening the effect of his presentation of a subject by qualification; 2d, That the Self he refers to is the higher self, man's share of divinity.

Note 1. The reference may be to Washington Allston or to William Blake.

Note 2. See "Days" in *Poems*.

Note 3. The phrase "preëstablished harmony" is a highly technical one taken from the celebrated system of Leibnitz. The mild assertion of the double negative "not without" conveys the suggestion with a touch of humor in the use of the learned system's vocabulary for such ends.

Note 4. The delicate humor and abiding humanity of Emerson are at their best in his characterization of youth, under *Domestic Life*, Cent. Ed. Vol. VII, p. 104: —

"But chiefly, like his senior countrymen, the young American studies new and speedier modes of transportation. Mistrusting the cunning of his small legs, he wishes to ride on the necks and shoulders of all flesh. The small enchanter nothing can withstand — no seniority of age, no gravity of character; uncles, aunts, grandsires, grandams, fall an easy prey; he conforms to nobody, all conform to him; all caper and make mouths and babble and chirrup to him. On the strongest shoulders he rides, and pulls the hair of laurelled heads."

Education, Cent. Ed. Vol. X, p. 139: "They know truth from counterfeit as quick as the chemist does. They detect weakness in your eye and behavior a week before you open your mouth, and have given you the benefit of their opinion quick as a wink. . . . If I can pass with them, I can manage well enough with their fathers."

Note 5. The question of grammar here is an interesting one. The cadence of the sentence was perhaps the determining consideration. Of course Milton and Mrs. Hemans afford similar constructions in "than whom" and "all but he."

NOTE 6. One of the Windward Islands in the British West Indies, of much interest to Abolitionists from its negro population.

NOTE 7. Cf. *History* for another treatment of this theme.

NOTE 8. The active form of this verb is unusual.

NOTE 9. The economy of expression in this phrase is worthy of attention. See the phrase, "let the ape and tiger die," Tennyson, *In Memoriam*, CXVII, 24.

NOTE 10. The variety of forms and associations in which this thought has been presented in the essays thus far is worthy of analysis and some attempt at classification. Is it inadvertent repetition?

NOTE 11. It may be interesting to reproduce here the version of the first edition, with a ruder vigor, more adapted to delivery in the Lyceum.

"With consistency a great soul has simply nothing to do. He may as well concern himself with his shadow on the wall. Out upon your guarded lips! Sew them up with pack-thread, do! else, if you would be a man, speak what you think to-day in words as hard as cannon-balls, and to-morrow speak what to-morrow thinks in hard words again, though it contradict everything you said to-day. Ah, then, exclaim the aged ladies, you shall be sure to be misunderstood! Misunderstood! It is a right fool's word. Is it so bad then to be misunderstood? Pythagoras was misunderstood, and Socrates, and Jesus, and Luther, and Copernicus, and Galileo, and Newton, and every pure and wise spirit that ever took flesh. To be great is to be misunderstood." *C. E.*

NOTE 12. Taken in connection with the word "acrostic," the allusion seems to be to the poem of Publius Optatianus Porphyrius. It is a eulogy of Constantine; the lines are acrostic: Porphyry was a pupil of Plotinus, in turn a pupil of Ammonius at Alexandria.

NOTE 13. See "Woodnotes" in *Poems*.

NOTE 14. In *Character*, Cent. Ed. Vol. X, p. 92, Emerson writes: "It were an unspeakable calamity if any one should think he had the right to impose a private will on others. That is the part of a striker, an assassin. All violence, all that is dreary and repels, is not power but the absence of power."

NOTE 15. An older phrase for "takes precedence of."

NOTE 16. See Induction to Shakespeare's *The Taming of the Shrew*.

NOTE 17. Iskander Bev, George Castriota, 1403–1468, is referred to. He maintained his independence of Amurath II and of Mohammed II in Albania.

NOTE 18. See Shakespeare's *Twelfth Night*, II, 3, 124. "Dost thou think because thou art virtuous, there shall be no more cakes and ale?"

NOTE 19. This is reminiscent of Wordsworth's Ode, *Intimations of Immortality*, IX : —

> Hence in a season of calm weather
> Though inland far we be
> Our souls have sight of that immortal sea
>   Which brought us hither,
> Can in a moment travel thither,
> And see the children sport upon the shore,
> And hear the mighty waters rolling evermore.

The entire Ode should be compared with the teaching of this essay concerning "the life by which things exist." With both should be compared *The Over-Soul*, Cent. Ed. Vol. I.

NOTE 20. See "The Sphinx" in *Poems*. "These roses," etc. is the constructive illustration to be added to previous expressions of Emerson's dislike and distrust of "reference." So also the "reverted eye."

NOTE 21. This use of "agent" is an example of Emerson's keen sense of etymology. From time to time, he is startlingly precise.

NOTE 22. This phrasing again depends upon strict etymology for its force. It is not common usage in speech.

NOTE 23. See the treatment of this theme in *Character*.

NOTE 24. Compare with *Domestic Life*. Cent. Ed. Vol. VII.

NOTE 25. This infrequent use of "allow" seems to be the one given in the Century Dictionary as meaning "to approve, justify, or sanction."

NOTE 26. The name of the Icenian Queen in the play usually attributed to Beaumont and Fletcher and performed before 1619. Caratach is General of the Britons, cousin to Bonduca, and a man of heroic mould. The quotation is from the close of the first scene of the third act, but does not have quite the introduction suggested by Emerson. Bonduca says, "I would know further, Cousin," after the god has replied by fire to Caratach's salutation in place of "fretful prayers," "whinings," and "tame petitions." Another extract from Act I, Sc. 1 of this play is given in *Parnassus*, where it is assigned to Beaumont and Fletcher. Emerson, however, may very well have chosen to exhibit some of his insight as a higher critic; for the lion's share of this play, as of others, belongs to Fletcher.

NOTE 27. In thus dealing with prayer, Emerson has lifted his opposition to reference, repetition, and slavery to the past to the highest level. Prayer seems thus the *n*th power of consecrated, impersonal will in character. The usual phrasing would be hindered *from*, not *of*, meeting. But the use of the older phrasing gives solemnity to the thought. Kipling's poem of *Tomlinson* is a satirical expression of this idea even more drastic than Emerson's.

NOTH 28. John Locke, 1632–1704, one of the most influential English philosophers of modern times. He was founder of the sensational philosophy and psychology. His chief work is the "Essay concerning Human Understanding." The skeptical development of his principles by Hume led Kant to the elaboration of his critical philosophy. Antoine Laurent Lavoisier, *b.* 1743, guillotined 1794, was a celebrated French chemist, founder of modern chemistry, reformer of chemical nomenclature. Charles Hutton, 1737–1823, an English mathematician. James Hutton, 1726–1797, a Scottish geologist and natural philosopher. Jeremy Bentham, 1748–1832, an English jurist and utilitarian philosopher. François Marie Charles Fourier, 1772–1837, a noted French socialist, propounder of the coöperative system of society known as Fourierism. It arranges society in groups, according to occupation, capacities, and attractions, to live in phalansteries, or common dwellings.

NOTE 29. The quite possible paradox of this phrase was perfectly understood and accepted by Emerson.

NOTE 30. See Lamb: " How would he chirp and expand over a muffin." *South Sea House.* See Goethe, *Faust,* " Prolog im Himmel:" —

> "Er scheint mir, mit Verlaub von Eu. Gnaden,
> Wie eine der langbeinigen Cicaden,
> Die immer fliegt und fliegend springt,
> Und gleich im Gras ihr altes Liedchen singt."

Roughly translated: " He (man) seems to me, by permission of your Grace, like one of these long-legged grasshoppers, that always flies and flying, jumps, and in the grass chirps its monotonous little old song."

Plato has a passage in the *Phædrus* which might easily have been the suggestion and served as a background for Emerson's expression.

"Soc. There is time yet, and I can fancy that the grasshoppers who are still chirruping in the sun over our heads are talking to one another and looking at us. . . . A lover of music like yourself ought surely to have heard the story of the grasshoppers, who are said to have been human beings in the age before the Muses. And when the Muses came and song appeared they were ravished with delight; and singing always, never thought of eating and drinking, until at last they forgot and died. And now they live again in the grasshoppers; and this is the return which the Muses make to them, — they hunger no more, neither thirst any more, but are always singing from the moment that they are born, and never eating or drinking; and when they die they go and inform the Muses in heaven who honors them on earth." Compare also "Let them rave," Tennyson, *A Dirge,* where the phrase is under a refrain.

NOTE 31. See "Written in Naples," "Written at Rome," in *Poems.*

NOTE 32. The vague and shifting meaning of "quaint" admirably fits it for the use Emerson makes of it in relation at once to grandeur of thought, to beauty, and to convenience.

NOTE 33. This expression in dignified writing is exceedingly rare. The phrase, however, is a kind of slang of *curio* hunters and providers. Atmospherically its appearance with this discussion of travelling for a background to the value of personality is dramatic, if also a trifle whimsical.

NOTE 34. An example of transferred epithet and of the use of suggestion in sculpture as an "utterance." The variety of phrasal form in this sentence is noticeable.

NOTE 35. This treatment of *Experience* in the concrete is paradoxical to the extent that it takes account of the principle of Compensation. This doctrine has been held, however, by great authorities in history. Doctor Edward Freeman repeatedly maintained its truth.

NOTE 36. Phocion, 402–317 B. C., Athenian statesman and general and leader of the aristocratic party. He opposed Demosthenes.

NOTE 37. See *Experience*. Note 46.

NOTE 38. Parry, Sir William Edward, 1790–1855, an English navigator and Arctic explorer.

NOTE 39. Franklin, Sir John, 1786–1847, English Arctic explorer. In 1845 he led an expedition in search of the northwest passage. It was last spoken July 26, 1845. Thirty-nine relief expeditions were sent out between 1847 and 1857. Captain Leopold McClintock found traces of the missing expedition in 1859, among them a paper giving the date of Franklin's death. His cenotaph in Westminster Abbey has this tribute from Tennyson:—

> "Not here! the White North has thy bones; and thou,
>   Heroic sailor-soul,
>   Art passing on thine happier voyage now
>   Toward no earthly pole."

NOTE 40. See second motto of *Compensation*.

NOTE 41. The dual thought closing this essay allies it with all that has gone before. It completes while it discriminates. The self honored by Emerson is no child of greed or appetite, but of renunciation and aspiration. Kipling's *Kim* gives the story of different quests after selfhood. The boy Kim's adventures, the old red Lama's effort to escape from the wheel of things, and Huree Babu, "the fearful" man's wish to be made a member of the Royal Society for taking Ethnological Notes The story of Kim's reinforcement of his own will by training is told dramatically, pp. 242 *et seq.:* —

"Yet the jar — how slowly the thoughts come!—the jar had been smashed before his eyes. Another wave of prickling fire raced down his neck, as Lurgan Sahib moved his hand.

"'Look! it is coming into shape!' said Lurgan Sahib. So far Kim had been thinking in Hindi, but a tremor came on him, and with an effort like that of a swimmer before sharks, who hurls himself half out of the water, his mind leaped up from a darkness that was swallowing it and took refuge in — the multiplication table in English!

"'Look! It is coming into shape!' whispered Lurgan Sahib.

"'The jar had been smashed — yes, smashed — not the native word, he would not think of that — but smashed into fifty pieces, and twice three was six and thrice three was nine, and four times three was twelve. He clung desperately to the repetition. The shadow-outline of the jar cleared like a mist after rubbing eyes. There were the broken shards; there was the spilt water drying in the sun, and through the cracks of the verandah showed, all ribbed, the white house-wall below — and thrice twelve was thirty-six!

"'Look! Is it coming into shape?' asked Lurgan Sahib.

"'But it is smashed — smashed,' he gasped. — Lurgan Sahib had been muttering softly for the last half-minute. Kim wrenched his head aside. 'Look! *Dekko!* It is there as it was there!'

"'It is there as it was there,' said Lurgan, watching Kim closely while the boy rubbed his neck. 'But you are the first of a many who have ever seen it so.' He wiped his broad forehead."

At the close of the matchless scene between the half drowned but illuminated lama and the Mohammedan horse-dealer, the latter in the full spirit of our essay's close addresses the lama: —

"Allah forbid it! Some men are strong in knowledge, Red Hat. Thy strength is stronger still. Keep it — I think thou wilt."

HEROISM

The following is part of the account of this essay given in the Centenary Edition: —

This essay is probably the lecture of that name essentially as delivered in the course on "Human Culture" in Boston, in the winter of 1837–38.

The homage which Mr. Emerson felt bound to render to the lowly virtues of Prudence after dealing with "the fine lyric words of Love and Friendship," made an interesting contrast for his hearers, the more effective by his leading them up to the heights of Heroism in the succeeding lecture.

In a lecture called "The Present Age," delivered in the following year, this expression occurs, — his recognition of the awakening of those days to the need of individual, social, and political reform: "Religion does not seem now to tend to a *cultus*, but to a heroic life. He who would undertake it is to front a corrupt society and speak rude truth, and he must be ready to meet collision and suffering."

The saying of Mahomet alone served for motto in the first edition.

NOTE 1. These names might properly enough be mere specimens of the grand style of nomenclature used by Emerson to keep up the level of literary suggestion, but as a matter of fact, Rodrigo is one of the rivals in the play called *The Pilgrim*,

Pedro is the other. Valerio is a gentleman in another play of Beaumont and Fletcher's, *A Wife for a Month*.

NOTE 2. In this list of plays, all from Beaumont and Fletcher, Mr. Emerson evidently trusted to his memory, and gave to one the name from a leading character. There is no play by the name of "Sophocles," but the extract given is from a piece called "Four Plays in One," the special play being "The Triumph of Honor." This is founded on a story of Boccaccio's in the *Decameron*, the tenth day and the fifth novel. *C. E.*

NOTE 3. See Scott's *Old Mortality*, chap. xlii.

NOTE 4. A selection of rare pamphlets from the library of Robert Harley, first Earl of Oxford (1661–1724).

NOTE 5. A small town in Saxony, the scene of two battles, one in 1632, when Gustavus Adolphus, though victorious, died, the other in 1813, when Napoleon Bonaparte gained an inconclusive victory.

NOTE 6. Simon Ockley, 1678–1720, an English Orientalist, whose chief work was a *History of the Saracens*.

NOTE 7. See essay on Plutarch, in *Lectures and Biographical Sketches*.

NOTE 8. The form of this phrase may illustrate the faint distinction between the personal and the impersonal in the usage of Emerson. The customary expression is "the hero's is a mind," etc. In the *Phædo* of Plato, Jowett's translation, occurs this passage: "Wherefore, I say, let a man be of good cheer about his soul, who has cast away the pleasures and ornaments of the body as alien to him, and rather hurtful in their effects, and has followed after the pleasures of knowledge in this life; who has adorned the soul in her own proper jewels, which are temperance, and justice, and courage, and nobility, and truth — in these arrayed she is ready to go on her journey to the world below when her time comes."

NOTE 9. See essay on *Prudence*, Cent. Ed., Vol. ii. "Prudence is the virtue of the senses. It is the science of appearances. It is the outmost action of the inmost life. It is God taking thought for oxen. It moves matter after the laws of matter. It is content to seek health of body by complying with physical conditions, and health of mind by the laws of the intellect.

"The world of the senses is a world of shows; it does not exist for itself, but has a symbolic character; and a true prudence or law of shows recognizes the co-presence of other laws and knows that its own office is subaltern."

NOTE 10. This is another way of putting the truth of the saying that there's only a step from the sublime to the ridiculous. Thomas Paine and Napoleon Bonaparte both make use of the idea, undoubtedly Paine's was the earlier.

NOTE 11. This very interesting passage is reminiscent of Shakespeare's characterization of the seven ages of man in *As You Like It*, II, vii, and of Wordsworth's picture of the boy in the Ode on *Intimations of Immortality*. It suggests also Emerson's own picture of his son in the *Threnody*. There is clearly to be seen his curious, quaint, other-worldly humor in the inversion of values and the unexpected close in "earnest nonsense."

NOTE 12. Shakespeare's *Henry IV*, Pt. II, II, ii.

NOTE 13. According to the Centenary Edition the author of an Oriental Geography, translated by Sir George Ously. The anecdote is somewhat differently worded.

NOTE 14. This phrase suggests the appeal of an enthusiastic teacher to his class that the members should help to make God possible. Reflection shows more than mere rhetoric, levity, or irreverence in the utterance. It is the paradox of truth with emphasis on the aspect now called "Pragmatism."

NOTE 15. John Eliot, 1604–1690, the "Apostle of the Indians." Author of a translation of the Bible into the Indian language, a catechism, and a grammar.

NOTE 16. The use of the word " temperance " here has a touch of Emerson's characteristic paradox. The event is narrated in 1 Chronicles xi, 16–19.

NOTE 17. An interesting comparison exists between this passage and Emerson's " to be great is to be misunderstood," where the implication is almost the obverse of the one here. Compare Matthew xii, 16–19, part of which is: "The Son of man came eating and drinking, and they say, Behold a man gluttonous, and a winebibber, a friend of publicans and sinners. But wisdom is justified of her children."

NOTE 18. Another version of this story is told by Plutarch in his " Apothegms of Kings and Great Commanders," in the *Morals:* "When Pætilius and Quintus accused him of many crimes before the people; 'On this very day,' he said, 'I conquered Hannibal and Carthage; I for my part am going with my crown on to the capitol to sacrifice; and let him that pleaseth stay and pass his vote upon me.' Having thus said, he went his way; and the people followed him, leaving his accusers declaiming to themselves." *C. E.*

NOTE 19. The use of " condemnation" here is paradoxical. Socrates finally accepted a formal condemnation, but he protested against its justice in the most emphatic way possible. The Prytaneum was the meeting-place of the presidents of the Senate, where they were entertained at the public charge together with those who were so honored for ancestral or personal service. Socrates declared that he should be honored in this way instead of being punished.

NOTE 20. In Anne Manning's delightful *The Household of Sir Thomas More* the entry in Meg's (his daughter's) journal is: " Dr. Clement hath beene with us. Sayth he (Sir Thomas More) went up as blythe as a bridegroom to be clothed upon with mortality." The traditional anecdotes are that as Sir Thomas was mounting the scaffold in the Tower he said to a bystander, " Friend, help me up; when I come down again I can shift for myself;" and after he had laid his head on the block he lifted it to arrange his beard, saying, "for it has never committed treason."

NOTE 21. An example of Emerson's abiding sense of the relations of things and his love of paradox. In the nature of the case, the world cannot have Blue Laws. In actual fact, the Blue Laws existed only in the imagination of persons opposed to the adoption by the early authorities of the New Haven Colony of the Scriptures as their code of law and government and their strict application of the Mosaic principles. Popularly the term means harsh and inquisitorial enactment of petty regulation.

NOTE 22. In the account given by Plutarch, Epaminondas, serving in the battle of Mantinea side by side with Pelopidas, who fell seemingly mortally wounded, protected him at the risk of his own life. This is thought to have laid the foundation of one of the most enduring of friendships.

NOTE 23. The use of "handsome" in this connection is quaint and archaic and peculiarly Emersonian.

NOTE 24. Bayard, Pierre du Terrail, Chevalier de, 1475–1524, a French national hero, — "the knight without fear and without reproach."

NOTE 25. Sidney, Algernon, c. 1622–1683, an English patriot, one of the leaders of the Independents.

NOTE 26. Hampden, John, 1594–1643, one of the "five members" impeached by Charles I, 1642.

NOTE 27. See "Musketaquid" in *Poems*.

NOTE 28. Called the "Tenth Muse," by Plato in the *Phædrus*. A Greek lyric poet who lived about 600 B. C. Aristotle accepts her as the "poetess" as he does Homer as the "poet."

NOTE 29. Sévigné, Marie de Rabutin-Chantal, Marquise de, 1626–1696. A French author famous for her letters to her daughter.

NOTE 30. De Staël (-Holstein), Anne Louise Germaine Necker, Baronne de, 1766–1817, a celebrated French writer greatly disliked by Napoleon Bonaparte. See *Social Aims*. She was "the most extraordinary converser that was known in her time."

NOTE 31. A Greek goddess of law, order, and abstract right.

NOTE 32. It is possible that Emerson had in mind the episode in *Antony and Cleopatra*, III, xi: —

> *Cleo.* O my lord, my lord,
> Forgive my fearful sails! I little thought
> You would have followed.
>   *Ant.* Egypt, thou knew'st too well
> My heart was to thy rudder tied by the strings,
> And thou shouldst tow me after. O'er my spirit
> Thy full supremacy thou knew'st, and that
> Thy beck might from the bidding of the gods
> Command me.

NOTE 33. This note in the Centenary Edition gives an interesting emphasis to this advice: "Scorn trifles, lift your aims; do what you are afraid to do: sublimity of character must come from sublimity of motive." These were the teachings which the Emerson boys received in their youth from their brilliant, loving, and eccentric aunt, Miss Mary Moody Emerson. Her nephew has left an account of her in *Lectures and Biographical Sketches*. His words concerning her are carved upon her gravestone in Concord Cemetery: "She gave high counsels. It was the privilege of certain boys to have this immeasurably high standard indicated to their childhood, a blessing which nothing else in education could supply."

NOTE 34. Born 402 B. C., put to death 317 B. C. A celebrated Athenian general and statesman, advocate of the policy of peace with Macedon in opposition to Demosthenes. He was a leading aristocrat. In *Uses of Great Men*: "I applaud a sufficient man, an officer equal to his office; captains, ministers, senators, I like a master standing firm on legs of iron, well-born, rich, handsome, eloquent, loaded with advantages, drawing all men by fascination into tributaries and supporters of his power. . . . But I find him greater when he can abolish himself and all heroes by letting in this element of reason, irrespective of persons, this subtilizer and irresistible upward force into our thought, destroying individualism; the power so great that the potentate is nothing. Then he is a monarch who gives a constitution to his people; a pontiff who preaches the equality of souls and releases his servants from their barbarous homages; an emperor who can spare his empire."

NOTE 35. In *Uses of Great Men*: "Our globe discovers its hidden virtues, not only in heroes and archangels, but in gossips and nurses. Is it not a rare contrivance that lodged the due inertia in every creature, the conserving, resisting energy, the anger at being waked or changed? Altogether independent of the intellectual force in each is the pride of opinion, the security that we are right. Not the feeblest grandame, not a mowing idiot, but uses what spark of perception and faculty is left to chuckle and triumph in his or her opinion over the absurdities of all the rest. Difference from me is the measure of wrong. Not one has a misgiving of being wrong."

NOTE 36. The Rev. Elijah P. Lovejoy, a Presbyterian minister of intelligence, courage, and blameless character, devoted himself to the cause of awakening public sentiment in the Southern and Border States to the wrong of slavery and its evil results, and became editor of the St. Louis *Observer*. His press was destroyed by a mob, and he and his family were driven from the city. He then settled in Alton, Illinois, and established his paper, maintaining anti-slavery views. Riots resulted, and three presses, furnished in succession by friends of the cause, were destroyed. Mr. Lovejoy sent for another press. A public meeting of citizens was called because of the excited state of public opinion in the city. Resolutions were passed requiring Lovejoy to retire from the charge of his paper. He stood upon his rights under the Constitution to publish his beliefs freely. To the demand that in deference to mob law he should yield up his post, he said: "This I *never* will do. God in his providence — so say all my brethren, and so I think — has devolved upon me the responsibility of maintaining my ground here; and, Mr. Chairman, I am determined to do it. A voice comes to me from Maine, from Massachusetts, from Connecticut, from New York, from Pennsylvania, — yea, from Kentucky, from Mississippi, from Missouri, calling upon me in the name of all that is dear in heaven or earth to stand fast, and by the help of God *I will stand*. I know I am but one and you are many. My strength will avail but little against you all. You can crush me if you will, but I shall die at my post, for I cannot and will not forsake it." The press arrived and was lodged by his friends in a stone warehouse belonging to one of a gallant little company who undertook to defend the right of free speech. On the night of November 7, 1837, the mob demanded the press. The city authorities gave no protection. Mr. Lovejoy's friends refused to surrender and were attacked. They resisted, and when the building was set on fire, Lovejoy, coming out to prevent it, was shot dead.

Mr. George P. Bradford, one of Mr. Emerson's nearest friends, described to me the occasion when he delivered this discourse in Boston. Towards the end of the lecture, while carrying his audience — the cultivated people of Boston — with him, in full sympathy with devoted courage in other times and lands, suddenly, looking his hearers in the eyes, he brought before them the instance in their own day and country, and told of the martyrdom of Lovejoy for the right of free speech. Mr. Bradford said that a cold shudder seemed to run through the audience at this calm braving of public opinion twenty years before its ripening in the great war for freedom. Of course Lovejoy had other defenders in Boston, notably Wendell Phillips, who first entered the lists as an anti-slavery champion at the time of his slaying. *C. E.*

NOTE 37. See Thomas à Kempis, Book I, chap. xx: " If thou wilt withdraw thyself from speaking vainly, and from gadding idly, as also from hearkening after novelties and rumors, thou shalt find leisure enough and suitable for meditation on good things. The greatest saints avoided the society of men, Heb. xi, 38, when they could conveniently; and did rather choose to live to God in secret. One said: 'As oft as I have been among men, I returned home less a man than I was before. [Seneca, Ep. VII.] . . . No man doth safely speak, but he that is glad to hold his peace. No man doth safely rule, but that is glad to be ruled.'"

NOTE 38. These lines were evidently quoted from memory from *A Dirge*, one of Tennyson's early poems. The burden, "Let them rave," runs through all the verses. The following one comes as near the lines as quoted as any of them: —

Thou wilt not turn upon thy bed;
Chaunteth not the brooding bee
Sweeter tones than calumny?
        Let them rave.
Thou wilt never raise thine head
From the green that folds thy grave —
        Let them rave.   *C. E.*

HISTORY

This is the essay first in the list of those presented to the
public as the "First Series" of Emerson's essays. Part of the introduction provided by the Centenary Edition gives these facts
and comments: —

After the publication of *Nature*, the first hint that appears
of the collection by Mr. Emerson of his writings into a second
book, occurs in the end of a letter to Mr. Alcott, written April
16, 1839, which Mr. Sanborn gives in his *Memoir of Bronson
Alcott:* "I have been writing a little, and arranging old papers
more, and by and by I hope to get a shapely book of Genesis."

In a letter written in April, 1840, to Carlyle, Mr. Emerson
thus alludes to the *Essays :* —

"I am here at work now for a fortnight to spin some single
cord out of my thousand and one strands of every color and
texture that lie ravelled around me in old snarls. We need to
be possessed with a mountainous conviction of the value of our
advice to our contemporaries, if we will take such pains to find
what that is. But no, it is the pleasure of the spinning that betrays poor spinners into the loss of so much good time. I shall
work with the more diligence on this book-to-be of mine, that
you inform me again and again that my penny tracts are still
extant; nay, that beside friendly men, learned and poetic men
read and even review them. I am like Scholasticus of the Greek
Primer, who was ashamed to bring out so small a dead child
before such grand people. Pygmalion shall try if he cannot
fashion a better, — certainly a bigger."

Soon after *Nature* had appeared, Carlyle had written to
his friend: "There is a man here called John Sterling, . . .
whom I love better than any one I have met with, since a certain sky-messenger alighted to me at Craigenputtock and vanished in the Blue again. . . . Well, and what then, cry you?
Why then, this John Sterling has fallen overhead in love with a
certain Waldo Emerson; that is all. He saw the little book *Nature* lying here; and, across a whole *silva silvarum* of prejudices,
discerned what was in it, took it to his heart, — and indeed into
his pocket. . . . This is the small piece of pleasant news, that
two sky-messengers (such they were, both of them, to me) have
met and recognized each other, and by God's blessing there shall
one day be a trio of us; call you that nothing?" Sterling wrote
to Emerson and a noble friendship resulted. Although they

never met in the body, these friends had more in common with each other in their hope, their courage, and their desire for expression in poetry than either had with Carlyle. Sterling died in 1844.

In a curious and characteristic preface, among other things, Carlyle said: —

"The name of Ralph Waldo Emerson is not entirely new in England; distinguished travellers bring us tidings of such a man; fractions of his writings have found their way into the hands of the curious here; fitful hints that there is in New England some spiritual notability called Emerson glide through the reviews and magazines."

In Berlin, Herman Grimm (who later wrote the lives of Michelangelo and Raphael), while waiting his turn in the parlor of the American dentist, chanced to pick up the *Essays* from the table; "read a page, and was startled to find that I had understood nothing, though tolerably well acquainted with English. I inquired as to the author. In reply I was told that he was the first writer in America, an eminently gifted man, but somewhat crazed at times, and often unable to explain his own words. Notwithstanding, no one was held in such esteem for his character and for his prose writings. In short, the opinion fell upon my ears as so strange that I re-opened the book. Some sentences, upon a second reading, shot like a beam of light into my very soul, and I was moved to put the book in my pocket, that I might read it more attentively at home. . . . I took Webster's Dictionary and began to read. The construction of the sentences struck me as very extraordinary. I soon discovered the secret: they were real thoughts, an individual language, a sincere man that I had before me; naught superficial, second-hand. Enough! I bought the book! From that time I have never ceased to read Emerson's works, and whenever I take up a volume anew it seems to me as if I were reading it for the first time."

" History " was not delivered as a single lecture, but in writing it Mr. Emerson made use of passages from lectures in three distinct courses; namely, that on " English Literature " (1835–36), on " The Philosophy of History " (1836–37), and on " Human Life " (1837–38), as is shown by Mr. Cabot in the chronological list of lectures and addresses in the Appendix (F) to his Memoir.

The course on " The Philosophy of History " (1836–37) had the following lectures, many of which appear as such or in their matter in the *Essays :* —

I. Introduction (History has been ill written ; its meaning and future, etc.)	VI. Religion.
	VII. Society.
	VIII. Trades and Professions.
II. Humanity of Science.	IX. Manners.
III. Art.	X. Ethics.
IV. Literature.	XI. Present Age.
V. Politics.	XII. Individualism.

In his Journal, Mr. Emerson thus lays out the course in advance, with the belief in the Over-Soul as the foundation of all.

There is one soul.

It is related to the world.

Art is its action thereon.

Science finds its methods.

Literature is its record.

Religion is the emotion of reverence that it inspires.

Ethics is the soul illustrated in human life.

Society is the finding of this soul by individuals in each other.

Trades are the learning the soul in nature by labor.

Politics is the activity of the soul illustrated in power.

Manners are silent and mediate expressions of soul.

NOTE 1. This is the upshot of Emerson's conception of History as a process. It is of course precisely the opposite of the ordinary notion of the subject. History is studied mainly to provide perspective and to help in distinguishing the great from the small. In *Uses of Great Men* he says: "The genius of humanity is the right point of view of history. . . . Once you saw phœnixes: they are gone; the world is not therefore disenchanted. . . . We have never come at the true and best benefit of any genius so long as we believe him an original force. In the moment when he ceases to help us as a cause, he begins to help us more as an effect. Then he appears as an exponent of a vaster mind and will. The opaque self becomes transparent with the light of the First Cause." In *Shakspeare: or, The Poet:* "We are very clumsy writers of history. We tell the chronicle of parentage, birth, birth-place, schooling, schoolmates, earning of money, marriage, publication of books, celebrity, death; and when we have come to an end of this gossip, no ray of relation appears between it and the goddess-born."

NOTE 2. This is characteristic. It reflects Emerson's reading in Oriental, Greek, and Old English literature. There is in it Platonic reminiscence, eastern and Teutonic mysticism.

NOTE 3. See *Nature*, and the duality of nature touched upon in *Compensation*.

NOTE 4. The word "consist" is used in its strict etymological sense and gives a startling emphasis to the idea.

NOTE 5. The paradox of dealing with exceptions and crises as being of the essence of nature is not merely verbal with Emerson. A similar principle animated the great scientist who advised, "Study the waste" for the key to discovery.

NOTE 6. See *Self-Reliance*.

NOTE 7. An example of the way in which the vague associations connected with a name may be made to rivet attention to a thought. One Hasdrubal died 207 B. C., and according to Livy his head was thrown into the camp of his brother Hannibal. Another died 221 B. C., assassinated by a slave whose master he had put to death. A third Hasdrubal was commander in the war against Masinissa, 150 B. C. After an obstinate resistance he surrendered to Scipio, and was allowed to live in honorable captivity; but his wife upbraided him for his surrender and threw herself and her children into the flames in the temple where they had taken refuge.

NOTE 8. Cesare Borgia, 1478–1507, a man of personal beauty, a patron of learning, a resolute soldier, and a master of cruel perfidy, lived violently, died in war, and was celebrated as a model ruler by Macchiavelli in *Il Principe.* Few persons have vivid memories of this, but the names impress.

NOTE 9. Reminiscent of Wordsworth's Ode on *Intimations of Immortality :* —

> "At length the Man perceives it die away
> And fade into the light of common day."

NOTE 10. This recalls the æsthetic theory of Kant. The "note of the universal" is really this taking for granted our own competence. We cannot imagine any dissent from our opinions or our pleasures or our virtues when we are really engaged with works of any sort of art that makes its own appeal.

NOTE 11. The position of the adjectives after the noun illustrates the way in which the rhythm of the sentence influenced Emerson's style.

NOTE 12. See Joshua, x, 12: "Stand thou still upon Gibeon."

NOTE 13. The note in the Centenary Edition suggests inaccuracy here: —

"I am indebted to Professor Charles Eliot Norton for calling my attention to the probable compounding of the name Marmaduke Robinson, through a slip of Mr. Emerson's memory, out of the names of the two Quakers hung on Boston Common in 1659, Marmaduke Stevenson and William Robinson."

NOTE 14. Stonehenge is a prehistoric monument in Salisbury Plain, Wiltshire: it seems to have consisted of two concentric circles of upright stones inclosing two ellipses. The Ohio circles are aboriginal fortifications on the Scioto River, twenty-six miles south of Columbus. Mexico is a way of suggesting the interesting features of native Aztec civilization. Memphis is the early capital of Egypt.

NOTE 15. Belzoni, Giovanni Battista, 1778–1823, an Italian traveler, explorer, and athlete (at Astley's, London). He transferred the bust of the so-called Young Memnon from Thebes to the British Museum.

NOTE 16. One of the most important and least appreciated of Emerson's contributions to the natural history of thinking.

NOTE 17. The word was introduced into philosophy by Giovanni Bruno to denote the minimum parts of substances, supposed by him to be at once psychical and material. Leibnitz conceived the monad as absolutely unextended substance existing in space, its existence consisting in its activities, which are ideas; and the universe was, in his belief, made up of such ideas.

The history of each monad followed an internal law, and all intercourse between the monads was impossible; but there was a preëstablished harmony between these laws of the different monads. The term is applied in biology to any simple single-celled organism. Huxley says: " There is reason to think that certain organisms which pass through a monad stage of existence . . . are, at one time of their lives, dependent upon external sources for their protein matter, or are animals; and, at another period, manufacture it, or are plants."

NOTE 18. This use instead of brutality is rare. The Century Dictionary cites another instance from Spenser's *Faerie Queene*, II, viii, 12.

NOTE 19. This is not a precise statement. Io appears in the *Prometheus* as a fair woman with a heifer's horns.

NOTE 20. Herodotus wrote a history of the Persian invasion of Greece. Thucydides began a history of the Peloponnesian War. Xenophon described the expedition of the ten thousand Greeks to the Black Sea. Plutarch, author of *Forty-six Parallel Lives* of Greeks and Romans.

NOTE 21. Cf. *Papers from The Dial*, particularly "Thoughts on Modern Literature," "Europe and European Books," "Past and Present," and "A Letter."

NOTE 22. Another famous description of sculpture is "frozen music."

NOTE 23. Cf. "Xenophanes" in *Poems*.

NOTE 24. It is hardly possible that Emerson had not in mind while writing this sentence the remarkable natural formation in the White Mountains known as "The Old Man of the Mountain."

NOTE 25. This reference has a peculiarly personal emphasis, as shown by the note in the Centenary Edition: —

" In the month of April, 1839, Carlyle sent Raphael Morghen's engraving of the Aurora, by Guido in the Rospigliosi palace in Rome, to Mr. Emerson, saying, "It is my wife's memorial to your wife. . . . Two houses divided by wide seas are to understand always that they are united nevertheless." The picture still hangs in the parlor of Mr. Emerson's home, with the inscription which accompanied it: 'Will the lady of Concord hang up this Italian sun-chariot somewhere in her Drawing Room, and, looking at it, think sometimes of a household here which has good cause never to forget hers. T. CARLYLE.'

" Mr. Emerson used to point out to his children how the varied repetition of the manes, heads, and prancing forefeet of the horses were imitations of the curved folds of a great cumulus cloud."

NOTE 26. Roos, Johann Heinrich, 1631–1685, a German painter of animals.

NOTE 27. A similar claim is made by Ruskin for a certain type of artist.

NOTE 28. This is to all intents a quotation from himself. He has made the sentiment his own in theory and in practice.

Note 29. See the essays on "Art" (*Essays, First Series,* and *Society and Solitude*) and "The Problem" in *Poems.*

Note 30. The cathedral of Strassburg is fabled to have been begun in 600. When the great wooden tower burned down, Erwin, an architect, was employed to restore it. He began the work of restoration in 1227, but did not live to complete it. His sons Johannes and Erwin carried on the work from his drawings, which are still at Strassburg. The façade, the galleries, and the rose windows are of great beauty.

Note 31. See *Hamlet,* III, ii.

Note 32. This derivation of an architectural feature from a snow landscape is unusual. The arching of trees has been suggested for the origin of the pointed arch, the lotus and the acanthus have served as factors in art systems, but what may be called the architecture of snow and ice is not a common factor in explanation. The suggestion is worked out elaborately in Whittier's *Snow-Bound,* and delicately in the second prelude in Lowell's *Vision of Sir Launfal.*

Note 33. See "The Snow-Storm" in *Poems.*

Note 34. Heeren, Arnold Hermann Ludwig, 1760–1842, a German historian, professor of philosophy and history at Göttingen.

Note 35. A river of Ethiopia mentioned by Strabo. *C. E.*

Note 36. See De Quincey's *Flight of a Tartar Tribe.*

Note 37. This active transitive use of the verb is vigorous and smacks of the market. The force is much greater than if some ethical or literary word had been used.

Note 38. This is rather half-hearted. The Germans do not say Fore-World but Vorwelt.

Note 39. The force of "costly" here seems to lie in the price that is paid in effort to get back to the simple, and also perhaps in the distaste we may acquire for newer literature.

Note 40. See Whistler's *Ten O'clock,* also Kipling's *The Conundrum of the Workshops.*

Note 41. A famous Greek archer in the Trojan war. He was friend and armor-bearer to Hercules. Hero of a play by Sophocles.

Note 42. Dr. Richard Moulton puts the distinction between the Greek-classic and English-romantic as being the effort to keep as much as possible out (the classic) and to get as much as possible in (the romantic).

Note 43. This judgment has been abundantly justified by recent criticism and discoveries in archæology. Classic and romantic are descriptions of stages and attitudes of all art rather than of fixed times or localities.

Note 44. See Shakespeare's *Macbeth,* I, iii.

Note 45. Menu or Manu. In Sanskrit "man," one of a class of demiurgic beings, each of whom presides over a Manvantara, or period of Manu.

Note 46. Simeon, *d.* 459, a Syrian ascetic who spent the

last thirty years of his life on a pillar near Antioch. The Thebais, a Greek epic of the Theban cycle and of unknown authorship; the theme, a mythical war between Argos and Thebes. Capuchins, a mendicant order of Franciscan monks, founded in Italy in 1528 by Matteo di Bassi, and named from the long capouch, or cowl, which they wore. They were to live by begging, were not to use gold or silver or silk in decoration of their altars, and the chalices were to be of pewter.

NOTE 47. A member of the learned and priestly caste in Persia. Brahmin, member of the highest or priestly caste of India. Druid, a priest of the ancient Celts. Inca, a chief or lord in ancient Peru.

NOTE 48. Son of Poseidon and Libya, a deity of several primitive nations.

NOTE 49. Champollion, Jean François, 1790–1832, a celebrated French archæologist, Orientalist, and explorer. He discovered the key to the Egyptian hieroglyphic inscriptions.

NOTE 50. An Indian town in Mexico. The tall mound was probably an ancient settlement on a base of sun-dried bricks, with a second platform of less extent and greater elevation, and a central mound the average elevation of which is now one hundred and seventy feet.

NOTE 51. A tragedy of Æschylus. Emerson means that the form of the work of art adds beauty to a process which is usually considered destructive and hideous.

NOTE 52. Orpheus was the son of Apollo or a Thracian river-god. He could charm all animate and inanimate things with his music. "Riddle" is here used as a synonym for meaning. Cf. "Come riddle me my riddle."

NOTE 53. See Plato's *Phædrus*, the myth of the charioteer and the vision of truth. The entire paragraph is very Platonic. See *Intellect, Essays*, "First Series," Cent. Ed., pp. 335–7.

NOTE 54. Cf. James Russell Lowell's *Extreme Unction*.

NOTE 55. The third act of the Second Part of Goethe's *Faust* is known in Germany as "the Helena." It is an independent poem dealing with Helen of Troy interpolated by Goethe very loosely into the drama of *Faust*.

NOTE 56. Chiron was a centaur, son of Kronos and Philyra.

NOTE 57. Imaginary creatures, part lion, part eagle.

NOTE 58. Three daughters of Darkness (Phorkys) and the Abyss (Keto). One of the forms in which Mephistopheles appears in the Second Part of *Faust*.

NOTE 59. The wife of Tyndareus, and mother of Helen, Clytemnestra, Castor and Pollux.

NOTE 60. The relation of modern science to obscure and occult practices of an earlier age was doubtless in Emerson's mind. Astronomy is astrology transformed, chemistry owes much to alchemy, and botany to the herbalist. One aspect of this relation is well set forth in Kipling's *Puck of Pook's Hill*, in the story entitled "The Joyous Venture."

Note 61. *Perceforest*, a mediæval French romance, the scene in Britain before the time of Arthur. *Amadis de Gaul*, a romance of the fourteenth century by Vasco de Lobeira of Portugal.

Note 62. See ballad in *Percy's Reliques;* or in Sargent and Kittredge, *English and Scottish Popular Ballads.*

Note 63. That is, he is the heir of all the ages.

Note 64. This passage is part of a lecture on "The Doctrine of the Hands," given in the course on *Human Culture* in 1837–38. This is the relativity of things so ever present in Emerson's thought.

Note 65. Shakespeare, *Henry VI*, Pt. I, II, iii.

Note 66. Laplace, Pierre Simon, Marquis de, 1749–1827, celebrated French astronomer and mathematician.

·Note 67. The use of " prophesied " here is very characteristic of Emerson's diction and his habit of thought. The word suggests more than he needs to say, but it gives dignity and scope and a certain liberality of attitude to the reader's mind. The ordinary term would be "implied" or "called for" or even "necessitated."

Note 68. Davy, Sir Humphry, 1778–1829, celebrated English chemist, inventor of the safety lamp.

Note 69. Gay-Lussac, Joseph Louis (1778–1850), French chemist and physicist, made the first balloon ascension for scientific purposes in 1804.

Note 70. Handel, George Frederick, 1685–1759, a celebrated German composer of music. He is best known for his oratorios, among them " The Messiah."

Note 71. There are two Whittemores, one Thomas (1800–1861), a Universalist preacher and ethical writer of Boston, Mass., compiler of *Songs of Zion.* In his youth he was "mechanic." The other, Amos, 1759–1826, an inventor who contrived a machine for puncturing the leather and setting the wire for cotton and wool cards. The efficient means out of one of his difficulties in this invention was revealed to him in a dream. In either case this name is an instance of the determined impartiality of Emerson's mind. The rating of Whittemore with Watt, Fulton, and Arkwright is little short of absurd, judged in the light of their subsequent reputations, but taking the chance doubtless seemed a duty of the hour to Emerson.

Note 72. This seems perhaps a concession to persons who have poor memories and cannot pass examinations, but Emerson's alternative is so much more difficult that the conventional demands seem easy in comparison. Cf. *The American Scholar* I and II, part of which is: "Meek young men grow up in libraries, believing it their duty to accept the views which Cicero, which Locke, which Bacon have given; forgetful that Cicero, Locke, and Bacon were only young men in libraries when they wrote those books."

Note 73. Cf. Robert Browning's *Popularity*, part of which is, —

" And there's the extract, flasked and fine,
    And priced and salable at last!
And Hobbs, Nobbs, Stokes, and Nokes combine
    To paint the future from the past,
Put blue into their line.

" Hobbs hints blue, — straight he turtle eats:
    Nobbs prints blue, — claret crowns his cup:
Nokes outdares Stokes in azure feats, —
    Both gorge. Who fished the murex up?
What porridge had John Keats? "

NOTE 74. An aboriginal inhabitant of the Hawaiian Islands.

NOTE 75. See "Limits" in *Poems;* also *Nature:* "To speak truly, few adult persons can see nature. Most persons do not see the sun. . . . In the woods, too, a man casts off his years, as the snake his slough, and at what period soever of his life is always a child. In the woods is perpetual youth." Also *Discipline:* "The moral influence of nature upon every individual is that amount of truth which it illustrates to him. Who can estimate this ? Who can guess how much firmness the sea-beaten rock has taught the fisherman ? how much tranquillity has been reflected to man from the azure sky, over whose unspotted deeps the winds forevermore drive flocks of stormy clouds, and leave no wrinkle or stain ? how much industry and providence and affection we have caught from the pantomime of brutes ? What a searching preacher of self-command is the varying phenomenon of Health ?" Also the motto for *Nature :* —

"A subtle chain of countless rings
The next unto the farthest brings!
The eye reads omens where it goes,
And speaks all languages the rose,
And, striving to be man, the worm
Mounts through all the spires of form."

POLITICS

The account in the Centenary Edition gives these facts about the essay in the form in which it was published: —

"This essay was based on a lecture in the Boston course of 1839–40 on 'The Present Age.' The lecture on 'Politics' followed 'Literature' and preceded 'Reforms' and 'Religion.' Much new matter was added in the essay. Some passages that were omitted it seemed well to give in these notes. In this essay one sees Emerson fearlessly apply his doctrine of the Universal Mind, or the *common* sense of man, to politics, and find therein good hope for democracy. And his faith in evolution encourages a fearless optimism when at last in the nineteenth Christian century he has found one man — it does not appear whether himself or another —'to whom no weight of adverse experience will make it for a moment impossible that thousands of human beings might exercise towards each other the grandest and simplest sentiments, as well as a knot of friends, or a pair of lovers.'"

NOTE 1. Merlin or Myrddhin was a half-legendary bard of the sixth century. No authentic work of his remains. As a legendary figure he plays a part in Tennyson's *Idylls of the King*, and in Malory's *Morte d'Arthur*. The Early English Text Society has published for the first time the Early English prose romance of Merlin, 1450–60, from the French original attributed to Robert de Borron. Borron's original was Geoffrey of Monmouth's *Vita Merlini* (1139), translated into French by Wace. The student should not be content with any characterization of Merlin that ignores this material.

NOTE 2. Pisistratus, 605–527 B. C., a tyrant of Athens, friend of Solon.

NOTE 3. Cromwell, 1599–1658, Lord Protector of the Commonwealth of England, Scotland, and Ireland. Carlyle's lecture on "The Hero As King," in which he gave a place to Cromwell, had been delivered in 1840. Compare with the classification given in the *Phædrus* of Plato, where the tyrant and the good king are opposed as examples of more or less disciplined and cultured wills, according to the share they had won of truth as opposed to mere will or passion. Jowett, Tr., p. 248.

NOTE 4. A proverbial expression for profitless labor. Ocnus twisted a rope, an ass ate it. Proverbially also a feeble union or tie.

NOTE 5. "Perishes in the twisting" is a variant of perishes in the using, to express an even briefer span of life.

NOTE 6. The more usual expression would be "greater" or "more of."

NOTE 7. "And" commonly connects similar types of speech. The use of brute as an adjective is archaic and gives dignity and force to the expression.

NOTE 8. A Syrian, father-in-law of Jacob. See Genesis xxx, 5.

NOTE 9. See *The Fortune of the Republic:* "The class of which I speak make themselves merry without duties. They sit in decorated club-houses in the cities, and burn tobacco and play whist; in the country they sit idle in stores and bar-rooms, and burn tobacco, and gossip and sleep." In nobler form the ideal objections were put in the form of experiments like those at Florence, Fruitlands, and Brook Farm. The purpose of the experiment may be said to be the higher life by way of agriculture, self-culture, and communism. Emerson considered its claims as presented to him by ardent advocates and decided against joining them. In different places he has expressed himself to the effect that he must "submit to the degradation of owning bank-stock and seeing poor men suffer," and that he did not "wish to remove from (his) my present prison to a prison a little larger." "I wish to break all prisons." "At the name of a society, all my quills rise and sharpen." "Diet, medicine, traffic,

books, social intercourse, and all the rest of our practices and
usages are equally divorced from ideas, are empirical and false.
I should like to put all my practices back on their first thoughts,
and do nothing for which I now ask the whole world for my
reason. If there are inconveniences and what is called ruin in
the way, because we have so enervated and maimed ourselves,
yet it would be like dying of perfumes to sink in the effort to
reattach the deeds of every day to the holy and mysterious
recesses of life." *Memoir of Ralph Waldo Emerson*, J. E. Cabot,
ii, 437.

Note 10. The Century Dictionary gives two instances of the
use of this word by Milton. See *The Fortune of the Republic:*
"Our people are too slight and vain. . . . We import trifles,
dancers, singers, laces, books of patterns, modes, gloves and
cologne, manuals of Gothic architecture, steam-made ornaments."

Note 11. This is a variation in English of the Latin *res
nolunt diu male administrari*, with its legal associations.

Note 12. This paragraph from the lecture was omitted here:
"The philosopher, who is never to stop at the outside or appearance of things, will find more to justify his faith in the harmony of politics with the constitution of man, than the mere
statute-book can furnish him. There is more history to a nation
than can be gathered from its code. Its code is only the high-
water mark showing how high the last tide rose, but at this
moment perhaps the waters rise higher still, only they have not
yet notched their place by a line of pebbles, shells, and seaweed.
Observe that the law is always the last and never the first step.
One person, a few persons, an increasing minority do the thing;
defend it; irresistibly urge it; until finally, against all reluctance,
roaring opposition, it becomes the law of the land. The thing
goes before, — the form comes after. The elements of power,
namely, persons and property, must and will have their just
sway." *C. E.*

Note 13. See *The American Scholar:* "The world of any
moment is the merest appearance. Some great decorum, some
fetish of a government, some ephemeral trade, or war, or man,
is cried up by half mankind and cried down by the other half,
as if all depended on this particular up or down. . . . Let him
not quit his belief that a popgun is a popgun, though the ancient
and honorable of the earth affirm it to be the crack of doom. . . .
Success treads on every right step. For the instinct is sure that
prompts him to tell his brother what he thinks. . . . He learns
that he who has mastered any law in his private thoughts, is
master to that extent of all men whose language he speaks, and
of all into whose language his own can be translated." This is the
aspect of self-reliance to which Emerson most often recurs, but
it is presented under a different guise — that of group efficiency."

Note 14. The original lecture had from this point the material supplied by the Centenary Edition, as follows: —

"It seems to follow from these doctrines that nothing is less important than the laws or forms of government. Power belongs to persons and to property. Property is merely the obedience of nature to human labor and follows of course the moral quality of the persons who create and hold it. With the progress of any society, with the cultivation of individuals, the existing forms become every day of less consequence. Every addition of good sense that a citizen acquires destroys so much of his opposition to the laws of nature and the well-being of society, and of course brings the power of his property on the side of justice. Knowledge transfers the censorship from the State House to the reason of every citizen, and compels every man to mount guard over himself, and puts shame and remorse for sergeants and maces. And we find in all times and countries every great man does, in all his nature, point at and imply the existence and well-being of all the orders and institutions of a state. He is full of reverence. He is by inclination (how far soever in position) the defender of the grammar-school, the almshouse, the holy day, the church, the priest, the judge, the legislator, the executive arm. Throughout his being is he loyal, even when by circumstance arrayed in opposition to the actual order of things. Such was Socrates, St. Paul, Luther, Milton, Burke.

" The education of every man is bringing him ever to postpone his private to the universal good, to comport himself, that is, in his proper person, as a state, and of course whilst the whole community around him are doing the like, the persons who hold public offices become mere clerks of business, in no sense the sovereigns of the people.

" It were very much to be wished that these laws drawn from the nature of things could become a part of the popular philosophy, that at least all endeavors for the reform of education or the reform of political opinion might be made where only they can have any avail, in the speculative views of the individual, for it was justly said by Bacon that the speculative opinions of men in general between the age of thirty and forty were the only sure source of political prophecy. The philosophy of property, if explored in its foundations, would open new mines of practical wisdom, which would in the event change the face of the world; would destroy the whole magazine of dissimulation, for so many ages reckoned the capital art of Government. It would purge that rottenness which has defamed the whole Science until *politic* has come to mean cunning; would show the pretenders in that science that they were their own dupes; would show that the cunningest man cannot cheat nature or do any wrong without suffering the same. It would go deep into ethics and touch all the relations of man. It would teach the subtle and inextricable compensation that attaches to property. Everything God hath made hath two faces. Every cent in a dollar covers its worth, and also covers its evil. The man who covets the wealth of London should know that whilst each pound and penny represents so much commodity, so much corn and wine and cloth, of necessity it also represents so much mould or sourness and moth as belongs to these commodities: if so much property, then so much risk; if so much power, then so much danger; if so much revenue, then so much tax. When his honest labor and enterprise attract to him a great estate, then his exertions stand over against his gains to make him whole. But could his wish without his honest labor transfer out of another's vaults a million pounds sterling into his own chest, so would also, against his wish, just so massive an ill will and fear concentrate its black rays on him in darkness that might be felt. All property must and will pay its tax. If it come not by fair means, then it comes by foul. The wise man who sees the unerring compensations which worked themselves out in the world, will pay the state its full dividend on his estate, if not for love of right, then for fear of harm.

"And as in respect to property, so also in respect to persons it takes an ounce to balance an ounce; the fair house of Seem is never an equivalent for the house of Be. Nor can the loudest Pretension supply the place of the smallest piece of Performance. A just view of human nature would convince men of that truth (how hard to learn) that it is the man makes the place. Alfred, Washington, Lafayette, appear half divine to the people followed in their office by a nation's eye. Ambitious but pitiful persons see them and think it is the place alone that makes them great, and that if they sat in the same chairs they would be as much admired. All means are used to this end; all sorts of shame accumulated; and by and by perhaps they sit in the high seat only to make subtleness and pitifulness quite bare to the view of all men.

"In our own times, without satire, this mistake is so common that all society and government seems to be making believe, when we see such ignorant persons with a grave countenance taking their places as legislators and statesmen. This could not be, but that at intervals throughout society there are real men intermixed, whose natural basis is broad enough to sustain the paper men in common times, as the carpenter puts one iron rod in his banister to five or six wooden ones. But inexorable time, which brings opportunity once to every man, brings also to every man the hour of trial to prove him whether he is genuine, or whether he is counterfeit.

"The last ages have been characterized in history by the immense creation of property. The population of the globe, by the nations of western Europe in whom the superiority of intellect and organization seems to reside, has set at work so many skilful hands that great wealth is added. Now no dollar of property is created without some direct communication with nature, and of course some acquisition of knowledge and practical power. The creation of all this property, and that by millions, not by a few, involves necessarily so much education of the minds of the proprietors. With power always comes the consciousness of power, and therefore indomitable millions have demanded forms of government more suited to the facts. Throughout Europe, throughout America, the struggle exists between those who claim new forms at all hazards, and those who prefer the old forms to the hazard of change. Of course on the whole is a steady progress of innovation. In London, they write on the fences, 'Of what use are the Lords?' In Spain and in Portugal, the liberal monarchists can scarce hold out against the mob. The South American States are too unsettled than that an ordinary memory can keep the run of the powers that be.

"The era seems marked in many countries by the separation of real power from its forms, and the continual interference of the popular opinion between the executive and its will. A levity before unknown follows. The word 'Revolution' is stripped of its terrors, and they may have many in a year. They say in Paris, There will be no revolution to-day, for it rains.

"The struggle is envenomed by the great admixture of ignorance and selfishness on both sides which always depraves human affairs, and also prevents the war from being one purely of ideas. The innovators are led not by the best, but by the boldest, and often by the worst, who drive their private trade on, take advantage of the march of the principle. The conservatives make up for weakness by wiles and oppose indiscriminately the good and evil measures of their antagonists. Meantime Party, that bellowing hound that barks or fawns, that defamer and bargainer and unreasoning self-lover, distorts all facts and blinds all eyes. Party counts popularity success. Its whole aim ever is *to get the hurrah on our side.* It infects from the bar-room and ward-caucus up, all the veins of the state, stealing even into literature and religion; and in our age every Party has written history for itself as Gibbon, Lingard, Brodie, Hume, Hallam, Mitford.

"Meantime if we rise above the hubbub of parties, and the uncovered selfishness of many of the actors, we shall see that humanity is always the gainer, that the production of property has been the education of the producers, that the creation of so many new households and so many forcible and propertied citizens, has been the creation of lovers of order, knowledge and peace, and hating war. Trade and war are always antagonists. The progress of trade has been the death of war, universally. In these days nations have stretched out the hand to each other. In our times, it is said for the first time, has the word 'International' been compounded. Some progress has been made by national compact in hindering offences against all the world, as piracy and kidnapping. Mediation is made to supersede armies and navies. The projects with which the minds of philanthropists teem, are themselves a sure mark of progress. The black colony at Liberia, the proposition of the congress of nations to arbitrate controversies arising between two states, and so to prevent war or at least aid the right cause by the moral force of a decision, these are projects the bare starting of which in any practicable shape, proves civilization and Christianity. The mutual helpfulness of nations and the sympathy of all in the projects of each and the continual approximation by means of mechanical improvements seem to point at stricter union and simpler legislation, at a legislation more purely official, such as shall not hold out such bribes to vanity and avarice.

"The philosopher must console himself amidst the harsh discord of what is called politics by the reflection that its errors, like the errors of the planets, are periodic; that a firm bound is set by counterchecks in man to every excess, that the discipline which the events of every day administer to every man, tend always to make him a better citizen, and to make him independent of the mutations of parties and states."

A comparison of these two endings is important as showing the different tone of Emerson's spoken and printed estimate of institutions. The mood of the second is much more confident and is certainly spiritually optimistic. In the first the doubt is at least suggested that law is the creature of a force, as malevolent as controlling. In short the first has the emphasis of a half-truth put as if it were a truth and a half. In the delivery it was doubtless ameliorated and chastened by Emerson's personality and the beneficence of his bearing.

NOTE 15. On the occasion of the passage of the Fugitive Slave Law, Emerson said in a wonderful address, part of which is here cited from the Centenary Edition: —

"The last year has forced us all into politics. There is infamy in the air. I wake in the morning with a painful sensation which I carry about all day, and which, when traced home, is the odious remembrance of that ignominy which has fallen on Massachusetts. I have lived all my life in this State and never had any experience of personal inconvenience from the laws until now. They never came near me to my discomfort before. *But the Act of Congress of September 18th, 1850, is a law which every one of you will break on the earliest occasion, — a law which no man can obey, or abet the obeying, without loss of self-respect and forfeiture of the name of a gentleman.*"

NOTE 16. See Burke's *Observations on a late Publication:* "Party divisions, whether on the whole operating for good or evil, are things inseparable from free government."

NOTE 17. This is unusually severe characterization. It must be taken rather as the expression of Emerson's attitude towards all radicalism as such, than as a condemnation of American radicalism in comparison with American excess of any other kind. It is the lack of love that Emerson deplores, and he forgets that he has not proved the facts on radicalism in America.

NOTE 18. A penal colony on an inlet of the eastern coast of New South Wales, Australia, five miles south of Sidney, sent out 1787–88 from England, but later transferred to Port Jackson.

NOTE 19. Fisher Ames, 1758–1808, Dedham, Mass., orator, statesman, and political philosopher. Federal member of Congress from Massachusetts, 1789–97. He declined the presidency of Harvard College.

NOTE 20. This is a beautiful expression of a very ugly fact, and one that Emerson particularly regretted when it came under his notice. Yet as an admirer of force and individuality, he always paid his tribute to efficient assertion of the moment's duty. He understood the honor there could be among thieves. Yet this is an overstatement. It is not really the want of liberty that strengthens law and decorum.

NOTE 21. A term said to be derived from Charles Lynch, 1736–1796, a Virginia planter, who with two neighbors undertook to secure order by punishing offenders with stripes or banishment without process of law.

NOTE 22. This is a brief review of the theories of government presented in Aristotle's treatises, Plato's characterization, and based on an ideal principle thoroughly Platonic in its interpretation of the course of political experiment. See Welldon's *Politics of Aristotle* and Jowett's *Plato's Republic*.

NOTE 23. At this passage the Centenary Edition supplies the following: —

" Mr. Cabot, in the Appendix F to his Memoir, giving an account of the lecture ' Politics,' printed the following passage as omitted in the essay. I cannot find it in the manuscript, and suppose it may have dropped out: —

"'The State and Church guard their purlieus with jealous decorum. I sometimes wonder where their books find readers among mere mortals, who must sometimes laugh, and are liable to the infirmity of sleep. Yet politics rest on real foundations and cannot be treated with levity. But the foundation is not numbers or force, but character. Men do not see that all force comes from this, and that the disuse of force is the education of men to do without it. Character is the true theocracy. It will one day suffice for the government of the world. Absolutely speaking, I can only work for myself. The fight of Leonidas, the hemlock of Socrates, the cross of Christ, is not personal sacrifice for others, but fulfils a high necessity of his proper character : the benefit to others is merely contingent.' "

NOTE 24. Compare with the analysis of the relation between liberty and taxing given by Burke in the *Speech on Conciliation with America :* "Abstract liberty, like other mere abstractions, is not to be found. Liberty inheres in some sensible object, and every nation has formed to itself some favorite point, which by way of eminence becomes the criterion of their happiness. It happened, you know, Sir, that the great contests for freedom in this country were from the earliest times chiefly upon the question of taxing."

NOTE 25. This is intended to supply an emphasis for the two sentences of conclusion rather than to delay thought upon itself. Emerson thinks of the beatitude of men when relations are angelic, memory myrrh, and presence frankincense and flowers; he does not literally prescribe personal isolation as a means to the end. At most he suggests the limited nature of personal relations. But the saying sounds stern and cold — to the unreflecting — cool possibly to the most reflective.

NOTE 26. Malthus, Thomas Robert, 1766–1834, an English political economist, known for his *Principle of Population*, 1798, which he states to be that population increases in a geometrical ratio, means of subsistence in an arithmetical ratio, and that vice and crime are necessary checks of this increase in numbers.

NOTE 27. Ricardo, David, 1772–1823, an English Jew celebrated for his original and influential treatment of economic problems. One of his books is *Political Economy and Taxation*.

NOTE 28. A valuable publication originated by Robert Dudley at the suggestion of Burke, who was for some years editor and principal contributor. The years from 1758 to 1790 cover the first series. It is still proceeding.

NOTE 29. Brockhaus's *Conversations-Lexikon*, a German Encyclopædia, extensive in range and precise in information.

NOTE 30. See "Fragments on the Poet" in *Poems*.

NOTE 31. A reminiscence of Carlyle's *Sartor Resartus* and its clothes vocabulary.

NOTE 32. See Genesis iii, 7. Professor Woodberry, in *Ralph Waldo Emerson*, p. 186, says: "The secret of his style is in diction. It may be described as seventeenth-century diction." The secret of this passage is adequately revealed by this characterization.

NOTE 33. The ordinary word here would be "consciousness;" greater force and the entire charm of the passage is gained from Emerson's variation.

NOTE 34. Compare this phrase, its meaning and associations, with the "perfect moment" of Walter Pater. The perfect moment is one of the experiences of Marius the Epicurean in Pater's study of that name. The renunciation, the restraint implied in it, are well fitted to bring out the full flavor of the suspicion Emerson expresses about "the splendid."

NOTE 35. "Not all there" is the homely phrase by which New Englanders describe the mentally deficient. The suggestion adds point to the awkwardness of ability in conventional society.

NOTE 36. This is a brilliantly suggestive characterization, but its meaning is elusive. What class of forest animals has nothing but a prehensile tail? Is it apes or snakes, or may he invent an imaginary creature to meet our needs?

NOTE 37. This is a curious phrase. The meaning seems to be "as far as code is concerned" or in the colloquial phrase "for all the code," *i. e.* "in spite of" or "without."

NOTE 38. This would seem more precisely expressed by "useless," but the use of "hopeless" makes the sentence dramatic within its own structure — competition is presented as without hope.

NOTE 39. An old-fashioned structure of the phrase.

NOTE 40. The earlier form of this substituted "fate" for "faith." *C. E.*

NOTE 41. This expresses Emerson's characteristic opposition to the classic conception of form and limit as imposed by the nature of things. In the *Laws* Plato sets forth the precise limits of the successful city state (*Laws*, Bk. V, 738. Jowett, Tr.). Few critics of institutions are free from the dread that they may be "too large." Perhaps still fewer can really subscribe to the truth of Emerson's closing sentence. How many dare act on it? Yet even Emerson did not always strike this note. In *Nominalist and Realist* he says in a quite different connection: "Though the uninspired man certainly finds persons a conveniency in household matters, the divine man does not respect them: he sees them as a rack of clouds, or a fleet of ripples which the wind drives over the surface of the water. But this is flat rebellion. Nature will not be Buddhist: she resents generalizing, and insults the philosopher in every moment with a million of fresh particulars." The view of property formally presented by Emerson in this essay may be well compared with a few sentences from Shaler's "The Individual" (Appleton), p. 135 *et seq.* "The possession and the sense of property, both essentially features of human society, have in certain ways been very effective in promoting the development of sympathy, though, like war, it has had at the same time a limiting effect on the range of the emotion. The first effect of the property sense is, of course, hedonistic, purely selfish; but more than any other influence, it has in a secondary way served to create a sense of the rights of others, to make men put themselves in the place of the neighbor. The very cornerstone of human society is an understanding of the fellow creature. It is clear that this sense has come forth from the earliest of them, *i. e.* the right of each man to his own possessions. In such ways as these the conception of the kindred man, as like one's self, has been greatly fostered by the development of social institutions." Far more congenial to this view of property and its influence are the positions held and set forth in Emerson's sympathetic essay on *Wealth* in *Conduct of Life.* In the motto to this essay: —

> " But, though light-headed man forget,
> Remembering Matter pays her debt :
> Still, through her motes and masses, draw
> Electric thrills and ties of Law,
> Which bind the strengths of Nature wild
> To the conscience of a child."

Finally in *An Imperial Rescript* by Kipling appears another version of the matter, in part: —

> "And over the German benches the bearded whisper ran : —
> Lager, der girls and der dollars, dey makes or dey breaks a man.
> If Schmitt haf collared der dollars, he collars der girls dere mit ;
> But if Schmitt bust in der pizness, we collars der girl from Schmitt."

BEHAVIOR

This essay is from a course of lectures on *The Conduct of Life* read to audiences in 1851, some time after Mr. Emerson's return from a stay of nine months in England. The publication of the book called out varied and somewhat contradictory opinions. The introduction to the volume in the Centenary Edition gives a full and valuable account of the important circumstances attending the course of lectures as well as the publication of the book. Two other volumes of Emerson's essays are closely related to this essay, *Representative Men* and *English Traits*. The essays *Behavior* and *Manners* are links in the chain from causes to events that reaches from the soul to men and their doings.

The motto well expresses in the closing couplet Emerson's attitude toward the conventional claims of behavior.

> " The much deceived Endymion
> Slips behind a tomb."

His explanation of the enduring deception is to be found in the suggestions of a note in the Centenary Edition: —

> " How near to what is good is what is fair!
> Which we no sooner see,
> But with the lines and outward air
> Our senses taken be."

"These lines of Jonson express the charm which the graces had for the solitary New England scholar who believed himself sadly deficient in them. He used these verses as the motto to what a writer in a recent journal has called "his fine essay on Manners, which was the first study for his finer essay on Behavior." The allusion, in the last lines of the motto of this essay, to Endymion, whom sleeping the moon stooped to kiss, leaving the influence of that benediction while life lasted, is a statement of the author's own case. It recalls the opening verses of the 'Ode to Beauty,' written perhaps ten years earlier."

NOTE 1. George Sand's novel *Consuelo* was one of the few novels read and valued by Mr. Emerson, who alludes to it in the essay on "Books," in *Society and Solitude*, and in *Representative Men. C. E.*

NOTE 2. Talma, François Joseph, and Madame Vanhove, a French tragic actor and a French actress, his wife. The husband introduced upon the stage the custom of wearing the costume of the period represented, was a critic of art, and friend of Napoleon.

NOTE 3. Talma's work did not prevent Emerson from seeing the real man under "the arts." In *Napoleon, or the Man of the World* in *Representative Men*, he says: "Napoleon is thoroughly modern, and at the highest point of his fortunes has the very spirit of the newspapers. . . . In short, when you have penetrated through all the circles of power and splendor, you were not dealing with a gentleman, at last, but with an impostor and a rogue; and he fully deserves the epithet of Jupiter Scapin, or a sort of Scamp Jupiter. . . . So this exorbitant egotist narrowed, impoverished, and absorbed the power and existence of those who served him; and the universal cry of France and of Europe in 1814 was, Enough of him; 'Assez de Bonaparte! '"

NOTE 4. See Shakespeare's *Merchant of Venice*, III, i.

NOTE 5. An example of the free way in which Emerson uses structure to suit his eyes rather than the gerund-grinders.

NOTE 6.

> I care not how you are dressed,
> In coarsest weeds or in the best;
>
> . . . .
>
> But whether you charm me,
> Bid my bread feed and my fire warm me.
> "Destiny," *Poems.*

NOTE 7. Asmodeus, a demon mentioned in the Book of Tobit in the Apocrypha, and in the Talmud. The keeping him out of mischief by setting him to spin sand into ropes is alluded to in several places in Mr. Emerson's work, as in *Politics* and *Resources*. In a fragment of verse he likens his own task of weaving his thoughts into a coherent tissue for an essay to that of this spirit. *C. E.*

NOTE 8. This is a vigorous provincialism of the kind Emerson delighted in.

NOTE 9. A famous school or university in Rome established by Hadrian. Also a club in London established 1824. Finally a local library of Boston.

NOTE 10. Titian, 1477–1576, a famous Venetian painter. He was portrait painter to the Doges.

NOTE 11. Claverhouse, John Graham, Viscount Dundee, *c.* 1649–1689, a Scottish soldier employed to put down the Covenanters, fell in the victorious battle of Killiecrankie against William III. The word "fop" has only relative significance as applied to him in this passage. He was a fierce soldier, but a precisian in forms, military and others.

NOTE 12. The Centenary Edition notes that the passage is thought to allude to John Quincy Adams.

NOTE 13. The Emir Abd-el-Kader, whose energy and courage made him for sixteen years a terror to the French army in Algiers, was finally captured in 1847. He became the friend of General Daumas, who edited an exceedingly interesting book entitled *Les Chevaux du Sahara*, in which he recorded what the Emir told him of the Arab horse, the tradition of his origin, the texts from the Koran concerning him, his breeding, treatment, and performance, and also of the customs and modes of thought and action of the Arabs of the Desert. Mr. Emerson took great pleasure in this book. *C. E.*

Note 14. See "The Initial, the Dæmonic and the Celestial Love." In the Old English epic of Beowulf there is mention of a woman who would let no man look into her eyes except her husband. The English sonnets of the Elizabethan period speak of lovers looking babies in each other's eyes. See Robert Browning's *Cristina* : —

> "She never should have looked at me
> If she meant I should not love her!
> There are plenty . . . men, you call such,
> I suppose . . . she may discover
> All her soul to, if she pleases,
> And yet leave much as she found them:
> But I'm not so, and she knew it
> When she fixed me, glancing round them," *et seq.*

Note 15. Cf. J. R. Lowell's *Studies for Two Heads*, part of which is : —

> "Her eye, — it seems a chemic test
> And drops upon you like an acid ;
> It bites you with unconscious zest,
> So clear and bright, so coldly placid;
> It holds you quietly aloof,
> It holds, — and yet it does not win you ;
> It merely puts you to the proof
> And sorts what qualities are in you;
> It smiles, but never brings you nearer,
> It lights, — her nature draws not nigh;
> 'T is but that yours is growing clearer
> To her assays: — yes, try and try,
> You'll get no deeper than her eye."

Note 16. The book of Winckelmann on Greek Art was often referred to by Mr. Emerson. Johann Caspar Lavater, the Swiss mystic, wrote a remarkable work on physiognomy in men and animals, in which he pushed his theories to a ludicrous extreme. His *Physiognomische Fragmente zur Beförderung der Menschenkenntniss und Menschenliebe* was published in 1775–78. *C. E.*

Note 17. Louis de Rouvroi, Duke of Saint-Simon, 1675–1755, a writer of interesting *Mémoires*, which because of their bold and satirical character did not obtain full publication until 1829. Jean François Paul de Gondi, Cardinal de Retz, 1614–79, a man of loose morals but much ability, became Cardinal, and Archbishop of Paris. He had many vicissitudes of fortune, being an opponent of Richelieu and Mazarin, and had to take refuge in Spain for some years. His *Mémoires* cover an interesting period. Pierre Louis, Count Roederer, 1754–1835, a man of letters who was a statesman of remarkable intelligence and address, which saved him, although of the moderate party, in the French Revolution, throughout which he was very active. Under Napoleon he occupied places of importance, but after the return of the Bourbons he devoted himself to literature. Among his writings are the *Chronique de Cinquante Jours* and *Mémoires pour servir à l'histoire de la Société polie en France. C. E.*

NOTE 18. Henry Richard Vassall Fox, third Baron Holland, 1773–1840, an English politician, nephew of Charles James Fox.

NOTE 19. The title of a powerful novel by Victor Hugo which appeared in 1831.

NOTE 20. Northcote, Sir Stafford Henry, 1818–1887, an English conservative statesman.

NOTE 21. Fuseli was banished from Switzerland for some political indiscretion. His drawing was praised by Sir Joshua Reynolds, and in time he became professor of painting in the Academy. He wrote a *Life* of Reynolds. James Northcote, a pupil of Reynolds, became a portrait painter. His disposition and manners made him unpopular. *C. E.*

NOTE 22. A man of a low caste performing the lowest menial services, literally "a drummer," the Pariahs being the hereditary drum-beaters. An outcast, a vagabond. De Quincey in *Autobiographic Sketches* has a remarkable treatment and analysis of the underlying idea. Kipling's *Without Benefit of Clergy* is a contribution of astounding pathos to the literature of the subject.

NOTE 23. Quoted from *Pericles and Aspasia* by Walter Savage Landor. For further characterization of the author see essay on Walter Savage Landor in the volume *Natural History of Intellect and Other Papers.*

NOTE 24. An illustration of this generalization is found in *Napoleon, the Man of the World:* "Bonaparte was singularly destitute of generous sentiments. The highest-placed individual in the most cultivated age and population of the world, — he has not the mind of common truth and honesty. . . . He is a boundless liar. . . . His manners were coarse. He treated women with low familiarity. He had the habit of pulling their ears and pinching their cheeks, when he was in good humor, and of pulling the ears and whiskers of men, and of striking and horseplay with them, to his last days. It does not appear that he listened at keyholes, or, at least, that he was caught at it."

NOTE 25. Cf. the incisive passage in Carlyle's *Sartor Resartus:* "Often in my atrabiliar moods when I read of pompous ceremonials, Frankfort Coronations, Royal Drawing-rooms, Levees, Couchees; and how the ushers and macers and pursuivants are all in waiting; how Duke this is presented by Archduke that, and Colonel A by General B, and innumerable Bishops,

Admirals, and miscellaneous Functionaries, are advancing gallantly to the Anointed Presence; and I strive in my remote privacy, to form a clear picture of that solemnity, — on a sudden, as by some enchanter's wand the — shall I speak it? — the clothes fly off the whole dramatic corps; and Dukes, Grandees, Bishops, Generals, Anointed Presence itself, every mother's son of them, stand straddling there, not a shirt on them; and I know not whether to laugh or weep. This physical or psychical infirmity, in which perhaps I am not singular, I have, after hesitation, thought right to publish for the solace of those afflicted with the like. . . . What would Majesty do, could such an accident befall in reality; should the buttons all simultaneously start, and the solid wool evaporate in very Deed, as here in Dream ? *Ach Gott !* How each skulks into the nearest hiding-place; their high State Tragedy (Haupt und Staats-Action) becomes a Pickleherring-Farce to weep at, which is the worst kind of Farce; *the tables* (according to Horace), and with them, the whole fabric of Government, Legislation, Property, Police, and Civilized Society, *are dissolved,* in wails and howls.

"Lives the man that can figure a naked Duke of Windlestraw addressing a naked House of Lords ?" *et seq.* After reading this one is impressed with the force of Emerson's "treat these reputations tenderly."

NOTE 26. The reference is thought to be applicable to Mary Moody Emerson.

NOTE 27. Journal, 1841. "Be calm, sit still in your chair, though the company be dull and unworthy. Are you not there ? There then is the choir of your friends; for subtle *influences* are always arriving at you from them, and you represent them, do you not ? to all who stand here.

"It is not a word that 'I am a gentleman, and the king is no more,' but is a fact expressed in every word between the king and a gentleman." *C. E.*

NOTE 28. This shows another of the harmful aspects of the compliancy so greatly disliked by Emerson. Woodberry says of him, p. 183: "In his personal nature there was a strain of haughtiness that belonged with the formality of his manners and his inherited pride, which underlay his independence and was in his blood; the superiority with which he looked upon both society and literature with confident criticism was allied to this."

NOTE 29. Junius Fromziskers, 1589–1677, a German student of Teutonic languages. Milton was indebted to him for part of his interest in Anglo-Saxon character and expression.

NOTE 30. See *History,* Note 49.

NOTE 31. Friedrich Heinrich Jacobi, the German philosopher and correspondent of Goethe.

NOTE 32. There is a similar plot admirably used by Prosper Mérimée, in his "Federigo" in *Dernières Nouvelles.*

Note 33. The description of Sir Philip Sidney bears out this experience of Emerson's.

Note 34. This was a favorite idea with Thomas Carlyle, expressed in the "rest of the spinning top." The phrase recurs in *Sartor Resartus.* The Centenary Edition notes that Emerson wrote also, Journal, 1850: "My prayer to women would be, when the bell rings, when visitors arrive, sit like statues."

Note 35. Compare the passage in "The Celestial Love" beginning, —

> For this is Love's nobility, —
> Not to scatter bread and gold.   *C. E.*

Note 36. This is of paradox all compact and is characteristic of the haughty strain, mentioned by Woodberry, in Emerson's make up. In the temper of Carlyle's discovery of motives, one wonders what would be the effect of a meeting between two persons each trying to put the other "in a good light" and each conscious of the other's effort.

Note 37. "Hear what the morning says and believe that," was one of Mr. Emerson's finest utterances. There is a passage on morning influences in "Inspiration," in connection with Goethe's poem "Musagetes," in *Letters and Social Aims.   C. E.*

Note 38. The close of this essay links it with the one on *Culture,* which precedes it in *Conduct of Life,* and which supplies a steady undercurrent of suggestion and reminiscence.

MANNERS

In the course of lectures, "The Philosophy of History," given by Mr. Emerson in 1836–37, was one called *Manners.* In 1841–42, he gave a course on "The Times," of which this essay was one. There was also a lecture, *Manners and Customs of New England,* in the five on New England, and the same theme is treated in *Behavior* in *Conduct of Life.* The first part of the motto is from Ben Jonson's Masque, *Love Freed from Ignorance and Folly;* the second from that of *Pleasure Reconciled to Virtue.*

Note 1. The use of "philosophical" here is intentionally and suggestively inaccurate. It illustrates again Emerson's sense of humor in connection with unpromising subjects. The primitive or the careless is hardly philosophical, but the results of the inconvenience may be borne in that temper.

Note 2. See *History,* Note 15.

Note 3. Borgu or Bussango, a kingdom in Sudan. It was in this country that Mungo Park met his death. See *Blackwood's Magazine,* 1899.

Note 4. Tibbus, Tibus or Tabus (rock people). A Nigritian people of Tibesti in the Sahara, reaching south into the Sudan. They traffic by caravan across the Sahara. Described by Nachtigal and Rohlfs.

NOTE 5. Borneo, a state of the Sudan. It was at the height of its power at the close of the 16th century. It has been described by Barth, Nachtigal, and later French and German explorers.

NOTE 6. This vigorous use of everyday English reminds the reader of Samuel Johnson and of Carlyle. This is more forceful English than the purist's advice.

NOTE 7. Emerson's translation by way of reference is characteristic of his self-reliance. The phrase of course means "as it should be." An example of Emerson's quick insight into verbal suggestion.

NOTE 8. "Gentilesse" means courtesy, delicacy; is obsolete, was used by Edmund Spenser and others.

NOTE 9. See "Fragments on The Poet" in *Poems*.

NOTE 10. This was a growing sentiment with the public of Emerson's time: Matthew Arnold gives somewhat satirical expression to it in making the aristocracy of England barbarians with physical prosperity for their chief interest.

NOTE 11. A road to the west from Niagara River where, in 1814, a battle was fought between the Americans and the British.

NOTE 12. Lord Falkland, Lucius Cary, 1610–43, an English politician and writer. He was member of Parliament and later Secretary of State.

NOTE 13. Two Persian monarchs of the name of Sapor, of the dynasty of the Sassanidæ, conquered the Roman emperors in battle in the third and fourth centuries A. D. *C. E.*

NOTE 14. Ruy Diaz de Bivar in the eleventh century, the *preux chevalier* of Spain, in the struggle against the Moors, was celebrated in ancient chronicles, romances, and ballads. Southey from these materials composed his noble *Chronicle of the Cid*. Mr. Emerson liked to read passages from this to his children. Many of the ballads about the Cid are translated by Lockhart in *Spanish Ballads*. *C. E.*

NOTE 15. Another example of the independence of the usual tyranny of time natural to Emerson. This he shared with certain poets and thinkers of mystic powers in all times.

NOTE 16. These are terms in fencing, but doubtless Emerson was willing that they should carry a double burden of suggestion.

NOTE 17. This is an unusual phrase in literature. It has its types in common speech, as "to bring clear or clean." In Shakespeare, *Measure for Measure*, I, 1, appears "that we may bring you something on your way."

NOTE 18. Emerson does not often repeat a word after so brief an interval.

The Centenary Edition notes that most of this paragraph is taken from a lecture on *Prudence* in the course on "Human Culture," 1838. The original text is as follows: —

"Thus we understand exceeding well in America the charm

of what is best in English manners, and, as we by age, cultivation, and leisure refine and ripen, come to set a high value on that species of breeding which foreigners, from a more sanguine temperament, and we too, from our democratic wantonness, usually blame in the English, — the mild, exact decorum, the cool recognition of all and any facts by a steadiness of temper which hates all starts, screams, faintings, sneezings, laughter, and all violence of any kind. The English, and we also, are a commercial people, great readers of newspapers and journals and books, and are therefore familiar with all the variety of tragic, comic, political tidings from all parts of the world, and are not to be thrown off their balance by any accident nearby, like villagers whom the overturn of a coach, or a robbery, or a dog with a kettle sets agape, and furnishes with gossip for a week."

NOTE 19. This is a careless construction and unusually awkward in Emerson's writing.

NOTE 20. A quarter of Paris, south of the Seine, celebrated as the headquarters of the royalists and long associated with wealth and fashion.

NOTE 21. The battle which completed Napoleon's conquest of northern Italy, July 14, 1800.

NOTE 22. The greatest naval victory of the British over Napoleon, Oct. 21, 1805. Nelson was first in command, Collingwood was second.

NOTE 23. The "only" here is out of place for the best effect of Emerson's sentence. The order should plainly be "only the day before yester that is city and court to-day."

NOTE 24. An example of the fine and delicate humor characteristic of Emerson.

NOTE 25. The reason for the use of this name as a place of banishment from society on account of offensive conduct is unknown. It was first used in military society to imply exclusion from the society of the mess.

NOTE 26. A rare word meaning an obsequious follower of fashion.

NOTE 27. The henchman of McIvor in Scott's *Waverley* thus expresses his wish that the young English officer could see the chief at the head of his clan. *C. E.*

NOTE 28. This is the favorite spiritual arithmetic of Emerson. The half-gods go and the great gods come. But little men have a great impatience and resent such teaching as cold comfort. It has its prototype, however, in the Calvinism that Emerson always admired whether he believed it or not. In the "application" of the sermon of Jonathan Edwards from Ezekiel XIX, 12, "Her strong rods were broken and withered," in *Selected Sermons of Jonathan Edwards*, edited by H. Norman Gardiner (Macmillan Company), the climax is: "But now this 'strong rod is broken and withered,' and surely the judgment of God therein is very awful, and the dispensation that which may well be for a lamentation. Probably we shall be more sensible of the worth and importance of such a strong rod by the want of it."

NOTE 29. Son of Alcæus and husband of Alcmene. Used to typify a host. Jupiter personated him in order to marry Alcmene, but was interrupted at the feast by the real Amphitryon.

NOTE 30. A provincial construction very common in New England. It gives a homely and familiar air to the statement.

NOTE 31. This is in various forms frequently asserted by Emerson: it is partly prudence, partly courage, and wholly paradox.

NOTE 32. This is characteristic of Emerson's contempt for trifles in human intercourse.

NOTE 33. A paraphrase of a sentiment quite ultimate in Emerson's theory and practice. It can be traced through all his writing.

NOTE 34. In this way society is made a meeting of such philosophers as are described in Plato's *Phædrus*.

NOTE 35. That is the dry light — an expression of Heraclitus meaning that which is nearest purity and the source of pure being.

NOTE 36. This is characteristic of what was called the transcendentalism of the day. "Infinite means to secure finite ends."

NOTE 37. "Impertinent" is used in the etymological sense of the word.

NOTE 38. This entire passage should be compared with the analysis of society and social conditions presented in George Meredith's chapter on the "Comic Spirit" in *The Egoist* or in his *Essay on Comedy*.

NOTE 39. This word illustrates Emerson's usage in emphasizing an understatement, a rhetorical impossibility to most persons. The opposite direction of energy they cannot maintain, so they pile up big adjectives or tear down little ones. Emerson reverses the process.

NOTE 40. An example of this is to be found in the story of Mrs. Mulock Craik, *John Halifax, Gentleman*.

NOTE 41. An instance of Emerson's incisive satire. The episode of Circe and Ulysses and the latter's transformed companions is made to serve as characterization for the alleged lions of Fashion.

NOTE 42. The clergy as distinguished from the laity, a body of clerks, the *literati*. This is the sense here.

NOTE 43. This is a rhetorical device for emphasizing the fashionable exclusiveness he wishes to characterize.

NOTE 44. An example of very adroit balance of form and meaning in parallel phrases.

NOTE 45. Another view of this subject is presented in George Eliot's "Debasing the Moral Currency" in *Impressions of Theophrastus Such.* See also *Social Aims:* "And beware of jokes; too much temperance cannot be used; inestimable for sauce, but corrupting for food, we go away hollow and ashamed."

NOTE 46. The Centenary Edition notes that the source of this epitaph is unknown. Doctor Emerson does not think his father composed it.

NOTE 47. Keats, *Hyperion.*

NOTE 48. "Ethnical" or "ethnic," pertaining to race. In *Social Aims* Emerson writes: "He whose word or deed you cannot predict, who answers you without any supplication in his eye, who draws his determination from within, and draws it instantly, — that man rules.

"The staple figure in novels is the man of *aplomb*, who sits among the young aspirants and desperates, quite sure and compact, and, never sharing their affections or debilities, hurls his word like a bullet when occasion requires, knows his way, and carries his points. They may scream or applaud, he is never engaged or heated. Napoleon is the type of this class in modern history; Byron's heros in poetry. But we for the most part are all drawn into the *charivari;* we chide, lament, cavil, and recriminate."

NOTE 49. This is essentially a Greek conception of the relation of life and art. It is Platonic in so far as it values art in life. The relation of this view of art to that known as art for art's sake is suggested.

NOTE 50. This use of the superlative is unexpected in the connection of Emerson's thought, and the choice of this particular adjective to describe the common estimate of feminine intuition illustrates the intellectual independence of the writer.

NOTE 51. See John ix, 6, 11, 15, 25.

NOTE 52. Hafiz, Shums-uddin Muhammad. An eminent Persian, died about 1388, one of the lyric poets of all time.

Firdusi, Abul Kasim Mansur, 940–1020, the great epic poet of Persia.

NOTE 53. The leading forms which characterize the Byzantine style are the round arch, the circle, the cross, and the dome supported on pendentives. The capitals of the pillars are of endless variety and full of invention. *Cent. Dict.*

NOTE 54. Part of the setting of the typical fairy story or didactic tale. Appears in our day as the title of a novel, *The Golden Book of Venice.*

NOTE 55. This use of "couple" is an example of easy, familiar colloquialism.

NOTE 56. The connection between royal blood and fire seems too remote for the clear expression of a truth until the reader reflects on the ultimate nature of each and its singular power of working after its kind. The touch of paradox adds to the force.

NOTE 57. The meaning here does not appear at once. The second clause is an understatement of the facts if literally taken. Briefly, it is vulgar to insist upon one's own advantage.

NOTE 58. The Centenary Edition points out the ideal character of the hero of this illustration. Osman is the ideal man of like conditions with Emerson.

Note 59. A vigorous alliterative expression in which banning means cursing.

NOTE 60. This fable was invented by Emerson. *C. E.*

FRIENDSHIP

The exhaustive and interesting introduction to this essay in the Centenary Edition contains the following account of the text: —

"This essay was not given as a lecture under this title and as a whole in any of the Boston courses. although very probably it served in that capacity in some of the Lyceums. As is shown in Mr. Cabot's Memoir (Appendix F), portions of it were taken from the lecture on 'Society,' in the course on 'The Philosophy of History' (1836–37), and others from 'The Heart' in the course on 'Human Culture,' given in Boston the following year. Several paragraphs come from 'Private Life,' in the course on 'The Present Age' (1839–40)."

The extracts from Emerson's *Letters* and *Journal* bearing on this theme and quoted in this edition are important. The motto, with its controlled ardor and in spite of the contrasting verse movement, inevitably recalls some of Shakespeare's Sonnets, as XXIX, XXX. Comparison is challenged by the famous essays on the same theme by Bacon and by Montaigne. The poetry and fiction of literature constantly offer this subject. The teaching gathered from Thackeray's *Esmond*, Lamb's *Essays*, Milton's poetry in *Comus*, *Lycidas*, and *Paradise Lost*, Tennyson's *In Memoriam* contribute to the appreciation of Emerson's insight and benevolence.

NOTE 1. Cf. *Macbeth*, II, ii : —

> ": Will all great Neptune's ocean wash this blood
> Clean from my hand? No: this my hand will rather
> The multitudinous seas incarnadine,
> Making the green one red."

NOTE 2. Cf. Milton's *Comus*, l. 5 : "The smoke and stir of this dim spot:" l. 7, "Confined and pestered in this pinfold here;" l. 17, "With the rank vapours of this sin-worn mould."

NOTE 3. This should be compared with the doctrine set forth in *Compensation*. The statement is hardly literally true and it requires a careful adjustment of its implications with the teachings of the *Over-Soul* and the larger self in *Self-Reliance* to make clear the element of truth that it embodies. In the perfect character all qualities help; in the imperfect, they too often hinder. The lover is proverbially bashful, the surgeon may be deserted by his skill if the patient is his own child. It was a wonder that William Tell could shoot the apple on the head of his son, and the story goes that he strengthened his courage and steadied his aim by the thought of the second arrow that he had for the tyrant in case the first went amiss.

NOTE 4. A description of the happiest results in ideal conditions only.

NOTE 5. A rare expression of the quality in Emerson's character described by George E. Woodberry as "a strain of haughtiness."

NOTE 6. The almost sublime height of this isolation from ordinary selfish demands is much more characteristic of Emerson. Affection which requires no return within a thousand years, or the beloved object nearer than a universe off, is peculiarly Emersonian.

NOTE 7. Here is the central thought of this conception of friendship, allying it to all the considerations presented in this group of essays.

NOTE 8. See Milton's *Comus*, l. 47.

NOTE 9. Cf. the point of view in *Self-Reliance*.

NOTE 10. The contraction and expansion of the heart and arteries in propelling the blood in circulation. This passage relates the experience of friendship to the principle of compensation.

NOTE 11. More precisely this should be the skeleton, or more precisely yet, the mummy, given a place at Egyptian banquets as a reminder of mortality.

NOTE 12. This thought should be traced through its elaboration in *Spiritual Laws* and in the essays on Plato and on Swedenborg.

NOTE 13. The spiritual detachment indicated by this energetic phrase is characteristic.

NOTE 14. This characterization of the soul's methods is morally possible only through the agency of the Over-Soul, or the all-encompassing Deity. On any other principle the doctrine is unworthy of Emerson.

NOTE 15. Cf. with the closing sentence of Bacon's *Essay on Friendship*.

NOTE 16. This shows the place of friendship in Emerson's system of compensation.

NOTE 17. The construction of this sentence deserves attention for its dramatic compression.

NOTE 18. This sentence supplies Emerson's reason for all the misadventures of social life. It supplies also his theory of the reasonableness of a discontent with conventional society.

NOTE 19. Cf. J. S. Mill's *On Liberty*, chap. ii.

Note 20. See Matthew v, 48: "Be ye therefore perfect, even as your Father which is in heaven is perfect."

Note 21. Shakespeare, *Sonnets*, XXV.

Note 22. This German compound means literally nature-slowness, and may be compared with Tennyson's phrase in *Locksley Hall*, "the process of the suns."

Note 23. See Matthew xi, 12: "The kingdom of heaven suffereth violence, and the violent take it by storm."

Note 24. See Shakespeare, *A Midsummer Night's Dream*, III, ii, "Lord, what fools these mortals be!"

Note 25. This curious figure has the force of a sudden change of pitch and of the homely association it suggests.

Note 26. Suggestion of the figures used by T. Carlyle in *Sartor Resartus*.

Note 27. Emerson's relations with Carlyle are an interesting commentary on this statement. The two volumes of *Correspondence* afford many side lights on this considered as a practical maxim. It must be remembered, however, that sincerity is an expensive form of self-expression.

Note 28. This is an example of Emerson's extreme optimism. Probably the statement is intended to be only approximately true, for Emerson is no stranger to the fact that men deceive themselves and have publics within themselves, before which they play their most elaborate parts.

Note 29. This note in the Centenary Edition gives life to this reference: —

"The allusion is to Jones Very, of Salem, a mystic and ascetic, of whom an interesting account is given in Mr. Cabot's *Memoir of Emerson*, vol. i, chapter x, and a fuller one by Mr. W. P. Andrews, in his introduction to *Essays and Poems by Jones Very*. In a letter to Miss Margaret Fuller, written in November, 1838, Mr. Emerson wrote: 'Very has been here lately and stayed a few days, confounding us all with the question whether he was insane. At first sight and speech you would certainly pronounce him so. Talk with him a few hours, and you will think all insane but he. Monomania or monosania, he is a very remarkable person; and though his mind is not in a natural, and probably not in a permanent state, he is a treasure of a companion, and I had with him most memorable conversations.'

"He records that Very said to him: 'I always felt, when I heard you read or speak your writings, that you saw the truth better than others, yet I felt that your spirit was not quite right. It was as if a vein of colder air blew across me.'"

Note 30. Probably the term "insanity" is used here to indicate the broken relations with the conventional man that would be the price paid for the experience.

Note 31. Cf. Bacon on this subject.

Note 32. Montaigne, Bk. I, xxxix.

Note 33. See *Social Aims*: "But we are not content with

pantomime; we say, This is only for the eyes. We want real relations of the mind and the heart; we want friendship; we want knowledge; we want virtue; a more inward existence to read the history of each other. Welfare requires one or two companions of intelligence, probity, and grace, to wear out life with, — persons with whom we can speak a few reasonable words every day, by whom we can measure ourselves, and who shall hold us fast to good sense and virtue; and these we are always in search of. He must be inestimable to us to whom we can say what we cannot say to ourselves. Yet now and then we say things to our mates, or hear things from them, which seem to put it out of the power of the parties to be strangers again. 'Either death or a friend,' is a Persian proverb. I suppose I give the experience of many when I give my own. A few times in my life it has happened to me to meet persons of so good a nature and so good breeding that every topic was open and discussed without possibility of offence, — persons who could not be shocked. One of my friends said in speaking of certain associates : ' There is not one of them but I can offend at any moment.' But to the company I am now considering were no terrors, no vulgarity. All topics were broached, — life, love, marriage, sex, hatred, suicide, magic, theism, art, poetry, religion, myself, thyself, all selves and whatever else, with a security and vivacity which belonged to the nobility of the parties and their brave truth. The life of these persons was conducted in the same calm and affirmative manner as their discourse. Life with them was an experiment continually varied, full of results, full of grandeur, and by no means the hot and hurried business which passes in the world."

NOTE 34. See Spenser, *On His Promised Pension;* Shakespeare, *As You Like It,* III, ii ; *Merry Wives of Windsor,* V, vi ; *Comedy of Errors,* II, ii. Sir Thomas More advised an author who had sent him his manuscript to read "to put it in rhyme." Which being done, Sir Thomas said, "Yea, marry, now it is somewhat, for now it is rhyme ; before it was neither rhyme nor reason." (Part of the account in *Familiar Quotations,* Bartlett.)

NOTE 35. Compare the different treatment of conversation to be found in *Social Aims* and note the agency attributed to women.

See also *Discipline :* "We are associated in adolescent and adult life with some friends, who, like skies and waters, are coextensive with our idea; who, answering each to a certain affection of the soul, satisfy our desire on that side; whom we lack power to put at such focal distance from us, that we can mend or even analyze them. He cannot choose but love them. When much intercourse with a friend has supplied us with a standard of excellence, and has increased our respect for the resources of God who thus sends a real person to outgo our ideal; when he has, moreover, become an object of thought, and, whilst his character retains all its unconscious effect, is converted in the mind into solid and sweet wisdom, — it is a sign to us that his office is closing, and he is commonly withdrawn from our sight in a short time."

NOTE 36. See *Social Aims :* " But there are people who cannot be cultivated, — people on whom speech makes no impression; swainish, morose people, who must be kept down and quieted as you would those who are a little tipsy; others, who are not only swainish, but are prompt to take oath that swainishness is the only culture; and though their odd wit may have some salt for you, your friends would not relish it. Bolt these out. And I have seen a man of genius who made me think that if other men were like him coöperation were impossible. Must we always talk for victory, and never once for truth, for comfort and joy? Here is centrality and penetration, strong understanding, and the higher gifts, the insight of the real, or from the real, and the moral rectitude which belongs to it : but all this and all his resources of wit and invention are lost to me in every experiment that I make to hold intercourse with his mind; always some weary, captious paradox to fight you with, and the time and temper wasted. And beware of jokes; too much temperance cannot be used: inestimable for sauce, but corrupting for food, we go away hollow and ashamed. As soon as the company give in to this enjoyment, we shall have no Olympus. True wit never made us laugh. Mahomet seems to have borrowed by anticipation of several centuries a leaf from the mind of Swedenborg, when he wrote in the Koran: —

"On the day of resurrection, those who have indulged in ridicule will be called to the door of Paradise, and have it shut in their faces when they reach it. Again, on their turning back, they will be called to another door, and again, on reaching it, will see it closed against them; and so on, *ad infinitum*, without end."

NOTE 37. See *Social Aims :* " Manners first, then conversation. Later, we see that as life was not in manners, so it is not in talk. Manners are external; talk is occasional; these require certain material conditions, human labor for food, clothes, house, tools, and, in short, plenty and ease, — since only so can certain finer and finest powers appear and expand. In a whole nation of Hottentots there shall not be one valuable man, — valuable out of his tribe. In every million of Europeans or of Americans there shall be thousands who would be valuable on any spot on the globe."

NOTE 38. This is a famous phrase of Emerson's. Cf. in *Social Aims :* —

" And yet there are trials enough of nerve and character, brave choices enough of taking the part of truth and of the oppressed against the oppressor, in privatest circles. A right speech is not well to be distinguished from action. Courage to ask questions; courage to expose our ignorance. The great gain is, not to shine, not to conquer your companion, — then you learn nothing but conceit, — but to find a companion who knows what you do not; to tilt with him and be overthrown, horse and foot, with utter destruction of all your logic and learning. There is a defeat that is useful."

NOTE 39. See *Uses of Great Men:* "Men who know the same things are not long the best company for each other."

NOTE 40. See George Colman, the younger, *Sylvester Daggerwood, or New Hay at the Old Market,* sc. i : "I had a soul above buttons."

NOTE 41. This is the outcome of the principles set forth in *The Over-Soul, Circles, Compensation,* and *Heroism.* It is the generalization that underlies the series of illustrations that Emerson found in men and events. Cf. Milton's *Comus.*

NOTE 42. Cf. *Social Aims,* where the intrusive visitor is treated of.

NOTE 43. Cf. *Hamlet,* I, ii: "Would I had met my dearest foe in Heaven ! "

NOTE 44. Emerson had other moods than this. See his poem, *The Amulet:* —

> " Your picture smiles as first it smiled;
>   The ring you gave is still the same:
> Your letter tells, O changing child!
>   No tidings *since* it came.

> " Give me an amulet
>   That keeps intelligence with you, —
> Red when you love, and rosier red,
>   And when you love not, pale and blue.

> " Alas! that neither bonds nor vows
>   Can certify possession ;
> Torments me still the fear that love
>   Died in its last expression."

NOTE 45. Another example of Emerson's interest in the literature of legal and ethical distinctions.

NOTE 46. See Kipling in *The Light that Failed:* "Be still and hear the desert talk."

NOTE 47. See *Social Aims:* "Of course those people, and no others, interest us, who believe in their thought, who are absorbed, if you please to say so, in their own dream. They only can give the key and leading to better society: those who delight in each other only because both delight in the eternal laws; who forgive nothing to each other; who, by their joy and homage to these, are made incapable of conceit, which destroys almost all the fine wits. Any other affection between men than this geometric one of relation to the same thing, is a mere mush of materialism."

NOTE 48. Cf. Tennyson's *Ulysses:* —

> "That which we are, we are;
> One equal temper of heroic hearts,
> Made weak by time and fate, but strong in will,
> To strive, to seek, to find, and not to yield."

NOTE 49. The use of this suggestion from electrical science is peculiarly vivid.

NOTE 50. See a similar treatment of this theme in *Social Aims*.

NOTE 51. Such sentences as these represent the teaching known as transcendental. The essays *Aristocracy* and *Nominalist and Realist* illustrate some of the contributing principles. See also the concluding sentences of *Nature:* —

"The world is mind precipitated, and the volatile essence is forever escaping again into the state of free thought. Hence the virtue and pungency of the influence on the mind of natural objects, whether inorganic or organized. Man imprisoned, man crystallized, man vegetative, speaks to man impersonated. That power which does not respect quantity, which makes the whole and the particle its equal channel, delegates its smile to the morning, and distils its essence into every drop of rain. Every moment instructs, and every object; for wisdom is infused into every form. It has been poured into us as blood; it convulsed us as pain; it slid into us as pleasure; it enveloped us in dull, melancholy days, or in days of cheerful labor; we did not guess its essence until after a long time."

It is possible that Emerson never said his last word on friendship. It was a subject that occupied his thoughts always more or less and upon which he never felt that he had satisfied himself. Indeed if such a term could be used of his serene and ample spirit, friendship was something about which he was a little uneasy. This means that Emerson was a kind man as well as a thinker and that his philosophy was not a veneer to his feelings. But the essay on *Friendship* is not his best essay nor most characteristic of his genius. Possibly it is the most widely known of his essays and undoubtedly has influenced readers who have found little else in his work that was congenial. To the confirmed reader of Emerson, this essay is a sort of *crux*. To it he returns; to its incompleteness and wise silences he confesses his indebtedness. The best commentary on it is all that Emerson wrote, particularly the *Poems*, and of these "Terminus" is indispensable.

> "As the bird trims her to the gale,
> I trim myself to the storm of time,
> I man the rudder, reef the sail,
> Obey the voice at eve obeyed at prime:
> · Lowly faithful, banish fear,
> Right onward drive unharmed;
> The port, well worth the cruise, is near,
> And every wave is charmed.'"

COLLEGE ENTRANCE REQUIREMENTS

IN THE RIVERSIDE LITERATURE SERIES

* indicates the years in which the book is required "for reading."
"s" indicates those in which it is required "for study."

NUMBER	1906	1907	1908	1909	1910	1911
132. Arnold. Sohrab and Rustum 6				*	*	*
— Bacon. Essays.2 (*Preparing*)				*	*	*
115. Browning. Poems 6 (selected)				*	*	*
109. Bunyan. Pilgrim's Progress, Part I 2				*	*	*
100. Burke. Speech on Conciliation	s	s	s	s	s	s
128. Byron. Poems 6 (selected)				*	s	s
105. Carlyle. Essay on Burns 8				s	s	s
166. Carlyle. Heroes and Hero Worship 5				*	*	*
135. Chaucer. Prologue 3				*	*	*
80. Coleridge. Ancient Mariner 6	*	*	*	*	*	*
164. De Quincey. Joan of Arc, and The English Mail-Coach 5				*	*	*
161. Dickens. Tale of Two Cities 4				*	*	*
83. Eliot. Silas Marner 4	*	*	*	*	*	*
42, 130, 131. Emerson. Essays 5 (selected)				*	*	*
19-20. Franklin. Autobiography 2				*	*	*
68. Goldsmith. Deserted Village 3				*	*	*
78. Goldsmith. Vicar of Wakefield 4				*	*	*
91. Hawthorne. House of Seven Gables 4				*	*	*
155. Irving. Life of Goldsmith	*	*	*			
51-52. Irving. Sketch Book 6 (selections)						
79. Lamb's Essays of Elia 5 (selected)				*	*	*
2. Longfellow. Miles Standish 6				*	*	*
30. Lowell. Vision of Sir Launfal 6	*	*	*	*	*	*
104. Macaulay. Essay on Addison	s	s	s			
45. Macaulay. Lays of Ancient Rome 6				*	*	*
102. Macaulay. Life of Johnson 8	s	s	s	s	s	s
72. Milton. L'Allegro, Il Penseroso, etc.	s	s	s	s	s	s
119. Poe. Poems 6 (selected)				*	*	*
147. Pope. Rape of the Lock 3				*	*	*
142. Ruskin. Sesame and Lilies (selections)5				*	*	*
86. Scott. Ivanhoe 4	*	*	*	*	*	*
53. Scott. Lady of the Lake 6	*	*	*	*	*	*
165. Scott. Quentin Durward 4				*	*	*
93. Shakespeare. As You Like It 1				*	*	*
163. Shakespeare. Henry V 1				*	*	*
67. Shakespeare. Julius Cæsar 1	s	s	s	*	*	*
136. Shakespeare. Macbeth	*	*	*	s	s	s
55. Shakespeare. Merchant of Venice 1	*	*	*	*	*	*
149. Shakespeare. Twelfth Night 1				*	*	*
60-61. Sir Roger de Coverley Papers 2	*	*	*	*	*	*
160. Spenser. Faerie Queene, Book I 3				*	*	*
156. Tennyson. Gareth and Lynette, etc. 6	*	*	*	*	*	*
140. Thackeray. Henry Esmond 4				*	*	*
24. Washington. Farewell Address 7				s	s	s
56. Webster. 1st Bunker Hill Oration 7				s	s	s

The following Requirements for 1909-1911 are not published in the Riverside Literature Series: *Palgrave's* Golden Treasury, 1st Series, Bks. II and III,3 Bk. IV,6 *Mrs. Gaskell's* Cranford,4 *Blackmore's* Lorna Doone.4

1, 4, 5, 6 *Two from each group to be selected for reading, 1909-1911.*
2, 3 *One from each group to be selected for reading, 1909-1911.*
7 *These two are an alternate for Burke's Speech, 1909-1911.*
8 *One to be selected for study, 1909-1911.*

HOUGHTON, MIFFLIN AND COMPANY

A Field Guide
to the Insects

THE PETERSON FIELD GUIDE SERIES

EDITED BY ROGER TORY PETERSON

THE PETERSON FIELD GUIDE SERIES

A Field Guide
to the Insects

of

America North of Mexico

by

DONALD J. BORROR

Faculty of Entomology
The Ohio State University

and

RICHARD E. WHITE

Systematic Entomology Laboratory
United States National Museum

Color and shaded drawings by Richard E. White
Line drawings by the Authors

HOUGHTON MIFFLIN COMPANY BOSTON

1970

First Printing W

Copyright © 1970 by Donald J. Borror
and Richard E. White

Library of Congress Catalog Card Number: 70-80420

Printed in the United States of America

Editor's Note

ENTOMOLOGISTS fall into two categories: those who find insects endlessly fascinating and those who would get rid of them. Those in the first group, likely as not, begin as obsessive butterfly collectors and never quite lose their sense of wonder about the six-legged world. Those who would get rid of insects are afflicted with an impulse to drop bricks on beetles and all other small crawly things. They may eventually wind up working for chemical companies, devising more sophisticated techniques of annihilation.

Seriously, insects, because of their astronomical number, are undeniably important in our lives. They cannot be ignored. Many are "beneficial"; others, in human terms, are obviously harmful. There is much talk of the damage they do. However, if we evaluate insects across the board according to the measure of our economy, we find that they fall on the credit side of the ledger. The authors of this book point out that whereas damage by insects in the United States has been estimated to run into huge sums annually, their pollinating services alone each year are probably worth considerably more than the damage costs.

So then, indiscriminate eradication is out. Some control is necessary, but we deplore the unscientific spraying that eliminates defoliator and pollinator alike; we resent the primitive methods that kill not only the noxious insects but also their natural controls, their predators and parasites. We regret the decline of attractive butterflies along the roadsides and in our gardens. Particularly upsetting is the widespread use of persistent chemicals, such as the chlorinated hydrocarbons, which poison the ecosystem and travel through the food chain until even bald eagles, ospreys, and peregrine falcons are lethally affected.

There is a strong case for less chemical control of insects and more biological control. This requires a more critical knowledge of insects and demands the ability to differentiate between our allies and our enemies. This *Field Guide* should be useful to the new breed of economic entomologists who have the responsibility of resolving the dilemma, but it is really written primarily for the larger audience that includes the general naturalist and the ecologist, as well as the aesthetically oriented citizen who finds pleasure in the psychedelic patterns of butterflies and moths and in the porcelainlike textures of beetles.

North of the United States–Mexican border the species of insects outnumber the birds by more than 100 to 1. To be precise, about 88,600 species have been catalogued. It would be hopeless to include even a tenth of them in a book of field guide size; however, on the family level comprehensive coverage is possible. In this book the authors go below the family level in a few groups. For a complete treatment of eastern butterflies we refer the reader to *A Field Guide to the Butterflies* by Alexander B. Klots. A western butterfly guide is in preparation.

The identification of insects is more like the identification of flowers than it is like the field recognition of birds. Tiny and catchable, they may be examined in the hand. Their recognition is still a visual process, nevertheless, but more comparable to the bird-in-hand technique of early ornithology than that of present-day fieldglass bird study. The approach is more technical and a fairly complex terminology is often unavoidable. Instead of the binocular, the hand lens becomes the most useful optical instrument.

The device of the arrow in the illustrations, first used in the eastern bird guide and later applied to other books in the Field Guide Series, is particularly useful when dealing with insects, because wing venation and structural detail may be more determinative than obvious patterns and marks.

A hand lens, a folding net, and this *Field Guide* will take up little space in your knapsack or coat pocket. Take them with you on your travels and tick off the many new things you find.

ROGER TORY PETERSON

Preface

INSECTS are a remarkable group of animals. They occur almost everywhere and make up more than half of all the living things on this planet, they play a significant role in the world of nature and affect man directly or indirectly in many ways, and they exhibit some unusual physiological and structural peculiarities.

There are several hundred thousand different kinds of insects (about 88,600 in the area covered by this book), and they occur in almost every type of habitat. The only habitat they have not invaded to any extent is the ocean. Most of them are small, and some are minute. Our species vary in length from less than a millimeter to about 6 inches, but more than half of them are less than $\frac{1}{4}$ inch long. This means that they can live in small situations, and a small but diversified area may contain many kinds — there may be more kinds of insects on an acre than species of birds in the entire United States, and their numbers may be as high as several million per acre.

From man's point of view the insects are extremely important animals; some are very destructive, and many are very beneficial. Insects may damage or kill cultivated plants, they may damage or contaminate stored foods and other products, and they may attack man or animals and bite, sting, or act as vectors of disease. Annual losses caused by insects in the United States have been estimated to be about $3½ billion. On the other hand, insects do a great deal of good. Many are important agents in the pollination of plants, including most orchard trees and many vegetables and field crops; some provide products of commercial value (honey, beeswax, silk, and shellac); many are important items in the food of birds, fish, and other animals; those parasitic or predaceous on other insects help keep noxious species under control; many are valuable scavengers; some have been used in the treatment of disease; many have been used in studies of heredity, evolution, stream pollution, and other biological problems; and insects are interesting and often very beautiful animals. Most people look upon insects as undesirable pests, but we believe insects do more good than harm: insects' pollinating services alone are probably worth about $4½ billion annually in this country.

Most insects have an enormous reproductive capacity, and if it were not for the many checks on their increase (enemies, adverse environmental conditions, and the like) we would soon be overrun by them. To cite an extreme example: a pair of pomace flies (*Drosophila*), in which the female can lay a hundred eggs, may have 25 generations a year and could (if there were no checks) increase in a year to about 10^{41} flies. This number of flies, packed a thousand to the cubic inch, would form a ball 96 million miles in diameter! Many insects can reproduce parthenogenetically (without a male fertilizing the eggs), and the eggs of some insects hatch into not just one young but into many — over a thousand in the case of some of the chalcids.

We are concerned in this book primarily with the problem of identification, which is a first step in getting acquainted with any group of animals, but we have included some information on the structure, habits, and importance of the various insect groups. We hope that those beginning the study of insects with this *Field Guide* will go beyond identification to further study of these animals.

We have been aided in the preparation of this book by a great many people. Some have read portions of the manuscript and have made helpful suggestions and criticisms, and others have provided information on specific points. Various specialists, particularly in the combined United States Department of Agriculture and Smithsonian staffs of the United States National Museum, have assisted by loaning specimens used in preparing the color plates and many of the drawings. We are particularly indebted to Donald M. Anderson, Barnard D. Burks, Kellie Burks, George W. Byers, Oscar L. Cartwright, Arthur D. Cushman, Donald R. Davis, W. Donald Duckworth, J. Gordon Edwards, William D. Field, Oliver S. Flint, Richard H. Foote, Paul H. Freytag, Richard C. Froeschner, Raymond J. Gagné, Ashley B. Gurney, Jon L. Herring, Ronald W. Hodges, John M. Kingsolver, Josef N. Knull, James P. Kramer, Karl V. Krombein, John D. Lattin, Paul M. Marsh, Frank W. Mead, Frank J. Moore, C. F. W. Muesebeck, Lois B. O'Brien, André D. Pizzini, Louise M. Russell, Curtis Sabrosky, David R. Smith, Thomas E. Snyder, Paul J. Spangler, Ted J. Spilman, George C. Steyskal, Alan Stone, Eileen R. Van Tassell, Edward Todd, Charles A. Triplehorn, George B. Vogt, Luella M. Walkley, Rose Ella Warner, Donald M. Weisman, Janice White, Willis W. Wirth, and David A. Young. We wish to thank those on the staff of Houghton Mifflin Company whose expert advice and assistance have made the production of this book possible.

Contents

Illustrations

How to Use This Book

Identification. The identification of insects is not fundamentally different from the identification of birds, mammals, ferns, or other forms of life. It is simply a matter of knowing what to look for, and being able to see it. Three things complicate the problem of insect identification: there are so many different kinds of insects (some 88,600 species in North America), many are small and the identifying characters often difficult to see, and many undergo rather radical changes in appearance and habits throughout their life cycle, with the result that one may learn to recognize an insect in one stage but be unable to recognize it in another.

It is impossible in a book of this size to include all the information necessary for identifying the huge numbers of insects, so we carry the identification only to the family level (further in a few families). This reduces the problem considerably, but adds a complicating factor: many families consist of species that vary greatly in size, shape, and color. Identification in such cases must be based on certain structural details rather than color and general appearance. We reduce the problem further here by dealing principally with adults and only incidentally with immature stages.

The part of this book dealing with identification is based primarily on an examination of the insect *in the hand*. After identifying an insect by a detailed examination of its structural details, one often can recognize it in the field without examining these details. Some means of magnification is needed for seeing many of the minute features of insect structure. A 10× hand lens is sufficient in many cases, but a microscope (usually a stereoscopic microscope) is necessary for identification of many of the smaller insects.

Identification of an insect may be based on one or more characteristics: its general appearance (size, shape, and color), the form or character of various body parts (antennae, legs, wings, bristles, or other parts), how it acts (if it is alive when examined), where it is found (the type of habitat, and the part of the country), and sometimes such characters as the sounds it produces, its odor, or the hardness of its body. Many insects can be recognized by their general appearance as belonging to a particular order or group of families, but further identification often requires an examination of individual parts of the insect.

Identification of an insect is a process of progressively narrowing down the group to which the insect belongs. We suggest the following steps:

1. Identify the order to which the insect belongs. This is done by using the pictured key on the front and back endpapers. A comparison of the specimen with the first pair of alternatives will lead to further alternatives, and eventually to the order; if you are not sure at any step which way to proceed, try both alternatives. Then check your identification by consulting the paragraphs on *Identification* and *Similar orders* in the general account of that order, the information in the table on pp. 57–59, and the illustrations.

2. Identify the group of families in the order (if the order contains only a few families, proceed to step 3). The larger orders are variously subdivided, but the major groups in the order (suborders, superfamilies, etc.) are indicated in the introductory account (under *Classification*), and the distinguishing characters of each group are given at the beginning of the discussion of a group. If such a group is further subdivided, information will be given on the subdivisions, so that eventually the specimen can be narrowed down to a small group of families.

3. Identify the family. This is done by checking the paragraphs on *Identification* and also the accompanying black and white illustrations for the families in the group.

If the beginner will spend a little time studying the illustrations in this book and the information in the table on pp. 57–59, he should soon be able to recognize the order of most insects he finds — and further identification will be by the steps 2 and 3 indicated above.

Illustrations. This book contains one or more illustrations for most North American insect families, with diagnostic arrows pointing to the important distinguishing features. The families for which there are no illustrations are small or rare, and not very likely to be encountered by users of this book. A few illustrations are designed to explain the characters used in identification; the majority are intended to show the characters of individual families, and consist of drawings of individual insects and isolated body parts.

Most of the illustrations have been made of a particular species, though the species (or genus) is not always indicated. These species were selected because they are more or less typical of the group, or are the ones most likely to be encountered. Some of the simpler drawings are rather generalized and intended to represent a group of species rather than any particular one. Some families are illustrated solely by drawings of isolated body parts; the insects in such families are similar in general appearance to those in related families illustrated by drawings of entire insects.

The arrows on the illustrations indicate major diagnostic characters; usually there are italics in the accompanying text or legend page to link with the pointed arrows. Arrows ending slightly off a figure are intended to call attention to general features (shape, number of segments, etc.) of the body part indicated. Two or more arrows from a common point refer to a single character. Arrows are generally omitted when they would not indicate clearly such easily observable features as general shape and color.

The actual size of most insects illustrated is shown by a line near the drawing; for some large insects this line is in 2 or more sections. These lines generally represent body length (from front of the head to tip of the abdomen, or to the wing tips if they extend beyond the abdomen); horizontal lines in some cases represent wingspread. If there is no size line, information on size will be found in the text.

Terms, Abbreviations, and Symbols. Many terms referring to body parts or areas are defined where they are used. For terms not so defined consult the Glossary (p. 363).

A few abbreviations and symbols are used in the descriptions: FW, front wing; HW, hind wing; ♂, male; ♀, female. Measurements, unless otherwise stated, refer to body length. Smaller measurements are given in millimeters. Comparison of millimeter and inch scales is shown below.

All venational characters, unless otherwise stated, refer to the front wing. Any reference to the number of cells in a specific part of the wing refers to the number of closed cells (those not reaching the wing margin) unless otherwise indicated.

Geographical Coverage. This book covers the families of insects occurring in North America north of Mexico. The characters given for each group apply to North American species, and may not apply to all the species occurring elsewhere. The terms "N. America" and "N. American" refer to that portion of the continent north of Mexico. Groups for which no information is given on geographic range are widely distributed in North America. Most of the figures given for the number of species in a group are conservative estimates.

CENTIMETERS (1 CM. = 10 MM.)

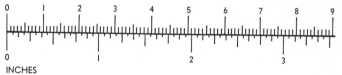

Comparison of millimeter and inch scales.

Collecting and Preserving Insects

COLLECTING and preserving insects is an ideal way to learn about them, and can be an interesting hobby. It provides the satisfaction of learning at first hand, and enables the collector to discover things about insects that he might not learn from books. It also provides material for the study of structural details that serve as identification characters. There are few restrictions against collecting insects compared to those for collecting other animals or plants. The average landowner has no objection to insect collecting on his property, and it is only in a few places such as parks where collecting may be restricted. Insects are so abundant that ordinary collecting has little or no effect on their numbers; the student of insects need not worry that his collecting activities will upset the balance of nature.

When and Where to Look for Insects

Insects occur almost everywhere, and the more places you examine the more kinds of insects you are likely to find. Insects are small and live in small habitats; different species may often be found only a few inches or a few feet apart. If you know where to look, you can find at least some insects virtually any time, but collecting will be more profitable from spring to fall than in the winter. Different insects are active at different times of the year, hence collecting throughout the year will yield a wider range of insects than collecting for only a part of the year.

You can begin your collecting at home, where you may find insects on pets, or infesting food, clothing, and other materials. On warm evenings outdoor insects are attracted to porch lights and windows of lighted rooms.

A good place outdoors to look for insects is on plants; each plant will attract certain species. Other insects occur in various concealed situations, such as in leaf litter or debris, under stones or other objects, in fungi, under bark, in dead logs, in decaying materials, and in the ground. Many insects live in water, either throughout their lives or during their immature stages, and may be found in different parts of specialized aquatic habitats. Adults of insects occurring in water only during their immature stages are usually found near water.

4

Collecting Equipment and How to Use It

The minimum equipment necessary to collect insects consists of your hands and a container for the insects collected. Certain tools are very helpful, nonetheless. For general collecting they include a net, killing jars, vials of preservative, envelopes, and small boxes; other tools are useful in some types of collecting. A pair of forceps is excellent for handling insects, as is a hand lens for examining them. Many of these items can be carried in a shoulder bag; the forceps and hand lens can be carried on a string around your neck.

The Net. A net for general collecting should be light and strong and have a fairly open mesh so that it can be swung easily and an insect can be seen through it. The size may depend on your personal preference, but most nets have a handle 2½ to 3 ft. long and a rim about 1 ft. in diameter; the bag should be about twice as long as the diameter of the rim, and rounded at the bottom. Marquisette, scrim, bobbinet, and bolting cloth are good materials for the bag, which should have a heavier material, such as muslin, around the rim. A fine-mesh bolting cloth is probably the best material for the bag of a net that will be used primarily for sweeping.

Insect nets can be purchased from a supply house (prices ranging upward from a few dollars) or they can be homemade; homemade nets cost considerably less. An insect net can be made with a broom handle or similar stick, a wire for the rim, and a cloth bag, as shown in the illustration on the next page. If you prefer a net that can be taken apart and carried inconspicuously, use the frame of a fish-landing net, which you can buy from a sporting-goods store.

An insect net can be used in 2 general ways: you may look for an insect and swing at it or you may simply swing the net through vegetation. The first method requires a certain amount of speed and skill, especially for active or fast-flying insects. The second method, usually called "sweeping," can yield a considerable quantity and variety of small insects.

Insects caught in a net can be removed in various ways. Take care to prevent their escaping before you take them out of the net. Remove them with as little resultant damage as possible and — in the case of insects that bite or sting — without injury to yourself. You can keep an active insect from escaping by quickly turning the net handle to fold the bag over the rim.

Most insects can be removed from a net by grasping them through the net with the fingers. Small or fragile insects, easily damaged by this method, can be removed in these ways: (1) by inserting a box or bottle into the net and getting the insect directly into this container; (2) by working the insect into a fold of the net and placing this fold into a killing jar to stun the insect; or (3) by removing the insect with an aspirator (see p. 9). The first method is the one used by many collectors to remove butterflies or moths

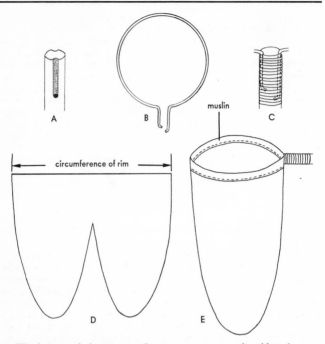

The homemade insect net. Cut grooves on opposite sides of one end of handle, as shown in A, 1 to about 2 in. from end and the other to about 3 in. from end; drill a hole about halfway through handle at end of each groove. Bend wire for rim (about No. 8 gauge) as shown in B, fit into holes and grooves, and fasten it there with fine wire or heavy cord (C). Cut material for bag as shown in D and sew. Completed bag, with muslin around rim, is shown in E.

from a net, since direct handling of the specimen often causes some of the scales to be rubbed off. If a butterfly or moth is grasped by the fingers through the net, grasp it by the body not the wings, and stun it by pinching the thorax before putting it into a killing jar (to reduce fluttering and wing damage in the jar).

Many beginners may be reluctant to grasp an insect for fear that it might bite or sting; such is much less likely than most people believe. An insect that bites does so by moving its jaws sideways and pinching or by piercing with the beak. Very few pinching insects are capable of causing pain or breaking the skin, and those that can are generally very large insects. Most biting insects are unable to bite if grasped firmly by the sides of the body.

An insect that stings does so with a structure at the posterior end of the body — usually quite readily. The only stinging insects are the bees, wasps, and some of the ants, and females alone can sting. Many flies and a few other insects strongly resemble bees or wasps but are quite harmless. If an insect in a net is one that might sting, remove it from the net in one of three ways: (1) put a fold of the net containing the insect into a killing jar until the insect is stunned (or pour an anesthetic such as chloroform over the fold of the net to stun the insect); (2) grasp the insect through the net with forceps and remove it; or (3) work the insect into a fold of the net, stun it by pinching the thorax, and then remove it. The third method is the simplest and quickest.

Insects caught by sweeping can be removed by shaking them to the bottom of the net and stunning them by the first method described above.

Killing Jars. Insects can be studied alive with considerable interest and profit, but it is well to kill and preserve a few. The characters that differentiate insects can be studied best in preserved specimens, and insect collections can be both attractive and instructive.

Killing jars are of various sizes and shapes, depending on the use they will receive. It is advisable to have 2 or more jars in the field, for insects of different types. Wide-mouthed jars are preferable to narrow-mouthed ones, and glass jars should be reinforced with tape to reduce the hazards of breakage. Several materials can be used as killing agents, but the best are probably ethyl acetate and cyanide. Ethyl acetate is a much safer material to use than cyanide, but does not kill as quickly, and jars made with it must be recharged frequently; specimens killed by ethyl acetate are usually more relaxed than those killed by cyanide, and less likely to be discolored. Cyanide jars last much longer, and are quite safe to use if certain precautions are observed. Most collectors prefer to use killing jars made with cyanide.

Ethyl acetate (an ingredient of nail polish) is a clear liquid, and its fumes act as the killing agent. Jars made with it must contain something absorptive. Cotton or cloth can be used as the absorbent material, but plaster of paris is better. Pour a mixture of plaster of paris and water into the jar and allow it to set and dry; then place a few eyedroppers of the acetate on the plaster (which absorbs it), and the bottle is ready for use. Take care not to put in too much acetate, because wet insects make poor specimens. Add more ethyl acetate every few days.

Cyanide jars can be made with calcium, sodium, or potassium cyanide. Calcium cyanide is a dark gray powder often used as a fumigant and ordinarily is obtained from a store that sells insecticides. Sodium cyanide comes in the form of balls about an inch in diameter, which must be crushed before use in a killing jar; it is obtained from a company dealing in insecticides or chemicals.

Potassium cyanide (which looks like sugar) is usually available at a drugstore. The toxic agent in a cyanide jar is hydrogen cyanide, an extremely poisonous gas given off by the action of moisture on the cyanide. Calcium cyanide releases this gas very rapidly, and is perhaps the most dangerous type of cyanide to use; jars made with it ordinarily last only a month or two. Sodium and potassium cyanides give off the gas less rapidly and are less dangerous to use; jars made with them may last a year or more. Cyanide jars are easy to make but we recommend that the beginner not attempt to make his own. He can ask someone experienced in handling cyanide to make them for him or else buy them from a supply house.

The chief hazard in the use of cyanide jars is not so much the gas given off (which is toxic if inhaled in quantity) as the possibility of a broken jar and a cut hand. This hazard can be greatly reduced by covering the bottom part of the jar with adhesive, masking, or electric tape. *All* killing jars should be so taped, and all should be conspicuously labeled POISON.

Other materials that can be used in a killing jar are carbon tetrachloride and chloroform. Carbon tetrachloride is the easier to obtain but is more dangerous. A killing jar made with either of these materials (which are liquids) is made in the same way as an ethyl acetate jar, and must be recharged frequently.

The efficiency of a killing jar depends to a large extent on how it is used. Never leave it open any longer than necessary. The hazard of an open jar, even one made with cyanide, is not very great, but the escaping gas reduces the strength of the jar. Keep the inside of the jar dry. Moisture from the insects or from the plaster sometimes condenses on the sides, particularly if the jar is exposed to bright sunlight. Moisture can be reduced by keeping a few pieces of cleansing tissue in the jar. When butterflies or moths are put into a jar, many of their scales come off and remain there; other insects put into this jar will become covered with the scales and look dusty. It is advisable to have a special jar for butterflies and moths and put other insects into different jars. All killing jars should be wiped out occasionally.

The time required for a killing jar to kill an insect depends on both the jar and the insect, and may vary considerably. Insects can be left in an ethyl acetate jar for long periods without damage, but if left too long in a cyanide jar they may become discolored. Remove insects from a jar within an hour or two after they are killed.

Specimens removed from a killing jar in the field may be stored temporarily in small boxes or envelopes; the boxes should contain some pieces of cleansing tissue. Letter envelopes, or triangular ones (see illus. opp.), are better for insects with small bodies and large wings (butterflies, moths, dragonflies, etc.). Place the specimen in the envelope with the wings together above the body and write collecting data on the outside of the envelope.

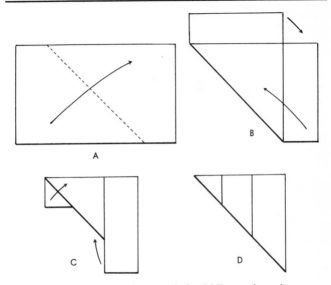

A triangular paper envelope, made by folding a piece of paper as shown in A, B, and C to form the completed envelope (D).

Beating. Many insects that occur on plants "play dead" and drop off the plant when it is jarred. You can collect such insects by placing a net or sheet under the plant and beating the plant with a stick. An insect net does not provide much collecting area. A better device is a sheet of white cloth about a yard square, held spread out by two slender pieces of wood along the diagonals of the cloth.

Sifters. Insects occurring in leaf litter or debris are most easily collected by some kind of sifting device. The simplest procedure is to shake a handful of the debris onto a sheet or cloth. Small animals present will be detected by their movement and can be picked up with forceps, an aspirator, or a wet brush. A more efficient method is to use a Berlese funnel, a large funnel with a circular piece of screen or hardware cloth in it. The material to be sifted is placed in the funnel on the screen, the funnel is held upright with a ringstand or other support, and a container (usually of alcohol) is placed below the funnel. As the material dries (this can be hastened by a light bulb over the material) the insects move downward, and eventually go into the container below the funnel. Generally it takes a few hours to get most of the insects out of the material by this method.

Aspirator. An aspirator is a device with which insects are sucked into a vial or other container. This container has intake and mouth-piece tubes entering it; the intake tube is usually a piece of ¼-in. glass tubing about 6 in. long, and the mouthpiece tube is ¼-in. glass tubing through the cork plus 1½ to 2 ft. of rubber tubing, with a piece of cloth over the inner end to prevent insects from being sucked into the mouth. Place the end of the intake tube close to the insect and suck through the mouthpiece. An aspirator is useful for collecting small, not too active insects, either from an insect net, a plant, or another situation. The insects so collected may be kept alive or transferred to a killing jar.

Traps. Insect traps can be constructed in various ways, and the attractant used will determine the types of insects likely to be caught. The attractant may be artificial light, decaying meat or fruit, or other things. The traps are constructed so that once the insects get in they cannot get out. Some traps (such as those with light as the attractant) may be constructed to direct the caught insects eventually into a container of alcohol or a killing jar; others (such as traps baited with decaying materials) may be constructed to direct the insects into a special chamber and not into the bait.

Insects attracted to lights or baits may often be collected by hand or with a net, without use of a trap. Insects attracted to a light, for example, can be collected directly into a killing jar or other container when they alight on some surface nearby (a light-colored wall or sheet). Thus you can collect only those specimens in which you are particularly interested.

Aquatic Collecting Equipment. Many aquatic insects can be collected by hand or with forceps from objects in the water; more can be collected with a net or other device. An aquatic net should be much sturdier than an aerial net, with a bag no deeper than the diameter of the rim. Kitchen strainers 4 to 6 in. in diameter make good dip nets.

If a dip net or strainer comes up full of mud and debris, the insects taken may be difficult to see unless they move. To locate them, dump the net contents into a white-bottomed pan of water. Insects are easily seen against this white background, and can be removed by hand, forceps, or eyedropper. Small free-swimming forms like mosquito larvae are best collected with a long-handled white enameled dipper, in which the insects similarly show up well. Remove them with an eyedropper.

Other Equipment and Methods. Many insects can be collected directly into a killing jar or other container, without the use of a net. This is the simplest way to collect insects that alight on a flat surface and do not fly too readily, and many insects on flowers. Various types of buildings often serve as insect traps; insects fly in and alight on the walls or ceiling and remain there, or they alight on windows — from which they can be collected directly into a jar.

A heavy knife is useful for cutting into logs or branches, opening galls, prying up bark, or digging into places that may harbor insects. Keep at hand a notebook and pencil for taking notes, and make triangular paper envelopes from the notebook pages.

Collecting some kinds of insects requires special equipment not mentioned above. An ingenious collector should be able to devise equipment and procedures for collecting such insects.

Mounting and Preserving Insects

Most insects are preserved dry, normally on pins, and once dry will keep indefinitely. Soft-bodied insects must be preserved in liquids, since they shrivel or become distorted if preserved dry. Minute insects that are hard-bodied may be mounted (dry) on "points," but many must be mounted on microscope slides for detailed study. Insects that are preserved dry should be pinned or mounted as soon as possible after they are collected; if allowed to dry first they become very brittle and may be broken in the process of mounting.

Relaxing Specimens. Dried specimens can be relaxed by placing them in a humid atmosphere for a few days; any airtight jar can be used as a relaxing chamber. Cover the bottom of the jar with wet sand (add phenol or ethyl acetate to prevent mold), put the insects into the jar in small open boxes or envelopes, and close the jar.

Pinning. Insects sufficiently hard-bodied to retain their shape when dry, and big enough to pin, are normally preserved by pinning. Common pins are too thick and too short, and they rust; insects should be pinned with *insect pins*, made especially for this purpose, which can be bought from a supply house. They are available in various sizes (thicknesses). The best sizes for general use are Nos. 1 (very slender), 2 (less slender), and 3 (thicker, for larger insects).

Most insects are pinned vertically through the thorax; a few are pinned sideways. Beetles and hoppers are pinned through the front part of the right wing, at a point where the pin on emerging from the underside of the body will not damage a leg. Bugs are pinned through the scutellum (p. 33) if it is large enough to take a pin or through the right wing, as for beetles. Grasshoppers and crickets are pinned through the rear edge of the pronotum, just to the right of the midline. A treehopper is pinned through the pronotum just to the right of the midline. Dragonflies and damselflies can be pinned vertically through the thorax with the wings horizontal, but it is better to pin them sideways, left side up, with the wings together above the body, the pin going through the thorax below the wing bases. If the wings are not together when the specimen is removed from the killing jar, place the specimen in an envelope (the wings together above the body) for a day or two until it has dried enough for the wings to stay in this position; then pin it.

The simplest way to pin an insect is to hold it between the thumb and forefinger of one hand and insert the pin with the other hand. All specimens and labels put on a pin should be at a uniform height; this is most easily accomplished with a pinning block.

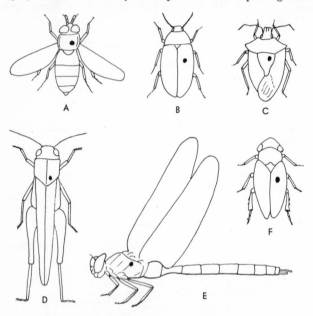

How insects are pinned. The black spots show the location of the pin in the case of flies (A), beetles (B), bugs (C), grasshoppers (D), dragonflies and damselflies (E), and leafhoppers, froghoppers, and planthoppers (F).

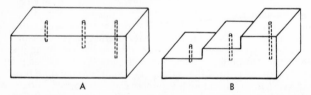

Pinning blocks. These may be made of a rectangular piece of wood (A) or one shaped like steps (B), with holes drilled to 1, ⅝, and ⅜ in. After placing a specimen on a pin, insert the pin in the 1-in. hole until it touches bottom. The ⅝-in. hole is used to position the locality-date label on the pin, and the ⅜-in. hole to position a second label, if there is one.

Mount the insect about an inch up on the pin. With large-bodied insects there should be enough of the pin above the insect to permit easy handling.

Sagging of the abdomen of a pinned insect (like a dragonfly) can be prevented in the following ways: (1) by sticking the pinned specimen onto a vertical surface, with the abdomen hanging down, and leaving it there until the abdomen dries; or (2) by placing a small piece of cardboard on the pin, just under and supporting the insect, and leaving it there until the insect dries; or (3) by supporting the sagging abdomen with crossed pins, the abdomen resting in the angle where the pins cross.

A sheet of cork, balsa wood, or other soft material is useful for the temporary storage of pinned specimens until they can be sorted and placed in boxes.

Mounting Small Insects on Pins. Insects hard-bodied enough to mount dry but too small to pin are usually mounted on "points." Points are small triangular pieces of cardboard, about 8 mm. long and 3 or 4 mm. wide at the base; the pin is put through the base of the point and the insect is glued to the tip. Points can be cut with scissors or punched out with a special punch (obtainable from a supply house), or they can be purchased from a supply house.

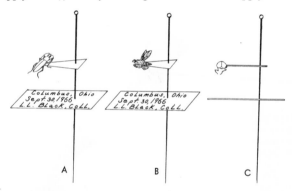

Mounting small insects on points. A, beetle, dorsal side up; B, fly, left side up; C, beetle mounted dorsal side up, attached by its side to the bent-down tip of the point.

Insects put on points should be glued so that the body parts to be examined in identifying the insect are not obscured. The best position for an insect is on its right side, with the head away from the pin (B, above). Flat insects that may be difficult to mount on their side are usually mounted dorsal side up at the extreme tip of the point.

Place an insect that is to be put on a point at the edge of a block,

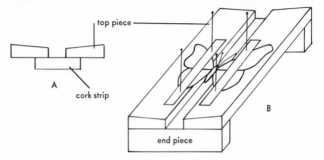

A spreading board. A, cross section showing relation of cork strip to groove in center of board; B, a board containing a spread specimen. Supply-house boards are generally 12 in. long and 4 to 6 in. wide; the top pieces are $\frac{3}{8}$ in. thick at the inner edge and $\frac{1}{2}$ in. thick at the outer edge. The center groove may be $\frac{1}{4}$ to $\frac{1}{2}$ in. or more wide, depending on the size of the insects to be spread on it; the width of this groove is adjustable in some supply-house boards. The top pieces should be of wood soft enough to take a pin easily.

grasp a pin containing a point by the sharp end, and touch the tip of the upper surface of the point to a drop of glue and then to the insect. Long and slender insects put on points should be put on 2 points that have their tips separated to form a V. Use glue or household cement, *not* mucilage.

Very small insects are sometimes mounted on "minuten" pins instead of points; they are short and very slender. Insert one end of the pin into the insect and the other into a small piece of cork on a regulation insect pin.

Spreading. The position of the legs and wings in a pinned insect is generally not important, as long as all parts can be seen and studied, but some insects (such as butterflies, moths, and perhaps some others) should have their wings spread before being put into the collection. An insect can be spread on a spreading board or spread upside down on a flat surface; the position of the wings depends on the type of insect. A spreading board (see illustration above), which can be bought from a supply house or can be home-made, is used for specimens going into a pinned collection. The specimens are usually spread dorsal side up. An insect to be mounted under glass, as in a Riker or glass mount (see pp. 19–20), is spread on any flat surface soft enough to take an insect pin and placed in an upside-down position. The spreading process consists of placing the wings in a standard position and fastening them there (with strips of paper), and leaving them to dry in that position.

The wings of a butterfly, moth, or other insect in which the front wings are more or less triangular are spread with the hind margin of the front wings at right angles to the body, and the hind wings far enough forward so that there is no large gap at the side between the front and hind wings (see illustrations of such insects in this book). In grasshoppers, damselflies, dragonflies, and other insects whose front wings are elongate rather than triangular, the wings are generally spread with the front edge of the hind wing at a right angle to the body and with the front wings far enough forward to just clear the hind wings. The front and hind wings of a butterfly, moth, or mayfly overlap at the base, with the front edge of the hind wing under the rear edge of the front wing, and should be so overlapped when spread. The front and hind wings of most other insects are not overlapped when spread.

For the beginner and those interested primarily in mounting a few large or showy insects for display, we recommend spreading the insect in an upside-down position and mounting it under glass; spreading is easier this way, and does not require a special spreading board. For the more advanced student, or anyone planning to specialize in insects that are normally spread, we recommend the use of a spreading board.

The steps in spreading a butterfly in an upside-down position are illustrated on p. 16. Butterflies and moths must be handled carefully (forceps preferred) to avoid rubbing scales off the wings. To spread a butterfly, grasp it by the thorax, ventral side up, and insert a pin through the thorax. Pin the insect on its back on a flat surface; if the wings are together above its back, spread them apart with forceps as the insect is lowered to the surface. Pin strips of paper over the wings on each side (A). Remove the lower pin on one side and, holding the strip fairly tight, raise the front wing. Do this with a pin, placing the pin behind a heavy vein near the front basal part of the wing; avoid pushing the pin through the wing because this leaves a hole. If the body tends to swivel, insert a pin alongside it at the base of the abdomen. When the wing is raised to the proper position (rear edge at a right angle to the body) insert a pin through the paper strip just in front of the front edge of the wing (B); pin the lower end of the strip down, anywhere behind the hind wing. Now do the same thing on the other side (C). Next raise one hind wing so that the notch at the side between the two wings is reduced, and pin the paper strip just behind the rear edge of the hind wing (D). Repeat the process on the other side (E). Next orient the antennae to a symmetrical position and hold them in place by pins placed alongside them (E). Now hold the body down with forceps at the pin through the body, and carefully remove this pin (F). If the legs project upward very far fasten them close to the body with a strip of paper across the entire specimen, at right angles to the body. Data on when and where the specimen was collected should be noted beside it, this information accompanying the specimen when it is later put into the collection.

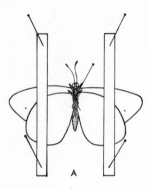
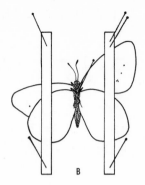
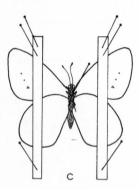
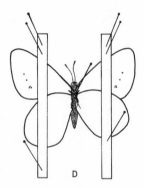
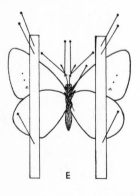
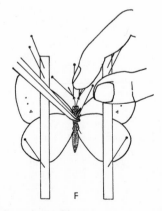

Steps in spreading a butterfly.

The time required for a spread specimen to dry will vary with its size and with temperature and humidity. A large butterfly or moth that might take several days to dry at normal room conditions can be dried in an hour or two with heat — in an oven or under an electric light. To determine if the specimen is dry, touch the abdomen gently with a pin; if the body is stiff the specimen is dry, but if the abdomen is still flexible the specimen is not yet dry.

A specimen spread on a spreading board is spread the same way, except that the insect is pinned through the thorax from above and placed at the standard height on the pin. The pinned specimen is then placed on the board, the pin going into (perhaps through) the cork strip at the bottom of the groove, until the base of the wings is even with the upper surface of the top piece of the board. Next the wings are spread and fastened down and the antennae oriented to a symmetrical position. Do not remove the pin in the insect's body after the spreading.

Mounting on Slides. Small insects, particularly soft-bodied forms that shrivel when preserved dry, and various insect parts (genitalia, wings, mouth parts, etc.) are often mounted on slides for detailed study. Insects and parts that are thick or dark-colored are usually cleared (made translucent) before mounting. Then they are mounted on microscope slides in some type of mounting medium (like Canada balsam). Such mounting involves treatment of the specimen with various reagents. Consult technical books for an explanation of the process.

Insect wings can be mounted on slides (preferably 2 x 2 in., which can be projected) without any mounting medium. If the wings are not folded they can be broken off a dried specimen, placed on a 2 x 2 slide and oriented, another slide put on top, and the slides taped together. Such a slide is permanent, and can be made in a few minutes. A folded wing must be relaxed and unfolded before it is mounted. This is done by putting the wing in alcohol or a special relaxing solution. The flattened wings are allowed to dry before the other slide is added. The wings of butterflies and moths can be mounted this way, but cannot be projected unless the scales are bleached or removed; directions for doing this are given on p. 221.

Preservation in Envelopes. Use envelopes for the permanent preservation of slender and relatively fragile insects such as dragonflies, damselflies, and crane flies. This method saves considerable space compared to mounting on pins, and the specimens are less apt to be broken (or if they are, the parts are not lost). The simplest type of envelope is a triangular one (see p. 9), labeled on the outside. If clear plastic envelopes are used, it is possible to study the specimens without removing them from the envelope. Labeling for specimens in plastic envelopes can be done on a white card (same size as the envelope) placed inside with the specimen.

Preservation in Fluids. Larvae, nymphs, and soft-bodied adults are usually preserved in fluids, since they shrivel when preserved dry. The best preservative is a 75–80 percent solution of ethyl alcohol. Alcohol is a killing agent for most insects but is unsatisfactory for killing larvae — it may distort or discolor them. Larvae should be killed by hot water or chemicals. A good killing solution for larvae is one containing 1 part of kerosene, 7–10 parts of 95 percent ethyl alcohol (less for very soft-bodied larvae), 2 parts of glacial acetic acid, and 1 part of dioxane. Isopropyl alcohol (rubbing alcohol) will serve if ethyl alcohol is not available.

Containers of specimens preserved in alcohol should be completely filled with alcohol and tightly stoppered to reduce or prevent evaporation. If a large number of specimens are killed in a small amount of alcohol, this alcohol should be replaced after a day or two. Rubber stoppers are better than cork ones. Periodically inspect containers of specimens in fluid and replace any evaporated fluid.

Arrangement and Care of the Collection

Labeling. All specimens should be labeled with at least the locality and date of their capture — specimens without such labels are of little value. The name of the collector and in some cases information on the habitat or food of the specimen are also helpful. For pinned insects put this information on one or two small pieces of paper on the pin below the insect; for specimens mounted on slides put it on a slide label, and on a piece of paper (in pencil or waterproof ink) placed inside the container for specimens preserved in fluid.

Labels on pinned specimens should be on fairly stiff white paper no larger than about $\frac{1}{4}$ x $\frac{3}{4}$ in. (or smaller), at a uniform height on the pin (achieved with a pinning block) and parallel with the insect (or point). Locality labels may be handwritten or printed. Printed labels can be obtained from a supply house or cut from a photograph of a sheet of typewritten labels. The locality given should indicate the capture site as closely as possible. The county may be sufficient in some cases, but if the county is large list the town or other site. Place these labels on the pins in the same way

Columbus Columbus Columbus Columbus	Lincoln Co., Lincoln Co., Lincoln Co.,
O. O. O. O.	Me. Me. Me.
Columbus Columbus Columbus Columbus	D.J. Borror D.J. Borror D.J. Borror
O. O. O. O.	Lincoln Co., Lincoln Co., Lincoln Co.,
Columbus Columbus Columbus Columbus	Me. Me. Me.
O. O. O. O.	D.J. Borror D.J. Borror D.J. Borror
Columbus Columbus Columbus Columbus	Lincoln Co., Lincoln Co., Lincoln Co.,
O. O. O. O.	Me. Me. Me.
	D.J. Borror D.J. Borror D.J. Borror

A   B

Sheets of locality labels, actual size, with locality alone (A) or locality and collector (B), each label with a space for writing in the date.

throughout the collection — whether they are read from the right or left is a matter of personal preference.

An insect collection should contain some identification labels. How these are best arranged will depend on the size of the collection and the extent to which it is identified. Most collections should be labeled at least to order and family, and the specimens so arranged that a single label can serve for all the specimens in a group. When specimens are labeled to species, an identification label is placed on each specimen or on the first in a group. This label is a plain piece of paper (about an inch square and at the base of the pin) containing the scientific name of the insect, the name of the person identifying it, and the date (month and year) the identification was made.

Boxes for Pinned Insects. Pinned insects are kept in boxes having a soft material in the bottom to permit easy pinning; they can be obtained from a supply house or be homemade. The most common supply-house type is a Schmitt box, a wooden box about 9 x 12 x 2½ in. with a tight-fitting lid and the bottom lined with sheet cork or similar material. Such boxes cost from a few to several dollars. Similar boxes made of heavy cardboard are available from supply houses and cost one half to one third as much. Homemade boxes may be made of wood or heavy cardboard, and the bottom lined with sheet cork, balsa wood, Styrofoam, or corrugated cardboard. The material in the bottom should fit tightly, and if corrugated cardboard is used it should be soft enough to take an insect pin. Large collections may be housed in Schmitt boxes, or in cabinets containing trays or drawers constructed like Schmitt boxes.

Riker Mounts. A Riker mount is a glass-topped box containing cotton, with insects on the cotton just under the glass. Insects spread for mounting in a Riker mount are spread in the upside-down position described on p. 15. Riker mounts may be of various sizes, and also can be purchased from a supply house or be home-

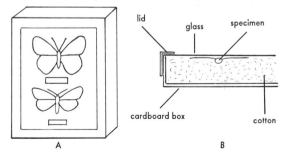

The Riker mount. A, a completed mount; B, sectional view showing a specimen in place under the glass.

made. Homemade boxes can be made from a cardboard box, a piece of glass cut to fit inside the lid, and binding tape. The box should be about an inch deep; cut deeper boxes down to this depth. Cut out a section of the lid, leaving about a ⅜-in. margin around the edge. Covering the lid with tape will improve its appearance. Fasten the glass inside the lid with strips of tape placed so that they do not show from the outside. If you want to hang up the mount put 2 brass fasteners on the bottom and reinforce them inside with tape, then tie a string or wire between them on the outside. Before putting a thick-bodied insect into a Riker mount, tease the cotton to make a small depression for the body. Fasten the lid on the mount with pins or tape.

Specimens in Riker mounts are easily displayed, and the mounts can take considerable handling without damage to the specimens. A repellent can be placed under the cotton to protect the specimens from pests. Riker mounts have 2 disadvantages: only 1 side of the specimen can be seen and many moths will fade after prolonged exposure to light.

Glass Mounts. Glass mounts are similar to Riker mounts, but have glass on both top and bottom and contain no cotton; both sides of the specimen(s) are visible. They generally contain only one or a few specimens, and can be made in various ways. The following procedure is relatively simple:

1. Spread specimen in an upside-down position and fasten legs close to the body.

2. Cut 2 identical pieces of glass for top and bottom of the mount, allowing a margin of at least ¼ in. on all 4 sides of the specimen(s).

3. Cut enough supporting glass to provide room for body of the insect. These pieces will be as long as 1 dimension (usually the shorter) of top and bottom pieces, and a width that will leave a

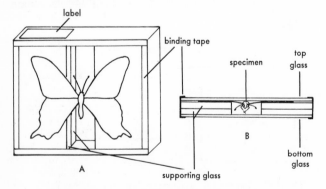

A glass mount. A, the finished mount; B, sectional view.

space in center of the mount 2 or 3 times as wide as body of the insect.

4. Clean the glass thoroughly, preferably with a glass cleaner; use a brush to remove lint from the glass.

5. Fasten the pieces of supporting glass to bottom piece with a small drop of cement (such as Duco household cement) on each outside corner; press each supporting piece into position, in line with the edges of bottom glass; remove any excess cement. Allow time for cement on one piece to set before the next piece is added.

6. When the supporting glass is in position, place specimen on the supporting pieces and center it. Put a small drop of cement on the 4 outer corners, then put on the top glass, being careful not to move the specimen. Press this glass down hard and put a small weight on it; leave the weight in place until cement sets (an hour or more).

7. Tape edges of the mount with slide-binding or electric tape; this covers any sharp edges of the glass, and gives the mount a finished look. The label is placed as shown.

Glass mounts are inexpensive, easy to make, and they provide a safe and attractive method for storage and display. If specimens put into these mounts are heat dried or otherwise made pest-free before mounting, they should remain pest-free. Two or more specimens can be put in a single mount by placing one above the other, or side by side (with 3 groups of supporting glass). The use of standard sizes will simplify glass cutting and mount storage.

Plastic Mounts. Plastic mounts may consist of 2 sheets of thick plastic with the insect mounted between them, or a plastic block in which the insect is embedded. If 2 sheets are used, each is bulged out where the insect's body will be, the 2 sheets are put together with the insect between them, and sealed around the edge with acetone or tape. Embedding an insect in a block of plastic is a rather involved process, but the final product is an attractive, durable, and permanent mount. Supply houses offer materials for this type of mounting and instructions for their use.

Protection of a Collection from Pests. Insect collections are subject to attack by dermestid beetles and other pests, which will ruin the collection if it is not protected. Insect boxes can be protected with a repellent such as naphthalene flakes or paradichlorobenzene (napthalene flakes last longer). The repellent in a box of pinned insects can be put in a small pillbox or wrapped in a piece of cloth firmly attached to a corner of the box. The repellent in a Riker mount is placed under the cotton. Collections should be examined periodically for signs of damage, and if pests are detected the collection should be fumigated or heat-treated. It is not possible to put repellent in a glass mount, so take care to make sure that specimens are pest-free when put in these mounts.

Handling Specimens. Insects are very brittle when dry. Careless handling of a pinned specimen can result in the loss of legs, antennae, or other parts. Broken-off parts often can be replaced by use of glue or cement. Experience (and accidental damaging of prize specimens) will impress on the collector the importance of care in handling mounted specimens.

Supply Houses

Much of the equipment necessary for making an insect collection can be homemade or purchased in local stores, but some items must be obtained from a supply house. A few of the leading supply houses are:

Bio Metal Associates, 316 Washington St., El Segundo, Calif. 90245. Eastern office: BioQuip East, 1115 Rolling Rd., Baltimore, Md. 21228. Western office: BioQuip West, P.O. Box 61, Santa Monica, Calif. 90406

Carolina Biological Supply Co., Burlington, N.C. 27216

General Biological Supply House, Inc., 8200 S. Hoyne Ave., Chicago, Ill. 60620

Powell Laboratories, Gladstone, Oregon 97027

Ward's Natural Science Establishment, Inc., P.O. Box 1712, Rochester, N.Y. 14603

Ward's of California, P.O. Box 1749, Monterey, Calif. 93942.

Work with Living Insects

THE STUDENT of insects who does nothing but collect, kill, and mount these animals and study the dead specimens will miss the most interesting part of insect study. Anyone who takes time to study *living* insects will find that they are fascinating and often amazing little animals. They can be studied in the field or in captivity. Many are very easy to keep in captivity, where they can be studied more easily and at closer range than in the field.

Some collectors try to catch an insect as soon as they see it. We suggest that you occasionally stop and watch an insect awhile before you try to collect it. In the case of fast-flying insects such as dragonflies, you will probably not be able to catch one the instant you see it and may be compelled to watch. This may try your patience, but in observing it you may learn things about its habits that you would not learn if you caught it immediately.

If insects are kept in captivity a short period and released (or put into the collection), they require only simple containers and relatively little care. If collected in immature stages and kept until the adults appear, they require more care and sometimes special containers. If cultures are maintained throughout one or more generations, special containers and even more attention are necessary.

Field Observations

You can insect-watch much as you might bird-watch — by going into the field and keeping your eyes and ears open. A binocular is seldom needed, as for bird-watching, except occasionally for such insects as dragonflies. A hand lens, however, is very helpful.

A pond is an excellent place for watching insects. it probably has water striders and whirligig beetles moving about on its surface, various beetles, bugs, and other insects in shallow water where they can be watched from shore, and dragonflies, damselflies, and other insects flying or resting near or over the pond. Brief observation of the dragonflies, for example, will reveal that each species has a definite zone (height) of flight above the water surface, each flies and rests in a characteristic manner, and each has a particular method of laying eggs, flying in tandem, and chasing other individuals. An observer will discover that some of the larger dragonflies patrol definite territories; they will attempt to mate with any female of their species entering this territory,

23

and will engage in characteristic dances or chases with other males of their species that enter the territory. An examination of the vegetation around the edge of a pond may reveal nymphs transforming into adults. This process — the adult emerging from the nymphal skin and expanding — takes from one-half hour to an hour, and at the right season it is not difficult to find emerging individuals.

Another good place to watch insects is at flowers. Many insects occur there, and although some of them are fairly small they can usually be observed at close range. Observation of the bees will reveal the basis of the expression "busy as a bee"; a butterfly may be seen uncoiling its proboscis and extending it down into the flower; and the sunlight striking the wings of a hovering syrphid fly will make it look like a small jewel. Some animals occurring on flowers are predators, and feed not on the flower but on the bees and flies that visit it. If you observe a flower containing a crab spider or an ambush bug for a while, you might see either animal catch its prey, and you will be surprised at how large an insect it can catch. The observant insect-watcher will see many instances of one animal eating another.

Ants are very interesting insects, especially at or near their nest, or on plants in association with aphids. The ground around a large mound nest may be almost alive with ants coming or going, perhaps carrying something. If a stone or board is lifted and an ant nest under it is exposed, the ants will busily transport their young to the shelter of their underground burrows. A few ants are often found around a large cluster of aphids on a plant; if you observe these for a time you may see the ants feeding on a watery fluid (honeydew) that issues from the end of the aphid's abdomen.

A plant selected at random and examined carefully will seldom fail to have some insects on it, and there are likely to be many kinds — each on a particular part of the plant and behaving in a characteristic fashion. The plant may also contain the eggs, larvae, or pupae of many types of insects.

If you visit a site at fairly regular intervals you may be able to follow the seasonal history and development of the insects there. The development of a wasp nest, galls, leaf miners, the activities of a group of webworms or tent caterpillars, or the development of the insects in a fallen log can be followed by such observations.

Keeping Insects in Captivity

Cages. There are many types of containers to use as insect cages. A few simple types are illustrated opposite (especially A–D). An insect can be kept for a time in an empty container (A or B), but it will generally live longer if something like natural conditions are provided.

Plants supplied as food must be kept fresh or regularly replaced.

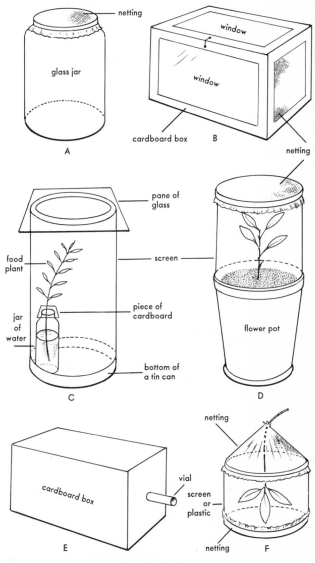

Cages for insects.

They can be kept fresh longer if placed in a jar of water, with a cover on the jar around the stem of the plant to prevent insects on the plant from falling into the water (C). Sometimes a plant can be grown in the cage, or a cylinder of screen can be placed over a potted plant (D). Since insects vary greatly in the type of food they eat, the kind provided for a caged insect will depend on the insect's food habits. Insects feeding on other living insects present the major food problems. Whatever the food, generally it must be replaced before it deteriorates.

Many insects, notably plant feeders, need not be provided with water, since they get enough in their food. Others, those feeding on drier foods, may require additional moisture, and a wet sponge or piece of cotton in the cage or a vial of water plugged with cotton and lying on its side can supply it. Take care to avoid an excess of moisture; this promotes the growth of mold, and droplets of water on the walls of the cage may trap insects.

It is often effective to approximate natural conditions in the cage by having sand, soil, or stones, and a plant or some object on which the insect can rest. If an insect being reared requires special conditions for pupation (soil or debris), these conditions should be provided.

Sometimes the best way to have caged insects under conditions as natural as possible is to cage them in the field in their normal habitat. Insects feeding on a plant can be caged in a bag or cylinder placed over the part of the plant on which they are feeding (F). Aquatic insects can be reared in cages partly submerged in their habitat; the screen of such cages should be fine enough to contain the insects but coarse enough to allow food material to get in.

Rearing. Rearing adults from immature stages enables one to follow the insect's life history, and provides the collector with excellent specimens for a collection. Many insects can be reared relatively easily.

A box like that shown in E can be used to rear adults from larvae living in debris or other materials. This material is put into the box and the box sealed; the emerging adults are usually attracted to light, and go into the vial.

Caterpillars are good insects to rear, since many are large and easily observed, and their transformations are very striking. The chief problem is providing suitable food, because most caterpillars feed on only a few kinds of plants. If the food plant is not known, you must either identify the caterpillar and determine its food from a reference book or try a number of plants in the hope of finding something the caterpillar will eat. The food plant can be kept fresh by placing it in water, as described above (C). If the caterpillar requires special condition for pupation (soil or debris), these conditions should be provided.

A caterpillar collected in the fall may overwinter before pupating, or it may overwinter as a pupa; sometimes it may not complete its development unless it is subjected to low temperatures. Cocoons collected in the fall and brought indoors may fail to develop, either because they dry out or require exposure to low temperature. Drying can be prevented by placing the cocoons in a container with a little soil and occasionally sprinkling the soil with water. Exposure to low temperature can be accomplished by placing the cocoons in a refrigerator for a few weeks, or by keeping them outdoors (for example, on the outside windowsill of a room).

Many aquatic insects, especially those living in stagnant water and feeding on microorganisms or debris, are easily reared indoors. They can be reared in some of the water from which they were collected, often without special equipment to aerate the water and without adding more food. If a stream-inhabiting insect is put into an aquarium, the water usually must be aerated and its temperature not allowed to go too high. Adult mosquitoes can be reared from larvae or pupae in containers as small as vials; cover the vials (with netting or a plug of cotton) to prevent the adults from escaping. Predaceous insects such as dragonfly or damselfly nymphs require other insects or small aquatic animals as food, and the aquarium must contain something extending out of the water — a stick or piece of screen — onto which the nymphs can climb when they are ready to transform into adults.

Meal-infesting insects generally are very easy to rear or maintain from generation to generation, since they normally live indoors and do not require extra moisture. They can be kept in containers of their food material; this material should be sifted at intervals, and the insects transferred to a fresh batch.

Spiders, and predaceous insects such as mantids or dragonfly nymphs, will prove interesting to keep in captivity if supplied with suitable insects as food. Many of these animals have unusual methods of capturing their prey. Caged spiders can be watched making their webs or egg sacs.

Adult crickets sing readily in captivity, and live a fairly long time; you can enjoy their songs and also see how the songs are produced. Chicken mash or ground-up dog food can be used as food, and a wet sponge or piece of cotton will provide adequate moisture.

With a little knowledge of an insect's food habits and habitat requirements, an ingenious student should be able to devise methods of rearing almost any type of insect. Anyone rearing adults from immature stages will sooner or later get parasites instead of the adults expected, and thus will learn something about the habits and hosts of parasitic insects.

The Projection of Living Insects

Living insects can be demonstrated to a group by means of projection, and the effect is much like a motion picture. Aquatic insects in a watch glass can be projected for small groups with a photographic enlarger or similar projector, or the insects can be put into a slide-sized water cell and projected for larger groups with a slide projector — the more practical method. The construction of such a water cell is illustrated below.

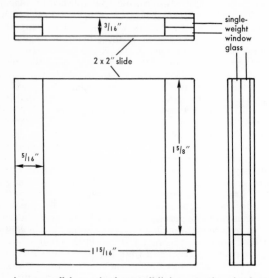

A water cell for projecting small living aquatic animals.

The Structure of Insects

A KNOWLEDGE of insect structure is essential to understanding descriptions and the characters distinguishing different groups. The following account is rather brief; more information is given in the accounts of some of the insect orders.

General Structure. The body of an insect is segmented and more or less elongated. The segments are grouped in 3 body regions, the head, thorax, and abdomen. The *head* bears the eyes, antennae, and mouth parts; the *thorax* bears the legs and wings; the *abdomen* usually bears no locomotor appendages but often has some appendages at its posterior end.

An insect's body wall is somewhat hardened (*sclerotized*). It serves as a shell to protect the internal organs and acts as a skeleton or, more properly, *exoskeleton* (muscles are attached to its inner surface). The surface of the body is divided by intersegmental and other lines into a number of platelike areas, or *sclerites*.

The Head. The head is the anterior capsulelike body region that bears the eyes, antennae, and mouth parts. It is usually quite hard. The surface is divided by sutures into a number of areas, each with a name; the same names are used in different insect groups — where the areas can be homologized — but special terms are used in some groups.

Insects generally have 2 kinds of eyes, simple and compound. For the majority there are 3 simple eyes (*ocelli*), located on the upper front part of the head. Some insects lack ocelli and others have only 2. The *compound eyes* are situated dorsolaterally on the head, each composed of many facets. In some insects they occupy most of the head and contain hundreds of facets.

The Antennae are usually located on the front of the head below the ocelli; they vary greatly in form and in the number of segments contained, and are often used to distinguish different insect groups. Various terms that describe the antennae are explained in the accounts of the groups in which antennal characters are used for identification.

Mouth Parts. The mouth parts of an insect generally are located on the ventral or anterior part of the head, and they vary a great deal in different insect groups. The mouth part structures typically present are a *labrum* (upper lip), a pair of jawlike *mandibles*, a pair of jawlike *maxillae*, a *labium* (lower lip), and a tonguelike structure called the *hypopharynx*.

Insect mouth parts are of 2 general types, chewing and sucking. Insects with chewing mouth parts have laterally moving mandi-

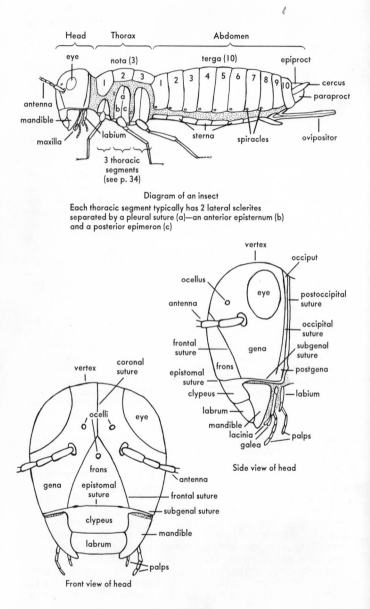

Diagram of an insect

Each thoracic segment typically has 2 lateral sclerites separated by a pleural suture (a)—an anterior episternum (b) and a posterior epimeron (c)

Side view of head

Front view of head

bles (see opp.) and generally chew their food; those with *sucking mouth parts* have the parts modified into a *beak* (proboscis) through which liquid food is sucked. The mandibles are either lacking in sucking mouth parts or are styletlike and form part of the beak; they do not move laterally. A few insects (such as bees) have laterally moving mandibles and a beaklike tongue, and suck liquid through the tongue; a few, like the larvae of dytiscid beetles (p. 154), have well-developed mandibles that move laterally but they suck their food in liquid form through channels in the mandibles.

Chewing mouth parts normally can be recognized by the laterally moving mandibles, visible on the lower front part of the head; most chewing insects do not have a beak. Scorpionflies have the head prolonged ventrally into a beaklike structure (see illus., p. 209), with mandibles that move sideways, and these insects chew. Snout beetles (see illus., p. 203) have the front of the head prolonged into a snout, but there are tiny laterally moving mandibles at the tip of the snout.

Mouth parts of sucking insects (see p. 32) vary in appearance and in how they operate. Many sucking insects (such as bug, froghopper, mosquito, and stable fly) pierce the tissue fed upon. What you see of the beak is usually (bug, mosquito, froghopper) not the part that does the piercing but a sheath enclosing the piercing structures. The piercing is done by a group of hairlike or swordlike *stylets*. When these stylets pierce something, the sheath folds up or back out of the way. If when about to be bitten by a mosquito you will let it alone and watch it in action, you will see that the beak bends in the middle as the 6 hairlike stylets inside it go into the skin. The proboscis of a butterfly or moth does no piercing; generally it is coiled like a watch spring on the ventral side of the head when not in use, and is uncoiled when the insect feeds. Some flies (like the House Fly) have a rather fleshy proboscis that is incapable of piercing.

The stylets of an insect with sucking mouth parts usually enclose the food and salivary channels (the proboscis of a butterfly or moth contains only a food channel). When you are bitten by a mosquito, for example, saliva is first injected through the salivary channel (this is what causes the irritation), then blood is sucked up through the food channel.

The maxillae and labium of most insects bear small feelerlike structures called *palps;* each maxilla bears 1, and the labium bears 2. Some insects lack 1 or both pairs of palps: the flies (Diptera) have only the maxillary palps, most butterflies and moths (Lepidoptera) have only the labial palps, and the bugs (Hemiptera) have no palps at all.

The Thorax (see opp. and p. 34). This, the middle section of the body (between head and abdomen), is divided into 3 segments: (1) *prothorax* (2), *mesothorax*, and (3) *metathorax*. Each segment

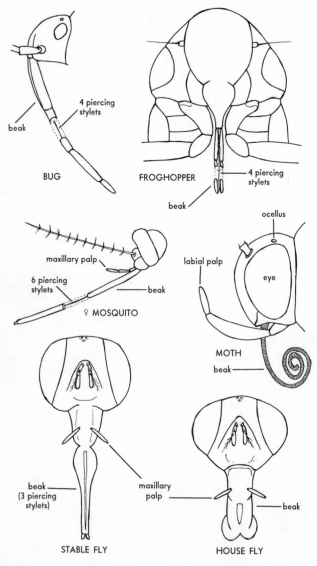

Sucking mouth parts.

typically bears a pair of legs lateroventrally, and the mesothorax and metathorax usually bear a pair of wings dorsolaterally. Some insects have only 1 pair of wings (generally borne by the mesothorax), and some are wingless.

Each thoracic segment bears 4 groups of sclerites (platelike areas), the *notum* (plural, nota) dorsally, a *pleuron* (plural, pleura) on each side, and the *sternum* (plural, sterna) ventrally. Any thoracic sclerite can be indicated as belonging to a particular segment by using the proper prefix. For example, the notum of the prothorax is the *pronotum*, the pleura of the mesothorax are the *mesopleura*, and so on. The pronotum in many insects is a large and conspicuous sclerite forming the dorsal surface of the body between the head and the base of the wings. The pleura of the mesothorax and metathorax are usually larger than the propleura.

The pronotum is a single sclerite, but may contain various grooves or ridges. Each of the other nota is usually divided into 3 sclerites — the *scutum*, *scutellum*, and *postnotum*. The *mesoscutellum* in bugs and most beetles is a conspicuous and more or less triangular sclerite between the pronotum and the base of the wings, and is often simply called the scutellum. Each pleuron is usually separated into 2 sclerites by the *pleural suture*, a line of division which extends from the base of the leg to the base of the wing; the anterior sclerite is the *episternum*, and the posterior one is the *epimeron*. The pleura sometimes contain sutures setting off additional sclerites, and frequently there are 1 or more small sclerites in the membranous area between the pleura and the base of the wings. The sternum is often divided by sutures into 2 or 3 sclerites.

The Legs (see p. 34). An insect leg typically contains the following segments: *coxa* (basal segment), *trochanter* (generally small, just beyond the coxa), *femur*, *tibia*, and *tarsus*. The tarsus usually bears at its apex a pair of *claws* and 1 or more padlike structures. Since the legs vary considerably in different insects, leg characters are often used in identification. The legs may differ in the relative size and shape of the various segments, the number of subdivisions of the tarsus (usually called tarsal "segments," though the entire tarsus technically constitutes a single leg segment), and the trochanter, the character of the claws, pads, and other structures at the apex of the tarsus, and the spines or hairs on the legs.

The Wings. Insect wings also vary considerably, and much use is made of this variation in classification and identification. Many insect order names end in *ptera* (from the Greek, meaning "wing"). The wings are located dorsolaterally on the mesothorax and/or the metathorax. Most of the muscles that move the wings are attached to the walls of the thorax rather than to the base of the wings, and the wing movements are produced largely by changes in the shape of the thorax.

Insect wings vary in number, size, shape, texture, venation,

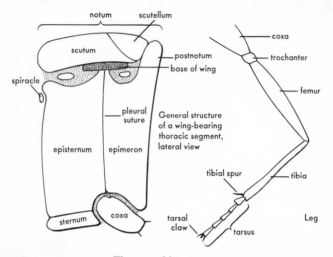

Thorax and leg structure.

and in the position held at rest. Most insects have 2 pairs of wings but many have only 1 pair and some are wingless. Although most insect wings are membranous (thin, like cellophane) some are thickened or leathery; many are covered with hair and some bear scales. Typically insects fold the wings over the abdomen at rest, but a few hold them vertically above the body and some hold them outstretched.

Certain terms are used in referring to different edges, regions, or angles of the wing: the anterior edge is the *costal margin*, and the base of the costal margin is the *humeral angle;* the posterior edge is the *anal margin*, and the posterior basal part of the wing is the *anal area;* an angle of the wing in the anal area is the *anal angle*, and an angle at the tip of the wing is the *apical angle*, or *apex*. There are 1 or 2 lobes in the anal area of the wing in some insects.

Wing Venation. Wing venation — the system of thickened lines in the wing — is frequently used in classification and identification. Although it is generally possible to homologize the veins of different insects and use a standard system of names for them, there are differences of opinion as to how these names should be applied for some insects. A special venational terminology is used in a few groups.

The most widely used terminology of wing venation is illustrated opposite. Longitudinal veins are indicated by capitalized abbreviations, and cross veins by small-letter abbreviations. Branches of the longitudinal veins are indicated by subscript numerals.

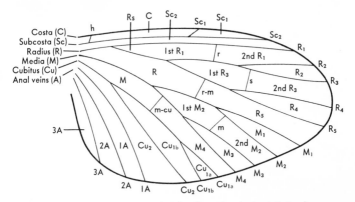

Generalized wing venation (explanation in text, below).

The vein forming the costal wing margin is the *costa* (C). The 1st vein behind the costa is the *subcosta* (Sc), which typically has 2 branches, Sc_1 and Sc_2. The next vein is the *radius* (R), which gives off basally a posterior branch, the *radial sector* (Rs); the radial sector usually forks twice. The anterior branch of R is R_1; the anterior branch of Rs is R_{2+3}, and its terminal branches are R_2 and R_3; the posterior branch of Rs is R_{4+5}, and its terminal branches are R_4 and R_5. The next vein is the *media* (M), which generally forks twice; the anterior branch beyond the first fork is M_{1+2}, and its terminal branches are M_1 and M_2; the posterior branch is M_{3+4}, and its terminal branches are M_3 and M_4. The next vein is the *cubitus* (Cu), which has 2 branches, Cu_1 and Cu_2; Cu_1 often has 2 terminal branches, Cu_{1a} and Cu_{1b}. The remaining veins are *anal veins* (A), and are numbered from anterior to posterior (1A, 2A, 3A). The usual *cross veins* are: the *humeral* (h) between C and Sc near the base of the wing; the *radial* (r) between R_1 and the anterior branch of Rs; the *sectorial* (s) between 2 branches of Rs; the *radio-medial* (r-m) between the radius and media; the *medial* (m) between 2 branches of M; and the *medio-cubital* (m-cu) between M and Cu.

Cells in the wing (spaces between veins) are named from the vein on the anterior side of the cell. Cells at the base of the wing are usually named without a subscript numeral. A cell behind a 2-parted or fused vein is named from the posterior component of that vein. Two or more cells with the same name are individually designated by numbering from the base of the wing (1st M_2 cell, 2nd M_2 cell). An *open cell* extends to the wing margin; a *closed cell* does not reach the margin.

A given insect may have more veins than shown in the figure above as a result of additional cross veins or additional branches of the longitudinal veins; it may have fewer veins because some fail to branch, fuse together, or are lost. Special terms are used for particular features of the venation in some orders and are discussed in this book under the accounts of those orders.

The Abdomen (see p. 30). The insect abdomen typically consists of 11 segments, but the last segment is usually represented by appendages only; so the maximum number of complete segments in most insects is 10. Many insects have fewer abdominal segments because of fusing or telescoping of some segments.

Each abdominal segment generally contains 2 sclerites, a dorsal tergum and a ventral sternum. The *terga* usually extend down the sides of the segments and overlap the sterna.

Most insects lack appendages on the abdomen except at the posterior end. The terminal appendages may be lacking or drawn into the body and hidden. When terminal appendages are present (top figure, p. 30) they usually consist of a pair of dorsolateral *cerci* (singular, cercus), a median dorsal *epiproct*, a pair of lateroventral *paraprocts*, and the *genitalia*. Cerci when present may be feelerlike or clasperlike; the epiproct, if present, may be short, or elongate and threadlike. The anal opening is at the posterior end of the abdomen, just below the epiproct if the latter is present.

The genitalia are structures associated with the genital openings — those of the male transfer sperm to the female and those of the female lay the eggs. Male genitalia are extremely variable and often quite complex; they provide valuable taxonomic characters in many groups. Some or all of the male genitalia may be withdrawn into the body and not be apparent without dissection. An *ovipositor* (egg-laying organ) is present in many insects. It is formed by structures on the 8th and 9th abdominal segments and extends beyond the body in some insects and in others is withdrawn into the body when not in use.

The sexes in many groups can be distinguished by the genital structures at the end of the abdomen. In groups having internal genitalia the sexes may differ in other ways (size or color), or they may be indistinguishable without dissection.

Internal Anatomy. Although space does not permit a detailed account here, we believe that some features of the internal anatomy of insects are of sufficient interest to warrant at least brief mention.

The *breathing system* of insects is very different from that of man. Insects have a system of tubes (*tracheae*) that open externally at the *spiracles* and branch internally to supply all parts of the body. There are usually 2 pairs of spiracles on the thorax and several pairs on the abdomen; abdominal spiracles are generally located on the lateral edges of the terga. Oxygen goes from the outside directly to the tissues by way of the tracheal tubes, and is not transported in the hemoglobin of the blood as in vertebrates.

Insects' blood is ordinarily not red, and it does not reach all parts of the body in blood vessels. The *heart* is a tube located in the abdomen above the digestive tract. Blood is pumped anteriorly from the heart through a dorsally situated vessel called the *aorta*, and in the neck region empties into the body cavity. It flows through the body cavity, and reenters the heart through lateral openings called *ostia*.

The *excretory system* of insects consists of a number of tubes (*malpighian tubules*) that empty into the alimentary tract. Wastes from the blood enter these tubes and pass into the alimentary track and to the outside by way of the anus.

The *nervous system* of insects consists of a ganglion called the brain, located dorsally in the head, a pair of connectives passing around the alimentary canal, and a ventral nerve cord; nerves extend from the brain and nerve cord to various parts of the body. There are many sense organs, located mainly in the body wall. Some of these respond to tactile stimuli, some to chemical stimuli, some to sound, some to light, and some to other stimuli. Chemical receptors (organs of taste and smell) are located principally on the mouth parts, antennae, and feet. Special auditory organs, when present, generally consist of drumlike structures (tympana) or special hairs sensitive to sound waves. Many insects can detect sounds pitched far above the hearing range of man.

The Growth and Development of Insects

Eggs. Insect eggs differ in shape and color, and some are ornamented with ridges, spines, or other processes. Most insects lay their eggs in a situation where the young on hatching will have conditions suitable for development. Many lay their eggs in characteristic masses, and a few cover their eggs with a protective material of some sort. The eggs of some insects develop internally, and the young are born alive.

Insect eggs ordinarily develop only if they have been fertilized but some undergo *parthenogenesis*, that is, they develop without fertilization. Fertilization sometimes determines sex. In Hymenoptera, for example, an unfertilized egg usually develops into a male and a fertilized egg into a female. Unfertilized eggs of most parthenogenetic insects develop into females, and in some species no males are known. A few Hymenoptera undergo *polyembryony* (a single egg develops into more than 1 young). This sometimes occurs in man, producing identical twins or triplets. In polyembryonic insects, from 2 to more than 1000 young may develop from 1 egg.

Growth. The growth of an insect is accompanied by a series of molts, in which the exoskeleton (outer shell) is shed and renewed. Insects change in form as they grow, and the amount and character of this differ from group to group. This change is called *metamorphosis*.

The exoskeleton of insects is generally rather hard, and the extent to which it can stretch is limited. An insect cannot grow continuously but must shed the exoskeleton at intervals and replace it with a larger one. This shedding process is called molting, or *ecdysis*. Molting involves a shedding of the outer surface of the body, the linings of the tracheae, and the lining of the anterior and posterior parts of the alimentary canal. It begins with a splitting of the old exoskeleton, usually on the dorsal side of the head or thorax. In some cases (caterpillars, for example) the shed exoskeleton shrinks into a small irregular mass, but in others it retains the shape of the insect.

The stages between molts are called *instars*. The number of molts is generally 4 to 8, but may be as many as 20 in some insects. Molting usually stops when the adult stage is reached. Only a very few insects (like bristletails) continue to molt after becoming adult.

Metamorphosis. Successive instars differ not only in size but in other features as well. This change during growth (metamorphosis) is relatively slight in some insects, very marked in others. There are 2 principal types of metamorphosis — simple and complete.

Simple Metamorphosis. In this type the wings (if present in the adult) develop externally during the early instars, compound eyes are present in the early instars if they are present in the adult, and there is no prolonged resting stage before the last molt. The immature instars of insects with this type of metamorphosis are called *nymphs*.

Nymphs usually resemble the adults except in size, body proportions, and the development of the wings; they generally live in the same habitat as the adult, and feed on the same foods. If the adults are wingless, the chief difference between nymphs and adults is in size. If the adult has wings, the wings are relatively small through the last nymphal instar, and expand to their adult size after the last molt.

Nymphs of mayflies, stoneflies, dragonflies, and damselflies differ from adults slightly more than in other insects with simple metamorphosis. They live in water and have gills, and when full-grown come to the surface of the water or crawl out of the water for their final molt.

Complete Metamorphosis. The eggs of insects with complete metamorphosis hatch into a wormlike stage called a *larva*. The larvae of insects vary in appearance: some have legs and others are legless and some lack a well-developed head. Larvae do not have compound eyes (but may have ocelli), and if the adult is winged the wings begin their development in the larval stage but develop internally. The larval stage lasts from a few to several instars, increasing in size and sometimes changing in color or other characters. After the molt of the last larval instar the insect changes to what is called a *pupa*. Pupae are usually inactive. They do not feed, and are sometimes enclosed in a protective covering, which may be a *cocoon* formed by the last larval instar before it molted or may be a *puparium* (formed of larval exoskeleton).

Insect larvae vary considerably in form. Several terms (eruciform, scarabaeiform, campodeiform, vermiform, elateriform, etc.) are used to describe them. *Eruciform larvae* are caterpillarlike, with a well-developed head, thoracic legs, and abdominal *prolegs* (see illus., p. 219); they occur in the Lepidoptera, Mecoptera, and some Hymenoptera (Symphyta). *Scarabaeiform larvae* are grublike, with thoracic legs but without abdominal prolegs, and are usually pale-colored and rather sluggish; they occur in certain Coleoptera (such as Scarabaeidae). *Campodeiform larvae*, which resemble diplurans in the family Campodeidae (see illus., p. 63), are elongate and somewhat flattened, with the antennae, cerci, and thoracic legs well developed, and are generally fairly active; they are found in the Neuroptera and many Coleoptera. *Vermiform larvae* are wormlike or maggotlike, without legs, and with or without a well-developed head; they occur in the Diptera, Siphonaptera, and most Hymenoptera (Apocrita), and in a few insects in other orders. *Elateriform larvae* are elongate and cylindrical, hard-bodied, and short-legged; they occur in certain Coleoptera (like Elateridae).

Most insect pupae look somewhat like mummified adults, with the appendages free and visible. Such pupae are called *exarate*, and occur in most insects with complete metamorphosis except the Diptera and most Lepidoptera. Some pupae have the appendages

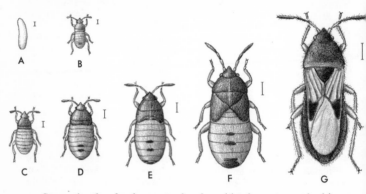

Stages in the development of a bug (simple metamorphosis).
A, egg; B–F, nymphal instars; G, adult.

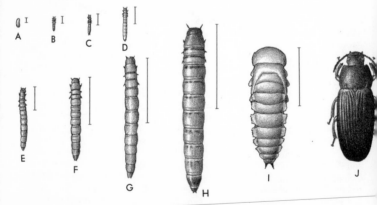

Stages in the development of a beetle (complete metamorphosis).
A, egg; B–H, larval instars; I, pupa; J, adult.

glued to the body, and look much less like the adults. Such pupae are called *obtect*, and occur in the Lepidoptera and some Diptera (Nematocera). The pupa of many Diptera (Brachycera and Cyclorrhapha) is enclosed in a puparium, and is termed *coarctate;* puparia are oval and brownish, and look rather like the fecal pellet of a small rodent.

The different larval instars of some insects with complete metamorphosis are not of the same type: the 1st instar is campodeiform and the remaining instars scarabaeiform or vermiform. This type of development is called *hypermetamorphosis*, and occurs in some parasitic insects. The active 1st instar larva seeks out and enters a host and, once there, molts to a less active type of larva.

The larvae and adults of insects with complete metamorphosis are usually so different that one unfamiliar with their life history would not believe them to be the same insect. They often live in dissimilar habitats and feed on dissimilar foods. The transformation of an insect with complete metamorphosis is a remarkable phenomenon — something well worth following in the field or with caged individuals.

Changes in the Adult. Immediately after its molt to the adult stage an insect is soft-bodied and pale-colored. If the adult has wings, these are usually small immediately after the molt — about the same size as they were in the pupal (or last nymphal) instar — and must expand to their full adult size. This expansion may occur in a few minutes, or take a half hour or more. The coming-out of the adult at the final molt is called *emergence*. Darkening to the adult coloration generally takes place in a short time (an hour or less), but in some insects it may be a week or more before the adult has developed its full coloration. Some adults (such as Hymenoptera) that emerge from cocoons may undergo these changes before emerging from the cocoon. Others (a butterfly) have the coloration fully developed at the time of the final molt and the wings expand to their full size *after* emergence. Once the adult has expanded to its full size it does not grow any more, and (with rare exceptions) does not undergo any more molts.

Life History. Most insects in our area have a single generation a year. The adults are present for a limited time during some part of the year, and the winter is passed in a dormant state. Insects overwinter in different stages — some as eggs, some as nymphs, some as larvae, some as pupae, and some as adults. A period of dormancy at low temperature is often an essential feature of the life cycle. Many insects (particularly those occurring in the northern part of the country) will not complete their development unless exposed to low temperature.

Some insects regularly have 2 generations a year and others may have several — continuing to reproduce as long as weather conditions are favorable. A few require more than a year to complete their development. Many of the larger insects in northern areas take 2 or 3 years; the record holders are some of the periodical cicadas, which take 17 years.

Adults of most insects live only a short time, ordinarily from a few days to a few weeks. An overwintering adult lives several months, and the queens of some social insects can live several years. Many insects that are short-lived as adults do not feed in the adult stage.

Classifying and Naming Insects

Classification. There are about a million kinds of described animals in the world, and their study calls for some plan of dividing them into groups. Zoologists classify animals chiefly on the basis of structure: those with certain structures in common are placed in one group and those with other structures are put in other groups. These groups are divided and subdivided. The result is a system of categories, each with certain structural features in common, and a name.

The animal kingdom is divided into a number of major groups called *phyla* (singular, phylum); each phylum is divided into *classes*, each class into *orders*, each order into *families*, each family into *genera* (singular, genus), and each genus into *species*. In many larger groups there are additional categories, such as subclasses, suborders, superfamilies, subfamilies, and tribes. The species is the basic category; it is a kind of animal. That is, it consists of individuals fundamentally similar in structure which interbreed to produce offspring but do not ordinarily interbreed with other groups. Sometimes species are divided into *subspecies*. Subspecies are generally geographic races that differ from one another only slightly and are capable of interbreeding.

The arrangement of animals into these categories is arbitrary: it is the opinion of the specialist that determines the limits of a category. Although specialists do not always agree on the limits of some categories, differences of opinion mostly are minor. This system is an indispensable tool in the study of animals. Anyone studying animals must be familiar with it.

Nomenclature. Animals have 2 types of names — scientific and common. Scientific names are the names used by scientists; they are used throughout the world, and every animal or group has one. Common names are vernacular names. They are less precise than scientific names, and many animals lack them. Some common names are used for more than 1 species or group, and a given animal or group may have several common names.

Scientific Nomenclature. The scientific naming of animals follows certain rules, only a few of which can be mentioned here. Scientific names are Latinized. They may be derived from various languages or from the names of people and places, but most are from Latin or Greek and refer to characteristics of the animal or group named. Names of groups above genus are single words in the nominative plural; names of genera are single words in the nominative singular; names of species are 2 words — the name of the genus plus a specific name; and names of subspecies are 3 words — the name of the species (2 words) plus a subspecific name. Specific and subspecific names may be adjectives or participles (in which case they must agree in gender with the genus name) or nouns in the nominative or genitive.

Names of genera, species, and subspecies are written in italics and are usually followed by the name of a person (the *author*). If the author name follows a species name it indicates the person who proposed the specific name; if it follows a subspecies name it indicates the person who proposed the subspecific name; if it is in parentheses it means that the author's species or subspecies was originally placed in a genus other than the present one. For example:

Musca domestica Linn. — the House Fly. Linnaeus (abbreviated "Linn." in this *Field Guide*) first described the House Fly and gave it the specific name *domestica* and placed it in the genus *Musca*.

Automeris io (Fabricius) — the Io Moth. Fabricius first described this moth and gave it the specific name *io*, and placed it in a genus other than *Automeris*.

Diabrotica undecimpunctata howardi Barber — the Spotted Cucumber Beetle. Barber proposed the name *howardi* and placed it in *Diabrotica*. There is no way of knowing from this name whether Barber originally described *howardi* as a subspecies of *undecimpunctata*, or as a subspecies of another species of *Diabrotica*, or as a species of *Diabrotica*.

Whenever a new group (from subspecies to superfamily) is described, the describer is supposed to designate a *type*. This type provides a reference if a question arises as to what the group includes, and type genera provide the basis of the name of certain higher categories. The type of categories from tribe to superfamily is a genus, the type of a genus is a species, and the type of a species or subspecies is a specimen.

Names of some categories have standard endings: -oidea for superfamily, -idae for family, -inae for subfamily, and -ini for tribe. The names are formed by adding the ending to the root of the type genus name. If 1 of these groups is divided into 2 or more subgroups, the subgroup containing the group's type genus will have the same name as the group except for the ending. An illustration: *Colletes* is the type genus of the family Colletidae (plasterer and yellow-faced bees); this family is divided into 2 subfamilies, the Colletinae (plasterer bees; with *Colletes*) and the Hylaeinae (yellow-faced bees; named for *Hylaeus*, the genus designated as the type of this subfamily).

This same principle applies when a species is divided into 2 or more subspecies — the subspecific name of one of the subspecies (the one containing the type of the species) will be the same as the specific name of the species. For example, the dragonfly *Tetragoneuria cynosura* (Say) is divided into 2 subspecies, *Tetragoneuria cynosura cynosura* (Say) and *Tetragoneuria cynosura simulans* Muttkowski. *T. c. cynosura* contains the type of *T. cynosura* and another specimen was designated as the type of *T. c. simulans*.

A given animal (or group) may be described by different people and thus may have more than 1 name. The first name proposed in such cases (provided the author followed certain rules) is the correct one and the other names become *synonyms*. It is not always easy to determine which of 2 or more names for an animal is the correct one: different names may be used by authorities who do not agree on which name has priority.

It sometimes happens that a person describing a new genus will use for it a name previously used for another genus. When this is discovered the later genus must be renamed, since the rules state that no 2 genera of animals may have the same name. Similarly, no 2 species or subspecies in the same genus may have the same specific or subspecific name. These rules relating to *homonyms* (cases of the same name being used for different groups) apply only within a particular category group, and they except the case mentioned above of 1 subspecies having the same specific as subspecific name. The category groups are: phylum through order, superfamily through subgenus, and species through subspecies. A name used in 1 of these 3 category groups can be used in another without violating the rules. For example, a specific or subspecific name may be the same as the name of a genus, or the same name may be used for both a genus and an order.

As our knowledge of animals increases it often becomes necessary to change scientific names. A group may be subdivided or combined with another group; a name widely used may become a synonym because of the discovery of an older name; or a group may be renamed because of the discovery of an earlier use of its name for another group. Problems encountered in scientific nomenclature are sometimes solved differently by taxonomists. For these reasons, the classification and nomenclature used by authorities may not always be the same. We follow in this book the opinions of most present-day entomologists. Other names and groupings most often encountered are included in the Index.

Common Names. Common names of insects mainly apply to groups rather than to individual species. The few species having common names are generally of some economic importance or are particularly striking in appearance. The name "beetle," for instance, refers to all the Coleoptera, of which there are some 290,000 world species (about 28,600 in the U.S.); the name "leaf beetle" refers to all the Chrysomelidae (about 25,000 world species, nearly 1400 in the U.S.); the name "tortoise beetle" refers to all the Cassidinae, a subfamily of the Chrysomelidae (about 3000 world species and about 24 in the U.S.); the name "Argus Tortoise

Beetle" refers to the single species *Chelymorpha cassidea* (Fabricius), which is of economic importance as a pest of sweet potato and other plants.

Most 1-word common names used for insects (beetle, bug, fly, termite, caddisfly, and others) refer to entire orders. Some (damselfly, grasshopper, lacewing, and others) refer to suborders or groups of families. Only a few (ants, Formicidae; cockroaches, Blattidae; and others) refer to families. Most common names of families — where the family has a common name — consist of 2 or more words, the last being the name of the larger group and the other(s) descriptive (robber flies, Asilidae; leaf beetles, Chrysomelidae; metallic wood-boring beetles, Buprestidae; and others).

The majority of the common names used in this book are in rather wide use; some are used by relatively few people, and a small number are used here for the first time. Many entomologists prefer scientific to common names because they are more precise and are widely used (at least among entomologists), and are sometimes easier to remember. An adjectival form of a group's scientific name is often used as a common name — a member of the order Orthoptera could be called an "orthopteran," or a member of the family Libellulidae could be called a "libellulid." If a family has no common name (and sometimes even when it does), it is standard practice to use the adjectival form of the family name as a common name. In a few cases (mantids, Mantidae; syrphid flies, Syrphidae; etc.) such names are widely used as common names.

"Fly" and "bug" are a part of the common names of many different insects. The "fly" of the name is written as a separate word if the insect is in the order Diptera (horse fly, robber fly, black fly), and together with the descriptive word if the insect is in another order (butterfly, dragonfly, scorpionfly). The "bug" of the name is written as a separate word if the insect is in the order Hemiptera (stink bug, bed bug, leaf bug), and together with the descriptive word if the insect is in another order (mealybug, lightningbug, ladybug).

Systematic
Chapters

Arthropods: Phylum Arthropoda
(Insects and Their Relatives)

Identification: Body segmented, segments usually grouped in 2 or 3 fairly distinct body regions. Paired, segmented appendages usually present. Body wall more or less hardened; forms an exoskeleton (external skeleton) periodically shed and renewed.

Similar phyla: Annelida (earthworms, leeches, various marine worms) have body segmented but with little or no differentiation of body regions. Appendages unsegmented or lacking. Body wall does not form an exoskeleton. Legless insect larvae differ from annelids in their internal anatomy (generally have tracheae and malpighian tubules, which annelids lack), and the body usually contains fewer segments (13 or fewer in insect larvae, ordinarily more in annelids).

Immature stages: Most arthropods other than insects undergo little or no metamorphosis and the young resemble the adults. A few (some crustaceans) have a larval stage markedly different from the adult; some (millipedes, some centipedes, some arachnids) have fewer legs in immature stages than in adult stages.

Habits: Very diversified. Practically every animal habitat contains some arthropods, and different arthropods vary greatly in their feeding habits.

Importance: The importance of insects has been outlined briefly in the Preface (p. vii). Other arthropods are important in similar ways. Many crustaceans (lobsters, crabs, shrimps) are used as food by man, and their collection and distribution constitute a sizable industry. Insects are rarely used as food by man (at least in this country), though certain insect products (honey) are.

Classification: Present-day arthropods are arranged in 2 subphyla, the Mandibulata and the Chelicerata, which differ principally in the number and character of the appendages. Each subphylum is further divided into classes.

No. of species: World, 840,000; N. America, 104,000.

Mandibulate Arthropods:
Subphylum Mandibulata

One or 2 pairs of antennae. 1st pair of appendages behind antennae are mandibles. Number of legs and body regions variable.

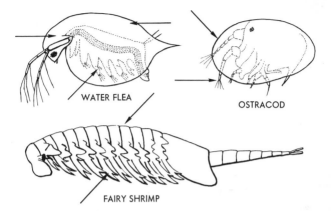

WATER FLEA

OSTRACOD

FAIRY SHRIMP

CRUSTACEANS   Class Crustacea

Identification: Appendages vary in number, but 2 pairs of antennae (1 pair may be quite small), a pair of appendages on each segment of cephalothorax (head and thorax) and sometimes on each abdominal segment; usually at least 5 pairs of leglike appendages. 2 body regions generally distinct (cephalothorax and abdomen), the cephalothorax often with a hardened covering (carapace). Mostly aquatic, gill-breathing.

Two major groups of crustaceans are usually recognized, Entomostraca and Malacostraca. Entomostraca include a large and varied assemblage of small aquatic forms, generally less than 5 mm., which lack appendages on the abdominal segments. Malacostraca are mostly larger forms, with appendages on the abdominal segments. Only the more common types in each group can be mentioned here.

Entomostraca. Members of this group occur in both salt- and freshwater; important chiefly as food of larger animals. Three types of entomostracans have a *bivalved carapace:* water fleas, clam shrimps, and ostracods. **Water fleas** (Cladocera) — sometimes extremely abundant in freshwater pools — have *4 to 6 pairs of flattened thoracic legs;* head is *outside the carapace.* **Clam shrimps** (Conchostraca) and **ostracods** (Ostracoda) have entire body *enclosed in the carapace,* and resemble tiny clams; clam shrimps have 10–32 pairs of legs and are sometimes fairly large (to 10 mm.), whereas ostracods have only *3 pairs of legs* and are always quite small. **Fairy shrimps** (Anostraca) are elongate, usually pale-colored, *without a carapace,* and have *11 pairs of flattened legs;* often abundant in temporary pools. **Tadpole shrimps** (Notostraca) have an oval carapace covering anterior part of body, 35–71 pairs of thoracic appendages, and 2 long threadlike appendages at posterior end of body; they are fairly large for entomostracans (½–2 in.); occur only in the West. **Copepods** (Copepoda) generally have a more or less elongate body that lacks a carapace, and 4–6 pairs of legs; females of many species carry their eggs in *2 laterally located egg sacs* near posterior end of body; copepods include freshwater and marine forms; most are free-living, but some (called fish lice) are parasites of fish. **Barnacles** (Cirripedia) are marine forms that as adults live attached to objects in the water (rocks, pilings, seaweeds, other marine animals, or boat bottoms); body usually enclosed in a shell of some sort.

Malacostraca. Most members of this group are marine, but a few occur in freshwater and a few are terrestrial. The **decapods** (Decapoda) include some of the largest and best-known malacostracans — lobsters, crayfish, crabs, and shrimps; entire cephalothorax is *covered by a carapace;* 5 pairs of cephalothoracic appendages are leglike; 1st pair of legs usually bears a *large claw.* Crayfish are the only decapods likely to be encountered in freshwater; most of the others are marine. **Amphipods** (Amphipoda) *lack a carapace* and have the body laterally flattened; 7 pairs of cephalothoracic appendages are *leglike.* This group includes freshwater and marine forms; some of the marine forms (beach fleas) are common along the seashore, where they live under stones or seaweed; freshwater amphipods are called scuds or sideswimmers. **Isopods** (Isopoda) *lack a carapace* and are dorsoventrally flattened, and the 7 pairs of cephalothoracic appendages are *leglike.* Most isopods are marine, but the group includes the sowbugs (pillbugs), which are common under stones or bark.

MILLIPEDES   Class Diplopoda
Identification: Wormlike, cylindrical or only slightly flattened. Many-legged, with 2 pairs of short legs *on most body segments. 1 pair of short, usually 7-segmented* antennae. Terrestrial.

Millipedes are common animals usually found in soil and debris or under stones and bark. They are slow-moving, and most of them feed on plants or decaying materials; they do not bite. Our species vary from a few mm. to about 4 in. Most are blackish, sometimes with light markings. Many give off an ill-smelling fluid from openings along sides of the body.

CENTIPEDES   Class Chilopoda
Identification: Elongate, wormlike. Similar to millipedes but body more flattened. Legs (15 or more pairs) arranged *1 pair per body segment.* Antennae with 14 *or more segments.* 1st pair of appendages behind head clawlike and functioning as *poison jaws.*

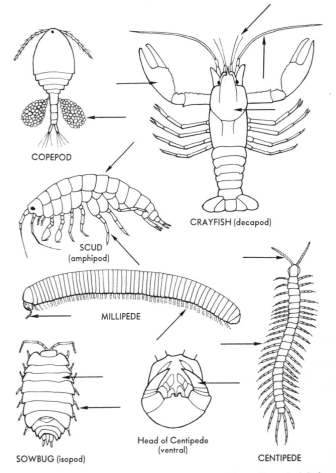

COPEPOD

CRAYFISH (decapod)

SCUD
(amphipod)

MILLIPEDE

SOWBUG (isopod)

Head of Centipede
(ventral)

CENTIPEDE

Centipedes are common animals found in soil and debris, under bark, in rotting wood, and in similar protected places. They are active and fast-running and are predaceous on insects and other small arthropods. They have poison jaws with which they paralyze their prey; the smaller centipedes are relatively harmless to man but some of the larger ones can inflict a painful bite. Our species are generally pale yellowish to dark brown, and vary from a few mm. to about 6 in.

PAUROPODS Class Pauropoda   **Not illus.**
Identification: Similar to centipedes but minute (1.0–1.5 mm.).
Only 9 pairs of legs. Antennae branched.

Pauropods are whitish and occur in soil and debris. They
are not common.

SYMPHYLIDS Class Symphyla   **Not illus.**
Identification: Similar to centipedes but with 10–12 pairs of
legs. 1–8 mm. Antennae not branched.

Symphylids occur under stones, in rotting wood, and in the
soil. They are not common.

INSECTS Class Insecta
Identification: Three pairs of legs. 3 body regions (head, thorax,
abdomen). Often 1 or 2 pairs of wings. 1 pair of antennae.
For additional characters, see p. 56.

Since the bulk of this book is concerned with insects, nothing
more need be said about them here.

Chelicerate Arthropods:
Subphylum Chelicerata

Usually 6 pairs of appendages: 1st pair (chelicerae) jawlike or
fanglike; 2nd pair (pedipalps) somewhat feelerlike (sometimes
clawlike, rarely leglike); remaining pairs leglike. Antennae absent.
Usually 2 body regions, cephalothorax (bearing the appendages)
and abdomen. Legs often with an extra segment (patella) between
femur and tibia.

SEA SPIDERS Class Pycnogonida   **Not illus.**
Identification: Long-legged, spiderlike marine animals, with a
small cephalothorax (head and thorax) and a very small abdomen. Usually 5 pairs of legs.

Sea spiders have a leg spread of 1 to several cm., and generally
occur beneath low tidemark. They have a sucking proboscis and
feed on other small animals.

HORSESHOE CRABS Class Xiphosura
Identification: Body with a *broadly oval shell* and a *long slender
tail.* Abdomen with leaflike gills on ventral side. Large animals,
up to 1½ ft.

Horseshoe crabs are marine animals with a very distinctive
appearance. They are fairly common along the seashore.

WATER BEARS Class Tardigrada   **Not illus.**
Identification: Minute animals, 1 mm. or less, with 4 pairs of
unsegmented legs, each leg with several claws.

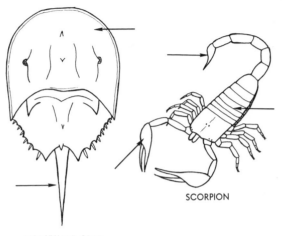

SCORPION

HORSESHOE CRAB

Water bears occur in fresh- and saltwater, mud, sand, and various other damp places. They are not often encountered.

TONGUEWORMS Class Linguatulida   **Not illus.**
Identification: Immature stages with 4–6 pairs of legs. Adults wormlike and legless, living as parasites in the mouth or respiratory track of various vertebrates.

This is an aberrant group, and may or may not be correctly placed in the Chelicerata. Tongueworms are not common, and are unlikely to be encountered by users of this book.

ARACHNIDS Class Arachnida
Identification: Adults nearly always with 4 pairs of segmented legs (rarely the pedipalps are leglike). Usually not wormlike.

This is the largest and most often encountered chelicerate class. Its members are very widely distributed. Several types within the class merit separate consideration.

Scorpions, Order Scorpionida. Relatively large arachnids (to 4 or 5 in.). Pedipalps *large and clawlike*. Abdomen *distinctly segmented* and ending in a *sting* usually curved upward. Scorpions occur in the South and West and are largely nocturnal. They feed chiefly on insects and spiders. The sting of a scorpion can be quite painful, and in some cases (2 species occurring in Arizona) may be fatal.

Whip-scorpions, Orders Microthelyphonida, Pedipalpida, Schizopeltida, and Amblypygi. Scorpionlike, but abdomen *oval*, *segmented*, and lacking a sting. Pedipalps *not clawlike*. 1st pair of legs *longer than others*. Some species have *a long whiplike tail*. Principally tropical; our species occur only in the southern states. They vary from a few mm. to 4 or 5 in. and are predaceous. A few of the larger species give off a vinegarlike odor when disturbed.

Wind-scorpions, Order Solpugida (not illus.). Spiderlike, but with body only slightly constricted behind cephalothorax, chelicerae very large, abdomen segmented. Solpugids occur in the desert areas of the Southwest; they are nocturnal, spending the day in burrows or under stones, cow chips, and other objects and foraging at night. They are fast-running animals about an inch long or less and are predaceous.

Pseudoscorpions, Order Chelonethida. Small (generally 5 mm. or less), flattened, oval-bodied arachnids with *large clawlike pedipalps*. Normally occur under bark or in debris. They are moderately common.

Daddy-long-legs or Harvestmen, Order Phalangida. Body oval and compact. Legs *extremely long and slender*. Abdomen *segmented*. These common and well-known animals are found in wooded areas or in fairly dense vegetation. Most feed on dead insects or on plants. The few long-legged spiders and mites that might be confused with daddy-long-legs have the abdomen unsegmented, and spiders have a strong constriction between the cephalothorax and abdomen.

Mites and Ticks, Order Acarina. Abdomen *unsegmented* and *broadly joined to cephalothorax*. Body more or less oval, usually minute (some ticks may be several mm.). This is the largest order in the class, and its members occur almost everywhere, often in considerable numbers. Many are free-living and many are parasites of other animals. The free-living **mites** are probably most abundant in the soil and in debris, where their populations may number several million per acre. Some parasitic forms are important pests of man and domestic animals (chiggers or harvest mites, scab and mange mites, ticks): **chiggers** are annoying pests of man, and a few act as disease vectors; **scab and mange mites** are pests of both man and animals; some of the **ticks** are also important disease vectors. **Spider mites** are serious pests of various cultivated plants, especially orchard trees and greenhouse plants. **Water mites,** many of which are reddish or orange, are common inhabitants of ponds. A few mites are gall makers, usually forming small pouchlike galls on leaves.

Spiders, Order Araneida. Abdomen *strongly constricted at base*, nearly always *unsegmented*, with a group of fingerlike spinnerets at posterior end. Spiders are common and well-known animals occurring in many habitats. They feed on insects and other small animals, paralyzing their prey with venom from glands opening on the chelicerae. Spiders are venomous but rarely bite man; only a few are dangerously venomous. Silk spun from the spinnerets is used in the construction of webs, snares, shelters, and egg sacs. Many spiders do not build webs; they forage or lie in wait for their prey. Webs of different spiders vary in form: many (called orb webs) are more or less circular, with spirally wound strands of sticky silk and radiating strands that are not sticky; some are sheetlike or funnel-like; others are irregular. Sexes of spiders can usually be distinguished by the pedipalps — slender in the female, somewhat clubbed in the male. The male is often smaller than the female and not as frequently seen. In some species the female kills and eats the male after mating.

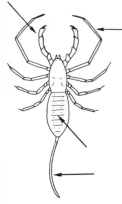

WHIP-SCORPION

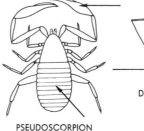

PSEUDOSCORPION

DADDY-LONG-LEGS

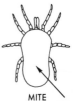

MITE

TICK

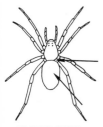

GROUND SPIDER

CRAB SPIDER

ORB-WEAVER SPIDER

Insects: Class Insecta

Identification: Three pair of legs. 3 body regions (head, thorax, and abdomen). Often 1 or 2 pairs of wings. 1 pair of antennae (antennae rarely absent). Mouth parts typically consist of a labrum, a pair of mandibles, a pair of maxillae, a hypopharynx, and a labium. Genital ducts open near posterior end of body. Winged insects differ from all other invertebrates in the possession of wings; wingless insects differ from most other arthropods in having 3 pairs of legs and a pair of antennae. Caterpillars appearing to have more than 3 pairs of legs have the first 3 pairs behind the head normally leglike in structure and the remaining pairs (prolegs) stout and fleshy and quite different in structure.

Similar groups: (1) Arachnida: larval mites with only 3 pairs of legs lack antennae, the body is not differentiated into 3 regions, and the abdominal region is not segmented. (2) Diplopoda: newly hatched millipedes, with 3 pairs of legs, have the head structure characteristic of millipedes (see illus., p. 51) and a single liplike structure (gnathochilarium) behind the mandibles instead of maxillae and a labium. (3) Annelida: some resemble legless insect larvae but have more than 13 body segments and lack a tracheal system.

Classification: The class Insecta is divided into 2 subclasses, the Apterygota and Pterygota. The **Apterygota** include the orders Protura, Thysanura, and Collembola, and the **Pterygota** include the remaining orders. The Apterygota are wingless, and most Pterygota have wings. The wingless Pterygota are thought to have evolved from winged ancestors because they have certain features of thoracic structure (for example, the thoracic pleura divided by a pleural suture into episternum and epimeron, and the meso- and metanotum divided by sutures) correlated with the development of wings; Apterygota have a simpler thoracic structure (these sclerites not divided by sutures). The Apterygota usually have stylelike appendages on the pregenital segments of the abdomen; such appendages are lacking in the Pterygota. The orders of insects are separated principally by the characters of the wings, mouth parts, legs, and the metamorphosis.

No. of species: World, 703,500; N. America, 88,600.

Some of the outstanding features of the 26 orders of insects are outlined in the following table.

CHARACTERS OF THE INSECT ORDERS

Order	Examples	Wings	Mouth parts	Usual no. of tarsal segments	Meta-morphosis	Usual size	Where usually found
Protura	proturans	none	sucking	1	simple	minute	in debris
Thysanura	bristletails	none	chewing	1-5	simple	medium	in debris, buildings
Collembola	springtails	none	chewing	1	simple	minute	in debris
Ephemeroptera	mayflies	4 (rarely 2); HW small	vestigial	3-5	simple; nymphs aquatic	medium	near water
Odonata	dragonflies and damselflies	4; many-veined; HW as large as FW	chewing	3	simple; nymphs aquatic	large	near water
Orthoptera	grasshoppers, crickets, cockroaches, mantids, walkingsticks	0-4; FW narrow and thickened; HW folded fanwise	chewing	3-5	simple	large	on ground or vegetation
Isoptera	termites	0-4; FW and HW similar in size	chewing	4	simple	small	in ground or wood
Plecoptera	stoneflies	4; FW narrow; HW with a large anal lobe	chewing	3	simple; nymphs aquatic	medium	near water
Dermaptera	earwigs	0-4; FW short and thickened; HW folded	chewing	3	simple	medium to small	in debris
Embioptera	webspinners	0-4; HW a little smaller than FW	chewing	3	simple	small	in debris

57

CHARACTERS OF THE INSECT ORDERS (contd.)

Order	Examples	Wings	Mouth parts	Usual no. of tarsal segments	Meta-morphosis	Usual size	Where usually found
Psocoptera	booklice and barklice	0–4; HW smaller than FW	chewing	2–3	simple	small to minute	in debris, buildings
Zoraptera	zorapterans	0–4; HW smaller	chewing	2	simple	minute	in debris
Mallophaga	chewing lice	none	chewing	1–2	simple	minute	on birds or mammals
Anoplura	sucking lice	none	sucking	1	simple	minute	on mammals
Thysanoptera	thrips	0–4; wings long, narrow, fringed	rasping-sucking	1–2	intermediate between simple and complex	minute	in debris or on vegetation
Hemiptera	bugs	0–4; FW thickened at base	sucking	2–3	simple	medium	on debris, on vegetation, on or in water
Homoptera	cicadas, hoppers, whiteflies, aphids, scale insects	0–4; FW membranous or thickened, uniform in texture	sucking	1–3	simple	minute to large	on vegetation
Neuroptera	dobsonflies, fishflies, alderflies, lacewings, antlions	4; many-veined; HW as large as FW	chewing	5	complete	medium to large	on vegetation, often near water

CHARACTERS OF THE INSECT ORDERS (contd.)

Order	Examples	Wings	Mouth parts	Usual no. of tarsal segments	Meta-morphosis	Usual size	Where usually found
Coleoptera	beetles	0–4; FW thickened and veinless; HW membranous and folded	chewing	3–5	complete	minute to large	all habitats
Strepsiptera	twisted-winged parasites	0–2 (FW clublike); HW fanlike; only male with wings	vestigial	2–5	complete, with hypermetamor-phosis	minute	in other insects, chiefly bees and hoppers (Homoptera)
Mecoptera	scorpionflies	0–4; FW and HW about same size	chewing; beaklike	5	complete	medium	on vegetation
Trichoptera	caddisflies	4; hairy	chewing; reduced	5	complete; larvae aquatic	small to medium	near water
Lepidoptera	butterflies and moths	0–4; scaly	sucking, with coiled proboscis	5	complete	minute to large	on vegetation
Diptera	flies	0–2 (HW reduced to halteres)	sucking	5	complete	minute to large	on vegetation
Siphonaptera	fleas	none	sucking	5	complete	minute	on birds or mammals
Hymenoptera	sawflies, ichneumons, chalcids, ants, wasps, bees	0–4; HW smaller than FW	chewing, chewing-sucking	5	complete	minute to large	on ground or vegetation

Proturans: Order Protura

Identification: Minute whitish insects, 0.6–1.5 mm. Eyes, wings, cerci, and *antennae lacking*. Front legs carried in an elevated position like antennae. Abdomen of adult 12-segmented, with a pair of short *styli* (fingerlike processes) on each of the 3 basal segments. Metamorphosis simple.

Similar orders: Other minute wingless insects have less than 12 abdominal segments, and either have antennae or lack styli on the 3 basal abdominal segments.

Immature stages: Similar to adult stage, but with fewer abdominal segments (a segment added each molt).

Habits: Proturans occur in moist soil, moss, leaf mold, under bark, and in rotting wood. They are rather rare, and are very infrequently collected.

Importance: This order is considered to be a very primitive one. Its members are not of economic importance.

Classification: Three families, separated principally on the basis of the presence or absence of a tracheal system and the character of the abdominal appendages.

No. of species: World, 90; N. America, 20.

Key to Families

1.   Tracheae present, with 2 pairs of spiracles on thorax; abdominal appendages with a terminal vesicle
Eosentomidae

1′.   Tracheae and spiracles absent; abdominal appendages with or without a terminal vesicle   2

2(1′).   At least 2 pairs of abdominal appendages with a terminal vesicle   **Protentomidae**

2′.   Only the 1st pair of abdominal appendages with a terminal vesicle   **Acerentomidae**

Bristletails: Order Thysanura

Identification: Elongate (rarely oval) wingless insects with 2 or 3 tail-like appendages at end of abdomen. Some abdominal segments with a pair of *styli* (fingerlike processes). Antennae long and many-segmented. Metamorphosis simple.

Similar orders: (1) Protura: no antennae or tails; minute size (Thysanura usually more than 1.5 mm.). (2) Collembola (p. 62): no tails, but usually a forked appendage at end of abdomen; no styli on abdomen, but generally a single short tubular structure (collophore) on 1st segment; antennae short. (3) Orders of Pterygota (larvae and wingless adults), p. 56: no styli on abdominal segments.

Immature stages: Similar to adult stage.
Habits: Most species occur in leaf litter, under bark and stones, or in debris; some species may be found in buildings.
Importance: A few sometimes are pests in houses.
Classification: Two suborders, Ectognatha and Entognatha, differing in the number of terminal abdominal appendages and the segmentation of the tarsi. Many authors give these groups order rank, the Thysanura including only the Ectognatha and the Entognatha being placed in the order Diplura.
No. of species: World, 700; N. America, 50.

Common Bristletails: Suborder Ectognatha

Three tail-like appendages at end of abdomen (cerci and a median caudal filament). Compound eyes usually present. Body generally covered with scales. Tarsi 3- to 5-segmented. Mostly active, fast-running or jumping insects.

SILVERFISH Family Lepismatidae
Identification: Compound eyes *small and widely separated*. Ocelli absent. Tarsi *3- or 4-segmented*. Coxae without styli.

The Silverfish, *Lepisma saccharina* Linn., and Firebrat, *Thermobia domestica* (Packard), the most commonly encountered members of this group, often are pests in houses and other buildings, where they feed on all sorts of starchy substances. They are 10–12 mm. The Silverfish is silvery, usually occurs in cool damp situations. The Firebrat is brownish, inhabits warm situations around furnaces and steam pipes.

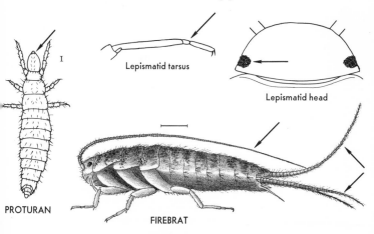

Lepismatid tarsus

Lepismatid head

PROTURAN

FIREBRAT

NICOLETIIDS   Family Nicoletiidae   **Not illus.**
   Identification: Similar to Lepismatidae but compound eyes
lacking and body sometimes not covered with scales.
   Nicoletiids may be elongate or oval: elongate forms lack scales,
occur in caves and mammal burrows; oval forms have scales,
live in ant and termite nests. All are quite rare but have been
found in Florida and Texas.

PRIMITIVE BRISTLETAILS   **Not illus.**
Family Lepidotrichidae
   Identification: Similar to Lepismatidae but body lacks scales,
ocelli are present, and tarsi are 5-segmented.
   A single rare species occurs in n. California, under bark and
in rotting wood of fallen Douglas fir. Yellowish gray, 12 mm.,
with antennae and tails quite long.

JUMPING BRISTLETAILS   Family Machilidae
   Identification: Similar to Lepismatidae but compound eyes
large and touching and there are styli on middle and hind coxae.
Tarsi 3-segmented.
   Machilids are active jumpers usually found in leaf litter,
under bark and stones, or among rocks along the seashore.
Most are brownish.

Diplurans: Suborder Entognatha

Only *2 appendages* (cerci) at end of abdomen. Body without
scales. Compound eyes lacking. Tarsi 1-segmented. Slender
whitish insects about 6 mm. or less. Usually found in soil and leaf
litter, under bark, or under stones and logs.

DIPLURANS
Families Campodeidae, Anajapygidae, and Japygidae
   Identification: Campodeidae: cerci and antennae *about equal
length*; 4–6 mm. Anajapygidae: similar, but cerci shorter than
antennae and fewer-segmented; less than 4 mm. Japygidae:
cerci *1-segmented and forcepslike.*
   The most commonly encountered diplurans are the campo-
deids. The other 2 families are small and rare (anajapygids are
represented by only 1 species, occurring in California).

Springtails: Order Collembola

Identification: Minute wingless insects, most less than 6 mm.
Body elongate or oval. Abdomen with 6 or fewer segments and
without cerci. Usually *a forked structure (furcula)* on 4th or 5th

abdominal segment, and *a small tubular structure* (*collophore*) on 1st abdominal segment. Antennae *short*, 4- to 6-segmented. Metamorphosis simple.

Similar orders: (1) Protura (p. 60): no antennae or furcula. (2) Thysanura (p. 60): cerci present; some abdominal segments with styli. (3) Small wingless Pterygota (p. 56): no furcula.

Immature stages: Similar to adult stage.

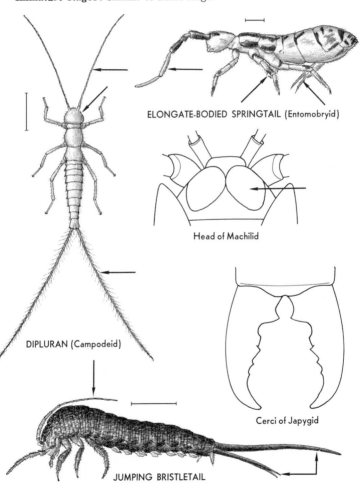

ELONGATE-BODIED SPRINGTAIL (Entomobryid)

Head of Machilid

DIPLURAN (Campodeid)

Cerci of Japygid

JUMPING BRISTLETAIL

Habits: Springtails occur in soil and leaf litter, under bark and in decaying wood, in fungi, and on the surface of water (freshwater ponds and along the seashore); a few occur on vegetation. Species with a furcula are jumpers; the furcula is normally folded forward under the abdomen, and the insect jumps by suddenly extending the furcula ventrally and posteriorly.

Importance: Important chiefly as scavengers, rarely as pests. Often very abundant, their populations sometimes numbering several million individuals per acre.

Classification: Two suborders, Arthropleona and Symphypleona, differing in body shape and segmentation.

No. of species: World, 2000; N. America, 314.

Suborder Arthropleona

Body elongate. Abdomen distinctly 6-segmented.

ELONGATE-BODIED SPRINGTAILS
Families Poduridae and Entomobryidae

Identification: Poduridae: minute, usually gray or black, with *short appendages;* integument (body covering) granular or tuberculate, without scales; pronotum *well developed* and visible from above; antennae *4-segmented.* Entomobryidae: similar, but integument usually smooth, pronotum reduced and usually not visible from above, and antennae *4- to 6-segmented.*

The family Entomobryidae is the largest in the order, and includes most of the springtails found in leaf litter and soil, in fungi, under bark, and in similar situations. The Marsh Springtail, *Isotomurus palustris* (Müller), is a common entomobryid occurring in moist woodlands. The Seashore Springtail, *Anurida maritima* (Guérin), is a slate-colored podurid occurring along the seashore, often in large numbers; it is frequently found in dense clusters on the surface of small pools between the tidemarks. *Podura aquatica* Linn. is common on the surface of freshwater ponds and streams. The Snow Flea, *Achorutes nivicolus* (Fitch), is a dark-colored podurid that sometimes occurs in large numbers on the surface of snow.

Suborder Symphypleona

Body oval or somewhat globular. Basal abdominal segments more or less fused.

GLOBULAR SPRINGTAILS Family Sminthuridae
Identification: By the characters of the suborder.

Sminthurids are minute insects, generally yellowish or mottled, with black eyes. They are often abundant on vegetation.

Mayflies: Order Ephemeroptera

Identification: Small to medium-sized, elongate, very soft-bodied, usually found near water. FW *large, triangular, many-veined.* HW small and rounded (rarely absent). Wings held together above body at rest. Abdomen with 2 or 3 hairlike tails. Antennae *small, bristlelike,* inconspicuous. Tarsi 3- to 5-segmented. Mouth parts vestigial. Metamorphosis simple.

Similar orders: (1) Odonata (p. 68): HW as large as FW or larger; terminal abdominal appendages relatively short; harder-bodied. (2) Hymenoptera (some ichneumons), p. 312: harder-bodied; antennae long; wings with fewer veins; tarsi 5-segmented. (3) Plecoptera (p. 92): HW with an anal lobe; wings held flat over abdomen at rest; antennae long and conspicuous.

Immature stages: Leaflike gills along sides of abdomen, and *3*

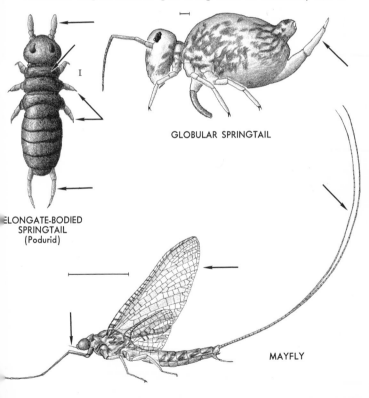

GLOBULAR SPRINGTAIL

ELONGATE-BODIED
SPRINGTAIL
(Podurid)

MAYFLY

hairlike tails. Common inhabitants of ponds and streams. Food consists of small aquatic organisms and organic debris.

Habits: The last nymphal instar molts to the winged form at the water surface or on an object just out of water. This winged stage, usually rather dull in appearance and somewhat pubescent, is not yet adult and is called a *subimago;* it molts once more to become adult (mayflies are unique among insects in undergoing a molt after the wings become functional). Adults seldom live more than a day or two, and do not feed. Males of many species engage in swarming flights, the members of the swarm flying up and down in unison. Eggs are attached to stones and other objects in the water, or are washed off the abdomen onto the water's surface. Adults often emerge in large numbers from lakes and ponds, and sometimes actually pile up along the shore.

Importance: Adults and nymphs are an important food of many freshwater fish. Artificial flies used by fishermen are often modeled after mayflies.

Classification: Three families, separated chiefly by wing venation and tarsal segmentation.

No. of species: World, 1500; N. America, 550.

BURROWING MAYFLIES
Family Ephemeridae

Identification: Most have clear wings; a few have spotted wings. Base of M_2 in FW *extends toward Cu_1, then bends abruptly distad.* R_{4+5} in HW *not forked.* Hind tarsi 4-segmented.

Nymphs occur in ponds, lakes, and large rivers, and are usually burrowing in habit. This group includes our largest mayflies. Some often emerge from lakes and rivers in enormous numbers.

STREAM MAYFLIES Family Heptageniidae

Identification: Base of M_2 in FW *nearly straight.* Cubital intercalaries in FW in 2 parallel pairs. R_{4+5} in HW *forked.* Hind tarsi 5-segmented.

Nymphs are flattened and streamlined, and occur on the underside of stones in streams. Adults are medium-sized to small, and usually clear-winged.

SMALL MAYFLIES Family Baetidae

Identification: M_2 in FW *as in Heptageniidae.* Cubital intercalaries in FW variable, but not in 2 parallel pairs. R_{4+5} in HW variable. Venation in HW often reduced (HW sometimes lacking). Hind tarsi 3- or 4-segmented.

Nymphs are more cylindrical than those of Heptageniidae, and occur in various aquatic habitats. Adults vary in size and appearance but are usually less than 15 mm.

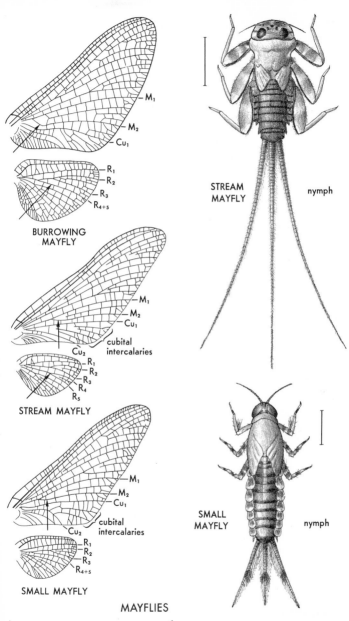

BURROWING MAYFLY

M_1
M_2
Cu_1

R_1
R_2
R_3
R_{4+5}

STREAM MAYFLY

M_1
M_2
Cu_1
cubital intercalaries
Cu_2

R_1
R_2
R_3
R_4
R_5

SMALL MAYFLY

M_1
M_2
Cu_1
cubital intercalaries
Cu_2

R_1
R_2
R_3
R_{4+5}

STREAM MAYFLY   nymph

SMALL MAYFLY   nymph

MAYFLIES

67

Dragonflies and Damselflies:
Order Odonata

Identification: Two pairs of elongate, membranous, many-veined wings. Wings at rest usually held outstretched (Anisoptera) or together above body (Zygoptera). FW and HW similar in size and shape (Zygoptera), or HW *broader at base than FW* (Anisoptera). Abdomen *long and slender*. Compound eyes large, often occupying most of head. Antennae *very short, bristlelike*, and inconspicuous. Prothorax small, the other 2 thoracic segments making up most of thorax. Tarsi *3-segmented*. Copulatory organs of ♂ located on ventral side of 2nd abdominal segment. Cerci present, 1-segmented, in male functioning as clasping organs during mating. Mouth parts chewing. Metamorphosis simple.

Similar orders: (1) Neuroptera (p. 140): antennae long; tarsi 5-segmented; wing venation different. (2) Hymenoptera (p. 312): antennae long; tarsi 5-segmented; HW smaller than FW; wings with fewer veins. (3) Diptera (p. 260): 1 pair of wings. (4) Ephemeroptera (p. 65): 2–3 long tails; HW smaller than FW; very soft-bodied.

Immature stages: Nymphs are aquatic, and occur in ponds and streams. They feed on other insects, which are captured with a peculiarly modified labium. When not in use, the labium is folded under the head, and when used is thrust forward very quickly to catch prey in a pair of clawlike structures at its apex. Labium when extended is sometimes as long as ⅓ body length. Gills of the nymph are located in rectum (Anisoptera) or are in form of 3 leaflike tails (Zygoptera).

Habits: Adults usually found near water (in which nymphs live), but many are strong fliers and can range many miles. Often fly in tandem, the male holding female by back of head or the prothorax with the appendages at end of his abdomen. Eggs generally laid in aquatic vegetation or are washed off end of the abdomen when female flies low over water. Adults relatively large insects (about 1–3½ in.), and many are brightly colored. Most are good fliers, and spend a large part of their time on the wing. They feed on other insects they catch on the wing.

Importance: All stages are predaceous, feeding on mosquitoes, midges, and other small insects, and help keep them under control. Adults attempt to bite when handled, but only the larger dragonflies can inflict a painful pinch; they do not sting.

Classification: Two suborders, Anisoptera and Zygoptera, which differ in wing shape, position of wings at rest, appendages at end of abdomen, and *characters of nymphs*. Principal characters separating families are those of wing venation.

No. of species: World, 4870; N. America, 420.

Dragonflies: Suborder Anisoptera

Relatively stout-bodied, about 1–3½ in. HW *broader at base than FW*, the wings at rest held outstretched. ♂ with 3 terminal abdominal appendages, 2 above and 1 below. ♀ with only 2 (dorsal) terminal appendages. ♀ of some groups with an ovipositor, located on ventral side of terminal abdominal segments, giving end of abdomen a somewhat swollen appearance. Nymphs robust, with gills in rectum; breathing is accomplished by drawing water into rectum through anus, and then expelling it; this expulsion of water serves as a means of locomotion, the insect thus moving by "jet" propulsion.

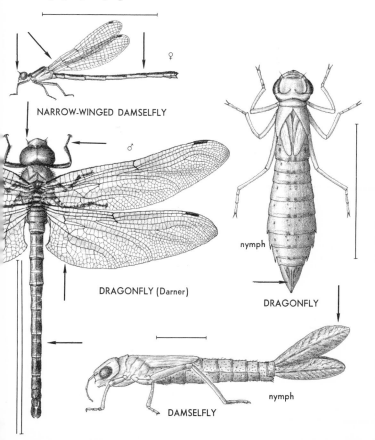

NARROW-WINGED DAMSELFLY

DRAGONFLY (Darner)

nymph

DRAGONFLY

DAMSELFLY

nymph

Graybacks, Clubtails, Darners, and Biddies: Superfamily Aeshnoidea

Triangles in FW and HW similar in shape and location. Most antenodal cross veins between C and Sc not in line with those between Sc and R. *A brace vein at proximal end of stigma* (except Cordulegastridae). Wings nearly always clear, without spots or bands. Ovipositor present or absent.

GRAYBACKS Family Petaluridae
Identification: Large grayish-brown or blackish dragonflies, about 3 in. Compound eyes do not meet on dorsal side of head. Median lobe of labium *notched*. Stigma at least 8 mm. Ovipositor well developed.

Two species of graybacks occur in the U.S., 1 in the East and 1 in the West; both are rare and local. Eastern species, *Tachopteryx thoreyi* (Hagen), is grayish brown and found along small streams in wooded valleys. Western species, *Tanypteryx hageni* (Selys), is blackish, and occurs at high elevations in mountains. Graybacks often alight on tree trunks, where their color blends with that of the bark.

CLUBTAILS Family Gomphidae   **See also Pl. 1**
Identification: Compound eyes *do not meet* on dorsal side of head. Median lobe of labium not notched. Stigma less than 8 mm. Terminal segments of abdomen sometimes dilated. ♀ lacks ovipositor.

Members of this large group occur along streams or shores of large lakes. Most species are 2–3 in., and dark brown with yellowish or greenish markings. Flight is usually steady, without periods of hovering; some occasionally fly with a very undulating flight. Adults often alight on a flat surface.

DARNERS Family Aeshnidae   **See also Pl. 1**
Identification: Compound eyes *in contact* for a considerable distance on dorsal side of head. Ovipositor *well developed*.

This group includes our largest dragonflies. Most species are 2¼–3¼ in., and a few may reach 3½ in. or more. All are strong fliers, difficult to catch. Most species are dark brown, often with bluish or greenish markings. The Green Darner (Pl. 1), *Anax junius* (Drury), a common species found around ponds, has a light green thorax, bluish abdomen and a targetlike mark on upperpart of the face. *Aeshna* is a large and widely distributed genus whose members are mostly dark-colored, with bluish markings. Darners generally occur around ponds and swamps.

BIDDIES Family Cordulegastridae
Identification: Large brownish to blackish dragonflies with yellowish markings. *No brace vein.* Ovipositor of ♀ conspicuous.
Biddies resemble river skimmers (*Macromia*, family Macromiidae), but have a slightly different wing venation (compare illustrations, pp. 71 and 73). The compound eyes are slightly separated on dorsal side of head or meet at a single point only. A small group, and its members are not common. They occur chiefly along small woodland streams.

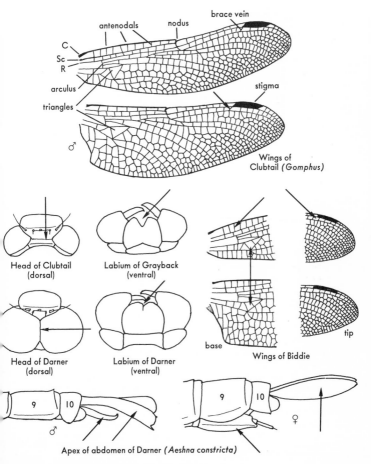

Wings of Clubtail (*Gomphus*)

Head of Clubtail (dorsal)

Labium of Grayback (ventral)

Head of Darner (dorsal)

Labium of Darner (ventral)

base

Wings of Biddie

tip

Apex of abdomen of Darner (*Aeshna constricta*)

Skimmers: Superfamily Libelluloidea

Triangles in FW and HW *different in shape*, and triangle in FW
farther beyond arculus than triangle in HW. Most antenodal cross
veins between C and Sc *in line with those between Sc and R. No
brace vein.* Ovipositor lacking.

BELTED and RIVER SKIMMERS Family Macromiidae
  Identification: Anal loop of HW rounded, without a bisector.
  ♂ with inner margin of HW *slightly notched*, and a small lobe on
  each side of 2nd abdominal segment. Wings never with spots
  or bands.
    Belted skimmers (*Didymops*) are brownish, with light mark-
  ings on the thorax, and 2¼–2¾ in. They occur along boggy
  pond shores but are not common. River skimmers (*Macromia*)
  are 2½–3¼ in., blackish, with yellow markings on thorax and
  abdomen, and the eyes in life are bright green; adults are fast
  fliers and are found along large streams and lakes.

GREEN-EYED SKIMMERS Family Corduliidae
  Identification: Anal loop in HW elongate, with a bisector,
  usually *not particularly foot-shaped.* ♂ with inner margin of
  HW *slightly notched*, and a small lobe on each side of 2nd abdominal segment. Hind margin of compound eyes *slightly lobed.*
    Corduliids are usually blackish or metallic, and seldom have
  conspicuous light markings. The eyes in life are bright green.
  Most species have the wings entirely clear or with only a small
  dark spot at the base, and are 1½–2¾ in. Members of the
  genus *Epicordulia* have a dark spot at base, middle, and tip of
  each wing, and are 2½–3¼ in. Corduliids generally occur about
  swamps and ponds; only a few are found along streams.

COMMON SKIMMERS Family Libellulidae   **See also Pl. 1**
  Identification: Anal loop in HW elongate, with a bisector, and
  usually *foot-shaped.* Inner margin of HW *rounded in both sexes.*
  ♂ without lateral lobes on 2nd abdominal segment. Hind
  margin of compound eyes *straight* or only very slightly lobed.
  Wing color variable.
    This is a large group and many species are very common.
  They occur chiefly about ponds and swamps; most dragonflies
  one sees in such places belong to this family. The majority are
  1–2½ in. (a few may be somewhat larger), and the wingspread
  is noticeably greater than the body length. Many are brightly
  colored, often with spots or bands on the wings; some have the
  sexes differently colored. Their flight is fast, sometimes interrupted by periods of hovering.

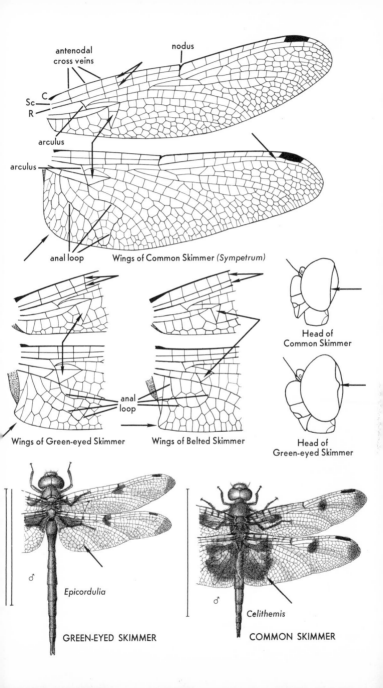

antenodal cross veins

nodus

C

Sc

R

arculus

arculus

anal loop

Wings of Common Skimmer *(Sympetrum)*

Wings of Green-eyed Skimmer

Wings of Belted Skimmer

anal loop

Head of Common Skimmer

Head of Green-eyed Skimmer

♂

Epicordulia

GREEN-EYED SKIMMER

♂

Celithemis

COMMON SKIMMER

Damselflies: Suborder Zygoptera

FW and HW similar in size and shape, at rest held together above body or somewhat divergent. Abdomen *very slender*. ♂ with 4 terminal appendages. ♀ with a well-developed ovipositor. Nymphs with *3 leaflike gills* at end of abdomen (illus., p. 69); swim by body undulations.

BROAD-WINGED DAMSELFLIES   See also Pl. 1
Family Calopterygidae

Identification: Wings *gradually narrowed at base*, with *10 or more antenodal cross veins;* usually blackish or with blackish markings (*Calopteryx*) or clear with a reddish spot at base (*Hetaerina*); wings at rest held together above body.

These are large damselflies that occur along streams. The male Black-winged Damselfly (Pl. 1), *Calopteryx maculata* (Beauvais), a common eastern species, has blackish wings and a metallic greenish-black body; female has dark gray wings with a white stigma and body is not metallic. The American Ruby-spot, *Hetaerina americana* (Fabricius), another common eastern species, is reddish, with a bright red spot at base of wings.

SPREAD-WINGED DAMSELFLIES   Family Lestidae

Identification: Wings *stalked at base; 2 antenodul cross veins*, M_3 rises *closer to arculus* than to nodus. Wings clear, usually held diverging above body at rest.

Spread-winged damselflies are 1¼–2 in., and are common around swamps and ponds. Most belong to the genus *Lestes*. They can be recognized in the field by *the way they hold their wings at rest*.

NARROW-WINGED DAMSELFLIES   See also p. 69 and Pl. 1
Family Coenagrionidae

Identification: Similar to Lestidae, but M_3 rises *behind nodus*, and wings at rest *held together above body*.

This group includes most of our damselflies (about 75 species). The majority occur around ponds and swamps (where often abundant), but a few are found along streams. Most species are 1–1¼ in. and clear-winged. *Argia fumipennis* (Burmeister), which occurs in the southern states, has smoky-brown wings. Many are very brightly colored. Most bluets (*Enallagma*, the largest genus in the family) are light blue with black markings, species of *Amphiagrion* are blackish with a red abdomen, and males of the Violet Dancer (Pl. 1), *Argia violacea* (Hagen), are largely violet. Color pattern usually differs in the sexes, males being more brightly colored than females.

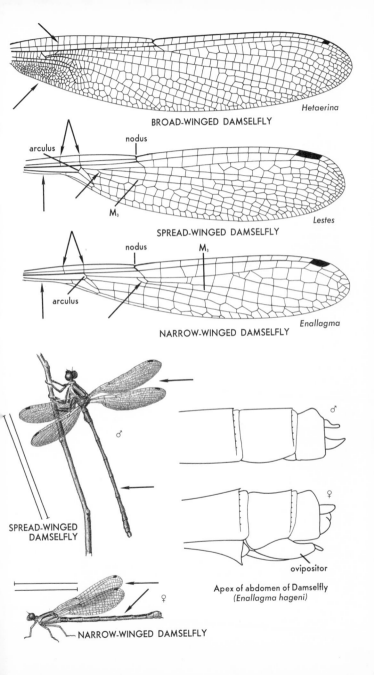

BROAD-WINGED DAMSELFLY

Hetaerina

SPREAD-WINGED DAMSELFLY

arculus

nodus

M₃

Lestes

NARROW-WINGED DAMSELFLY

nodus

M₃

arculus

Enallagma

SPREAD-WINGED DAMSELFLY

♂

♀

ovipositor

Apex of abdomen of Damselfly
(*Enallagma hageni*)

NARROW-WINGED DAMSELFLY

♀

Grasshoppers, Katydids, Crickets, Mantids, Walkingsticks, and Cockroaches: Order Orthoptera

Identification: Usually 2 pairs of wings: FW long, narrow, many-veined, and somewhat thickened (called *tegmina*); HW membranous, broad, with many veins, and folded fanwise at rest under FW; 1 or both pairs of wings sometimes small or absent. Antennae many-segmented, often long and hairlike. Cerci present, sometimes short and clasperlike, sometimes long and feelerlike. ♀ usually has ovipositor, which may be long and slender or short. Tarsi generally 3- to 5-segmented. Mouth parts chewing. Metamorphosis simple.

Similar orders: (1) Coleoptera (p. 146): FW thickened but veinless; cerci lacking; antennae rarely with more than 11 segments; HW longer than FW, with relatively few veins and not folded fanwise at rest. (2) Hemiptera (p. 112): mouth parts sucking; FW usually with base thickened and tip membranous; HW with few veins; antennae with 5 or fewer segments. (3) Dermaptera (p. 98): FW thickened but short; cerci forcepslike. (4) Homoptera (p. 128) (hoppers): rarely over 12 mm.; mouth parts sucking; antennae short and bristlelike. (5) Isoptera (p. 88): FW and HW of winged forms similar in size and shape, HW not folded at rest; cerci short and inconspicuous; antennae short, threadlike, or beadlike; tarsi 4-segmented.

Immature stages: Similar to adult but wings short or absent.

Habits: Many Orthoptera "sing" by rubbing one body part against another. Long-horned grasshoppers (p. 80) and crickets (p. 82) rub a sharp edge (*scraper*) of one front wing over a filelike ridge (*file*) on underside of other front wing. Slant-faced grasshoppers rub hind legs against the tegmina. Band-winged grasshoppers snap hind wings in flight. Males generally do the singing; females of a few species produce soft noises. Song most often heard ("calling" song) functions mainly in getting the sexes together. Each species has a distinctive song and some Orthoptera can produce more than one type of sound.

Importance: Most orthopterans are plant feeders and some are very destructive to cultivated plants; a few species sometimes increase to enormous numbers and migrate long distances, completely destroying large areas of crops on the way. A few are predaceous and a few rather omnivorous. Some orthopterans (like cockroaches) may be pests in buildings.

Classification: Six suborders, separated chiefly by characters of legs, antennae, body form, and ovipositor.

No. of species: World, 22,500; N. America, 1015.

Suborder Caelifera

Grasshopperlike jumping insects, with hind femora more or less *enlarged*. Tarsi with 3 or fewer segments. Antennae *relatively short*. Tympana (eardrums) usually present on sides of 1st abdominal segment. Ovipositor short.

PYGMY MOLE CRICKETS Family Tridactylidae
Identification: Length *10 mm.* or less. Front tibiae *enlarged* and

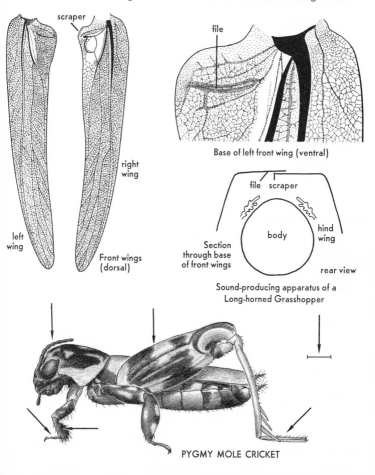

scraper

file

right wing

left wing

Front wings (dorsal)

Base of left front wing (ventral)

file scraper

body

hind wing

Section through base of front wings

rear view

Sound-producing apparatus of a Long-horned Grasshopper

PYGMY MOLE CRICKET

fitted for digging. Front and middle tarsi *2-segmented*, hind tarsi *1-segmented* or lacking. Antennae *11-segmented*. Body not pubescent.

These insects occur chiefly in moist sandy situations along shores of ponds and streams. They burrow in the ground but are sometimes found on the surface. They are not common.

PYGMY GRASSHOPPERS   Family Tetrigidae

Identification: Pronotum *extends back over abdomen* and is pointed posteriorly. Hind tarsi *3-segmented*, other tarsi *2-segmented*. Tegmina (FW) very short. 18 mm. or less.

Pygmy grasshoppers overwinter as adults and are most often encountered in spring and early summer. They are moderately common but are not of much economic importance.

SHORT-HORNED GRASSHOPPERS   See also Pl. 2
Family Acrididae

Identification: Pronotum *not prolonged back over abdomen*. Wings usually well developed. Tarsi *3-segmented*.

This group contains our most common grasshoppers. Many are important pests of cultivated plants. Most of them oviposit in the ground and overwinter in the egg stage.

Spur-throated Grasshoppers, Subfamily Cyrtacanthacridinae (see also Pl. 2). Spine or *tubercle* on prosternum. Pronotum flat dorsally and *broadly rounded posteriorly*. Face usually vertical. HW generally clear. This group contains many common species, including most of the pests. A few species sometimes increase to epidemic proportions and migrate long distances; these migrating swarms contain millions of grasshoppers and cause enormous damage.

Slant-faced Grasshoppers, Subfamily Acridinae. Similar to Cyrtacanthacridinae but with face *slanting backward* and without prosternal spine. Often occur in wet meadows or near marshes. Less abundant than other Acrididae.

Band-winged Grasshoppers, Subfamily Oedipodinae (see also Pl. 2). HW usually *colored*. A median *longitudinal keel* on pronotum. Posterior margin of pronotum *triangularly extended backward*. Face vertical or nearly so. Bandwings are often very common in sparse vegetation and along roadsides. They are conspicuous in flight because of color of the hind wings and the crackling noises they sometimes make but very inconspicuous when they alight, because the hind wings are concealed and the front wings are usually colored like the background.

EUMASTACIDS and MONKEY GRASSHOPPERS   Not illus.
Families Eumastacidae and Tanaoceridae

Identification: Similar to Acrididae but wingless. Medium-sized to small, usually brownish. Tympana generally absent.

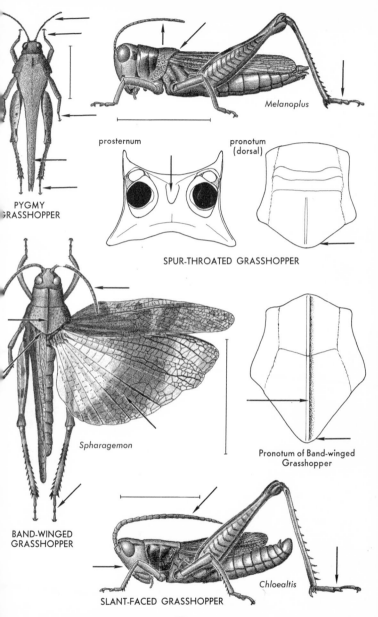

PYGMY
GRASSHOPPER

Melanoplus

prosternum

pronotum
(dorsal)

SPUR-THROATED GRASSHOPPER

Spharagemon

Pronotum of Band-winged
Grasshopper

BAND-WINGED
GRASSHOPPER

Chloealtis

SLANT-FACED GRASSHOPPER

79

Antennae shorter than front femora (Eumastacidae) or considerably longer (Tanaoceridae).

These 2 families contain several species of relatively uncommon grasshoppers that are found in the chaparral country of the Southwest, where they usually occur on the uppermost branches of bushes.

Suborder Ensifera

Similar to Caelifera but antennae *long, slender,* usually as long as body or longer. Tympana (eardrums), when present, located *at base of front tibiae.* Ovipositor *long and slender,* sometimes as long as body or longer. Tarsi 3- or 4-segmented.

LONG-HORNED GRASSHOPPERS   See also Pl. 2
Family Tettigoniidae

Identification: Large insects, usually greenish (sometimes brownish). Tarsi *4-segmented.* Ovipositor sword-shaped. Wings present (sometimes small), with less than 8 principal longitudinal veins. ♂ with sound-producing structures on FW (p. 77).

The best-known members of this group are greenish and the males are noted songsters. Most of the front wing surface slopes over the sides of the body, only a small portion being horizontal and dorsal; the base of the left tegmen is usually uppermost. Most species are plant feeders, and lay their eggs on or in plant tissues; winter is generally passed in the egg stage. Our species are grouped into 8 subfamilies, the most important of which are the following.

True Katydids, Subfamily Pseudophyllinae. FW *broadly oval, somewhat convex.* Prosternum with pair of short spines. Pronotum *about as long as wide* and with 2 transverse grooves. Arboreal and not often seen, but their *katy-did, katy-didn't* song is well known; they sing only at night. Principally eastern in distribution.

Bush and Round-headed Katydids, Subfamily Phaneropterinae. Usually green and over 1 in. FW *flat,* long and narrow or *elongate-oval.* HW usually longer than FW. Dorsal surface of 1st tarsal segment smoothly rounded (laterally grooved in the following subfamilies). Vertex somewhat rounded. Prosternal spines lacking. These katydids occur on weeds, bushes, and trees. Bush katydids (*Scudderia,* Pl. 2) have long, narrow, and nearly parallel-sided tegmina (FW). Angular-winged katydids (*Microcentrum*) have tegmina *widened* and *somewhat angulate in the middle,* and hind femora extend only a little beyond middle of tegmina. Round-headed katydids (*Amblycorypha*) have oval tegmina and hind femora extend almost to tips of tegmina. The songs of these katydids usually consist of a series of high-pitched lisps or ticks.

Cone-headed Grasshoppers, Subfamily Copiphorinae. Green-

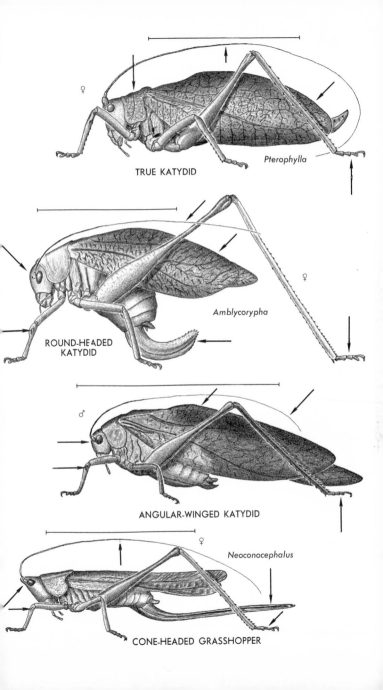

TRUE KATYDID

Pterophylla

ROUND-HEADED KATYDID

Amblycorypha

ANGULAR-WINGED KATYDID

CONE-HEADED GRASSHOPPER

Neoconocephalus

ish, usually over 1 in. Head *conical*, vertex *extending well beyond basal antennal segment*. Tegmina long and narrow. Ovipositor *nearly or quite as long as body*. Usually found in high grass or weeds. Songs high-pitched and buzzy.

Meadow Grasshoppers, Subfamily Conocephalinae (see also Pl. 2). Slender, greenish, seldom over 1 in. Vertex *does not extend beyond basal antennal segment*. Prosternum usually with a pair of small spines. Found principally in wet meadows or in grassy areas near ponds and streams. Songs usually consist of relatively long buzzes separated by zips (*bzzzzzz-zip-zip-zip-zip-bzzzzzz*).

Shield-backed Grasshoppers, Subfamily Decticinae. Brownish to black, usually 1 in. or longer, generally short-winged, with pronotum *extending back to abdomen*. Most eastern species belong to the genus *Atlanticus*, and occur in dry upland woods. Some western species often are serious pests of field crops; the most important of these is the Mormon Cricket, *Anabrus simplex* Haldeman.

CAMEL CRICKETS and OTHERS Family Gryllacrididae
  Identification: Similar to Tettigoniidae but usually wingless, gray or brown. Wings if present with 8 or more principal longitudinal veins, and FW of ♂ lacking sound-producing structures. Auditory organs generally lacking.

  Cave or Camel Crickets, Subfamily Rhaphidophorinae. Brownish, somewhat humpbacked appearance. Antennae *contiguous at base or nearly so*. Hind femora *long*. Occur in caves, cellars, under logs and stones, and in similar dark moist places. Most of our species belong to the genus *Ceuthophilus*.

  Leaf-rolling Grasshoppers, Subfamily Gryllacridinae (not illus.). Tarsi lobed, somewhat flattened dorsoventrally. Hind femora extend beyond apex of abdomen. Ovipositor upturned. Our only species, *Camptonotus carolinensis* (Gerstaecker), which occurs in the East, is brownish and 13–15 mm. Nocturnal, feeding on aphids and spending the day in a leaf it has rolled up and tied with silk.

  Jerusalem or Sand Crickets, Subfamily Stenopelmatinae. Large, robust, somewhat brownish. Tarsi *not lobed*, and *more or less flattened laterally*. Hind femora *do not extend beyond apex of abdomen*. These insects are western, occurring chiefly along the Pacific Coast. Nocturnal; spend the day under stones or in loose soil.

CRICKETS Family Gryllidae   See also Pl. 2
  Identification: Somewhat flattened insects. Tarsi *3-segmented*. Ovipositor usually long and cylindrical. Cerci long and feeler-like.

  This group contains many common insects, and the males are well-known songsters. Most of the tegminal (FW) surface is

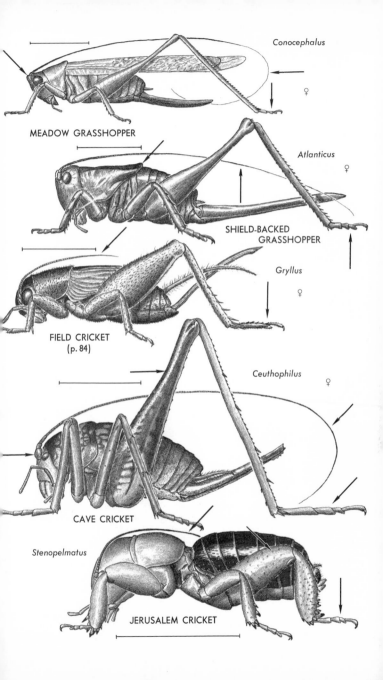

Conocephalus
♀

MEADOW GRASSHOPPER

Atlanticus
♀

**SHIELD-BACKED
GRASSHOPPER**

Gryllus
♀

FIELD CRICKET
(p. 84)

Ceuthophilus
♀

CAVE CRICKET

Stenopelmatus

JERUSALEM CRICKET

dorsal in position, with a narrow lateral portion bent down abruptly; the right tegmen is usually uppermost at rest. The front wings of females are thickened and leathery; those of males contain large membranous areas and are often wider. Songs generally are rapid trills or chirps — more musical and less lisping than songs of Tettigoniidae. Only the more common subfamilies can be mentioned here.

Mole Crickets, Subfamily Gryllotalpinae. Brownish, very pubescent. Usually 1 in. or longer. Front legs *broad and spade-like.* Antennae *relatively short.* Ovipositor not visible externally. Tegmina usually short, covering only about half of abdomen. Mole crickets burrow in the ground, ordinarily in moist places, and are not often encountered.

Bush Crickets, Subfamilies Eneopterinae and Trigonidiinae (see also Pl. 2). Most bush crickets are less than 9 mm. and brownish. 2nd tarsal segment *heart-shaped and flattened dorsoventrally* (small and flattened laterally in the remaining subfamilies). Eneopterinae have *small teeth on hind tibiae* between the spines and the ovipositor is cylindrical and nearly straight. Trigonidiinae lack teeth between the tibial spines and the ovipositor is somewhat sword-shaped (Trigonidiinae are sometimes called sword-bearing crickets). Found in bushes; they resemble the more common ground crickets (Nemobiinae) but do not live on the ground. Relatively uncommon in the North and more common in the South.

Tree Crickets, Subfamily Oecanthinae. Differ from the following subfamilies in lacking ocelli. Most species are pale green, have *small teeth between the spines on hind tibiae.* Many species are very common and all are excellent singers. Some occur on trees and shrubs, and others on high grass and weeds. The tree- and bush-inhabitants generally sing only at night, whereas the weed-inhabitants usually sing both day and night. Song of most species is a prolonged trill, but a few chirp. The chirping of the Snowy Tree Cricket, *Oecanthus fultoni* Walker, a bush inhabitant, is a common night sound in much of the country, and is at a very regular rate. All insects sing more slowly as the temperature drops (in the case of crickets the pitch of the song also falls with decreasing temperature), and the chirp rate of the Snowy Tree Cricket provides a means of estimating the temperature: the number of chirps in 13 seconds plus 40 gives a good estimate of the temperature in degrees Fahrenheit.

Ground Crickets, Subfamily Nemobiinae. Length 12 mm. or less; brownish. Spines on hind tibiae *long* and movable. Ground crickets are common insects, and occur on the ground in pastures, lawns, and in wooded areas. The songs are soft and high-pitched, and usually consist of pulsating trills or buzzes.

Field and House Crickets, Subfamily Gryllinae. Spines on hind tibiae *short, stout,* fixed. 12 mm. or longer. Field crickets (*Gryllus,* p. 83) are common and widely distributed; occur in fields, pastures, lawns, along roadsides, and in woods. The different species of *Gryllus*, which were formerly thought to represent a single species, are very similar in appearance but differ in seasonal life history, habitat, and song. The House Cricket, *Acheta domesticus* (Linn.), is a species introduced from

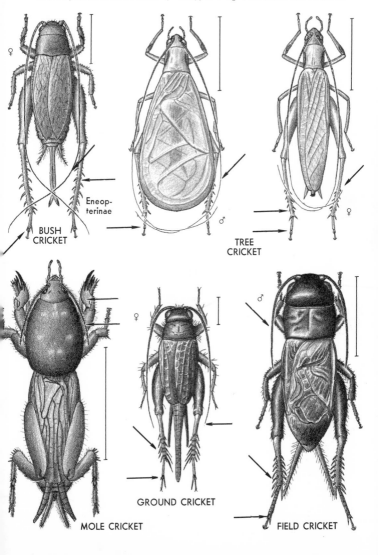

BUSH CRICKET

Eneopterinae

TREE CRICKET

MOLE CRICKET

GROUND CRICKET

FIELD CRICKET

Europe that often enters houses; it differs from field crickets in having the head light-colored with dark crossbands. Gryllinae sing both day and night, and most species chirp.

Suborders Mantodea, Phasmatodea, Blattodea, and Grylloblattodea: Nonjumping Orthoptera

MANTIDS Family Mantidae
Identification: Large insects, usually over 1 in., with a distinctive appearance. Prothorax and front coxae *greatly lengthened*. Front femora and tibiae armed with spines and *fitted for grasping prey*. Middle and hind legs slender, their coxae shorter. Tarsi *5-segmented*. Antennae *short*.

Mantids are predaceous, and usually lie in wait for their prey with the front legs upraised. Eggs are laid in papier-mâché-like cases attached to weeds or twigs; the eggs overwinter in the case. Mantids mostly are tropical. Our native species occur mainly in the South. The only ones common in the North are 2 introduced species: the European Mantid, *Mantis religiosa* Linn. (pale green, about 2 in.), and the Chinese Mantid, *Tenodera aridifolia sinensis* Saussure (3–4 in.). The latter is rather widely distributed and the former is largely restricted to the eastern states. In the West, *Litaneutria minor* (Scudder) occurs all the way to British Columbia.

WALKINGSTICKS Family Phasmatidae
Identification: Body and legs *very long and slender*. Wingless (1 species in s. Florida has very short wings). Tarsi usually *5-segmented* (3-segmented in *Timema* — small, stout-bodied, earwiglike forms occurring in the far West). Cerci 1-segmented. Antennae usually *long and slender*.

These insects strongly resemble twigs, and are usually found on trees or shrubs. They are plant feeders. Largely tropical and more common in the South; only a few species occur in the North. Most of them are at least 2 in.; 1 southern species reaches 6 in. or more.

COCKROACHES Family Blattidae   **See also Pl. 2**
Identification: Body flattened and oval, the head *concealed from above by pronotum*. Wings usually present. Antennae *long and slender*. Tarsi 5-*segmented*. Cerci many-segmented.

The best-known cockroaches are those that invade houses, where they may be serious pests. They feed on a variety of foods, and have an unpleasant odor, hide in cracks during the day, and feed at night. All are active, fast-running insects; many species seldom if ever fly. Cockroaches are much more abundant in the South than in the North; the few northern species that occur out of doors (wood cockroaches) are usually found in woods under dead logs and stones.

GRYLLOBLATTIDS Family Grylloblattidae   **Not illus.**
Identification: Elongate, cylindrical, wingless, 15–30 mm.
Antennae about half as long as body or less. Tarsi 5-segmented.
Cerci long, 8- or 9-segmented. Ovipositor long, sword-shaped.

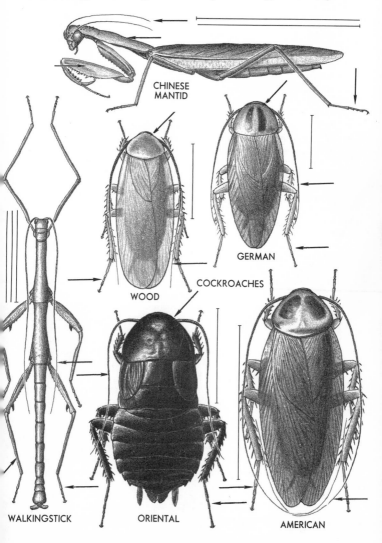

CHINESE MANTID

WALKINGSTICK

WOOD

GERMAN

COCKROACHES

ORIENTAL

AMERICAN

Compound eyes small or absent. Ocelli absent. Head relatively large, mouth parts situated anteriorly.

Grylloblattids occur in the mountains of nw. U.S. (California, Montana, Idaho, Washington, and Oregon) and w. Canada, usually at high elevations. They are generally found under logs or stones or at the edge of glaciers. Probably feed as scavengers.

Termites: Order Isoptera

Identification: Small, soft-bodied, usually pale-colored. Social, with caste differentiation. Antennae generally *short, thread- or beadlike*. Tarsi 4-segmented. Cerci usually short. Winged or wingless; winged forms with *2 pairs of wings similar in size and shape*, relatively long and narrow (as long as body or longer), at rest held flat over abdomen; wings eventually broken off along a basal fracture. Mouth parts chewing (vestigial in nasuti, p. 91). 2 ocelli or none. Metamorphosis simple.

Similar orders: (1) Hymenoptera (ants, p. 344): abdomen constricted at base (not so in termites); hard-bodied, dark-colored; antennae elbowed; HW smaller than FW. (2) Embioptera (p. 100): tarsi 3-segmented; basal segment of front tarsi greatly enlarged. (3) Zoraptera (p. 101): tarsi 2-segmented; antennae 9-segmented. (4) Orthoptera (p. 76): cerci usually longer; antennae hairlike. (5) Psocoptera (p. 102): tarsi 2- or 3-segmented; FW larger than HW; wings at rest rooflike over body; cerci absent.

Immature stages: Similar to adult but wings short or absent.

Habits: Termite colonies occur in ground or in wood. Food consists principally of wood or other vegetable materials. The 4 castes usually present are the reproductive caste, supplementary reproductives, workers, and soldiers; some species have a 5th (nasutus) caste. Reproductives have fully developed wings, compound eyes, and are generally dark-colored; they are produced in large numbers at certain seasons and leave the colony in a swarm. Mating occurs at this time, and individual pairs establish new colonies; reproductives shed their wings after mating. Female reproductives (queens) do all or most of the egg laying and ordinarily are long-lived. Supplementary reproductives have shorter wings, smaller eyes, and are generally lighter in color; they are able to reproduce. Most workers are sterile adults; they are palecolored and lack compound eyes, and their mandibles are small. They do the main work of the colony — collecting food, feeding the queen, soldiers, and young, constructing galleries, and the like. Some termites lack a worker caste and nymphs of other castes act as workers. Soldiers are usually sterile adults with *large heads and mandibles;* they attack intruders in the colony. A few termites lack a soldier caste. Some termites have a nasutus caste; nasuti have the head drawn out anteriorly into a slender snout, and they function in the defense of the colony.

Importance: Many species cause considerable damage to buildings, furniture, utility poles, fence posts, and other materials; infested timbers are hollowed out and may eventually collapse. Termites are beneficial in their important role of converting dead trees and other plant materials into substances useful to plants.

Classification: Four families in the U.S. Winged forms are separated mainly on basis of head and wing characters. Soldiers are separated on basis of head shape, leg and antennal characters, and characters of the mandibles.

Identification of Termites: The *fontanelle* is a depressed pale spot on front of head between the eyes. *Radius* is a longitudinal vein behind the costal margin of the wing. Wingless termites are best identified by association with winged forms and by habits. Termites found in the nest often can be identified by character and location of the nest, and by area in which it is found.

No. of species: World, 2100; N. America, 41.

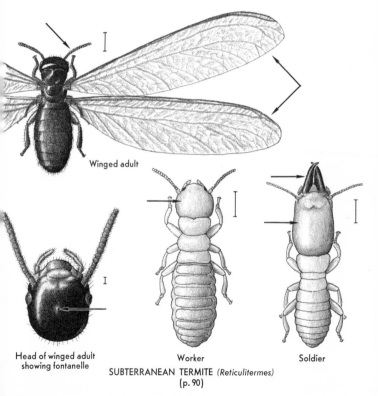

Winged adult

Head of winged adult
showing fontanelle

Worker

Soldier

SUBTERRANEAN TERMITE *(Reticulitermes)*
(p. 90)

SUBTERRANEAN and DAMP-WOOD TERMITES   p. 89
Family Rhinotermitidae

Identification: Widely distributed with colonies in the ground (subterranean termites), or occurring in Florida in damp wood (damp-wood termites). Winged adults with *a fontanelle*. Scale of FW (basal portion left after wing breaks off) longer than pronotum. R usually without anterior branches.

Subterranean termites nest in the ground and burrow into wood, usually fallen trees and stumps. They enter the wood of buildings or other structures where it comes in contact with the ground, or they may get into buildings by way of tunnels through cracks in the foundation. The Eastern Subterranean Termite, *Reticulitermes flavipes* (Kollar), a widely distributed and destructive species, is the only termite occurring in the Northeast; winged forms appear in spring. The damp-wood termites in this family (*Prorhinotermes*) occur in moist dead wood or tree roots and are found only in Florida.

SOLDIERLESS, DESERT, and NASUTIFORM TERMITES
Family Termitidae

Identification: Occur in Southwest. Colonies in wood with a ground contact, or in ground. Winged adults similar to Rhinotermitidae, but scale of FW shorter than pronotum.

Soldierless termites (lacking a soldier caste) burrow under logs or cow chips. Desert termites nest in the ground, and sometimes damage the wood of buildings and poles. Nasutiform termites attack wood in contact with the ground; they have a nasutus caste.

DRY-WOOD, DAMP-WOOD, and POWDER-POST TERMITES
Family Kalotermitidae

Identification: Occur in s. and w. U.S., the colonies in dry wood above ground (dry-wood and powder-post termites), or in moist dead wood or tree trunks (damp-wood termites). Winged adults without a fontanelle but *with ocelli*, and R usually with *anterior apical branches*.

Dry-wood termites (*Incisitermes* and others) attack buildings, furniture, utility poles, and piled lumber; they are important in the South, from S. Carolina to Texas. Powder-post termites (*Cryptotermes*, *Calcaritermes*), which occur in the South, attack dry wood and reduce it to a powder. Damp-wood termites (*Neotermes*, *Paraneotermes*) occur in Florida and the western states.

ROTTEN-WOOD TERMITES   Not illus.
Family Hodotermitidae

Identification: Similar to Kalotermitidae but winged adults without ocelli. Occur in western and southwestern states. Colonies in dead wood.

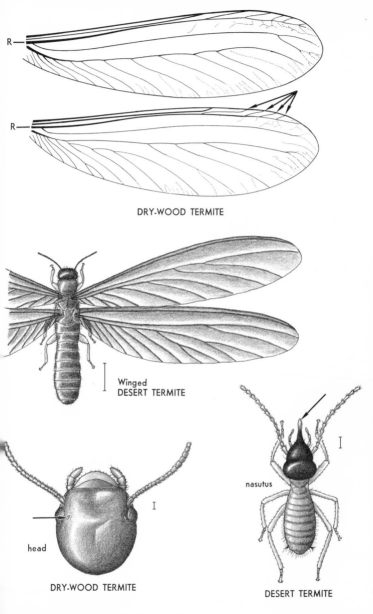

R

R

DRY-WOOD TERMITE

Winged
DESERT TERMITE

nasutus

I

head

DRY-WOOD TERMITE

DESERT TERMITE

This group includes only 3 species of *Zootermopsis*, which often damage buildings, utility poles, and lumber. They can live in wood without a ground contact but there must be some moisture in the wood.

Stoneflies: Order Plecoptera

Identification: Elongate, flattened, soft-bodied, usually found near streams. 4 membranous wings (a few males have wings reduced or lacking): FW long and narrow, HW shorter and nearly always with *a large anal lobe;* wings often with many veins, FW with a series of *cross veins between M and Cu_1 and between Cu_1 and Cu_2;* wings at rest held flat over abdomen, with anal lobe of HW folded fanwise. Antennae *long*, threadlike. Tarsi *3-segmented*. Cerci present, *often long* and many-segmented. Usually 3 (rarely 2) ocelli. Mouth parts chewing, sometimes reduced. Metamorphosis simple, nymphs aquatic.

Similar orders: (1, 2) Trichoptera and Neuroptera (pp. 210, 140): tarsi 5-segmented; HW without an anal lobe. (3) Orthoptera (cockroaches, p. 86): tarsi 5-segmented: generally not found near streams. (4) Ephemeroptera (p. 65): HW small or absent, wings held together above body at rest; antennae short and bristlelike.

Immature stages: Nymphs are elongate and flattened, with *long antennae and cerci*, and with *filamentous gills* on thorax about bases of legs (some nymphs lack gills); mayfly nymphs have 3 tails, and the gills are leaflike and located along the sides of the abdomen. Some nymphs are plant feeders, others are predaceous. When a nymph is full-grown it climbs out of the water onto a stone or other object, and there molts to the adult. Nymphal development takes about a year in most species, 2 years in some.

Habits: Most stoneflies are poor fliers, and seldom found far from water. Many are nocturnal, spending the day resting on stones, trees, under bridges and on bridge abutments, and other places near water; many are attracted to lights. Most adults appear in summer, but a few emerge and mate during fall and winter. Eggs are usually deposited in masses on surface of water. Many adults have poorly developed mandibles and do not feed; others, with well-developed mandibles, feed on blue-green algae and various plant materials. In general, stoneflies appearing in fall and winter are diurnal and feed as adults; those appearing in summer are chiefly nocturnal and do not feed as adults.

Importance: Of no economic importance except as food for fish and other animals.

Classification: Two suborders, Systellognatha and Holognatha, separated chiefly by mouth-part structure. Families are separated by characters of the wing venation, cerci, tarsi, gill remnants on the ventral side of the thorax, genitalia, and size. The characters likely to cause trouble for the beginner are those of the *gill remnants*, since these structures are often shriveled in dry pinned specimens and are difficult to evaluate; they are more easily studied in specimens preserved in alcohol. Length is measured from front of head to wing tips (wings in a resting position).

No. of species: World, 1550; N. America, 400.

Suborder Systellognatha

Cerci much longer than greatest width of pronotum. First tarsal segment much shorter than 3rd. Usually no forked vein rising from basal anal cell in FW. Adults appear in late spring and summer, usually nocturnal and nonfeeding.

COMMON STONEFLIES Family Perlidae
   Identification: Color variable but usually yellowish to brownish and not green. Mostly 15–40 mm. *Remnants of branched nymphal gills* on ventral side of thorax, usually immediately behind bases of legs.

   This family is the largest in the order, and its members are the stoneflies most often collected. Most nymphs are predaceous. One of the largest and commonest genera is *Acroneuria;* some species in this genus are quite large (to 40 mm.) and resemble pteronarcids but lack the rows of cross veins in the anal area of the front wings.

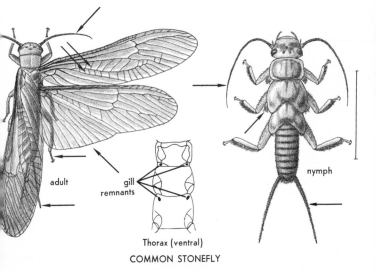

adult

gill
remnants

Thorax (ventral)

nymph

COMMON STONEFLY

GREEN-WINGED STONEFLIES Family Isoperlidae

Identification: Body greenish or yellowish, wings usually greenish. 6–15 mm. No remnants of nymphal gills on thorax. Front corners of pronotum acute or *narrowly rounded*. Anal lobe of HW *well developed*, with 4 or more veins reaching wing margin. ♂ without a lobe on 8th sternum, and 10th tergum usually *not notched*. ♀ subgenital plate generally small.

These are fairly common stoneflies, and adults are often seen running about on foliage near streams; many are pollen feeders. Nymphs vary in habits. This family contains a single N. American genus, *Isoperla*.

PERLODID STONEFLIES Family Perlodidae

Identification: Similar to Isoperlidae but 10–25 mm. and brownish or blackish; wings not greenish. Either no remnants of nymphal gills on ventral side of thorax or a remnant of a finger-like gill on each side of base of labium. ♂ usually with a lobe on posterior margin of 7th abdominal sternum, and 10th tergum with *a deep median notch*. ♀ subgenital plate generally large.

Nymphs occur in medium-sized to large streams, and adults appear in the spring or early summer. Most species are northern or western, and they are not common.

GREEN STONEFLIES Family Chloroperlidae

Identification: Length 6–24 (mostly 6–15) mm. Usually yellowish or greenish. No remnants of nymphal gills on ventral side of thorax. Front corners of pronotum *broadly rounded*. Either *a forked vein rising from basal anal cell in FW or anal lobe in HW reduced* (with 3 or fewer veins) or absent. ♂ without a lobe on either 7th or 8th abdominal sternum.

Nymphs usually occur in small streams, and adults appear in spring.

Suborder Holognatha

Cerci variable in length but usually short, no longer than greatest width of pronotum. Often a forked vein comes off basal anal cell in FW. Mandibles generally well developed. Most adults diurnal and plant feeding.

GIANT STONEFLIES Family Pteronarcidae

Identification: Length 1½–2½ in. Usually brown or gray. Anal area of FW with *2 or more rows of cross veins.*

Nymphs are plant feeders and occur in medium-sized to large rivers. Adults appear in spring and early summer. Adults are largely nocturnal and do not feed; often are attracted to lights.

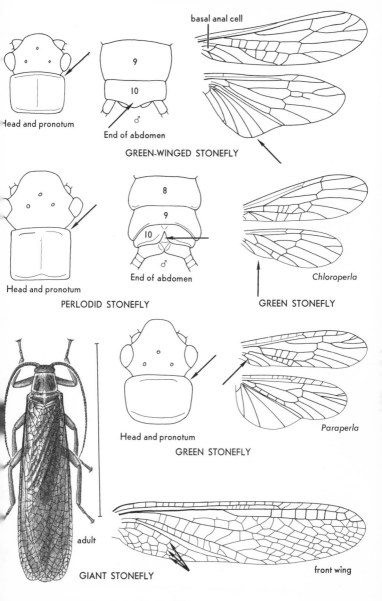

basal anal cell

Head and pronotum

End of abdomen ♂

GREEN-WINGED STONEFLY

Head and pronotum

End of abdomen ♂

PERLODID STONEFLY

Chloroperla

GREEN STONEFLY

adult

Head and pronotum

GREEN STONEFLY

Paraperla

GIANT STONEFLY

front wing

95

ROACHLIKE STONEFLIES Family Peltoperlidae
Identification: Brownish. 12–18 mm. FW with *10 or more costal cross veins*, and *without a forked vein rising from basal anal cell.* Cerci short. *2 ocelli.*

The common name refers to the roachlike appearance of the nymphs. The group is small, and chiefly northern and western. All the N. American species are in the genus *Peltoperla*, and only 2 of these occur in the East.

WINTER STONEFLIES Family Taeniopterygidae
Identification: Dark brown to blackish. *Usually 15 mm.* or less. Cerci short, 1- to 6-segmented. FW *with a forked vein rising from basal anal cell.* 2nd tarsal segment *about as long* as other tarsal segments.

Nymphs occur in large streams and rivers, and adults appear from January to April. Both nymphs and adults are plant feeders; adults sometimes feed on flowers.

ROLLED-WINGED STONEFLIES   Family Leuctridae
Identification: Body appears very slender because wings at rest are bent down over sides of body. Generally 10 mm. or less. Cerci short, 1-segmented. FW *with a forked vein rising from basal anal cell*, and *without a cross vein just behind costa* in apical portion of wing; 2nd tarsal segment *much shorter* than other segments.

Leuctrids are brownish or blackish, and are most common in hilly or mountainous areas. Nymphs usually occur in small streams, and adults appear from December to June.

SPRING STONEFLIES Family Nemouridae
Identification: Similar to Leuctridae but sometimes larger (to 15 mm.). FW flat at rest and *with a cross vein just behind costa* in apical portion of wing.

Nymphs are plant feeders and occur chiefly in small streams with sandy bottoms. Adults are brownish or blackish and appear from April to June. There are about 2 dozen N. American species, all in the genus *Nemoura.*

SMALL WINTER STONEFLIES Family Capniidae
Identification: Length usually *10 mm. or less.* Blackish. Cerci longer than greatest width of pronotum. 1st tarsal segment *about as long as 3rd.* Venation reduced. FW with few cross veins.

Nymphs usually occur in small streams, adults appear from November to April. Nymphs are plant feeders, and adults feed on blue-green algae. In some members of this group (species of *Allocapnia*) the anal lobe of hind wing is *nearly as long as rest of the wing.*

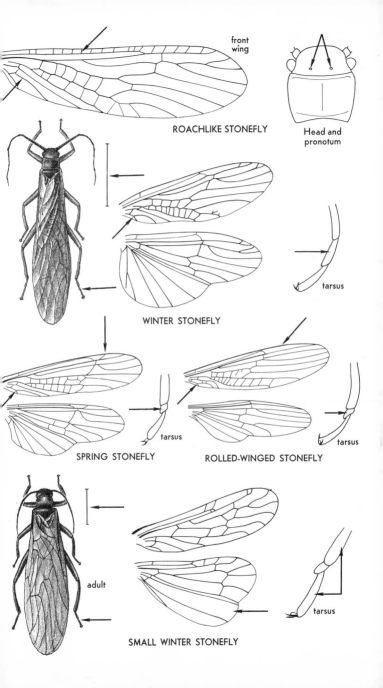

ROACHLIKE STONEFLY

front wing

Head and pronotum

WINTER STONEFLY

tarsus

SPRING STONEFLY

tarsus

ROLLED-WINGED STONEFLY

tarsus

adult

SMALL WINTER STONEFLY

tarsus

Earwigs: Order Dermaptera

Identification: Small to medium-sized, elongate, flattened. 4 wings (rarely wingless): FW (elytra) thickened, leathery, *short, meeting in a straight line down back;* HW membranous, at rest folded beneath FW. Cerci well developed and *forcepslike.* Antennae *threadlike, about half as long as body or less.* Tarsi 3-segmented. Mouth parts chewing. Metamorphosis simple.

Similar orders: (1) Coleoptera (p. 146) with short elytra: no forcepslike cerci. (2) Orthoptera (p. 76): cockroaches have short feelerlike cerci and 5-segmented tarsi; walkingsticks in the western genus *Timema* (which have 3-segmented tarsi) have antennae more than half as long as body.

Immature stages: Similar to adult but wings small or absent.

Habits: Earwigs are nocturnal, spending the day in debris, under bark, and in other protected situations; they are chiefly plant feeders or scavengers. Some species when disturbed eject a foul-smelling liquid from glands near base of the abdomen; this serves as a means of protection. Eggs are laid in burrows in the ground or in debris, and the female usually guards the eggs until they hatch. Cerci usually differ in shape in the sexes, being straight, stout, and closely approximated in the female, and more slender, curved, and pincerlike in the male.

Importance: The name "earwig" comes from an old superstition that these insects get into people's ears; this belief is without foundation. A few earwigs occasionally are pests in buildings and some may damage cultivated plants. The pincerlike cerci are used in defense, and can sometimes inflict a painful pinch.

Classification: Four families in N. America, separated chiefly by form of tarsi and antennae.

No. of species: World, 1100; N. America, 18.

COMMON EARWIGS Family Forficulidae

    Identification: Brownish. 2nd tarsal segment *lobed beneath,* expanded laterally, and *prolonged distally beneath 3rd segment.* Antennae *12- to 15-segmented.* Widely distributed.

    The most common species in this family is the European Earwig, *Forficula auricularia* Linn., 10–15 mm. It sometimes damages cultivated plants.

BLACK EARWIGS Family Chelisochidae   **Not illus.**

    Identification: Similar to Forficulidae but black, and 2nd tarsal segment not expanded laterally.

    Our only representative of this family is *Chelisoches morio* (Fabricius), a large earwig occurring in California.

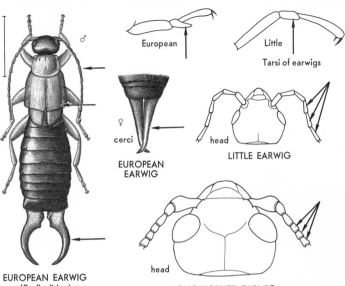

EUROPEAN EARWIG
(Forficulidae)

EUROPEAN EARWIG

LITTLE EARWIG

LONG-HORNED EARWIG

LONG-HORNED EARWIGS Family Labiduridae

Identification: Second tarsal segment cylindrical and not prolonged distally beneath 3rd segment. Antennae 16- to 30-segmented; *segments 4–6 together rarely longer than 1st segment.* Wings present or absent.

A common wingless species in this group is the Seaside Earwig, *Anisolabis maritima* (Géné), which occurs along Atlantic and Pacific Coasts; it is 18–20 mm. and has 24-segmented antennae. A common winged labidurid is the Striped Earwig, *Labidura bidens* (Olivier), 13–20 mm., found in the eastern states. The wingless labidurids (*Anisolabis* and *Euborellia*), which have the male cerci asymmetrical (the right one more curved), are sometimes placed in a separate family, the Psalididae.

LITTLE EARWIGS Family Labiidae

Identification: Tarsi *as in Labiduridae.* Antennae 11- to 15-segmented; *segments 4–6 together longer than 1st segment.* Wings usually present. Generally 4–7 mm.

The most common little earwig is *Labia minor* (Linn.), which is 4–5 mm. and light brown; it has been introduced into this country from Europe. The Handsome Earwig, *Prolabia pulchella* (Serville), 6.0–6.5 mm. and dark brown, is fairly common in the southern states.

Webspinners: Order Embioptera

Identification: Small (mostly 4–7 mm.), slender-bodied, usually yellowish or brownish. Tarsi *3-segmented*, basal segment of front tarsi *greatly enlarged*. Legs short, hind femora *thickened*. Antennae *short, threadlike, 16- to 32-segmented*. Ocelli absent. Wings present or absent in ♂ and always absent in ♀; 4 wings when present are membranous, HW slightly smaller than FW, and venation weak, *each vein in the middle of a brown band;* wings at rest held flat over body. Cerci present, *1- or 2-segmented*, usually asymmetrical in ♂ and always so in ♀. Mouth parts chewing. Metamorphosis simple.

Similar orders: (1, 2, 3) Isoptera, Zoraptera, and Psocoptera (pp. 88, 101, 102): basal segment of front tarsi not enlarged; Isoptera have 4-segmented tarsi, and their galleries are not silk-lined; Zoraptera have 2-segmented tarsi and 9-segmented antennae; Psocoptera have 2- or 3-segmented tarsi, and lack cerci.

Immature stages: Similar to adult but wings small or absent.

Habits: Webspinners live in colonies in silk-lined galleries in soil or debris and among mosses or lichens. Silk is spun from glands in basal segment of front tarsi; both adults and nymphs have silk glands. These insects are active and run rapidly, usually backward; sometimes play dead when disturbed. They feed chiefly on dead plant materials. The eggs are laid in the galleries and are often covered with chewed food particles; eggs are attended by the females. Both winged and wingless males occur in some species. Webspinners are not common, and are restricted to the southern states.

Importance: Not of economic importance.

Classification: Three families in N. America, which differ in wing venation and in the character of cerci and mandibles.

No. of species: World, 149; N. America, 9.

Key to Families

1. R_{4+5} in wings of ♂ forked; left cercus 2-segmented; Gulf
    Coast, Florida to s. Texas   **Teratembiidae**

1'. R_{4+5} in wings of ♂ not forked; if wings are absent, left
    cercus is 1-segmented   2

2. Mandibles without apical teeth; 10th tergum of ♂ com-
    pletely divided by a median membranous area that
    reaches 9th tergum; left cercus of ♂ usually with peglike
    spines on inner side of basal segment; lower Mississippi
    Valley and Southwest   **Anisembiidae**

2'. Mandibles with distinct apical teeth; 10th tergum of ♂
    incompletely divided by a median membranous area
    that does not reach 9th tergum; left cercus of ♂ smooth
    on inner side; southern states   **Oligotomidae**

Zorapterans: Order Zoraptera

Identification: *Minute* insects, 3 mm. or less. Tarsi *2-segmented*. Antennae *threadlike or beadlike, 9-segmented.* Wings present or absent; if present, 4, membranous, FW a little larger than HW, and with few veins; wings eventually shed, leaving short stubs attached to thorax. Wingless forms without eyes, winged forms with compound eyes and 3 ocelli. Cerci *short, 1-segmented,* and terminating in a long bristle. Mouth parts chewing. Metamorphosis simple.

Similar orders: Isoptera, Psocoptera, Embioptera (pp. 88, 102, 100), and others: differ in form of tarsi, antennae, and cerci.

Immature stages: Similar to adult but wings small or absent.

Habits: Zorapterans are usually found under slabs of wood buried in piles of old sawdust, under bark, or in rotting logs; often occur in colonies. They feed chiefly on mites and other small arthropods. Zorapterans occur in the southeastern states from Maryland, Illinois, Arkansas, and Oklahoma south to Florida and Texas. They are not common.

Importance: Not of economic importance.

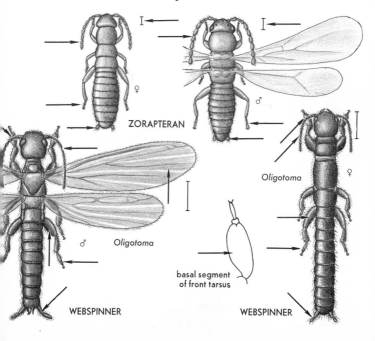

ZORAPTERAN

Oligotoma

Oligotoma

basal segment
of front tarsus

WEBSPINNER

WEBSPINNER

Classification: One family, the Zorotypidae.
No. of species: World, 22; N. America, 2.

Booklice and Barklice: Order Psocoptera

Identification: Small, soft-bodied, usually less than 5 mm. Wings present or absent, if present 4 in number, membranous, FW larger than HW, and held rooflike over body at rest; wing venation reduced. Face somewhat bulging. Ocelli present or absent. Antennae long and slender. Tarsi 2- or 3-segmented. Cerci absent. Mouth parts chewing. Metamorphosis simple.

Similar orders: (1, 2) Mallophaga and Anoplura (pp. 106, 108): ectoparasites of birds and mammals; tarsi 1- or 2-segmented; antennae short. (3) Isoptera (p. 88): tarsi 4-segmented; antennae usually short; FW and HW of winged forms similar in size. (4) Zoraptera (p. 101): antennae 9-segmented; cerci present, 1-segmented. (5) Embioptera (p. 100): tarsi 3-segmented, basal segment of front tarsi greatly enlarged. (6) Small Neuroptera (p. 140): tarsi 5-segmented.

Immature stages: Similar to adult but wings small or absent.

Habits: Feed chiefly on dry organic matter, molds, or fungi. They occur in debris, under bark or stones, and on bark of trees; a few are found in buildings. Some species are gregarious and live in silken webs on trunks or branches of trees. Winged forms are commonly called barklice, and wingless forms booklice; most are active, fast-running insects.

Importance: Some species occasionally are pests in buildings, where they may damage books by feeding on starchy materials in bindings.

Classification: Three suborders and 11 families; suborders are separated by the characters of the antennae and labial palps, and families chiefly by characters of the legs, wings, and mouth parts. Some mouth-part characters cannot be seen in dried material and can be satisfactorily studied only in material preserved in alcohol or mounted on microscope slides.

No. of species: World, 1100; N. America, 143.

Suborder Trogiomorpha

Antennae *long and hairlike*, with 20 or more segments. Labial palps *2-segmented*. Tarsi *3-segmented*.

TROGIID BOOKLICE Family Trogiidae
  Identification: Wings usually lacking or rudimentary, if well developed then FW broadly rounded apically. Body and wings without scales. Hind femora *slender*.

  Trogiids most likely to be encountered are wingless forms

occurring in houses, barns, or granaries. They differ from liposcelid booklice in having slender hind femora.

SCALY BARKLICE   Family Lepidopsocidae   **Not illus.**
Identification: Minute forms having the body and wings covered with scales.
  Only 3 rare species in this group occur in the U.S. They are found out of doors.

PSYLLIPSOCIDS   Family Psyllipsocidae   **Not illus.**
Identification: Pale-colored. Head in profile short and vertical. Wings and body not covered with scales.
  Psyllipsocids occur in dark damp places such as cellars and caves; 1 species often occurs in cellars around wine or vinegar barrels. A few have 1 or both pairs of wings short.

Suborder Troctomorpha

Antennae with 17 or fewer segments. Labial palps *2-segmented.* Tarsi *3-segmented.*

PACHYTROCTIDS   Family Pachytroctidae   **Not illus.**
Identification: Body short and arched. Legs long and slender, hind femora not thickened. Compound eyes in winged individuals composed of many facets.
  The 2 U.S. species in this group are quite rare.

LIPOSCELID BOOKLICE   Family Liposcelidae
Identification: Body elongate and flattened. Legs short, hind femora *thickened.* Usually wingless, but if winged then compound eyes are composed of 2–8 facets.
  The most common member of this group is *Liposcelis divinatorius* (Müller), the booklouse most often found in buildings.

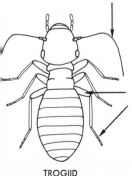

labial palps

Labium of Trogiid

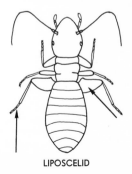

TROGIID

BOOKLICE

LIPOSCELID

It is a minute wingless insect recognized generally by its enlarged
hind femora.

Suborder Eupsocida

Antennae with less than 20 segments. Labial palps 1-*segmented*.
Tarsi 2- or 3-segmented.

POLYPSOCIDS   Family Polypsocidae
Identification: Tarsi *2-segmented*. Labial palps triangular,
tapering distally. Laciniae tapering to a point apically, *without
teeth*.

The members of this small group occur out of doors, and are
not common.

EPIPSOCIDS   Family Epipsocidae
Identification: Tarsi 2-segmented. Labial palps oval. Laciniae
widened distally, with *several small apical teeth*. Labrum with
2 diagonal internal ridges that often unite anteriorly.

The 2 U.S. species in this group are relatively rare.

COMMON BARKLICE   Family Psocidae
Identification: Tarsi *2-segmented*. Labial palps oval. Laciniae
straight, with *a few relatively large apical teeth*. Labrum with only
2 small tubercles internally. Cu_{1a} in FW *fused with M*.

Most barklice with 2-segmented tarsi belong either to this
family or to the Pseudocaeciliidae. Cu_{1a} in the front wing is
nearly always separate from M (rarely completely lacking) in
the Pseudocaeciliidae. The most common barklice belong to
the Psocidae.

PSEUDOCAECILIID BARKLICE   Family Pseudocaeciliidae
Identification: Similar to Psocidae but Cu_{1a} in FW *nearly always
separate from M* or lacking.

The majority of these barklice occur out of doors; only a few
may occur indoors. One southern species makes rather unsightly
webs on tree trunks and branches.

MESOPSOCID and MYOPSOCID BARKLICE   Not illus.
Families Mesopsocidae and Myopsocidae
Identification: Differ from other families in this suborder in
having 3-segmented tarsi, and from families in the other 2 suborders in having the labial palps 1-segmented. Cu_{1a} in FW fused
with M in the Myopsocidae, and usually free from M in the
Mesopsocidae.

The 6 species of Mesopsocidae and 4 of Myopsocidae in the
U.S. occur principally out of doors. They are not common.

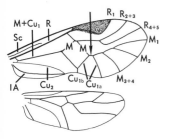

COMMON BARKLOUSE

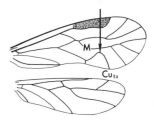

PSEUDOCAECILIID BARKLOUSE

Labium of Polypsocid

Labrum of Epipsocid

Labrum of Common Barklouse

Lacinia of Polypsocid

Lacinia of Epipsocid

Lacinia of Common Barklouse

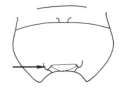

Hind tarsus
of Common
Barklouse

POLYPSOCID

Chewing Lice: Order Mallophaga

Identification: Small (mostly less than 5 mm.), wingless, flattened ectoparasites of birds and mammals. Mouth parts with *chewing mandibles*. Antennae short, 3- to 5-segmented, sometimes concealed in grooves on head. Compound eyes small. Head as wide as or wider than thorax. Legs short, the tarsi 1- or 2-segmented, with 1 or 2 claws. Cerci lacking. Metamorphosis simple.

Similar orders: Anoplura (p. 108): parasites of mammals only, including man (Mallophaga do not attack man); head generally narrower than thorax; 1 large tarsal claw; mouth parts sucking.

Immature stages: Similar to adult stage.

Habits: Chewing lice spend their entire life on their host; transmission from one host to another usually occurs when hosts come in contact, since lice are unable to survive long off a host. Each species attacks one or a few related species of hosts, and lives on a particular part of host's body. Eggs are laid on the host, usually attached to hair or feathers.

Importance: Lice are quite irritating to their hosts; heavily infested animals are often emaciated. No chewing lice attack man but several are important pests of domestic animals, especially poultry; they feed on feathers or hair of the host.

Classification: Two suborders and 6 families. Suborders differ in structure of the antennae and maxillary palps. Families are separated by various head characters and number of tarsal claws. These characters are most easily studied in specimens mounted on microscope slides. The host of a louse provides an important clue to its identity.

No. of species: World, 2675; N. America, 318.

Suborder Amblycera

Antennae clubbed, usually 4-segmented, *concealed in grooves* on head. Maxillary palps *4-segmented*.

GUINEA PIG LICE   Family Gyropidae   **Not illus.**
  Identification: Tarsi with 1 claw or none. Parasites of guinea pigs.
   Most members of this group occur in Cent. and S. America. Only 2 species occur in the U.S.

BIRD LICE   Family Menoponidae
  Identification: Tarsi with *2 claws*. Head *broadly triangular*, and *expanded behind eyes*. Antennae *in grooves on sides of head*. Parasites of birds.

This is a large group whose members attack various types of birds. Two species are important pests of poultry.

BIRD LICE Family Laemobothriidae
Identification: Similar to Menoponidae but head less triangular, with *a swelling on each side at base of antennae;* antennal grooves *open ventrally.* Parasites of birds.

These lice attack water birds and birds of prey.

BIRD LICE Family Ricinidae
Identification: Similar to Laemobothriidae but *without swellings on head at bases of antennae.* Parasites of birds.

The members of this small group attack chiefly sparrows and hummingbirds.

Suborder Ischnocera

Antennae threadlike, *not concealed in grooves,* and 3- to 5-segmented. Maxillary palps lacking.

BIRD LICE Family Philopteridae **Not illus.**
Identification: Tarsi with 2 claws. Antennae 5-segmented. Parasites of birds.

This is the largest family in the order, and its members attack a wide variety of birds. Two species are important pests of poultry.

MAMMAL CHEWING LICE Family Trichodectidae
Identification: Tarsi with *1 claw.* Antennae usually 3-segmented. Parasites of mammals.

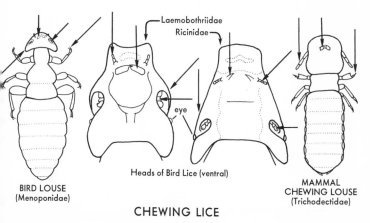

Laemobothriidae
Ricinidae

eye

Heads of Bird Lice (ventral)

BIRD LOUSE
(Menoponidae)

MAMMAL
CHEWING LOUSE
(Trichodectidae)

CHEWING LICE

These lice attack a number of different mammals, but not man. Some are important pests of domestic animals.

Sucking Lice: Order Anoplura

Identification: Small (usually less than 4 mm.), flattened, wingless ectoparasites of mammals. Mouth parts sucking, withdrawn into head when not in use; when used, everted through a short beaklike structure at front of head. Antennae short, threadlike or tapering distally, 3- to 5-segmented. Head small, nearly always narrower than thorax. Without ocelli and with compound eyes small or absent. Tarsi 1-segmented, with *1 large claw.* Cerci lacking. Metamorphosis simple.

Similar orders: Mallophaga (p. 106): mouth parts chewing; head usually as wide as or wider than thorax; 1 or 2 small tarsal claws; parasites of birds and mammals.

Immature stages: Similar to adult stage.

Habits: Sucking lice feed on the blood of their host, and their bites are often very irritating. Each species usually attacks one or a few related species of hosts, and generally lives on a particular part of the host's body. Eggs are usually attached to hairs of the host; eggs of the Body Louse are laid on clothing. Sucking lice spend their entire life on their host, and do not survive long away from the host.

Importance: These lice are irritating pests of man and animals, and 1 of the species that attacks man is an important disease vector.

Classification: Three families, separated chiefly by body shape and the development of compound eyes; these characters are best seen in specimens mounted on microscope slides.

No. of species: World, 250; N. America, 62.

SPINY SUCKING LICE Family Echinophthiriidae **Not illus.**
   Identification: Body thickly covered with short stout spines or with spines and scales. Parasites of marine mammals.
      The members of this small group attack seals, sea lions, and walruses.

MAMMAL SUCKING LICE Family Haematopinidae
   Identification: *Eyes lacking.* Parasites of various mammals (but not man or other primates).
      This is a large group, and includes most of the sucking lice that attack mammals other than man. Some species are pests of domestic animals.

HUMAN LICE Family Pediculidae
   Identification: *Eyes or eye tubercles present.* Parasites of man.
      This group contains 2 species, *Phthirus pubis* (Linn.), the Crab

or Pubic Louse, and *Pediculus humanus* Linn., the Head and Body Lice. These are the only lice that attack man.

The Crab Louse is 1.5–2.0 mm., broadly oval, with the head *much narrower* than thorax, and *with lateral lobes on the abdominal segments*. It usually occurs in the pubic region, but in very hairy individuals may occur almost anywhere on the body. Eggs are attached to body hairs.

P. humanus is 2.5–3.5 mm., more elongate, with head *only slightly narrower* than thorax, and *without lateral lobes on the abdominal segments*. Head and Body Lice are similar in appearance but differ somewhat in habits. The Head Louse (*P. h. capitis* De Geer) occurs on the head, and attaches its eggs to hairs. The Body Louse (*P. h. humanus* Linn.) occurs on the body, and its eggs are laid on clothing.

People who bathe and change clothes frequently seldom encounter these lice; lousiness generally occurs in people who live in crowded conditions and go for long periods without bathing or changing clothes. Head lice may be transmitted from one person to another on combs, hair brushes, or hats. Body lice may be transmitted by clothing or bedding, or they may migrate at night from one batch of clothing to another.

Lice are very annoying pests, and the Body Louse acts as a disease vector. The most important disease it transmits is epidemic typhus, which often occurs in epidemic form and has a high mortality rate. A louse becomes infective after biting a typhus patient; infection of another individual results from scratching the feces of this louse, or the louse itself, into the skin. The Body Louse also transmits relapsing fever. Infection in this case results from a crushed louse being scratched into the skin.

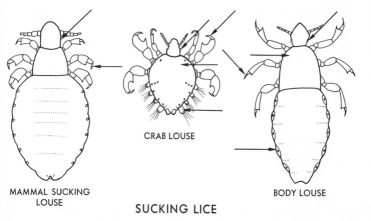

MAMMAL SUCKING
LOUSE

CRAB LOUSE

BODY LOUSE

SUCKING LICE

Thrips: Order Thysanoptera

Identification: Slender, minute (mostly 0.5–2.0 mm.), pale to blackish. Antennae *short, 6- to 9-segmented*. Wings when present 4 in number, *long and narrow*, with few or no veins and *fringed with long hairs*. Legs short. Tarsi 1- or 2-segmented and swollen at tip. Mouth parts sucking, asymmetrical, *in form of a conical beak* at base of head on ventral side. Metamorphosis intermediate between simple and complex.

Similar orders: Thrips are not likely to be confused with insects in other orders. They can be recognized by the characteristic form of the mouth parts and wings.

Immature stages: First 2 instars similar to adult but wingless, and called larvae; remaining 2 or 3 preadult instars usually with short wing pads, inactive and nonfeeding; last preadult instar (pupa) sometimes enclosed in a cocoon.

Habits: Most thrips are plant feeders, and many are abundant on vegetation or in flowers. A few are predaceous on other small arthropods, and many feed on fungus spores.

Importance: Many plant-feeding thrips damage cultivated plants by their feeding. A few act as vectors of plant diseases.

Classification: Two suborders, Terebrantia and Tubulifera, differing in shape of abdomen and development of ovipositor.

No. of species: World, 4000; N. America, 600.

Suborder Terebrantia

Terminal abdominal segment conical in ♀, *rather broadly rounded* in ♂. ♀ nearly always with an ovipositor. FW, when present, with 2 longitudinal veins. Antennae 6- to 9-segmented.

BANDED THRIPS Family Aeolothripidae   **Not illus.**
  Identification: Bicolored or dark. Wings usually dark, banded or longitudinally striped; FW relatively broad, rounded apically. Ovipositor upcurved. Antennae 9-segmented. Body not flattened.

  Most banded thrips, especially larvae, feed on small insects and mites. They are sometimes common on flowers.

MEROTHRIPIDS Family Merothripidae   **Not illus.**
  Identification: Ovipositor curved downward, often reduced. Pronotum with a dorsal longitudinal suture on each side. FW if present narrow, pointed. Front and hind femora thickened.

  This is a small group, and the only common species is one occurring in the East in fungi and debris or under bark.

COMMON THRIPS   Family Thripidae
 Identification: Ovipositor usually well developed, curved down-ward. FW pointed apically. Body somewhat flattened. An-tennae *6- to 9-segmented*, sensory areas (sensoria) on segments 3 and 4 conelike or fingerlike and projecting.
 Thripids make up the bulk of the Terebrantia, and nearly all species are plant feeders; some are serious pests of cultivated plants. Most are 1.5 mm. or less.

HETEROTHRIPIDS   Family Heterothripidae   **Not illus.**
 Identification: Similar to Thripidae, but antennae 9-segmented, and 3rd segment with an apical band of small blisterlike sensoria.
 Seldom encountered in our area. One fairly common species feeds in the flowers of jack-in-the-pulpit.

Suborder Tubulifera

Terminal abdominal segment *tubular* in both sexes. ♀ without an ovipositor. FW when present veinless or with a short median vein. Antennae with *4–8 (usually 8) segments*.

TUBE-TAILED THRIPS   Family Phloeothripidae
 Identification: By the characters of the suborder.
 This is a large group, and its members vary in habits. Some are plant feeders and are often abundant on vegetation, some are predaceous, and many feed on fungus spores.

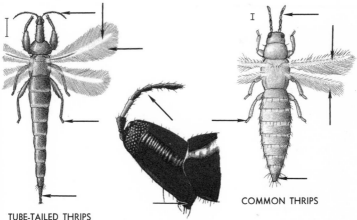

TUBE-TAILED THRIPS

Lateral view of Thrips head

COMMON THRIPS

Bugs: Order Hemiptera

Identification: FW usually *thickened at base, membranous at tip.* HW *membranous*, shorter than FW. Wings at rest held flat over body, tips of FW usually overlapping (some bugs are wingless, and a few have FW uniformly thickened). Mouth parts sucking. Beak generally *rises from anterior part of head*, and consists of 4 hairlike stylets in a segmented sheath. Palps lacking. Antennae of 5 or fewer principal segments, long and conspicuous or short and concealed. 2 ocelli or none. Tarsi with 3 or fewer segments. Metamorphosis simple.

Similar orders: (1) Homoptera (p. 128): FW uniform in texture, membranous or thickened; beak rises from hind part of head; antennae short and bristlelike or long and containing more than 5 segments. (2) Coleoptera (p. 146): FW uniformly thickened, nearly always meeting in a straight line down back; mouth parts chewing; antennae usually with 8 or more segments; tarsi often 4- or 5-segmented. (3) Orthoptera (p. 76): mouth parts chewing; FW uniformly thickened; HW with many veins; antennae many-segmented.

Immature stages: Similar to adult but wings small or absent.

Habits: This is a large order and its members vary in habits. Most bugs are terrestrial, but many are aquatic and a few are external parasites of vertebrates. Many bugs are plant feeders, and many are predaceous on other insects.

Importance: A number of bugs are pests of cultivated plants; a few are bloodsucking and are irritating pests, and some of these are disease vectors. Some predaceous bugs are of value in keeping pest species under control.

Classification: Two suborders, Cryptocerata and Gymnocerata, differing in the character of the antennae. The principal characters used in separating families of Hemiptera are those of the beak, antennae, front wings, and legs.

No. of species: World, 23,000; N. America, 4500.

Short-horned Bugs: Suborder Cryptocerata

Antennae *short and usually concealed* in grooves on ventral side of head. Ocelli generally absent. Aquatic or shore-inhabiting.

WATER BOATMEN   Family Corixidae

Identification: Elongate-oval, aquatic, usually 12 mm. or less. Dorsal surface of body flattened, with *narrow dark crosslines.* Front legs short, tarsi *1-segmented and scoop-shaped.* Hind legs *elongate* and functioning as oars.

Water boatmen are common insects in ponds. A few occur in streams, and a few are found in the brackish water of pools along the seashore above the high tidemark. They swim rapidly and somewhat erratically, and spend much time clinging to submerged vegetation. Most species feed on algae and other minute aquatic organisms. They do not bite man.

BACKSWIMMERS   Family Notonectidae

Identification: Resemble Corixidae but dorsal surface of body convex and *often light-colored*, without dark crosslines; front tarsi *not scoop-shaped*. 15 mm. or less.

Backswimmers are so named because they swim upside down. They are common insects in ponds. They swim in a less erratic fashion than water boatmen and spend much time resting at the surface, the body at an angle and the head down. They feed on

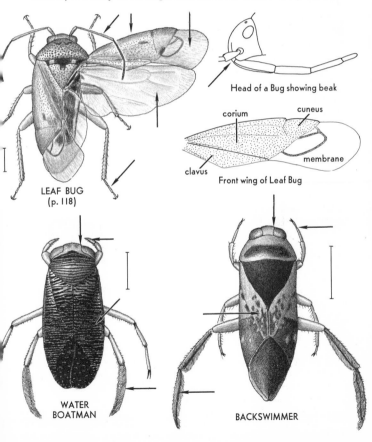

LEAF BUG
(p. 118)

Head of a Bug showing beak

corium   cuneus

clavus   membrane

Front wing of Leaf Bug

WATER
BOATMAN

BACKSWIMMER

other aquatic insects, and sometimes on small vertebrates. If handled carelessly they will bite, and the effect is rather like that of a bee sting.

WATERSCORPIONS Family Nepidae
Identification: *Slender and elongate* with long slender legs (*Ranatra*) *or elongate-oval* (*Nepa, Curicta*). Front legs *raptorial.* Terminal abdominal appendages *long, slender,* forming a non-retractable breathing tube. Usually 20–40 mm.

Waterscorpions in the genus *Ranatra* are brownish and resemble walkingsticks. They are common in ponds. Our only species of *Nepa* (*N. apiculata* Uhler) is elongate-oval; it is widely distributed but not very common. Two species of *Curicta* occur in the Southwest; they are somewhat more elongate than *Nepa.* Waterscorpions are predaceous on other insects, and can inflict a painful bite if handled carelessly.

GIANT WATER BUGS Family Belostomatidae
Identification: Brownish, oval, flattened, *about 1–2 in.* Front legs *fitted for grasping prey,* hind legs *somewhat flattened.* Terminal appendages *short,* retractile.

These bugs are fairly common in ponds, where they feed on various insects and small vertebrates. They can inflict a painful bite. Females of *Belostoma* (about 1 in.) lay their eggs on the back of the male, which carries them around until they hatch. Most larger giant water bugs belong to the genus *Lethocerus;* they lay their eggs on aquatic vegetation. Members of this group sometimes leave the water and fly about, and are often attracted to lights.

CREEPING WATER BUGS Family Naucoridae
Identification: Dark brown to brownish black, oval, *5–16 mm.* Membrane of FW *without veins.* Front femora *greatly thickened.*

These bugs are fairly common in ponds, where they feed on various aquatic animals. They can inflict a very painful bite if handled carelessly.

TOAD BUGS Family Gelastocoridae
Identification: Small *toad-shaped* bugs, *10 mm. or less.* Ocelli *present.* Front legs shorter than middle legs.

Toad bugs occur along the shores of ponds and streams, where they feed on smaller insects. They resemble toads in appearance and hopping habits.

VELVETY SHORE BUGS Family Ochteridae   **Not illus.**
Identification: Oval-bodied, 4–5 mm. Velvety bluish or black. Ocelli present. Antennae exposed. Front legs similar to middle legs in form and length. Beak long, extending at least to hind coxae.

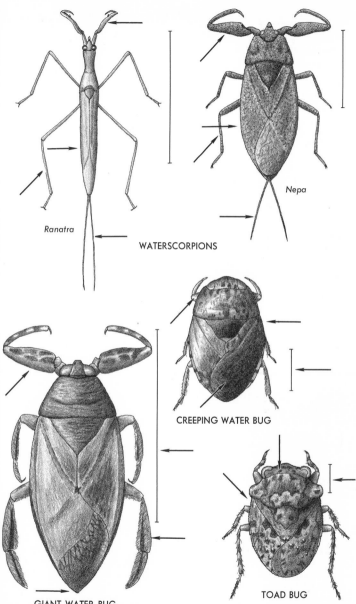

Ranatra

Nepa

WATERSCORPIONS

CREEPING WATER BUG

GIANT WATER BUG

TOAD BUG

These bugs occur along the shores of ponds and slow streams, and are predaceous. They are rather rare.

Long-horned Bugs: Suborder Gymnocerata

Antennae exposed, and longer than head. Mostly terrestrial (aquatic forms are generally surface-inhabiting).

WATER STRIDERS   Family Gerridae
Identification: Usually found running about on surface of water. Middle legs *rise closer to hind legs* than to front legs. Tarsi *2-segmented*. Usually over 5 mm.

Gerrids are common on the surface of slow streams and ponds. They are generally slender, elongate, and blackish, the front legs short and the *other legs long and slender*. Some are winged and some are wingless. They feed on various small insects that fall onto the water surface. They do not bite man.

RIPPLE BUGS   Family Veliidae
Identification: Small water striders, *usually less than 5 mm.*, found near riffles of streams. Middle legs *rise about equidistant* from front and hind legs (except in *Rhagovelia*, which has 1-segmented front tarsi). Legs short. Tarsi 1- to 3-segmented, claws located *before tip*.

Ripple bugs are brown or black, often with silvery markings. They are fairly common insects generally occurring in swarms. They are sometimes called broad-shouldered water striders because the body is widest near bases of middle or hind legs and the abdomen tapers posteriorly.

JUMPING GROUND BUGS
Families Dipsocoridae and Schizopteridae
Identification: Length 1–2 mm. Antennae 4-segmented, the 2 basal segments short and stout, and the 2 apical segments long and slender. Ocelli present. Tarsi and beak 3-segmented. Dipsocoridae: eyes project outward, not overlapping front edges of pronotum; head and tibiae with strong bristles. Schizopteridae: eyes project outward and backward, overlapping front edges of pronotum; head and tibiae without strong bristles.

These bugs occur on the ground in moist places, usually beneath dead leaves, and jump actively when disturbed. They are chiefly southern in distribution and are quite rare.

BED BUGS   Family Cimicidae
Identification: Flat, oval, usually reddish brown. *6 mm. or less.* Wings *vestigial*. Antennae *4-segmented*. Beak and tarsi *3-segmented*. Ocelli *absent*.

Bed bugs feed by sucking blood from man and animals; 1

species, *Cimex lectularius* Linn., is often a serious pest in houses, hotels, and other living quarters, and it also attacks various animals. Other bed bugs attack bats and birds. This group is a small one but widely distributed.

MINUTE PIRATE BUGS Family Anthocoridae

Identification: *Small* (mostly 3–5 mm.), oval, flattened, and black with white markings. FW with *a cuneus*, the membrane with *few or no veins* and no closed cells. Beak and tarsi *3-segmented*. Ocelli present. Antennae *4-segmented*.

Anthocorids are fairly common bugs usually found on flowers (they are sometimes called flower bugs), but some species occur

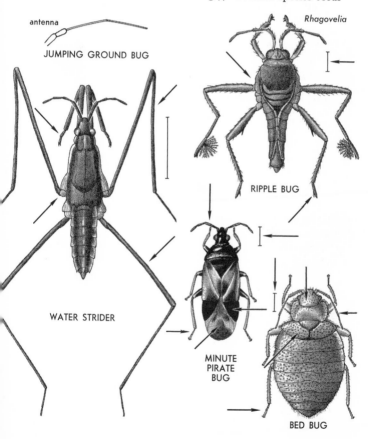

antenna

JUMPING GROUND BUG

Rhagovelia

RIPPLE BUG

WATER STRIDER

MINUTE PIRATE BUG

BED BUG

under bark, in leaf litter, or in fungi. They are predaceous on other insects and insect eggs.

LEAF or PLANT BUGS   See also p. 113 and Pl. 3
Family Miridae

Identification: Small, oval or elongate, soft-bodied, mostly less than 10 mm. FW with *a cuneus*, and membrane with *2 closed cells* (rarely membrane is lacking and cuneus is not distinct, in which case hind femora are enlarged). Ocelli *absent*. Beak 4-segmented. Tarsi *3-segmented*.

This is the largest family of bugs, with several hundred N. American species. They occur on vegetation, and are often abundant. All are rather soft-bodied, many are brightly colored. Nearly all the leaf bugs feed on plants, and some are serious pests of cultivated plants. Fleahoppers (*Halticus*), which are active jumpers, have short, uniformly thickened front wings and enlarged hind femora.

JUMPING TREE BUGS   Family Isometopidae   Not illus.
Identification: Similar to Miridae but with ocelli. Less than 3 mm.

Five rare species in this group occur in the East. They are usually on bark or twigs and jump when disturbed.

MICROPHYSID BUGS   Family Microphysidae   Not illus.
Identification: Broadly oval and somewhat flattened, shining black, 1.2 mm. Ocelli present. Antennae 4-segmented. Middle and hind tarsi 2-segmented. FW with a cuneus.

One very rare species of microphysid, *Mallochiola gagates* (McAtee and Malloch), occurs in the U.S. It has been recorded from Maryland and the District of Columbia.

GNAT BUGS   Family Enicocephalidae   Not illus.
Identification: Slender, gnatlike, about 5 mm. FW entirely membranous. Front femora and tarsi thickened. Middle and hind tarsi 2-segmented. Head elongate, constricted behind eyes. Ocelli present. Antennae and beak 4-segmented.

At least 4 rare species of *Systelloderes* occur in the e. U.S.

AMBUSH BUGS   Family Phymatidae   See also Pl. 3
Identification: Antennae 4-segmented, *slightly clubbed*. Beak short and 3-segmented. Ocelli present. Front femora *greatly thickened*. Middle and hind tarsi 3-segmented. Abdomen *wider in distal half*, extending laterally beyond wings.

Ambush bugs are common predaceous insects that usually occur on flowers, where they lie in wait for their prey. They often are found on goldenrod, where their greenish-yellow and brownish color provides camouflage. Though small (12 mm. or less), they are able to capture insects as large as bumble bees. They do not bite man.

ASSASSIN BUGS Family Reduviidae   See also Pl. 3
  Identification: Body shape *generally oval, sometimes* (Emesinae, see illus., p. 121) *greatly elongate and resembling a walkingstick.* Beak *short, 3-segmented,* usually curved and *fitting into a groove in prosternum.* Head *elongate, a transverse groove between eyes.* Antennae 4-segmented, sometimes with 1 or more segments divided into subsegments. Ocelli usually present (absent in Emesinae). Front femora generally *thickened.* Edges of abdomen often *extend laterally beyond wings.*

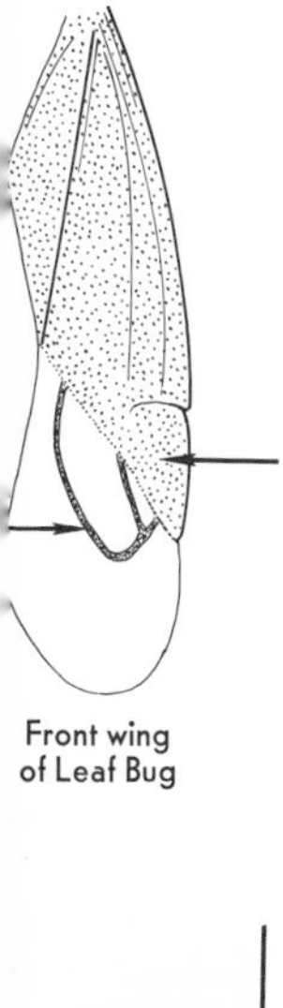

Front wing
of Leaf Bug

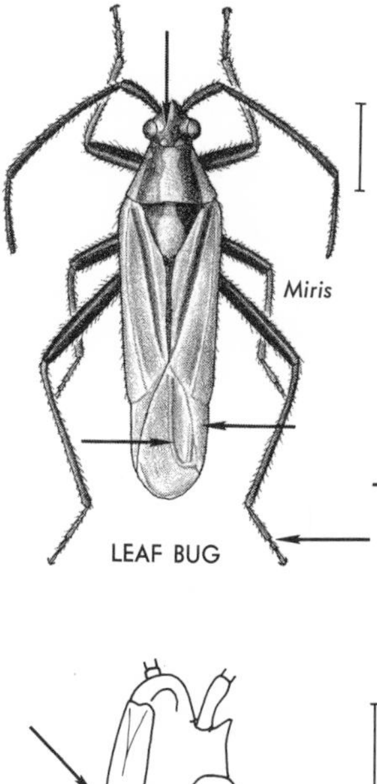

LEAF BUG

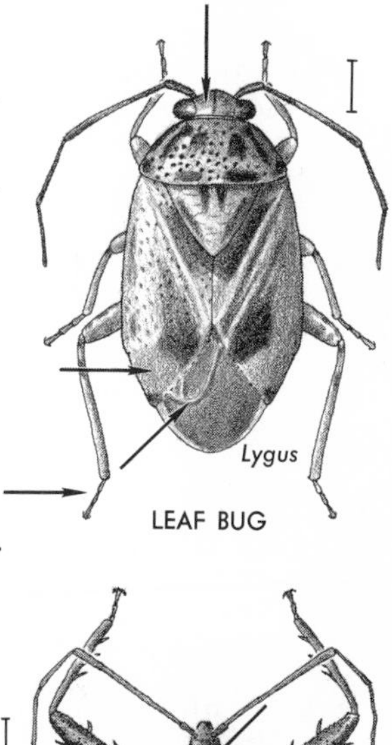

Miris

Lygus

LEAF BUG

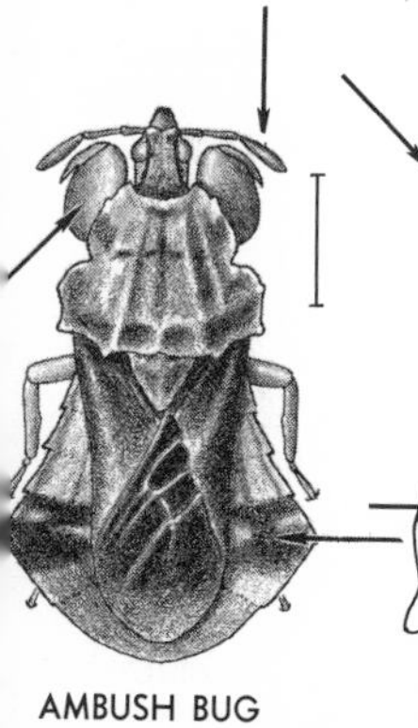

AMBUSH BUG

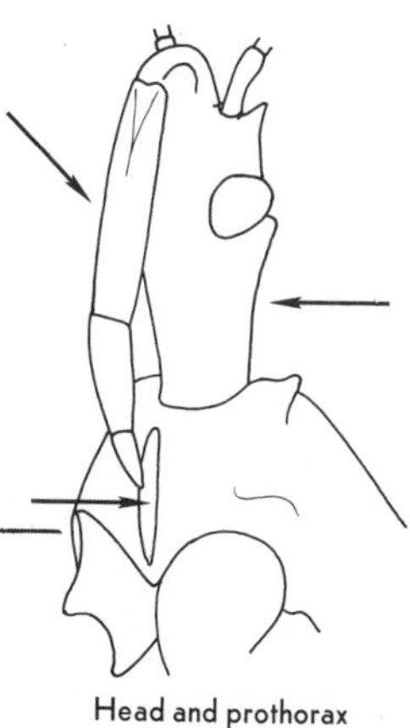

Head and prothorax
of Assassin Bug

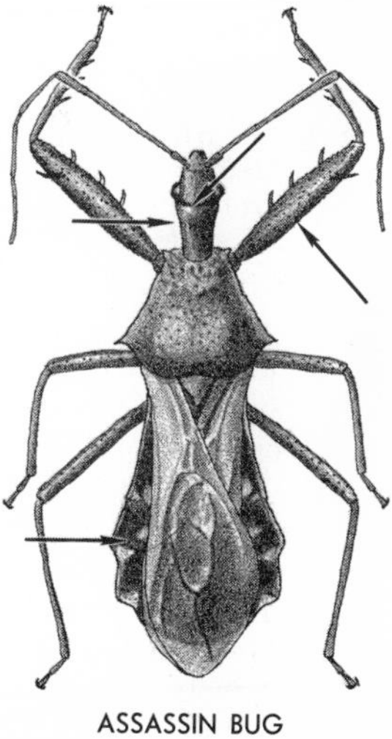

ASSASSIN BUG

Assassin bugs are generally brownish to black and 10–25 mm. Many are fairly common. Most species occur on foliage, although a few sometimes enter houses. The majority are predaceous on other insects, but a small minority are bloodsucking. Many can inflict a painful bite.

Subfamily Emesinae (considered by some authorities to be a separate family, the Ploiariidae). These resemble small walking-sticks, and are called thread-legged bugs (see opp.). They are generally found in old buildings, cellars, and similar places. Most northern species are 30–35 mm., but many southern species are 5–10 mm.

DAMSEL BUGS Family Nabidae

Identification: Elongate-oval. Antennae usually 4-segmented (rarely, subfamily Prostemminae, 5-segmented). Beak generally 4-segmented. Ocelli *present*. Front femora *slightly thickened*. Membrane of FW, when developed, with *a number of small cells around margin*.

Most damsel bugs are yellowish brown and about 8 mm., the body somewhat narrowed anteriorly and the wings well developed; some are slightly larger and shining black, and a few of these have very short front wings that lack a membrane. Nabids are common insects and usually occur on low vegetation. They are predaceous.

BAT BUGS Family Polyctenidae   Not illus.

Identification: Wingless, lacking eyes and ocelli, and ectoparasites of bats. 3.5–5.0 mm. Front legs short, femora thickened; middle and hind legs long and slender.

Two rare species of bat bugs occur in the U.S., 1 in Texas and the other in California.

LACE BUGS Family Tingidae

Identification: Body and wings with *reticulate sculpturing*. Pronotum has *a triangular posterior extension* over scutellum. Antennae and beak 4-segmented. Ocelli absent. Tarsi 1- or 2-segmented. Usually *5 mm. or less*.

Most lace bugs are grayish and somewhat rectangular, with a hoodlike extension of the pronotum forward over the head and a lacelike pattern of ridges on the pronotum and wings. Other (less common) species are narrower, with ridges on dorsal side of body forming a finer network, and some lack the extension of the pronotum forward over the head. Lace bugs feed on the foliage of trees and shrubs, and sometimes cause extensive defoliation.

ASH-GRAY LEAF BUGS Family Piesmatidae

Identification: Small, gray, *oval*, mostly *about 3 mm.* Dorsal side of body with *numerous small pits*. Pronotum without a posterior extension over scutellum. Antennae and beak 4-segmented.

Ocelli present. *A pair of fingerlike processes on front of head.*

These bugs feed on various weeds and trees. They are not common.

STILT BUGS   Family Berytidae

Identification: *Slender*, usually brownish, 5–9 mm. Legs and antennae *long and slender;* antennae 4-segmented, 1st segment *very long*, 4th segment *short and spindle-shaped*. Beak 4-segmented. Ocelli present. Tarsi 3-segmented.

Stilt bugs are fairly common and usually found on vegetation. They are plant feeders.

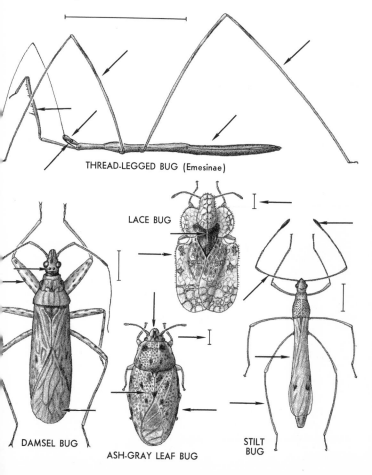

THREAD-LEGGED BUG (Emesinae)

LACE BUG

DAMSEL BUG

ASH-GRAY LEAF BUG

STILT BUG

SEED BUGS   Family Lygaeidae   **See also Pl. 3**

Identification: Small to medium-sized, elongate to oval, and fairly hard-bodied. Antennae and beak *4-segmented*. Tarsi *3-segmented*, with a pad at base of each claw. Front femora sometimes thickened. Membrane of FW with *only 4 or 5 veins*. Ocelli nearly always *present*.

Members of this large group are often common on vegetation. They are 3–15 mm. but most are less than 10 mm. Color varies considerably: majority are brownish, though some are brightly patterned; 2 species that feed on milkweed seeds (for 1, see Pl. 3) are red and black. Most species feed on seeds. The Chinch Bug, *Blissus leucopterus* (Say), which feeds on the sap of the host plant, is a serious pest of wheat and other grains. Members of the subfamily Geocorinae, often called big-eyed bugs, sometimes feed on other insects.

RED BUGS or STAINERS   **See also Pl. 3**

Family Pyrrhocoridae

Identification: Similar to Lygaeidae but *without ocelli* and with *more veins in membrane of FW*. Front femora never thickened. 8–18 mm. Usually brightly colored with red and black.

Red bugs occur chiefly in the southern states and are sometimes fairly common. Most are elongate-oval and brightly colored. A few have short front wings and are somewhat antlike in appearance. All are plant feeders. The Cotton Stainer (Pl. 3), *Dysdercus suturellus* (Herrich-Schäffer), is a serious pest of cotton.

LEAF-FOOTED BUGS   Family Coreidae   **See also Pl. 3**

Identification: Similar to Lygaeidae but with *many veins in membrane of FW*. Usually dark-colored and over 10 mm. Head *narrower* and most often shorter *than pronotum*. Hind tibiae *sometimes dilated and leaflike*.

This is a large group, and most of its members are relatively large bugs. They are widely distributed but are more common in the South. Some are plant feeders and others are predaceous. One of the plant feeders, the Squash Bug (Pl. 3), *Anasa tristis* (De Geer), is a serious pest of cucurbits. Coreids often give off an unpleasant odor when handled.

SCENTLESS PLANT BUGS   Family Corizidae   **Pl. 3**

Identification: Similar to Coreidae but usually pale-colored, less than 14 mm., and lacking scent glands.

Scentless plant bugs occur chiefly on grass and weeds, and are plant feeders; they are common in late summer and early fall. One species, the Boxelder Bug (Pl. 3), *Leptocoris trivittatus* (Say), is blackish with red markings and 11–14 mm.; it feeds on box elder trees, and often enters houses in the fall.

BROAD-HEADED BUGS Family Coriscidae
Identification: Similar to Coreidae but head *nearly as wide and as long as pronotum.* Scent glands well developed.

Most coriscids are yellowish brown or black and 10–18 mm. They give off an unpleasant odor when disturbed. Some of the black species have a reddish band across middle of dorsal side

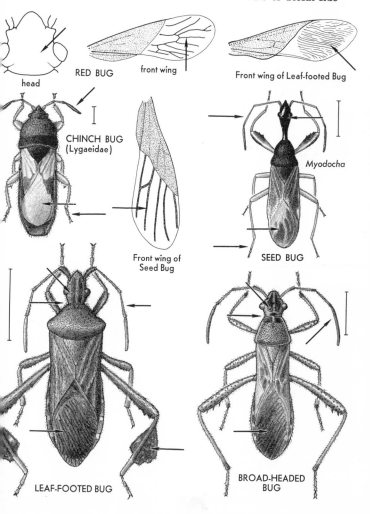

head

RED BUG   front wing

Front wing of Leaf-footed Bug

CHINCH BUG
(Lygaeidae)

Myodocha

Front wing of
Seed Bug

SEED BUG

LEAF-FOOTED BUG

BROAD-HEADED
BUG

of the abdomen, and their nymphs resemble ants. Broad-headed bugs are plant feeders and are usually found on vegetation.

FLAT or FUNGUS BUGS Family Aradidae
  Identification: Small, oval, dark, very flat. Wings *narrow*, *abdomen extends beyond them*. Antennae and beak 4-segmented, 1st segment of beak very short. Ocelli *absent*. Tarsi *2-segmented*.
  Flat bugs are usually found under decaying bark or in woody fungi, and are sometimes fairly common.

TERMATOPHYLID BUGS Family Termatophylidae **Not illus.**
  Identification: Similar to Miridae (p. 118) but with only 1 closed cell in membrane of FW (2 in Miridae), and basal segment of beak scarcely longer than wide (longer than wide in mirids).
  One rare species has been reported from New Hampshire and Arizona. It is 4 mm. and dark brown with a white scutellum.

SHORE BUGS Family Saldidae
  Identification: Small, *oval*, flattened, usually brownish. Membrane of FW with *4–5 long closed cells*. Antennae 4-segmented. Beak and tarsi *3-segmented*. Ocelli *close together*.
  Saldids are fairly common along grassy shores. When disturbed they fly a short distance and crawl down into the vegetation or into a crevice. They are predaceous.

SPINY SHORE BUGS Family Leptopodidae **Not illus.**
  Identification: Saldidlike, 3.5 mm., with long spines over most of body, including eyes. Last 2 antennal segments very slender. Beak short. Ocelli close together on a tubercle.
  One species in this Old World family, *Patapius spinosus* (Rossi), has been introduced into California.

WATER TREADERS Family Mesoveliidae
  Identification: Small, slender, usually greenish or yellowish, 5 mm. or less. Only anterior basal part of FW thickened, clavus *membranous;* membrane *veinless*. Antennae *long, slender, 4-segmented*. Beak slender, 3-segmented, 3rd segment long. Ocelli *present*. Tarsi 3-segmented, 1st segment very small.
  These insects are usually found on aquatic vegetation or running about on the surface of the water. They are sometimes fairly common around ponds. They feed on small aquatic organisms found on surface of the water.

ROYAL PALM BUGS Family Thaumastocoridae **Not illus.**
  Identification: Minute (2–3 mm.), flattened, oblong-oval. Pale yellow, with red eyes. Antennae 4-segmented. Beak 3-segmented. Tarsi 2-segmented. Ocelli present. Membrane of FW without veins.
  This group is represented in the U.S. by a single species,

Xylastodoris luteolus Barber, which occurs in Florida. It feeds on the royal palm.

VELVET WATER BUGS Family Hebridae

Identification: Length *3 mm. or less*. Somewhat oblong, with *a broad-shouldered appearance*. Body densely covered with velvety pubescence. Antennae *4- or 5-segmented*. Membrane and clavus of FW similar in texture, *without veins*.

Hebrids are usually found running or walking on surface of water, and they differ from other bugs found in this situation in being very pubescent. Only 7 species occur in N. America, and they are relatively rare.

WATER MEASURERS Family Hydrometridae

Identification: Grayish, most *about 8 mm.*, the body and legs *very long and slender*. Usually wingless. Head *long and slender*, the eyes bulging and located slightly behind middle of head. Antennae 4-segmented. Tarsi 3-segmented.

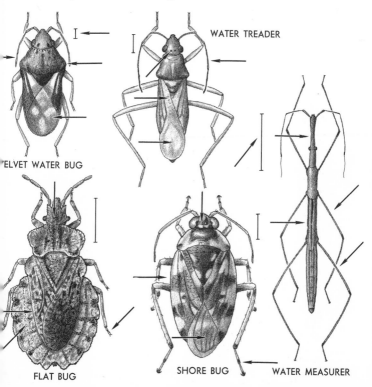

VELVET WATER BUG

WATER TREADER

FLAT BUG

SHORE BUG

WATER MEASURER

Water measurers resemble tiny walkingsticks, and are usually found around the edges of ponds, either on aquatic vegetation or walking slowly over surface of water. They are fairly common insects.

Superfamily Scutelleroidea

This group includes the remaining families of bugs, which have *5-segmented antennae* and are somewhat shield-shaped (with a broad-shouldered appearance).

BURROWER BUGS Family Cydnidae
   Identification: Black, generally 7 mm. or less. Similar to Pentatomidae (below) but with *strong spines on tibiae.*
   Burrower bugs usually occur under stones and boards or around the roots of grass tufts. They are not common.

NEGRO BUGS Family Corimelaenidae
   Identification: Broadly oval, convex, shining black, *3–6 mm.* Scutellum *large, covering most of abdomen and wings.* Tibiae with slender spines or none.
   Negro bugs resemble beetles but can be recognized as bugs by the 5-segmented antennae and 4-segmented beak. The wings under the large scutellum are typically hemipterous. These bugs are common on vegetation and flowers.

SHIELD-BACKED BUGS Family Scutelleridae
   Identification: Similar to Pentatomidae but scutellum *very large, broadly oval,* and *extending to apex of abdomen.* Pronotum *without a prominent tooth on each side* in front of humeral angle. Usually brownish. 8–10 mm.
   These bugs occur on vegetation, and are plant feeders. They are fairly common but not as common as stink bugs.

TERRESTRIAL TURTLE BUGS Family Podopidae
   Identification: Similar to Scutelleridae but smaller (*3.5–6.5 mm.*). Scutellum *U-shaped. A prominent tooth on each side of pronotum* just in front of humeral angle.
   This is a small group, and its members are quite rare.

STINK BUGS Family Pentatomidae   **See also Pl. 3**
   Identification: Broadly oval and somewhat shield-shaped. Scutellum *large and triangular* but not longer than corium and not reaching apex of abdomen. Tibiae with *weak or no spines.* Usually over 7 mm.
   This is a large and well-known group, and many of its members are very common bugs. The common name refers to the rather disagreeable odor these bugs produce. Some stink bugs are rather plain-colored, brownish or grayish, but many are brightly colored. Although most of them are plant feeders, some are

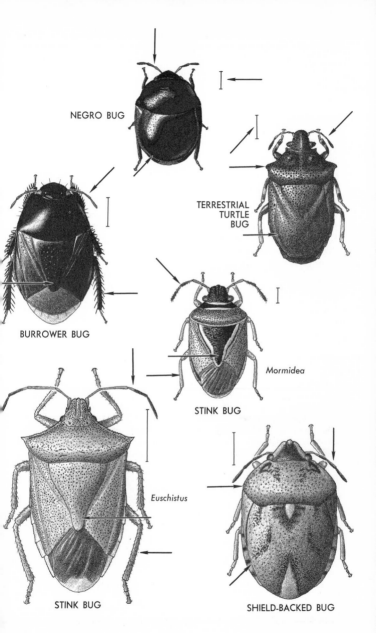

NEGRO BUG

TERRESTRIAL
TURTLE
BUG

BURROWER BUG

Mormidea

STINK BUG

Euschistus

STINK BUG

SHIELD-BACKED BUG

predaceous. A few of the plant feeders occasionally damage
cultivated plants, especially fruits.

Cicadas, Hoppers, Whiteflies, Aphids, and Scale Insects: Order Homoptera

Identification: Mouth parts similar to those in Hemiptera, but
beak usually short and rising at back of head, sometimes appearing to rise between front coxae. Winged or wingless. Winged
forms with 4 wings (rarely only 2), FW membranous or thickened,
HW membranous and a little shorter than FW, wings at rest
usually held rooflike over body. Tarsi 1- to 3-segmented. Antennae variable, sometimes short and bristlelike, sometimes long and
threadlike, rarely absent. ♀ often with a well-developed ovipositor. Metamorphosis usually simple.

Similar orders: (1) Hemiptera (p. 112): FW nearly always thickened at base and membranous at tip; beak usually rising at front
of head. (2, 3) Coleoptera and Orthoptera (pp. 146, 76) mouth
parts chewing.

Immature stages: Usually similar to adult but with wings absent
or vestigial.

Habits: Homoptera are plant feeders, and each species usually
feeds on a particular part of a few species of plants. The feeding
results in discoloration, distortion, wilting, or stunting of the
plant, and heavily infested plants are sometimes killed. A few
homopterans cause the development of plant galls.

Importance: Many members of this order are serious pests of
cultivated plants, causing damage by feeding and sometimes by
serving as vectors of plant diseases.

Classification and identification: Two suborders, Auchenorrhyncha
and Sternorrhyncha, each of which is divided into superfamilies.
Most families are separated by easily seen characters, but scale
insects can generally be identified to family only from specimens
mounted on microscope slides. Many wingless Sternorrhyncha
will be difficult or impossible to identify unless one is familiar
with their life history.

No. of species: World, 32,000; N. America, 6500.

Cicadas and Hoppers: Suborder Auchenorrhyncha

Tarsi *3-segmented*. Antennae *short, bristlelike*. Active insects.

Cicadas, Treehoppers, Froghoppers, and Leafhoppers: Superfamily Cicadoidea

Antennae rise *in front of or between compound eyes*. Middle coxae short, contiguous. No Y-vein in anal area of FW. Usually 2 ocelli (3 in cicadas). Jumping insects (except cicadas).

CICADAS Family Cicadidae   See also Pl. 4
Identification: Large insects, mostly 1–2 in. FW *membranous*. *3 ocelli*. ♂ usually with sound-producing organs at base of abdomen on ventral side. Nonjumping insects.

Cicadas are common insects, but are more often heard than seen since the majority are arboreal. Song is produced only by males, and is usually a loud (sometimes pulsating) buzz. Most cicadas are large blackish insects, often with greenish markings, that appear each year in July and August; their life cycle lasts 2–5 or more years, but the broods overlap and adults are present each year. The periodical cicadas (*Magicicada*) have a life cycle of 13 or 17 years, and adults are present in a given area only in certain years. These cicadas occur in the East, and adults appear in May and June; they are 19–33 mm. and have the eyes and wing veins reddish. The 17-year cicadas (3 species) are principally northern. The 13-year cicadas (3 species) are principally southern. The species in each life-cycle group differ in size, color, and song; most emerging broods of periodical cicadas contain 2 or 3 species. Eggs are laid in twigs, which usually die and break off; nymphs live in the ground and feed on roots. Nymphs are stout-bodied, brownish, with expanded front tibiae; they usually crawl up on a tree trunk for their molt to the adult. Cicadas are generally of little economic importance,

head

nymph   adult

CICADA

but the egg laying of large numbers of periodical cicadas often causes serious damage to young trees.

TREEHOPPERS   Family Membracidae
Identification: Small jumping insects, usually 12 mm. or less. Pronotum *prolonged backward over abdomen.*

Treehoppers are common insects occurring on all types of vegetation. They vary in shape, owing to variations in shape of the pronotum; most of them appear humpbacked and some are shaped like thorns. Adults of most species feed on trees and shrubs, but some feed on weeds and grasses, especially in the nymphal stage. Eggs are usually laid in twigs, and the terminal portion of such twigs generally dies.

FROGHOPPERS and SPITTLEBUGS   Family Cercopidae
Identification: Small jumping insects, generally less than 12 mm. Pronotum does not extend back over abdomen. Hind tibiae with *1 or 2 stout spines*, and usually a circlet of spines at apex.

Adults are called froghoppers because many are somewhat wider posteriorly and are shaped rather like tiny frogs; nymphs produce and become surrounded by a spittlelike mass, and are called spittlebugs. These insects are very common, and spittle masses are often abundant on grass and weeds; a few spittlebugs feed on trees. One of the most common species is the Meadow Spittlebug, *Philaenus spumarius* (Linn.), which varies considerably in color but is usually brownish; it often causes considerable damage to clovers.

LEAFHOPPERS   Family Cicadellidae   **See also Pl. 4**
Identification: Similar to Cercopidae but body usually tapers posteriorly or is parallel-sided, and hind tibiae have *1 or more rows of small spines.*

This is a very large group; many species are common and abundant insects. Most of them are less than 10 mm., and many are brightly colored. They occur on a diversity of plants but each species is usually rather specific in its selection of a food plant. Many are serious pests of cultivated plants, causing injury by their feeding, and a few serve as vectors of plant diseases. Leafhoppers often discharge from the anus a clear watery fluid called *honeydew*, to which other insects (particularly ants) may be attracted.

Planthoppers: Superfamily Fulgoroidea

Antennae rise *on sides of head beneath eyes.* Middle coxae elongate and separated. Two anal veins in FW usually meet distally to form a Y-vein. Jumping insects, mostly 10 mm. or less. Many species have very short wings that cover only the basal abdominal segments. Both short- and long-winged individuals occur in some species. There is usually a distinct angle between the front (or dorsal) and lateral surfaces of the head; antennae, eyes, and lateral ocelli are on the lateral surface. Planthoppers constitute a large group but are seldom as abundant as other hoppers.

The N. American families of planthoppers may be divided into 2 groups on the basis of the structure of the 2nd segment of the hind tarsus: (1) this segment small to minute, its apex rounded and with a small spine on each side: Tropiduchidae, Acanaloniidae,

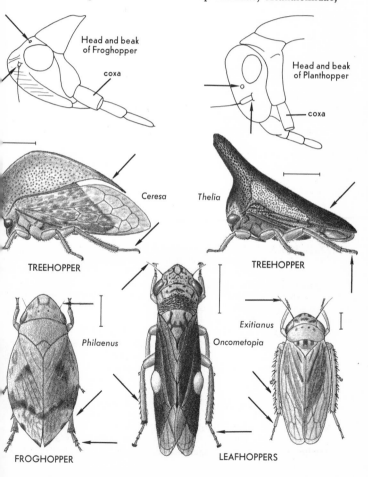

Head and beak of Froghopper
coxa

Head and beak of Planthopper
coxa

Ceresa
Thelia

TREEHOPPER
TREEHOPPER

Philaenus
Oncometopia
Exitianus

FROGHOPPER
LEAFHOPPERS

Flatidae, and Issidae; (2) this segment longer, its apex truncate or emarginate and with a row of small spines: the 7 remaining families.

TROPIDUCHID PLANTHOPPERS   Not illus.
Family Tropiduchidae
    Identification: Slender, yellowish to brownish, 7–9 mm. Apical portion of FW set off from rest of wing by a series of cross veins, the apical portion more densely veined than rest of wing. Hind trochanters usually directed backward.
    This is a tropical group. There are 3 rather uncommon species in the southeastern states.

ACANALONIID PLANTHOPPERS   Pl. 4
Family Acanaloniidae
    Identification: Shape characteristic: FW *broadly oval, held almost vertical at rest.* Costal area of FW reticulate. Hind tibiae with apical spines only.
    The members of this small group are usually greenish, sometimes with brown markings. Most of them belong to the genus *Acanalonia.*

FLATID PLANTHOPPERS Family Flatidae   Pl. 4
    Identification: Body somewhat wedge-shaped. FW elongate-triangular, held almost vertical at rest, and with *numerous costal and/or apical cross veins.* Hind tibiae with spines on sides in addition to apical ones.
    This is a large and widely distributed group, and most of its members are brownish or greenish.

ISSID PLANTHOPPERS Family Issidae
    Identification: Body not particularly wedge-shaped. FW often short, the costal area without numerous cross veins. Hind tibiae with *spines on sides in addition to apical ones.*
    Many species in this group are short-winged and some have a weevil-like snout.

FULGORID PLANTHOPPERS Family Fulgoridae   Not illus.
    Identification: Anal area of HW with many cross veins (such cross veins are lacking in remaining families).
    This group includes some of our largest planthoppers, but they are not very common. Most of them are brownish.

DERBID PLANTHOPPERS Family Derbidae
    Identification: Terminal segment of beak *about as long as wide* (remaining families have this segment longer).
    Most derbids have long narrow front wings and are rather delicate in build; many are brightly colored. These planthoppers feed on woody fungi.

DELPHACID PLANTHOPPERS   Family Delphacidae
Identification: Hind tibiae with *a large apical spur*.

This is the largest family of planthoppers. Its members are often very common insects. Most of them are quite small and many are short-winged.

ACHILID PLANTHOPPERS   Family Achilidae
Identification: Body flattened. FW *overlap at apex*, and the claval suture does not reach wing margin.

Most achilids are brownish, and occur in coniferous forests. Nymphs usually live in dead wood and under bark.

DICTYOPHARID PLANTHOPPERS   Family Dictyopharidae
Identification: Head *strongly prolonged anteriorly*, or front with 2 or 3 carinae (keels), or tegulae absent and claval suture obscure. Median ocellus lacking.

Most dictyopharids have the head produced forward into a long, slender, beaklike structure. If the head is not so produced, the body is usually oval and the front femora are broad and flattened.

CIXIID PLANTHOPPERS   Family Cixiidae
Identification: Head *little or not at all extended anteriorly;* front with only a median carina (keel) or none. Median ocellus often present. Tegulae present. Claval suture distinct.

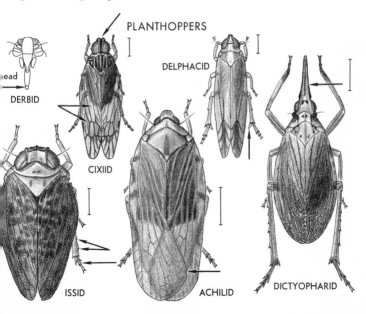

PLANTHOPPERS

head

DERBID

DELPHACID

CIXIID

ISSID

ACHILID

DICTYOPHARID

This is a relatively large group. Its members have *membranous* front wings, often with dark spots along the veins.

KINNARID PLANTHOPPERS Family Kinnaridae   **Not illus.**
Identification: Pale-colored, 3–4 mm. Similar to cixiids but abdominal terga 6–8 with wax-secreting pores. Vertex narrow and troughlike, narrower anteriorly.

Six species in the genus *Oeclidius* occur in the West.

Psyllids, Whiteflies, Aphids, and Scale Insects: Suborder Sternorrhyncha

Tarsi 1- or *2-segmented* (legs rarely lacking). Antennae long and threadlike (rarely absent). Mostly rather inactive insects.

Superfamily Psylloidea

PSYLLIDS Family Psyllidae   **See also Pl. 4**
Identification: FW membranous or thickened. Wings usually *held rooflike over body at rest*. Tarsi *2-segmented*. Antennae *10-segmented*. Active jumping insects, *2–5 mm*.

Most psyllids are free-living and feed on a variety of plants. A few are gall makers, generally forming galls on hackberry leaves. Nymphs are oval and flat and look very little like the adults; many produce a large amount of waxy filaments, making them look like little blobs of cotton. Some psyllids resemble tiny cicadas. A few species are pests of orchard trees or garden plants. One western species acts as vector of a plant disease known as "psyllid yellows."

Superfamily Aleyrodoidea

WHITEFLIES Family Aleyrodidae
Identification: *Minute* whitish insects, generally 2–3 mm. Body and wings covered with a white powder. *HW nearly as large as FW*. Wings held horizontal over body at rest. Tarsi *2-segmented*. Antennae *7-segmented*. Compound eyes somewhat elongate vertically and narrowed in middle.

Whiteflies are chiefly tropical, and our most common species are those attacking citrus or greenhouse plants. The 1st instar is an active insect; subsequent instars become covered with a blackish scalelike covering. Early instars are called larvae and the next to last instar, which is quiescent and does not feed, is called the pupa.

Aphids and Phylloxerans: Superfamily Aphidoidea

Wings, when present, membranous and not covered with a whitish powder. *HW much smaller than FW*. Tarsi 2-segmented. Body oval or pear-shaped, often with *a pair of fingerlike cornicles* near posterior end of abdomen. Many with a complex life cycle.

APHIDS Family Aphididae   **See also Pl. 4**
 Identification: Soft-bodied, usually somewhat pear-shaped, 4–8 mm., *nearly always with a pair of cornicles* near posterior end of abdomen. FW of winged forms with *Rs present and M branched.* Wings at rest usually held vertical above body.

This is a large group, and its members are often found in considerable numbers on the stems, leaves, and flowers of various plants. Many are serious pests of cultivated plants; their feeding causes a curling or wilting of the plant, and some aphids serve as vectors of plant diseases.

Most aphids have a complex life cycle, involving bisexual and parthenogenetic (♀) generations, winged and wingless individuals or generations, and often a regular alternation of food plants. Aphids generally overwinter as eggs, which hatch in the spring into wingless females that reproduce parthenogenetically (without fertilization) and give birth to young (rather than eggs). Two or more generations of such females may be produced; a generation of winged females eventually appears that usually migrate to a different food plant. These winged females also reproduce parthenogenetically, giving birth to young. Late in the season winged forms return to the original food plant, and

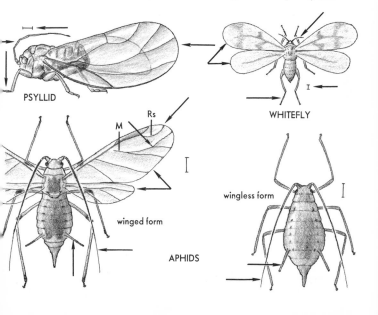

PSYLLID

WHITEFLY

M   Rs

winged form

wingless form

APHIDS

a generation of males and females appears; these mate, and the females lay the eggs that overwinter.

Aphids discharge from the anus a clear watery liquid, called honeydew, to which ants and other insects are attracted. Some ants live closely associated with aphids. They gather aphid eggs and keep them over winter in their nest and transport the aphids to a food plant in spring, tending them during the season and transferring them from one food plant to another. The ants feed on honeydew produced by the aphids.

WOOLLY and GALL-MAKING APHIDS
Family Eriosomatidae

Identification: Most produce *large amounts of a woolly or waxy material* that may nearly or completely cover the body, particularly in nymphal stages. Similar to Aphididae but cornicles very small or absent, and M in FW of winged forms *not branched.*

The life cycle is similar to that in Aphididae, but individuals of the bisexual generation lack mouth parts and a mated female lays only 1 egg. The Woolly Apple Aphid, *Eriosoma lanigerum* (Hausmann), is an important pest of apple and related trees; it usually overwinters on elm, and later in the season migrates to apple; still later some individuals migrate back to the elm, where the bisexual generation is produced, and others migrate to the roots of the apple, where they form gall-like growths. Many members of this family are gall makers, producing galls on leaves, stems, or buds of various plants.

PINE and SPRUCE APHIDS   Family Chermidae   See also Pl. 4
Identification: Live on needles or twigs of pine or spruce, or in galls on these trees. Cornicles absent. FW with Rs absent, and Cu_1 and Cu_2 *separated at base.* Wings held rooflike over body at rest. Wingless females often covered with waxy threads. Antennae of winged forms 5-segmented. Feed on conifers.

Adults are usually dark-colored. Many species alternate in their life cycle between 2 different conifers, forming galls only on 1. Both bisexual and parthenogenetic generations occur in most species. *Chermes abietis* Linn. is a common member of this group; it forms pineapple-shaped galls on twigs of spruce (see Pl. 4).

PHYLLOXERANS   Family Phylloxeridae
Identification: Similar to Chermidae but Cu_1 and Cu_2 in FW *stalked at base,* and wings held horizontal at rest. Wingless individuals sometimes covered with a waxy powder, but never with waxy threads. All forms with 3-segmented antennae. Feed on plants other than conifers.

Members of this group often have a very complex life history. The Grape Phylloxera, *Phylloxera vitifoliae* (Fitch), a serious pest of some varieties of grapes, attacks and forms galls on both the leaves and the roots; different generations occur on these

2 parts of the plant. The chief damage is done by individuals attacking the roots. European varieties of grapes are more susceptible to damage by this insect than American varieties. Where European varieties are grown, damage by the Phylloxera is reduced by grafting European vines to American rootstocks.

Scale Insects: Superfamily Coccoidea

Tarsi usually 1-segmented, with 1 claw, or legs absent. ♂ midge-like, with *1 pair of wings* (rarely wingless) and without a beak. ♀ wingless, often also legless, and usually with a waxy or scalelike covering. Male scale insects differ from Diptera in having 1-segmented tarsi (5-segmented in Diptera) and a long stylelike process (rarely 2) at end of abdomen.

The 1st instar has *legs and antennae* and is an active insect. Subsequent instars are less active and are often sessile. Legs and antennae of sessile scale insects are lost at the 1st molt, and the insect becomes covered with a scalelike covering. The last preadult instar of the male (called a pupa) is quiescent and does not feed.

Many scale insects are serious pests of cultivated plants, particularly orchard trees, shrubs, and many greenhouse plants, and when numerous may kill the plant. A few species are of value because of their secretions: shellac is made from the waxy secretions of a scale insect in India and some cochineal insects have been used as the source of a crimson dye.

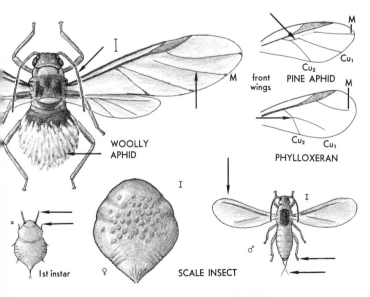

WOOLLY APHID

PINE APHID
front wings

PHYLLOXERAN

1st instar

♀

SCALE INSECT

♂

Identification of scale insects to family is based largely on characters of the female that can be seen only when the specimen is mounted on a microscope slide. Since most users of this book will not have facilities for mounting scale insects, structural features that distinguish each family have been omitted in the following accounts.

ENSIGN COCCIDS Family Ortheziidae
Females have well-developed legs and antennae. Body is covered with white waxy plates. These coccids occur on plant roots, and are not often encountered.

GIANT COCCIDS and GROUND PEARLS   Not illus.
Family Margarodidae
Female margarodids are large and rounded; some tropical species are nearly 1 in. long. Wax cysts of female *Margarodes*, some of which are metallic bronze or gold, are sometimes used as beads. The Cottony Cushion Scale, *Icerya purchasi* Maskell, is an important pest of citrus in the West.

ARMORED SCALES Family Diaspididae
Female armored scales are small, flattened, and disclike, lack legs, antennae, and eyes. They live under a scale formed of wax secretions of the insect and cast skins of early instars. Scales vary in shape and color in different species; male scales are usually smaller and more elongate than those of females. This is the largest family of scale insects, and it contains many important pest species. Most armored scales feed on trees and shrubs, and sometimes almost completely incrust twigs or branches. Two important pests of orchard and shade trees are the San Jose Scale, *Aspidiotus perniciosus* Comstock, and the Oystershell Scale, *Lepidosaphes ulmi* (Linn.); see opp. The former has a circular scale, the latter a scale shaped like an oyster shell.

ACLERDID SCALES Family Aclerdidae   Not illus.
Most members of this small group attack grasses and sedges. Generally feed under the leaf sheaths.

WAX and TORTOISE SCALES Family Coccidae
Female coccids are flattened and oval, the body hard and smooth or covered with wax. Antennae reduced or absent. Legs may be present or absent. The Cottony Maple Scale, *Pulvinaria innumerabilis* (Rathvon), about 6 mm., lays its eggs in a cottony mass that protrudes from posterior end of body (see opp.). Some coccids are pests of citrus and greenhouse plants.

LAC INSECTS Family Lacciferidae   Not illus.
This group is chiefly tropical, but a few species occur in the

Southwest on cactus and other desert plants. A species occurring in India, *Laccifer lacca* (Kern), is the source of lac, which is used in making shellac and varnishes.

PIT SCALES Family Asterolecaniidae   **Not illus.**
Female pit scales are small and oval. Body covered with a tough waxy film or embedded in a mass of wax. Legs vestigial or lacking. Antennae short and 4- to 6-segmented. The wax of *Cerococcus quercus* Comstock, a pit scale occurring on oak in the Southwest, has been used as chewing gum by the Indians.

MEALYBUGS Families Pseudococcidae and Eriococcidae
These are elongate-oval insects with well-developed legs. Bodies of most of them (Pseudococcidae) are covered with a waxy secretion; some (Eriococcidae) have body bare or only lightly covered with wax. Mealybugs often are pests of citrus and greenhouse plants.

COCHINEAL INSECTS Family Dactylopiidae   **Not illus.**
Cochineal insects are similar to mealybugs but are red, and the body is covered with white waxy plates. They occur in the Southwest on cactus. One species has been used by Indians as the source of a crimson dye.

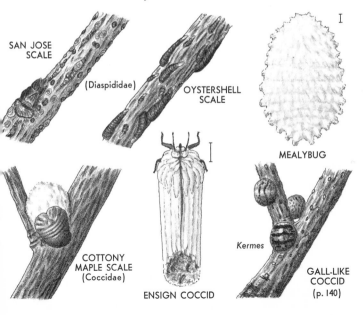

SAN JOSE SCALE

(Diaspididae)

OYSTERSHELL SCALE

MEALYBUG

COTTONY MAPLE SCALE (Coccidae)

ENSIGN COCCID

Kermes

GALL-LIKE COCCID (p. 140)

GALL-LIKE COCCIDS Family Kermidae   **p. 139**
Females of this group are somewhat spherical; lack legs but have 6-segmented antennae. Members of the genus *Kermes* live on oak twigs and resemble tiny galls. Females of a species occurring in Israel produce a large amount of honeydew; this honeydew accumulates on the leaves of the host plant to form a sugarlike substance called manna.

Fishflies, Snakeflies, Lacewings, and Antlions: Order Neuroptera

Identification: Four membranous wings: FW and HW about same size or HW a little wider at base; wings usually held rooflike over body at rest; wings generally with many veins, including numerous cross veins in costal area. Antennae long, many-segmented, thread-like, pectinate, or clubbed. Tarsi 5-segmented. Cerci absent. Mouth parts chewing. Metamorphosis complete.

Similar orders: (1) Odonata (p. 68): wings at rest held outstretched or together above body; tarsi 3-segmented; antennae short and bristlelike; wing venation different; harder-bodied. (2) Plecoptera (p. 92): tarsi 3-segmented; cerci present. (3) Mecoptera (p. 208): long-faced; few costal cross veins.

Immature stages: Larvae are campodeiform, and usually have large mandibles; majority terrestrial but a few aquatic. Larvae of most groups are predaceous. Pupation usually occurs in a silken cocoon; silk is spun from the anus.

Habits: Most Neuroptera are relatively poor fliers, and most are predaceous. Many are attracted to lights at night.

Importance: Some species, especially lacewings, are important predators, of value in keeping such pests as aphids under control. Larvae of the aquatic forms are an important item in the food of many freshwater fish, and some (like hellgrammites) are frequently used as fish bait.

Classification: Three suborders, Megaloptera, Raphidiodea, and Planipennia. Families of Planipennia are arranged in 3 super-families. Families are separated chiefly by wing and antennal characters.

No. of species: World, 4670; N. America, 338.

Dobsonflies, Fishflies, and Alderflies: Suborder Megaloptera

HW a little wider at base than FW. Anal area of HW folded fan-wise at rest. Larvae aquatic.

DOBSONFLIES and FISHFLIES Family Corydalidae
Identification: Large soft-bodied insects with a rather fluttery

flight; generally found near streams. Length usually *1 in. or more*. Ocelli *present*. 4th tarsal segment *cylindrical*.

Larvae occur in streams, generally under stones. Dobsonflies (*Corydalus* in the East and Southwest, *Dysmicohermes* in the West) are large insects with front wings over 2 in. long; males have mandibles *about 3 times as long as head*. Dobsonfly larvae, or hellgrammites (see illus.), are often used as fish bait. Fishflies are smaller (FW less than 2 in.), and many have serrate or pectinate antennae; some have clear wings, others extensive black or gray areas in the wings. Corydalid larvae have *a pair of hooked anal prolegs* and *8 pairs of lateral filaments*, and lack a terminal filament.

ALDERFLIES Family Sialidae
Identification: Similar to Corydalidae but smaller (usually *less than 1 in.*), *without ocelli*, and with 4th tarsal segment *dilated and deeply bilobed*.

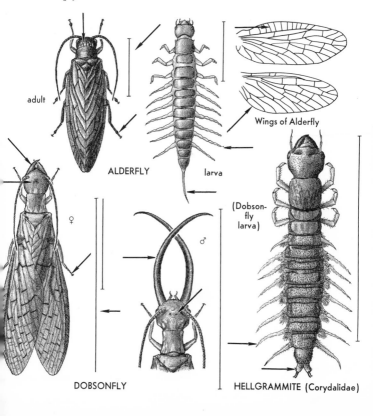

adult

ALDERFLY   larva

Wings of Alderfly

(Dobson-fly larva)

♀

♂

DOBSONFLY   HELLGRAMMITE (Corydalidae)

Alderflies are blackish or gray, somewhat lacewinglike in appearance but with the hind wings slightly wider at the base than the front wings. They are usually found near ponds or streams. Larvae are similar to those of Corydalidae but have a *terminal filament* and no hooked anal prolegs, and *only 7 pairs of lateral filaments*.

Snakeflies: Suborder Raphidiodea

Prothorax *elongate*. Front legs rise *from posterior end of prothorax* and are *similar to other legs*.

SNAKEFLIES   Families Raphidiidae and Inocelliidae
   Identification: Raphidiidae: stigma in FW *bordered proximally by a cross vein;* basal m-cu in HW transverse; ocelli present. Inocelliidae: stigma in FW *not bordered proximally by a cross vein;* basal m-cu in HW oblique; ocelli absent.
   Snakeflies occur only in the West, where they are represented by about 17 species of *Agulla* (Raphidiidae) and 2 species of *Inocellia* (Inocelliidae). Adults and larvae are predaceous; larvae are usually found under bark.

Dusty-wings, Lacewings, Antlions, and Owlflies: Suborder Planipennia

FW and HW similar in size and shape, anal area of HW not folded at rest. Either prothorax not lengthened or front legs mantidlike and rising from anterior end of prothorax.

Dusty-wings: Superfamily Coniopterygoidea

Length 3 mm. or less. Covered with a whitish powder. Wings with relatively few veins, Rs with *only 2 branches*.

DUSTY-WINGS   Family Coniopterygidae
   Identification: By the characters of the superfamily.
   Dusty-wings might be confused with psocopterans (p. 102) or whiteflies (p. 134), but can be recognized by their long threadlike antennae, chewing mouth parts, 5-segmented tarsi, and *characteristic wing venation*. They are rather rare.

Superfamily Hemerobioidea

Antennae threadlike, serrate, or pectinate, never clubbed.

MANTIDFLIES   Family Mantispidae
   Identification: Mantidlike in appearance: prothorax *elongate*, front legs *fitted for grasping prey* and rise from *anterior end of prothorax*.
   Mantidflies are widely distributed but are more common in

the South. Adults, less than 1 in., are predaceous. Larvae are parasitic in egg sacs of ground spiders.

PLEASING LACEWINGS Family Dilaridae **Not illus.**
Identification: Superficially resemble small moths, since wings are rather hairy and at rest are often held outspread. Antennae of ♂ pectinate. ♀ with an ovipositor as long as body. Costal cross veins not forked. FW more or less triangular and 3.0–5.5 mm.
Only 2 species occur in N. America, and they are quite rare.

GIANT LACEWINGS Family Polystoechotidae **Not illus.**
Identification: Wingspread 1½–2½ in. Humeral vein in FW recurved and branched. 1st r-m cross vein in HW longitudinal.
Only 2 species of giant lacewings occur in N. America, and they are quite rare.

ITHONID LACEWINGS Family Ithonidae **Not illus.**
Identification: Similar to Polystoechotidae, but FW with Sc and R_1 not fused distally and Rs with only a few branches, and 1st r-m in HW short and oblique.

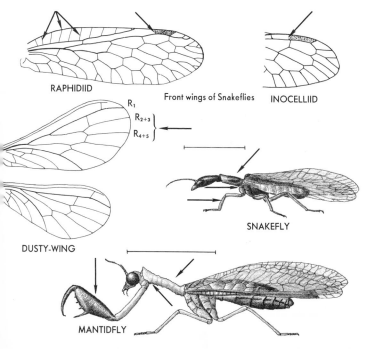

RAPHIDIID

Front wings of Snakeflies

INOCELLIID

R_1
R_{2+3}
R_{4+5}

SNAKEFLY

DUSTY-WING

MANTIDFLY

A single very rare member of this group, *Oliarces clara* Banks, has been reported from s. California. It has a wingspread of about 1½ in.

BEADED LACEWINGS   Family Berothidae   **Not illus.**
   Identification: Some costal cross veins forked. Vertex flattened. Outer margin of FW sometimes indented behind apex. Over 8 mm.
   Berothids resemble caddisflies, and are often attracted to lights. The group is small, its members quite rare.

GREEN LACEWINGS   Family Chrysopidae
   Identification: Wings usually greenish, eyes *golden or copper-colored*. FW with *apparently 1 radial sector*, Sc and R_1 *not fused at wing tip*, and costal cross veins *not forked*.
   Green lacewings are very common insects, found on grass, weeds, and shrubs, usually in relatively open areas. They often give off an unpleasant odor when handled. Adults and larvae feed principally on aphids and are important agents in the control of these insects. Eggs are laid *at ends of tiny stalks*, usually on foliage; the larvae, which have *long sickle-shaped mandibles*, pupate in small pea-shaped silken cocoons.

BROWN LACEWINGS   Family Hemerobiidae
   Identification: Similar to Chrysopidae but brownish and generally much smaller. FW with *apparently 2 or more radial sectors*. Some costal cross veins *forked*.
   Brown lacewings are less common than green lacewings, and are most likely to be encountered in wooded areas. They are widely distributed. Adults and larvae are predaceous.

SPONGILLAFLIES   Family Sisyridae
   Identification: Lacewinglike, 6–8 mm. Costal cross veins *not forked*. Sc and R_1 *fused near wing tip*. Vertex convex.
   Sisyrids resemble small brownish lacewings, and are found near water. Larvae feed on freshwater sponges.

Antlions and Owlflies: Superfamily Myrmeleontoidea

Large insects resembling damselflies or dragonflies but with longer antennae that are *clubbed*.

ANTLIONS   Family Myrmeleontidae
   Identification: Damselflylike, the antennae *about as long as head and thorax together. An elongate cell* behind point of fusion of Sc and R_1.
   Antlions resemble damselflies but are softer-bodied and have conspicuous knobbed antennae. Larvae (sometimes called doodlebugs) have long sicklelike jaws and usually live at the bottom of a conical pit in dry sandy or dusty areas. They feed on ants and other insects that fall into this pit.

OWLFLIES Family Ascalaphidae

Identification: Large insects resembling dragonflies but with antennae *nearly or quite as long as body.* Cell behind fusion point of Sc and R₁ is *short.*

Owlflies are fairly common in the South and Southwest, relatively rare in the North. Larvae are similar to those of the Myrmeleontidae but do not dig pits; they lie in wait for their

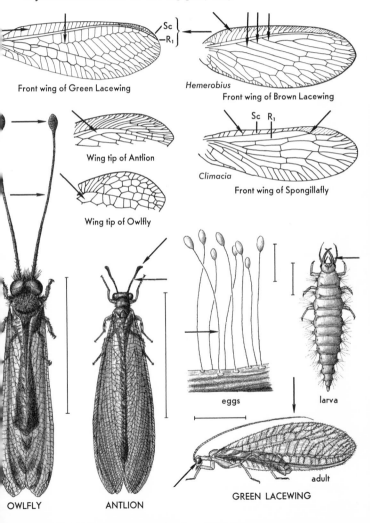

Front wing of Green Lacewing

Hemerobius
Front wing of Brown Lacewing

Wing tip of Antlion

Climacia
Front wing of Spongillafly

Wing tip of Owlfly

eggs

larva

adult

OWLFLY   ANTLION   GREEN LACEWING

prey on surface of the ground, often covered with dirt or
debris.

Beetles: Order Coleoptera

Identification: FW (*elytra*) horny or leathery, nearly always meeting in a straight line down back and covering HW. HW (the ones
used in flight) membranous, usually longer than FW, and folded
beneath FW when not in use. FW occasionally short and not
covering all of abdomen. 1 or both pairs of wings rarely reduced
or absent. Antennae usually with 11 segments, rarely with more,
often with 8–10, rarely with as few as 2; antennae variable in
form. Mouth parts chewing. Tarsi usually 3- to 5-segmented.
Abdomen commonly with 5 segments visible ventrally, sometimes
with up to 8. Metamorphosis complete.

Similar orders: (1) Dermaptera (p. 98): abdomen with pincerlike
appendages at tip. (2) Hemiptera (p. 112): mouth parts sucking;
front wings rarely meeting in a straight line down the back, nearly
always overlapping at tip; antennae with 4 or 5 segments. (3)
Homoptera (p. 128): mouth parts sucking. (4) Orthoptera (p. 76):
front wings with distinct veins (beetle FW lack veins); antennae
usually long, threadlike, many-segmented.

Immature stages: Larvae quite variable in form, hardness of body,
and development of appendages: campodeiform (like *Campodea;*
see illus., p. 63), grublike, or wormlike; some are wirewormlike,
and a few are greatly flattened. Feed in the open or burrow into
the food material. Occur in a great variety of habitats; many are
aquatic.

Habits: This is the largest order of insects. Its members are
almost everywhere and feed on all sorts of plant and animal materials. They are abundant on vegetation; they occur under bark,
stones, and other objects; many are found on or in the ground, in
fungi, rotting vegetation, dung, and carrion. Some are aquatic.
A few are parasites of other animals.

Importance: Many plant-feeding beetles are serious pests, and
different species attack nearly all parts of plants. Some beetles
feed on various stored foods and other materials. Many beetles
are of value because they prey upon and help to control injurious
insects or act as scavengers.

Classification: Three suborders, Archostemata, Adephaga, and
Polyphaga. Archostemata are a primitive group with only 2 rare
families. Adephaga have the 1st abdominal sternum interrupted
in the middle by the hind coxae. At least the hind part of this
sternum extends completely across the abdomen in the Polyphaga.
The superfamilies and families of beetles are usually separated by
characters of the antennae, legs, head, pronotum, front wings
(elytra), thoracic sclerites, and abdomen.

No. of species: World, 290,000; N. America, 28,600.

Identification of beetles: The pictured key (pp. 148–149) to the more common families of beetles should be of help to those not well acquainted with these insects. A comparison of the specimen to be identified with the 1st pair of alternatives will lead to further pairs, and eventually to a group of families in which the specimen belongs. Families marked with a dagger are the most common, and descriptions and illustrations of these should be checked first. Families with an asterisk (somewhat less common) should be checked next, and families without symbols are least common and can be checked last. If, from the descriptions and illustrations

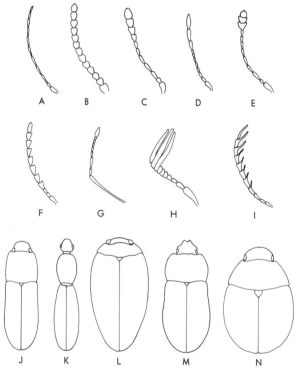

Types of antennae (A–I) and body shapes (J–N) in beetles. A, threadlike; B, beadlike; C, D, and E, clubbed (E, capitate); F, serrate; G, elbowed; H, lamellate; I, pectinate; J, elongate-slender, nearly parallel-sided; K, elongate-slender; L, elongate-oval; M, elongate-robust; N, broadly oval.

Key to the Principal Families of Coleoptera

†—the most common families
*—less common families
no symbol—least common

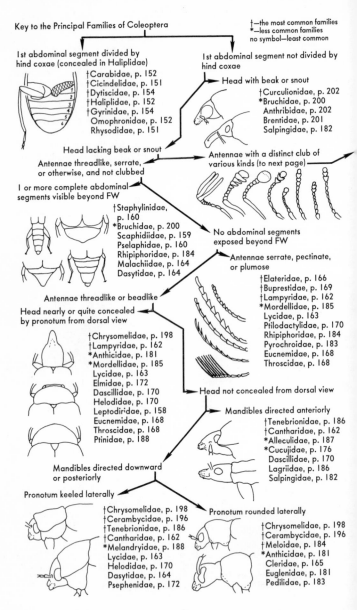

1st abdominal segment divided by hind coxae (concealed in Haliplidae)

†Carabidae, p. 152
†Cicindelidae, p. 151
†Dytiscidae, p. 154
†Haliplidae, p. 152
†Gyrinidae, p. 154
Omophronidae, p. 152
Rhysodidae, p. 151

1st abdominal segment not divided by hind coxae

Head with beak or snout

†Curculionidae, p. 202
*Bruchidae, p. 200
Anthribidae, p. 202
Brentidae, p. 201
Salpingidae, p. 182

Head lacking beak or snout

Antennae threadlike, serrate, or otherwise, and not clubbed

Antennae with a distinct club of various kinds (to next page)

1 or more complete abdominal segments visible beyond FW

†Staphylinidae, p. 160
*Bruchidae, p. 200
Scaphidiidae, p. 159
Pselaphidae, p. 160
Rhipiphoridae, p. 184
Malachiidae, p. 164
Dasytidae, p. 164

No abdominal segments exposed beyond FW

Antennae serrate, pectinate, or plumose

†Elateridae, p. 166
†Buprestidae, p. 169
†Lampyridae, p. 162
*Mordellidae, p. 185
Lycidae, p. 163
Ptilodactylidae, p. 170
Rhipiphoridae, p. 184
Pyrochroidae, p. 183
Eucnemidae, p. 168
Throscidae, p. 168

Antennae threadlike or beadlike

Head nearly or quite concealed by pronotum from dorsal view

†Chrysomelidae, p. 198
†Lampyridae, p. 162
*Anthicidae, p. 181
*Mordellidae, p. 185
Lycidae, p. 163
Elmidae, p. 172
Dascillidae, p. 170
Helodidae, p. 170
Leptodiridae, p. 158
Eucnemidae, p. 168
Throscidae, p. 168
Ptinidae, p. 188

Head not concealed from dorsal view

Mandibles directed anteriorly

†Tenebrionidae, p. 186
†Cantharidae, p. 162
*Alleculidae, p. 187
*Cucujidae, p. 176
Dascillidae, p. 170
Lagriidae, p. 186
Salpingidae, p. 182

Mandibles directed downward or posteriorly

Pronotum keeled laterally

†Chrysomelidae, p. 198
†Cerambycidae, p. 196
†Tenebrionidae, p. 186
†Cantharidae, p. 162
*Melandryidae, p. 188
Lycidae, p. 163
Helodidae, p. 170
Dasytidae, p. 164
Psephenidae, p. 172

Pronotum rounded laterally

†Chrysomelidae, p. 198
†Cerambycidae, p. 196
†Meloidae, p. 184
*Anthicidae, p. 181
Cleridae, p. 165
Euglenidae, p. 181
Pedilidae, p. 183

148

Key to the Principal Families of Coleoptera *(contd.)*

Last 3 or 4 (or more) antennal segments markedly prolonged laterally

†Scarabaeidae, p. 192
*Lucanidae, p. 190
*Passalidae, p. 191
Sandalidae, p. 166
Ostomidae, p. 164
Cleridae, p. 165
Heteroceridae, p. 172

Terminal antennal segments not prolonged laterally

1 or more abdominal segments visible beyond FW

†Staphylinidae, p. 160
*Nitidulidae, p. 177
*Histeridae, p. 156
*Silphidae, p. 158
*Bruchidae, p. 200
Pselaphidae, p. 160
Scaphidiidae, p. 159
Monotomidae, p. 174

No abdominal segments exposed beyond FW

Very compact, nearly or quite spherical from dorsal view

†Coccinellidae, p. 180
†Chrysomelidae, p. 198
†Dermestidae, p. 164
*Erotylidae, p. 176
*Hydrophilidae, p. 156
*Nitidulidae, p. 177
*Phalacridae, p. 178
Leiodidae, p. 158
Byrrhidae, p. 173
Anobiidae, p. 188

Elongate or linear, not spherical from dorsal view

Head nearly or quite concealed by pronotum from dorsal view

†Chrysomelidae, p. 198
†Dermestidae, p. 164
*Mordellidae, p. 185
*Anthicidae, p. 181
Anobiidae, p. 188
Bostrichidae, p. 189
Cisidae, p. 164
Scolytidae, p. 204
Mycetophagidae, p. 181
Leptodiridae, p. 158
Byturidae, p. 178
Throscidae, p. 168

Head not concealed from dorsal view

Antennal club asymmetrical

*Hydrophilidae, p. 156
*Silphidae, p. 158
Ostomidae, p. 164
Psoidae, p. 190
Dryopidae, p. 172
Elmidae, p. 172
Heteroceridae, p. 172
Cleridae, p. 165

Antennal club symmetrical

Pronotum narrower than FW at base

*Cucujidae, p. 176
Derodontidae, p. 174
Cleridae, p. 165
Lathridiidae, p. 178
Lyctidae, p. 190

Pronotum not narrower than FW at base

Mandibles directed forward

†Tenebrionidae, p. 186
*Hydrophilidae, p. 156
*Cucujidae, p. 176
*Languriidae, p. 175
*Silphidae, p. 158
*Erotylidae, p. 176
Derodontidae, p. 174
Silvanidae, p. 178
Colydiidae, p. 180
Mycetophagidae, p. 181

Mandibles directed downward

†Chrysomelidae, p. 198
*Hydrophilidae, p. 156
*Anthicidae, p. 181
*Erotylidae, p. 176
Throscidae, p. 168
Mycetophagidae, p. 181
Cryptophagidae, p. 175
Mycetaeidae, p. 179
Endomychidae, p. 180
Leptodiridae, p. 158

given, the specimen does not appear to belong to any of the families in the group, descriptions and illustrations of related groups
should be examined. Should there be doubt at any point in the
key as to which way to proceed, try both alternatives. After
practice you will recognize the most common groups, and identification of subsequent specimens will be easier. The key is so
arranged that some variable families key out in more than one
place. In the following text, tarsal segmentation is indicated by
a 3-number formula (like 5-5-5), representing the number of segments in the front, middle, and hind tarsi.

Suborder Archostemata

Tarsi 5-5-5. Antennae threadlike or beadlike. This is a primitive
group and its members are relatively rare.

RETICULATED BEETLES   Family Cupedidae
   Identification: *Shape distinctive* (resembling leaf-mining leaf
   beetles, p. 198): body elongate, rather flattened. FW long,
   parallel-sided, with *rows of square punctures between longitudinal
   ridges.* Body clothed with broad scales. Antennae *long, threadlike.* 7–20 mm.
      Only 5 species of cupedids occur in N. America, and they are
   infrequently collected. Adults are found in logs where larvae
   occur, on vegetation, or flying in the sunlight. Larvae bore in
   rotting oak, chestnut, and pine logs.

MICROMALTHID BEETLES   Not illus.
Family Micromalthidae
   Identification: Resemble small soldier beetles (p. 162). Antennae short, beadlike, 11-segmented. Pronotum widest anteriorly, head slightly wider than pronotum. FW short, exposing
   2 or 3 abdominal segments. 1.5–2.5 mm.
      This family contains only 1 species, *Micromalthus debilis*
   LeConte, which occurs in the Northeast. This beetle is unique
   as the only known member of the order in which *paedogenesis*
   (reproduction by larvae) occurs. Larvae bore in oak that has
   reached the red-rotten stage of decay, or in rotten, yellowish-
   brown chestnut. Larvae are common in these situations; adults
   are very seldom collected, but they can be reared in numbers
   from infested logs.

Suborder Adephaga

First abdominal segment divided by hind coxae. Notopleural
sutures present. Tarsi usually *5-5-5.* Antennae 11-segmented and
usually threadlike (rarely beadlike or clubbed). Nearly always
predaceous.

Superfamily Rhysodoidea

Antennae beadlike. These beetles are considered to be primitive members of the Adephaga.

WRINKLED BARK BEETLES   Family Rhysodidae
Identification: *Shape distinctive:* elongate-slender, body widest near apex of FW, tapering anteriorly. Antennae *short, beadlike.* Pronotum *grooved.* FW striate. Dorsal surface black or reddish, shiny. 5–8 mm.

Larvae of these beetles bore beneath bark of decaying beech, ash, elm, and pine. Adults are found beneath bark, and often hibernate in groups.

Superfamily Caraboidea

Antennae *threadlike.* Terrestrial, aquatic, or semiaquatic.

TIGER BEETLES   Family Cicindelidae
Identification: Shape distinctive: FW nearly parallel-sided or somewhat wider apically, pronotum *narrower than FW,* head at eyes *as wide as or wider than pronotum.* Antennae inserted above base of mandibles. Legs long, slender. Brownish, black, or green, often patterned, some iridescent and very colorful. 6–40 (mostly 10–20) mm.

Tiger beetles are active, fast-running, fast-flying, and quite a challenge to collect. They are common and occur in bright sunlight in open sandy areas, on sandy beaches, and on open paths or lanes. Their dexterity and strong mandibles make

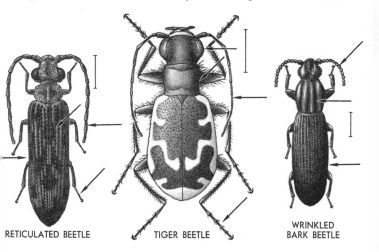

RETICULATED BEETLE   TIGER BEETLE   WRINKLED BARK BEETLE

them well fitted for their predaceous habits. They must be handled carefully when caught, because some can administer a painful bite. The larvae construct vertical tunnels in the ground; they wait at the top of tunnel for passing insects and feed on those they manage to subdue. About ¾ the 130 or so species in N. America belong to the genus *Cicindela*.

GROUND BEETLES Family Carabidae   See also Pl. 5
Identification: Head at eyes nearly always *narrower than pronotum*. Antennae inserted between eyes and base of mandibles. Legs usually long, slender. Generally black and shiny or dark, sometimes brightly colored. 2–35 (mostly 5–15) mm.

This is one of the largest families of beetles, and its members are probably as common and abundant — at least in the East — as any other beetles. Carabids are generally found on the ground beneath objects; some are found on vegetation and flowers. They commonly fly to lights. Most species are nocturnal, and hide during the day. They often run rapidly when disturbed, and seldom fly. Larvae usually occur in the same situation as adults. Adults and larvae are nearly always predaceous and many are very beneficial — they feed on some of our worst pests, including Gypsy Moth larvae, cankerworms, and cutworms. The species of *Calosoma* are called caterpillar hunters; adults and larvae often climb trees or shrubs in search of prey. Many ground beetles give off an unpleasant odor when handled. *Brachinus* species are called bombardier beetles because of their habit of ejecting from the anus a glandular secretion that literally explodes when released, producing a popping sound. This secretion is foul-smelling and irritating, and serves as a means of protection.

ROUND SAND BEETLES Family Omophronidae
Identification: *Shape and size distinctive:* oval, tapering at each end, very convex, 5–8 mm. Head large. Scutellum *apparently absent*. Brown or black, with light markings. Prosternum enlarged between coxae, concealing mesosternum.

The infrequently collected beetles of this small family occur in burrows in sand or mud along shores of streams and lakes. Throwing water over the banks forces them into the open, where they are easily collected. Larvae occur in similar situations; larvae and adults are predaceous.

CRAWLING WATER BEETLES Family Haliplidae
Identification: *Shape and size distinctive:* oval, tapering at each end, convex, 2.5–4.5 mm. Hind coxae greatly enlarged and concealing 2 or more abdominal segments. Yellow or brownish, with *black spots*. Head small. Antennae short.

These beetles are fairly common in or around ponds, streams, and lakes, and are usually found creeping or crawling over submerged vegetation. They are not good swimmers.

TROUT-STREAM BEETLES Family Amphizoidae **Not illus.**
  Identification: Elongate-oval, rather convex dorsally, somewhat flattened ventrally. Dull brownish to dull black. 11–16 mm. Aquatic, occurring in streams in far West.

Adults and larvae live in the icy waters of swift mountain streams. They cling to driftwood, debris, or to stones in eddies where the water level remains fairly constant. One species lives in relatively warm quiet water in streams near Seattle. Adults

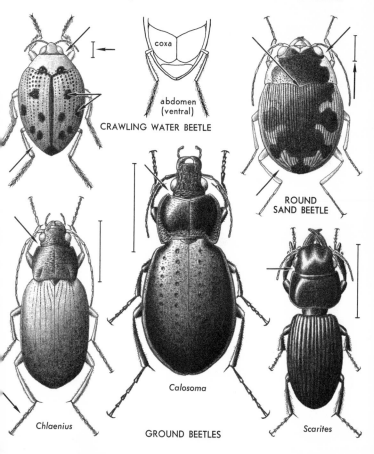

CRAWLING WATER BEETLE

ROUND SAND BEETLE

Chlaenius

Calosoma

Scarites

GROUND BEETLES

swim very feebly or not at all. Adults and larvae are apparently predaceous.

PREDACEOUS DIVING BEETLES Family Dytiscidae

Identification: Shape often distinctive: elongate-oval, convex, streamlined; hind legs *flattened and fringed* with hairs. Hind tarsi with 1 or 2 claws. Front tibiae lacking spines. Antennae *threadlike*. Scutellum usually visible. Black, brown, or yellowish, often with light markings. 1.4–35.0 mm.

Members of this fairly large group are abundant in ponds, lakes, and streams. They are excellent swimmers, and when swimming move the hind legs in unison; water scavenger beetles (Hydrophilidae, p. 156), with which dytiscids may be confused, move the hind legs alternately when swimming. Predaceous diving beetles frequently fly to lights. Adults and larvae are highly predaceous, and feed on various small aquatic animals, including fish. Larvae (called water tigers) have large sicklelike jaws, and suck the body contents of the prey through channels in the jaws; they do not hesitate to attack an animal larger than themselves.

BURROWING WATER BEETLES Family Noteridae

Identification: Similar to Dytiscidae but scutellum *hidden* and front tibiae *often with a curved spine*. Hind tarsi with 2 claws. Black to reddish brown. 1.2–5.5 mm.

This is a small group whose members are similar in appearance and habits to dytiscids. They are most common in the southeastern states but a few occur in the Northeast. Larvae burrow into the mud near the roots of aquatic plants (hence common name of the group).

Superfamily Gyrinoidea

This group contains a single very distinctive family that differs from nearly all other beetles in having 2 pairs of eyes, and from other Adephaga in having short clubbed antennae.

WHIRLIGIG BEETLES Family Gyrinidae

Identification: Elongate-oval, flattened, 3–15 mm. *2 pairs of compound eyes*, 1 dorsal and 1 ventral. Black, rarely dark metallic green. Front legs *long*, slender, middle and *hind legs very short*, flattened, not fringed with hairs. Antennae *short and clubbed*.

These beetles are often seen swimming in groups in an odd gyrating fashion on the surface of ponds and streams. Their 2 pairs of eyes enable them to watch for enemies and prey both above and below the water surface. They swim rapidly and are as much at home below water as on the surface. Adults and larvae are predaceous. Some adults when handled give off an odor similar to that of pineapples.

Suborder Polyphaga

First abdominal segment not divided by hind coxae, its posterior margin extending completely across abdomen. Prothorax nearly always lacking notopleural sutures. This suborder includes the remaining families of beetles.

Superfamily Lymexylonoidea

Maxillary palps enlarged in ♂. Antennae short, threadlike or serrate. Tarsi 5-5-5. Infrequently collected beetles.

SHIP-TIMBER BEETLES   Family Lymexylonidae   **Not illus.**
   Identification: Body narrow, elongate, 9.0–13.5 mm. Maxillary palps of ♂ long, flabellate. Antennae short, 11-segmented.
   Two rare species of ship-timber beetles occur in the eastern states, where they are found in decaying wood and under bark. Larvae bore into the heart and sapwood of dead chestnut, poplar, and other trees.

TELEGEUSID BEETLES   Family Telegeusidae   **Not illus.**
   Identification: Resemble rove beetles (p. 160): body elongate and slender, FW short and exposing much of abdomen; HW extending back over abdomen. Terminal segment of maxillary and labial palps greatly enlarged. 5–6 mm.
   Three very rare species occur in Arizona and California. They are presumed to live under bark. Larvae are unknown.

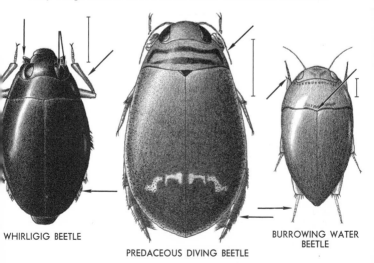

WHIRLIGIG BEETLE

PREDACEOUS DIVING BEETLE

BURROWING WATER BEETLE

Superfamily Hydrophiloidea

Tarsi usually 5-5-5. Mostly aquatic in habit.

HISTER BEETLES   Family Histeridae

Identification: Antennae *elbowed, clubbed*. FW *short, truncate*, exposing 1 or 2 abdominal segments. Body usually oval, sometimes greatly flattened, or elongate and cylindrical. Hardbodied, shiny, black (some with red markings). 1–10 mm.

These beetles usually occur around decaying organic matter — carrion, dung, decaying plants, and oozing sap — and apparently feed on other insects attracted to these materials. Some species are very flat and live under loose bark. The elongate cylindrical species live in the galleries of wood-boring insects. Larvae have much the same habits as adults.

WATER SCAVENGER BEETLES   Family Hydrophilidae

Identification: Maxillary palps *elongate*, usually longer than antennae. Metasternum frequently prolonged posteriorly as a sharp spine. Body generally oval or elliptical, convex dorsally. Antennae *short, clubbed*. Hind legs *flattened, usually with a fringe of hairs*. Black, brown, or yellow, sometimes patterned. 1–40 mm.

This is a fairly large group of common insects very similar to the Dytiscidae (p. 154). Most species are aquatic, both as adults and larvae. Adults are principally scavengers, but larvae are predaceous. Larvae feed on a variety of aquatic animals, and are very voracious. The members of 1 subfamily (Sphaeridiinae) are terrestrial, and feed in dung, humus, and decaying leaves.

MINUTE MOSS BEETLES   Family Limnebiidae   **Not illus.**

Identification: Similar to Hydrophilidae but with 6 or 7 abdominal segments (5 in Hydrophilidae). Elongate-oval, darkcolored. Maxillary palps elongate. 1.2–1.7 mm.

Members of this small family are found in matted vegetation along streams, in decaying moss near the shore, and in swampy places. Larvae are predaceous.

SKIFF BEETLES   Family Hydroscaphidae   **Not illus.**

Identification: Similar to rove beetles (p. 160) in having FW short and truncate, exposing 3 abdominal segments, but oval, body widest at base of FW, and with notopleural sutures. Tarsi 3-3-3. Tan to brown. About 1.5 mm.

This family contains a single species that occurs in Arizona, s. Nevada, and s. California. Adults and larvae occur in streams, and are found on filamentous algae growing on rocks, especially in shallow water.

Superfamily Staphylinoidea

FW often short, exposing some abdominal segments. Usually small. Most families, except Staphylinidae and Silphidae, are infrequently encountered.

BEAVER PARASITES Family Platypsyllidae **Not illus.**
    Identification: Body elongate-oval, flattened. FW short, exposing 4 abdominal segments. Eyes and HW absent. Tarsi 5-5-5. Antennae 11-segmented, not clubbed. About 2.5 mm.
    The single species in this family, *Platypsyllus castoris* Ritsema, is an ectoparasite of the American beaver; adults and larvae spend nearly all their life in fur of the host.

HORSESHOE CRAB BEETLES **Not illus.**
Family Limulodidae
    Identification: Body finely pubescent and shaped like a horseshoe crab. Antennae clubbed. FW short, exposing 4 abdominal segments. Eyes reduced or absent. 1.7–3.2 mm.
    Our 4 species of limulodids are found associated with ants; they feed on body exudates of the ants.

GRASS-ROOT BEETLES Family Brathinidae **Not illus.**
    Identification: Shape distinctive: elongate-slender, long-legged, antlike; head as wide as pronotum, narrower posteriorly, necklike. Antennae long, threadlike. Dorsal surface smooth, shiny. Coxae large, contiguous. 3.5–6.0 mm.

WATER SCAVENGER BEETLES

Hydrochara   *Hydrophilus*   HISTER BEETLE

Only 3 species occur in this country, 2 in the East and 1 in California. They are found in roots of grasses growing near water. They are very rare and their habits are not well known.

FEATHER-WINGED BEETLES   Family Ptiliidae   **Not illus.**
Identification: Antennae clubbed, each segment with a whorl of long hair. HW with a fringe of long hair. Oval, often pubescent. 0.25–1.0 mm.

Certain members of this group are not only the smallest beetles known but are among the smallest insects; some species are smaller than many Protozoa. Ptiliids occur in rotten wood, fungus-covered logs, vegetable detritus, and dung. They feed chiefly on fungus spores.

MAMMAL-NEST BEETLES   Family Leptinidae   **Not illus.**
Identification: Brownish, oval, flattened. Eyes reduced or absent. Antennae clubbed. FW with dense golden pubescence. 2.0–2.5 mm.

The few members of this group occurring in the U.S. are found in nests and fur of mice, shrews, moles, and beavers; 1 species has also been found in nests of social Hymenoptera. They probably feed on the eggs and young of mites and other small arthropods.

ROUND FUNGUS BEETLES   Family Leiodidae
Identification: Shape distinctive: oval to nearly spherical, strongly convex, often *capable of rolling into a ball.* Black or brown, shiny. Antennae *clubbed.* 1.5–6.5 mm.

Leiodids occur under the bark of dead trees, in rotten wood, decaying vegetable matter, and rotting fungi. Many species roll into a ball and play dead when disturbed.

SMALL CARRION BEETLES   Family Leptodiridae
Identification: Shape distinctive: elongate-oval, head partly visible dorsally. Antennae clubbed, 8th segment *much smaller than 7th or 9th.* Body with rather dense flattened pubescence. Thorax and FW usually with *cross ridges.* 2–5 mm.

The more common members of this small family feed on carrion. Others are found in fungi, ant nests, or are associated with mammals, and apparently are scavengers.

CARRION BEETLES   Family Silphidae   **See also Pl. 5**
Identification: FW *broad posteriorly,* loosely covering abdomen, or *short, truncate, and exposing 1–3 segments.* Black, often with yellow, orange, or red markings. Body usually soft, flattened. Antennae *clubbed,* last 2 or 3 segments pubescent. 1.5–35.0 (usually over 10.0) mm.

These beetles are commonly found on carrion and decaying

vegetation. They are the largest beetles found in such situations and are often easily recognized by their bright colors. Species of *Silpha* are broadly oval, 10–24 mm., and the elytra (front wings) nearly cover the abdomen. Species of *Nicrophorus* (for 1, see Pl. 5) have short elytra and are called burying or sexton beetles: they burrow under and bury carrion such as dead mice and other small animals. Adults and larvae are scavengers on carrion and decaying vegetation.

SHINING FUNGUS BEETLES Family Scaphidiidae
Identification: Shape distinctive: broadly spindle-shaped, convex. Usually black, shiny, some with red spots. FW *short and*

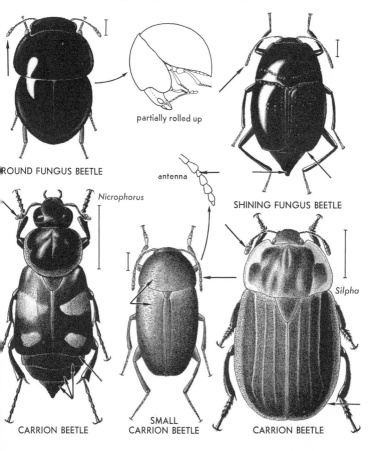

partially rolled up

ROUND FUNGUS BEETLE

antenna

SHINING FUNGUS BEETLE

Nicrophorus

Silpha

CARRION BEETLE

SMALL CARRION BEETLE

CARRION BEETLE

truncate, exposing *pointed tip of abdomen*. Legs long, slender. Antennae *clubbed*. 2–7 mm.

The members of this small family are found in fungi, dead wood, rotting leaves, and under bark. When disturbed they play dead or run with a characteristic uneven gait. Their habits are not well known.

ROVE BEETLES   Family Staphylinidae

Identification: Form often characteristic: nearly always elongate-slender, parallel-sided. FW *short* and exposing 3 to (often) 5 or 6 abdominal segments. Abdomen flexible, in life often bent upward. Antennae threadlike to clubbed. 1–20 (mostly 1–10) mm.

This is a large family, with nearly 3000 species in the U.S., many very common. Rove beetles occur in a variety of habitats: some larger species are found on carrion, others occur on the ground or under objects, along shores of streams and lakes, under bark, in fungi, on flowers, in ant and termite nests, or in decaying vegetable matter. They often run fast, usually with tip of the abdomen bent upward, and are good fliers. The hind wings when not in use are tucked under the short elytra (front wings) with aid of the abdomen. The beginning collector may be rather wary of these beetles because of their habit of holding the abdomen as if they were about to sting. Actually, none can sting but some of the larger species bite readily when handled. Most adults and larvae are predaceous on insects; some feed on decaying organic matter, and a few are parasitic.

SHORT-WINGED MOLD BEETLES   Family Pselaphidae

Identification: Similar to rove beetles, but with abdomen wider than pronotum and head. Chestnut-brown to dark brown. Maxillary palps often with segments enlarged. 0.5–5.5 mm.

This is a fairly large group whose members are found under bark, in or under rotting logs, in moss, on the ground, and in ant nests. They apparently feed on mold.

ANT-LOVING BEETLES   Family Clavigeridae   Not illus.

Identification: Similar to Pselaphidae, but antennae with only 2 or 3 segments. Head and pronotum slender. Eyes present or absent. Tarsi with a single claw. Brownish yellow. 1.8–2.5 mm.

Only 9 species occur in the U.S., and all are found in ant nests. They are fed by the ants, which in turn feed on a substance secreted by the beetles.

FRINGE-WINGED BEETLES   Family Clambidae   Not illus.

Identification: Broadly oval, convex. Capable of partially rolling into a ball. Hind coxae expanded. HW with a fringe of long hairs. Antennae clubbed. Tarsi 4-4-4. About 1 mm.

Most of our 9 species of clambids live in decaying vegetable matter; a few live in ant nests. They are at times fairly numerous, and occasionally fly in numbers at dusk.

ANTLIKE STONE BEETLES Family Scydmaenidae
Identification: Form characteristic: antlike, FW *oval*, head and pronotum *slender*, long-legged. FW shiny, with sparse pubescence. Antennae *slightly clubbed*. Brownish or reddish brown. 1–5 mm.

These beetles occur under bark, in tree holes, under logs, in decaying vegetation, in moss, under stones, and in ant and termite nests. Because of their secretive habits they are seldom observed, but they sometimes fly about in large numbers at twilight. Very little is known about the habits of the larvae.

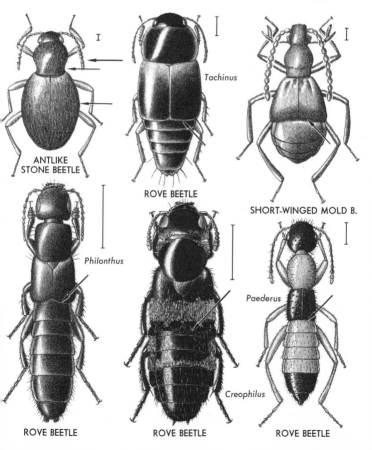

ANTLIKE STONE BEETLE

Tachinus

ROVE BEETLE

SHORT-WINGED MOLD B.

Philonthus

ROVE BEETLE

Creophilus

ROVE BEETLE

Paederus

ROVE BEETLE

FALSE CLOWN BEETLES Family Sphaeritidae   **Not illus.**
Identification: Oval, convex. Blackish, with a greenish or bluish luster. FW truncate, exposing last abdominal segment. Antennae clubbed. Similar to hister beetles (p. 156), but FW longer and antennae not elbowed. 4.5–5.5 mm.
The single N. American species occurs along the Pacific Coast (California to Alaska); lives under bark, in decaying fungi, moss, and dung, and is attracted to flowing sap.

MINUTE FUNGUS BEETLES Family Orthoperidae **Not illus.**
Identification: Body rounded or oval. Pronotum usually expanded anteriorly, shelflike, concealing head from above. Black or brownish. Antennae clubbed. HW fringed with hairs. 1 mm. or less.
This is a small group whose members usually occur under decaying bark, in or near rotting fungi, and in decaying vegetable matter. One fairly common species occurs on vegetation and flowers. Adults are predaceous, or feed on fungi.

MINUTE BOG BEETLES Family Sphaeriidae   **Not illus.**
Identification: Nearly spherical in shape, convex. Black, sometimes with light markings. Antennae with an abrupt 3-segmented club. Hind coxae large, touching. 0.5–0.75 mm.
This group is represented in the U.S. by 3 species that occur from Texas to California and Washington. These beetles live in mud or under stones near water, in moss, and among the roots of plants in boggy places.

Superfamily Cantharoidea

FW leathery and flexible. Moderate-sized, rather soft-bodied. Tarsi 5-5-5. Abdomen with 7 or 8 segments.

SOLDIER BEETLES Family Cantharidae   **See also Pl. 5**
Identification: Body *elongate, parallel-sided* or nearly so. Head *not concealed from above.* Soft-bodied. Black or brown, often with red, yellow, or orange; some predominantly yellow. 1–15 (mostly 5–15) mm.
Soldier beetles are common insects, usually found on flowers or foliage. Many feed on pollen and nectar. Species of *Chauliognathus* are common on goldenrod. Larvae live under bark or on the ground and feed on other insects.

LIGHTNINGBUGS or FIREFLIES   **See also Pl. 5**
Family Lampyridae
Identification: Similar to Cantharidae, but head *concealed from above* by pronotum, and last 2 or 3 abdominal segments often luminous. Usually brownish or blackish, frequently with yellow or orange. 5–20 mm.
Lampyrids are unique in that they can flash their lights on

and off; other luminescent insects glow continuously. They are common in spring and early summer and are conspicuous by their blinking lights. Species differ in rhythm of their flashes. Flashing is a recognition signal enabling the sexes to find each other. Some species lack light-producing organs. Larvae live on the ground, under bark, and in moist swampy places. They feed on various invertebrates, including snails.

NET-WINGED BEETLES Family Lycidae   **See also Pl. 5**
Identification: FW *reticulate, with longitudinal ridges* and less distinct cross ridges, and often broadest posteriorly. Soft-bodied. Head *concealed from above.* Usually yellow or reddish, with black markings. 5–18 mm.

Members of this small group are fairly common, and live on vegetation, flowers, and foliage of trees and shrubs, usually in wooded areas. Some large species are attractively colored. Adults feed on plant juices or on other insects. Larvae are predaceous and occur under bark.

GLOW-WORMS Family Phengodidae   **Not illus.**
Identification: ♂: broad, flat, soft-bodied; antennae plumose; FW short, pointed, HW extending beyond FW and covering abdomen; black or brownish, with red or yellow markings; 10–30 mm. ♀: resemble larvae but with compound eyes.

This is a small group of uncommon beetles. Males occur on foliage or beneath objects, and often fly to lights. Larvae and females are luminescent. Larvae are predaceous and live under bark or beneath objects on the ground.

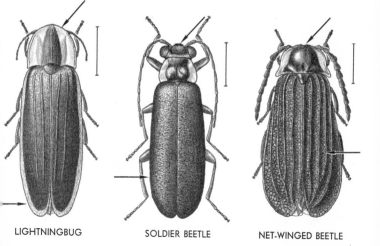

LIGHTNINGBUG   SOLDIER BEETLE   NET-WINGED BEETLE

Superfamily Cleroidea

Size small to moderate. Rather soft-bodied. Tarsi usually 5-5-5. Abdomen with 5 or 6 segments.

DERMESTID BEETLES Family Dermestidae   **See also Pl. 5**
  Identification: Elongate to broadly oval. Often covered with scales or *hair*. Black or brownish, sometimes patterned. Antennae *short, clubbed*, fitting in grooves below sides of pronotum. A median ocellus frequently present. 1–12 mm.
  The collector who fails to protect his collection with a repellant or fumigant will eventually find it infested with these beetles. Larvae feed on dried animal or plant materials and can completely ruin an insect collection; a pile of powdery material below a specimen is evidence of their activity. Dermestids feed on a great many things, including cereal products, grains, rugs and carpets, various stored foods, upholstery, fur coats, mounted birds or mammals, and museum specimens of plants and insects. Some species are destructive pests, and most of the damage is done by the larvae. Adults of some species occur on flowers, where they feed on pollen and nectar. Larvae are subcylindrical, brownish, and densely clothed with long hair.

SOFT-WINGED FLOWER BEETLES   **See also Pl. 5**
Families Malachiidae and Dasytidae
  Identification: FW *broadest posteriorly*. Body wedge-shaped, soft, often with erect hair. Antennae *serrate* or threadlike, basal segments sometimes enlarged. Black, dark blue, or green, often with orange, yellow, or red. 1.5–7.0 mm.
  Adults of these 2 families are fairly common on flowers and vegetation. Some feed on pollen, others are predaceous. Malachiidae differ from Dasytidae in having protrusible vesicles along the sides of the abdomen, and in bearing a lobe beneath each tarsal claw.

MINUTE TREE-FUNGUS BEETLES   Family Cisidae
  Identification: Elongate, cylindrical, head *concealed from above*. Brownish, body with erect pubescence. Tarsi 4-4-4, *1st 3 segments short*. Antennae with a 3-segmented club. Pronotum and/or head sometimes with a horn. 1–3 mm.
  Adults and larvae of this small family can be found in numbers in shelf fungi, under bark, and in wood. A few species occur in galleries of bark beetles (Scolytidae).

BARK-GNAWING BEETLES   Family Ostomidae
  Identification: Two body forms: either elongate-narrow, usually parallel-sided, head broad, pronotum and FW rather widely separated *at sides;* or oval or elliptical, head not broad, pronotum

and FW closely joined, margins of pronotum and FW broadly flattened. Tarsi 5-5-5, *1st segment very short*. Antennae *clubbed*, the club segments often extended laterally. Black, brown, blue, or metallic green. 6–20 mm.

Adults and larvae of this small family normally live under bark, in fungi, and in dry vegetable matter One species is common in granaries, where larvae and adults feed on other insects or on damaged grain.

CHECKERED BEETLES Family Cleridae   See also Pl. 5
Identification: Body *elongate-narrow*, with long erect pubescence.

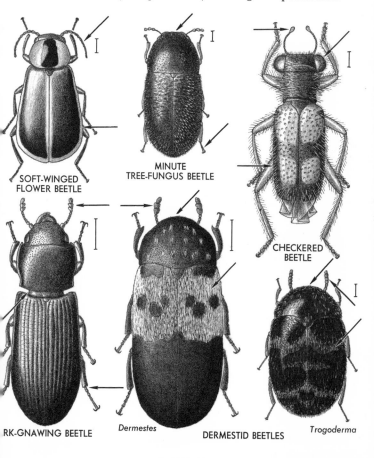

SOFT-WINGED FLOWER BEETLE

MINUTE TREE-FUNGUS BEETLE

CHECKERED BEETLE

RK-GNAWING BEETLE

Dermestes

DERMESTID BEETLES

Trogoderma

Pronotum narrower than FW, almost cylindrical. Head usually as wide as or *wider than pronotum*. Often marked with red, orange, yellow, or blue. Antennae variously *clubbed* or thread-like. 3–24 (mostly 3–10) mm.

Clerids are fairly common on trunks of dying or recently killed trees and on flowers and foliage. Most larvae and adults are predaceous on larvae of various wood-boring insects. Some species are beneficial in controlling bark beetles; they track down and devour bark beetle larvae in their burrows. Some adults and a few larvae are pollen feeders. One species, the Red-legged Ham Beetle, *Necrobia rufipes* (De Geer), is destructive to stored meats.

Superfamily Elateroidea

Prosternum often prolonged posteriorly into a lobe that fits into a depression in mesosternum. Abdomen usually 5-segmented. Tarsi 5-5-5. Mostly moderate-sized. Most beetles in this group are plant feeders and some are important pests.

SANDALID BEETLES Family Sandalidae
  Identification: Elongate-robust. FW nearly parallel-sided. Pronotum *tapers anteriorly*. Antennae *short, serrate*, pectinate, or flabellate. Mandibles large, prominent. First 4 tarsal segments each with 2 lobes beneath. Brownish to black. 16–24 mm.

The 5 N. American species of sandalids are usually found around elm and ash trees in spring or fall. They are excellent fliers. Larvae are parasites of cicada nymphs.

CEDAR BEETLES Family Rhipiceridae **Not illus.**
  Identification: Elongate-oval, black, similar to Sandalidae but smaller (11–15 mm.), tarsal segments not lobed, mandibles small, and antennae serrate.

The single N. American species in this family, *Zenoa picea* (Beauvois), occurs from Florida to Texas, where it is found under logs and bark. This insect is quite rare and little is known of the habits of either adults or larvae.

CLICK BEETLES Family Elateridae
  Identification: Shape distinctive: body elongate-narrow, somewhat flattened, usually parallel-sided, and rounded at each end or FW rather pointed at tip; posterior corners of pronotum *prolonged backward into sharp points*. Prosternum with an elongate lobe extending posteriorly into a mesosternal depression (this feature, plus a loose articulation of the prothorax, enables these beetles to "click"). Antennae usually *serrate*, sometimes threadlike or pectinate. Prosternum broadly lobed

anteriorly. Brown or black, sometimes lightly patterned. 3–45 mm.

Click beetles are named for their ability to click and jump. If one is turned onto its back, the head and prothorax are bent backward and then the body is suddenly straightened. This straightening produces an audible click and the beetle is propelled into the air. If it does not land right side up, the performance is continued until it does.

This is a large group, and many species are very common. Adults occur on foliage and flowers, under bark, or in rotting wood. Many apparently do not feed. Larvae (wireworms) are slender, shiny, and hard-bodied; they feed on plant or animal materials, and are found in rotten wood or soil. Some larvae are predaceous but most feed on roots or seeds. A few are very injurious to agricultural crops — they feed on newly planted seeds and the roots of various plants, including vegetables, cereals, and cotton. The Eyed Elater, *Alaus oculatus* (Linn.), is one of the largest (25–45 mm.) and most easily recognized species in this group; it has a salt-and-pepper color, and the pronotum bears 2 eyelike spots. The species of *Pyrophorus*, which occur in the southern states, are dark brown, 12–23 mm., and have 2 light spots at the rear corners of the pronotum that are luminous.

CEROPHYTID BEETLES Family Cerophytidae **Not illus.**
Identification: Elongate-robust. Hind trochanters enlarged, nearly as long as femora. Antennae pectinate in ♂ and serrate

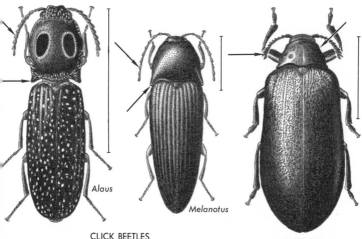

Alaus

Melanotus

CLICK BEETLES

SANDALID BEETLE

in ♀. Hind margin of prosternum with a rounded lobe. Black or brown. 7.5–8.5 mm.

Two very rare species of cerophytids occur in the U.S., one in the East and the other in California; they live under bark and in rotting wood.

CEBRIONID BEETLES   Family Cebrionidae
Identification: Body *elongate, broadest at base of FW*. Mandibles *large*, thin, projecting forward in front of head. Abdomen 6-segmented. Brownish, with long, dense, suberect pubescence. 15–25 mm.

Most of the 17 species of cebrionids in the U.S. occur in the Southwest. They are found under bark, on the ground, and beneath objects, and are nocturnal. Males are good fliers, with wasplike flight; females are wingless and live in the ground. Larvae live in or on the ground and feed on roots.

FALSE CLICK BEETLES   Family Eucnemidae
Identification: Similar to Elateridae (p. 166), but pronotum *somewhat stouter and more convex above*, anterior margin of prosternum straight across (not lobed), and prothorax more firmly attached to mesothorax, with little capacity for movement. Antennae serrate, pectinate, or flabellate, often fitting into prosternal grooves. Brown or black, sometimes with pale markings. 3–18 mm.

About 70 species of eucnemids occur in N. America, but they are infrequently collected. They are found on foliage, under bark, and in or on rotten wood (especially beech and maple). Adults quiver their antennae continuously (a habit not found in Elateridae). Larvae feed in rotting wood.

PEROTHOPID BEETLES   Family Perothopidae   **Not illus.**
Identification: Similar to Eucnemidae, but tarsal claws pectinate and prothorax loosely attached to mesothorax. Prosternum narrowly lobed anteriorly. Brownish. 10–18 mm.

Perothopids are rare beetles living on the trunks and branches of old beech trees. The 3 U.S. species occur from Pennsylvania to Florida and in California.

THROSCID BEETLES   Family Throscidae
Identification: Similar to Elateridae (p. 166), but body *more compact (broadest near base of FW)*, and prosternal lobe firmly attached to mesothorax and not movable. Antennae serrate or with *a loose 3-segmented club*. Brown or black, sometimes with pale markings. 2–5 mm.

Adults of this small family occur on flowers and vegetation but are not common. Larvae are found in worm-eaten wood, and are probably predaceous.

METALLIC WOOD-BORING BEETLES   See also Pl. 5
Family Buprestidae

Identification: Nearly always metallic or bronzed, especially on ventral surface. Dorsal surface frequently metallic, always shiny, usually lacking pubescence. Hard-bodied; body elongate-slender and parallel-sided to elongate-robust and even strongly oval. Antennae short, serrate or nearly threadlike, rarely pectinate. 3–40 (mostly 5–20) mm.

Buprestid larvae generally bore under bark, in wood, in roots of trees and shrubs, or in leaves, and attack living, dying, or dead plants; these larvae, often called flat-headed borers, are serious pests in orchards and on ornamental plants, and in logs

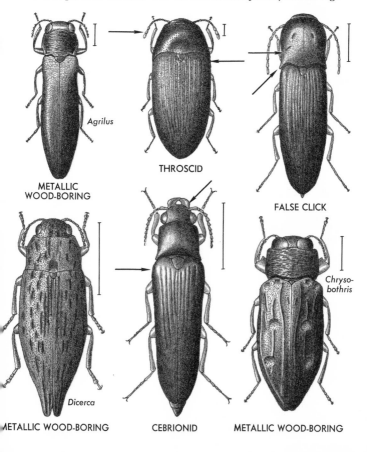

Agrilus

METALLIC
WOOD-BORING

THROSCID

FALSE CLICK

Dicerca

METALLIC WOOD-BORING

CEBRIONID

Chryso-bothris

METALLIC WOOD-BORING

cut for lumber. Many species are stem miners and some produce galls on certain plants. Adults feed on foliage and bark, or are attracted to flowers. They are frequently found basking in the sun on trunks and branches of dying or unhealthy trees. Many are quite wary and difficult to collect — they may run rapidly to evade the collector, or take flight if approached too closely. This group is a large one, and many species are common. Larvae of *Chrysobothris femorata* (Olivier) attack various trees and shrubs, and are frequently serious pests in orchards. Adults of the large genus *Agrilus* are elongate and slender; most are dark-colored and somewhat metallic; their larvae bore in stems and roots of trees and shrubs, including raspberries, black-berries, apple, and pear.

Superfamily Dascilloidea

Usually soft-bodied. Tarsi 5-segmented. Mostly small beetles, occurring on vegetation in moist areas.

SOFT-BODIED PLANT BEETLES   Family Dascillidae
   Identification: Tarsi with 2nd, 3rd, and 4th segments strongly lobed beneath or hind coxae greatly expanded. Antennae *serrate*. FW quite pubescent. 3–9 mm.
      The members of this small group are found on flowers and foliage in moist shady places, under bark, and in fungi, and are not common. Larvae live in the ground. Both adults and larvae are probably predaceous.

PTILODACTYLID BEETLES   Family Ptilodactylidae
   Identification: Antennae distinctive: *long, segments 4–10 bearing a long basal process*. Head nearly or quite concealed from above by pronotum. Scutellum *heart-shaped*, notched anteriorly. Yellowish brown. 4–6 mm.
      Only 6 species of ptilodactylids occur in N. America. They are found on vegetation in moist shady places. Larvae live in decaying logs and leaf mold, or are aquatic.

MARSH BEETLES   Family Helodidae
   Identification: Body oval to nearly spherical. Pronotum appears abbreviated, sometimes expanded anteriorly and shelflike, *conceals head*. Tarsi with 4th segment lobed beneath. Hind femora sometimes thickened. Black or brown, sometimes with orange or red markings. 2–4 mm.
      Marsh beetles are found on vegetation in swampy places or along lakes and streams. Some live in rotten stumps or tree holes. Species with enlarged hind femora are active jumpers and resemble flea beetles; they differ from flea beetles in having the tarsi distinctly 5-segmented (apparently 4-segmented in flea beetles). Larvae are aquatic and occur in both stagnant and

flowing water; some live in the water in tree holes or in wet decaying material. The larvae have very long, many-segmented antennae.

Superfamily Dryopoidea

Small (1–8 mm.). Legs frequently long, with strong claws; 5th tarsal segment usually very long. These beetles are aquatic, semi-aquatic, or occur in mud and on foliage beside streams.

MINUTE MUD-LOVING BEETLES   Not illus.
Family Georyssidae
    Identification: Shape distinctive: in dorsal view resembles small snout beetle without the snout, the head concealed from above by pronotum. Antennae clubbed. Body surface roughened, without pubescence. 1.5–3.0 mm.
    This group includes 2 rare species that live in muddy or sandy shores of streams, where they conceal themselves with a coating of mud. One species occurs in Nebraska, the other in Idaho and California.

MINUTE MARSH-LOVING BEETLES   Not illus.
Family Limnichidae
    Identification: Small (1–2 mm.) oval beetles similar to Dryopidae (p. 172), but middle coxae widely separated and hind coxae touching or nearly so. Antennae 10-segmented, short, most segments broader than long. Densely pubescent, golden or gray.
    Adults and larvae of this small family live in the wet sand or

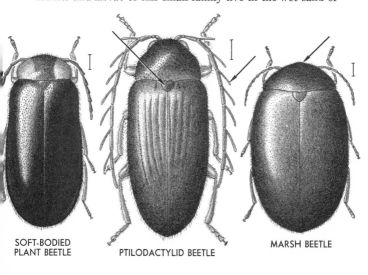

SOFT-BODIED
PLANT BEETLE   PTILODACTYLID BEETLE   MARSH BEETLE

soil along the margins of streams, or are aquatic. Their habits are not well known.

LONG-TOED WATER BEETLES   Family Dryopidae

Identification: Body oval or elongate-oval. Legs very long, strongly developed, claws *large*. Antennae *short*, most segments broader than long, usually concealed. Pubescence dense, low-lying, or absent. Front coxae transverse. Black, brown or dull gray. 1–8 mm.

These beetles are usually found on partly submerged sticks and stones in moving water or riffle areas of streams. They hang on firmly with their stout claws or creep slowly over the surface but do not swim. If a stick or stone is removed from the water and placed in the sun to dry, these beetles will be seen to move and can be captured — they are very difficult to see unless they move. Some adults are terrestrial and plant-feeding. Larvae are aquatic.

WATER-PENNY BEETLES   Family Psephenidae

Identification: *Oval*, flattened, black or brownish. FW broadest posteriorly, loosely covering abdomen. Dorsal surface sparsely pubescent, ventral surface densely pubescent. Abdomen with 5–7 ventral segments. 4–6 mm.

Water-penny beetles occur on vegetation along streams and on partly submerged rocks in riffles. Larvae are found on the underside of stones in rapidly flowing water; they are brownish, greatly flattened, and nearly circular, hence the common name of the group. Adults and larvae are plant feeders.

RIFFLE BEETLES   Family Elmidae

Identification: Form distinctive: body *oval* to cylindrical, legs long, strongly developed, claws *large*. Black to grayish. Antennae short or moderate in length, clubbed or threadlike. 1–8 mm.

Most riffle beetles occur on stones, logs, and other debris in flowing water; a few are terrestrial. The aquatic species spend most of their lives under water. Larvae are aquatic; some are long and slender, but others are flat and oval and resemble larvae of water-penny beetles.

VARIEGATED MUD-LOVING BEETLES
Family Heteroceridae

Identification: Shape and color distinctive: body elongate-robust; black or brownish, FW often with *undulating yellowish bands or spots;* densely pubescent. Front and middle tibiae flattened, *outer margin spiny.* Tarsi *4-4-4.* Mandibles of ♂ *extended forward,* flattened. Antennae short, serrate. 4.0–6.5 mm.

Members of this small family live in galleries in muddy or sandy shores of streams and lakes. They may be driven from their burrows by flooding the shore with water. They often fly to lights at night. Larvae are found in the same habitat as adults, and are very active.

Superfamily Byrrhoidea

Size small to moderate (1.0–9.5 mm.). Oval, convex, or more or less pill-shaped. Uncommon to rare beetles.

PILL BEETLES Family Byrrhidae
Identification: *Shape distinctive:* body oval, strongly convex, pill-shaped, the head deflexed and nearly or quite concealed from above. Tibiae usually flattened, often with spines. Tarsi 4-4-4 or 5-5-5. 1.2–10.0 mm.

Pill beetles are found beneath logs and objects on the ground,

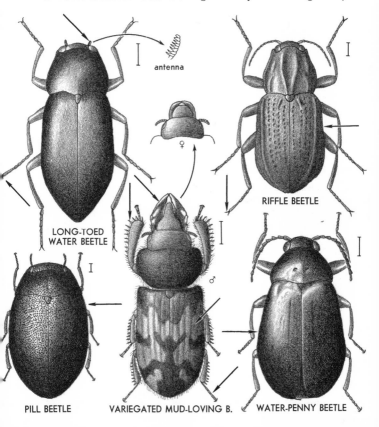

antenna

♀

RIFFLE BEETLE

LONG-TOED WATER BEETLE

♂

PILL BEETLE   VARIEGATED MUD-LOVING B.   WATER-PENNY BEETLE

often in sandy places or associated with mosses. Larvae live in moist soil and sand, in moss, and under objects. Adults and larvae are plant feeders.

WOUNDED-TREE BEETLES   Not illus.
Family Nosodendridae
   Identification: Similar to Byrrhidae (p. 173), but head visible dorsally and FW with rows of short hair tufts. Body oval, convex, black. Antennae with a 3-segmented club. Tibiae broad, with spines. Tarsi 5-5-5. 5–6 mm.
   Only 2 species of nosodendrids occur in the U.S., 1 from the Northeast west to Kansas, the other in California; both are quite rare. They are found under bark or in the wounds of trees, where they probably feed on fly larvae. Larvae live in hollow stumps and tree holes.

CHELONARIID BEETLES   Family Chelonariidae   **Not illus.**
   Identification: Elongate-oval. Head withdrawn into prothorax and concealed from above; strongly contractile. FW black, with patches of dense white pubescence. Pronotum reddish. Antennae threadlike. Tarsi 5-5-5. 5–7 mm.
   This family contains a single rare species, *Chelonarium lecontei* Thomson, which occurs in N. Carolina and Florida. Adults are found on foliage, and larvae are aquatic.

Superfamily Cucujoidea

This superfamily serves as a sort of dumping ground for families that cannot be placed elsewhere. The included families have little in common, in either morphology or habits.

TOOTH-NECKED FUNGUS BEETLES   Family Derodontidae
   Identification: Form of pronotum often distinctive: *lateral margins strongly toothed* or broadly flattened and bent upward. Brownish, often mottled. Head with a pair of ocelli. Antennae with *an elongate 3-segmented club.* FW with rows of punctures. Tarsi 5-5-5 or 4-4-4. 3–6 mm.
   The 6 N. American species of derodontids are relatively rare. They occur in shelf fungi, under the bark of willow and tulip trees, and in slime molds. When located, they are sometimes found in large numbers.

SMALL FLATTENED BARK BEETLES   Not illus.
Family Monotomidae
   Identification: Form distinctive: elongate, flattened, slender, parallel-sided. FW truncate, exposing tip of abdomen. Antennae with a club of 1 or 2 segments. Front coxae globular. 1.5–3.0 mm.
   Members of this group usually occur under bark. They are generally very infrequently collected, but may sometimes be

taken in large numbers in molasses traps set in dense woods. Very little is known of the habits of either adults or larvae.

SILKEN FUNGUS BEETLES Family Cryptophagidae
Identification: Usually light yellowish brown, sometimes brown or black, the body nearly always with fine silky pubescence. FW rounded, *broadest near middle.* Pronotum narrower, rounded laterally and broadest near middle; sides of pronotum often toothed or notched. Antennal club *3-segmented.* Tarsi usually 5-5-5, 5-5-4 in some males. 1–5 mm.

Silken fungus beetles are found on flowers and foliage, in fungi and decaying vegetable matter. Some species live in nests of wasps or bumble bees. The group is fair-sized, with more than 160 N. American species.

LIZARD BEETLES Family Languriidae   See also Pl. 6
Identification: Shape distinctive: *very elongate-slender, parallel-sided,* the FW, pronotum, and head nearly equal in width. Shining black or blue-black, the *pronotum* and sometimes also the head and FW *reddish, orange, or yellow.* Antennal club *4-segmented.* Tarsi 5-5-5. 5–10 mm.

Lizard beetles are common on flowers, leaves, and stems of various plants. Larvae are stem borers, and some are of economic importance. The Clover Stem Borer (Pl. 6), *Languria mozardi* Latreille, often causes considerable damage to clover.

ROOT-EATING BEETLES Family Rhizophagidae Not illus.
Identification: Similar to Monotomidae (p. 174), but with front coxae transverse. FW short, truncate, exposing tip of abdomen. 2–5 mm.

Adults and larvae of these beetles are usually found in rotten,

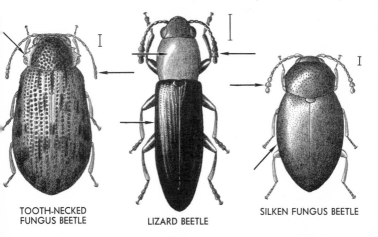

TOOTH-NECKED
FUNGUS BEETLE

LIZARD BEETLE

SILKEN FUNGUS BEETLE

fungus-infested wood. They are predaceous on wood-boring insects and live in the tunnels of these insects. A few species live in ant nests.

DRY-FUNGUS BEETLES Family Sphindidae **Not illus.**
Identification: Broadly cylindrical, pronotum broad and distinctly convex, head not or only barely visible dorsally. Brownish to black; pubescence sparse, short, suberect. Antennal club 3-segmented. Tarsi 5-5-4. 1.5–3.0 mm.

Sphindids are found in dry fungi and in debris from decaying logs and stumps. They are often difficult to see because of their small size and protective coloration. The 6 U.S. species are relatively rare.

MURMIDIID BEETLES Family Murmidiidae **Not illus.**
Identification: Small, oval, somewhat flattened. Antennae clubbed, club usually received in cavity of prothorax. Coxae widely separated. Legs retractile. Tarsi 4-4-4. 1st abdominal segment considerably longer than others. 1–2 mm.

The 5 N. American species are relatively rare, and little is known of their habits; they are probably predaceous.

MONOMMID BEETLES Family Monommidae **Not illus.**
Identification: Shape distinctive: elongate-oval, convex dorsally, flat ventrally. Appendages retractile. Black to brownish. Antennal club 2- or 3-segmented, fitting into grooves on underside of prothorax. Tarsi 5-5-4. 5–12 mm.

Monommids occur on foliage, under rotten wood, and in debris. Our 5 species are in the South, from Florida to s. California. They are not common. Larvae live under rotten wood or bore in the roots of agave.

PLEASING FUNGUS BEETLES **See also Pl. 6**
Family Erotylidae
Identification: *Elongate to broadly oval.* Black, shiny, lacking pubescence, often marked with red, orange, or yellow. Antennal club *3-segmented.* Tarsi 5-5-5, 4th segment often small. 3–20 mm.

Erotylids are usually found on fungi or in rotten wood; some are fairly common. Adults hibernate under bark, often in groups. Larvae occur in fleshy fungi or in decaying wood; some feed in fungus-infested stored products. Some erotylids are attractively patterned with red or orange and black.

FLAT BARK BEETLES Family Cucujidae **See also Pl. 6**
Identification: Body often greatly flattened; *elongate, usually narrow, parallel-sided.* Brown, black, or reddish. Antennae threadlike, sometimes clubbed. Tarsi 5-5-5, sometimes appearing 5-5-4. 2.0–13.5 mm.

Most cucujids can be recognized by their greatly flattened body; a few are not so flattened. They are common under loose bark and in dry or decaying plant material, and some are pests of stored grain. Most are predaceous on mites or small insects. A few feed on stored products.

SAP BEETLES Family Nitidulidae   **See also Pl. 6**
Identification: Antennal club *abrupt, 3-segmented.* Shape variable, usually elongate, robust, sometimes broadly oval; rarely long and slender with short FW. Abdomen often exposed beyond FW. Black or brown, often marked with red or yellow. Tarsi 5-5-5 or 4-4-4. 1.5–12.0 mm.

Many nitidulids are common on decaying fruits, fermenting plant juices, and in fungi; some occur on flowers, some are found in nests of bees and ants, a few breed in carrion, and a few are

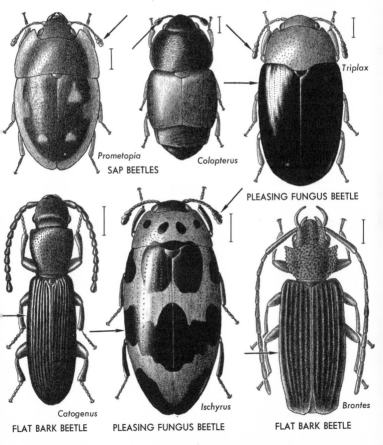

Prometopia
SAP BEETLES

Colopterus

Triplax
PLEASING FUNGUS BEETLE

Catogenus
FLAT BARK BEETLE

Ischyrus
PLEASING FUNGUS BEETLE

Brontes
FLAT BARK BEETLE

predaceous on scolytids or scale insects (pp. 204, 137). Species of *Conotelus* (found in flowers of morning glory) resemble rove beetles but have clubbed antennae. Larval habits are similar to those of adults.

FLAT GRAIN BEETLES Family Silvanidae
Identification: *Elongate, rather flattened.* Antennal club *3-segmented*, 3rd segment shorter than 2nd. Tarsi 5-5-5, never lobed. 1–5 mm.

Some silvanids occur under bark, others in stored plant materials (fruit, grain, meal, and flour). The most important grain-infesting species is the Saw-toothed Grain Beetle, *Oryzaephilus surinamensis* (Linn.), named for the teeth along margins of the pronotum.

SHINING FLOWER BEETLES Family Phalacridae
Identification: *Broadly oval to nearly spherical,* dorsal surface very convex. Black or brownish, shining. Antennal club *3-segmented.* Tarsi 5-5-5, 4th segment small. 1–3 mm.

These beetles are common on the flowers and foliage of various plants, especially goldenrod and other composites. Larvae feed in the heads of these flowers.

MONOEDID BEETLES Family Monoedidae   **Not illus.**
Identification: Reddish yellow, antennae and scutellum black, and 5 long black marks on each FW. FW parallel-sided, a little wider than pronotum. Tarsi 4-4-4, 1st segment broad, flat, oval, 2nd and 3rd minute, 4th large and long with stout claws. Antennal club 1-segmented. 2 mm.

A single rare species is found in s. Florida, where it occurs on a species of milkweed that grows near wet hammocks along the coast.

MINUTE BROWN SCAVENGER BEETLES
Family Lathridiidae
Identification: Shape distinctive: FW *oval, widest at middle,* pronotum and head progressively narrower, pronotum often nearly circular from above. FW with distinct rows of punctures. Antennal club 2- or *3-segmented,* loose. Brown or black. Tarsi *slender, 3-3-3,* 2-3-3, or 2-2-3. *1–3 mm.*

These beetles are fairly common and are usually associated with moldy material. Both adults and larvae occur in rotting vegetation, woodpiles, mammal nests, and sometimes on flowers; they are also found in warehouses, but are thought to feed on fungus and mold and not on stored products.

FRUITWORM BEETLES Family Byturidae
Identification: *Elongate-robust, FW parallel-sided.* Light brown to dark orange, with dense yellowish or grayish hairs. Antennal club *3-segmented.* Tarsi 5-5-5. 3.5–8.0 mm.

Adults of the eastern species are common on flowers and

foliage. Larvae feed on fruits of raspberry, blackberry, and related plants. Larvae of *Byturus unicolor* Say, the Raspberry Fruitworm, often seriously damage the fruit of raspberry. One western species has been reared from oak galls; adults of this species occur on oak foliage There are 5 species of byturids in the U.S.

MYCETAEID FUNGUS BEETLES Family Mycetaeidae
Identification: Shape distinctive: FW *oval, widest at middle*, margins of pronotum S-shaped and *extending forward, partly enclosing head*. Tarsi *4-4-4*. Black or brown, often with red or orange markings. Shiny, not pubescent. Pronotum often with 2 grooves at base. Antennal club *3-segmented*. 1–4 mm.

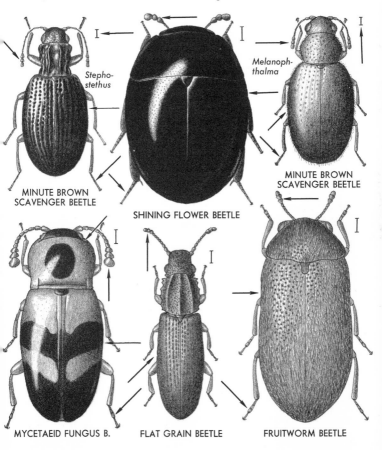

Stepho-
stethus

MINUTE BROWN
SCAVENGER BEETLE

SHINING FLOWER BEETLE

Melanoph-
thalma

MINUTE BROWN
SCAVENGER BEETLE

MYCETAEID FUNGUS B.   FLAT GRAIN BEETLE   FRUITWORM BEETLE

Members of this small family are found in decaying materials and on flowers, and are not common. One species occurs in granaries, where it feeds on fungus or mold, and may become a pest by spreading mold through the grain.

HANDSOME FUNGUS BEETLES See also Pl. 6
Family Endomychidae

Identification: Similar to Mycetaeidae (p. 179), but 3rd tarsal segment very small, the tarsi *appearing 3-segmented*. Forward angles of pronotum *prolonged*, partly enclosing head. Shining black or brown, often with red or orange markings. Antennal club *3-segmented*. 3.5–10.0 mm.

Members of this usually uncommon group occur in fungi, under bark, beneath logs, and in rotting wood. They are smooth, shiny, attractively colored, and resemble ladybird beetles. When disturbed they often draw in their appendages and play dead. Larvae occur in the same situations as adults and feed on fungi or rotten wood.

LADYBIRD BEETLES Family Coccinellidae See also Pl. 6
Identification: Shape often *distinctive:* broadly oval *to nearly spherical*, strongly convex dorsally, nearly flat ventrally. Tarsi *apparently 3-3-3, actually 4-4-4* (3rd segment minute). Head partly or completely concealed by pronotum. Often brightly colored — yellow, orange, or reddish with black markings or black with yellow to reddish markings. Antennae *short, club 3- to 6-segmented*. 0.8–10.0 mm.

This is a large group with many abundant and well-known species. Both adults and larvae of most species are predaceous on aphids, scale insects, mites, and other injurious forms, and are often quite numerous where these pests occur. Some species have been used commercially to combat scale insects injurious in orchards. Adults frequently overwinter in groups, sometimes in tremendous numbers. Adults of the Two-spotted Ladybird Beetle (Pl. 6), *Adalia bipunctata* (Linn.), often overwinter indoors, and may be seen at windows in fall or spring. Two species of *Epilachna* are plant feeders, both as larvae and adults, and are serious garden pests: the Mexican Bean Beetle, *E. varivestis* Mulsant, is yellowish, with 8 small dark spots on each elytron (front wing); the Squash Beetle, *E. borealis* (Fabricius), is yellowish, with 7 large dark spots on each elytron.

CYLINDRICAL BARK BEETLES Not illus.
Family Colydiidae

Identification: Usually slender and elongate to very elongate, narrow, parallel-sided, rarely oval and flattened. Antennal club 2- or 3-segmented. Black or brown. Pronotum often with ridges or grooves. Tarsi usually 4-4-4, rarely 3-3-3. 1–18 (mostly 1–8) mm.

Many colydiids are predaceous on wood-boring insects and are found under bark and in infested wood. Some are plant feeders and live in shelf fungi, vegetable detritus, or in ant nests. Larvae of a few species are ectoparasites of wood-boring larvae; such parasitic habits are rare among beetles. Few of the 102 N. American species are common.

ANTLIKE FLOWER BEETLES   Family Anthicidae
Identification: Shape distinctive: body antlike, FW elongate-oval, pronotum *distinctly narrower*, often rounded, head oval. Pronotum often with a hornlike process extending forward over head. Antennae threadlike, beadlike, or clubbed. Abdomen 5-segmented. Usually black or brown, often with red or yellow. Tarsi *5-5-4*. 2–12 mm.

These beetles are common on flowers and foliage as well as on the ground. Many species possess a distinctive hornlike process on the pronotum. Larvae feed chiefly on vegetable detritus; at least 1 species is predaceous. This group is of moderate size, with 188 N. American species.

ANTLIKE LEAF BEETLES   Family Euglenidae   **Not illus.**
Identification: Similar to Anthicidae, but abdomen 4-segmented and eyes notched. Black to reddish yellow. Hind femora or antennae often modified. 1.5–3.0 mm.

These beetles are principally eastern in distribution and are found on foliage or flowers. They are not common and their habits are poorly known.

HAIRY FUNGUS BEETLES   **Not illus.**
Family Mycetophagidae
Identification: Elongate-oblong, hairy or pubescent. Black or

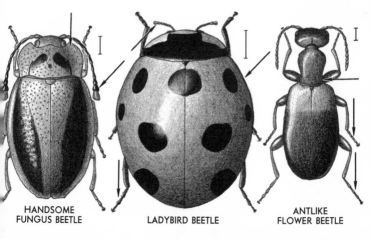

HANDSOME
FUNGUS BEETLE   LADYBIRD BEETLE   ANTLIKE
                                                            FLOWER BEETLE

brownish, FW often with orange or reddish. Antennal club 2- to 5-segmented. Tarsi usually 3-4-4 or 4-4-4. 1.5–6.0 mm.

These feed on fungi and are found under fungus-covered bark, in shelf fungi, and in moldy vegetable materials. A few feed on pine pollen.

FALSE LONGHORN BEETLES   Not illus.
Family Cephaloidae
   Identification: Elongate, slender, somewhat cylindrical. Similar to Cerambycidae (p. 196), but with tarsi 5-5-4. Tarsal claws pectinate, with a fleshy lobe beneath each claw. Yellowish to brown or black. 8–20 mm.
   This is a small, relatively rare group (10 N. American species). The habits are not well known, but adults are usually found on flowers and vegetation in wooded areas.

FALSE BLISTER BEETLES   Family Oedemeridae
   Identification: Slender, elongate, soft-bodied, similar to Meloidae (p. 184) or Cerambycidae (p. 196). Tarsi *5-5-4*, next to last tarsal segment wide and densely hairy beneath. Pronotum *broadened anteriorly*, much narrower at base than FW; rounded laterally. Often with yellow, red, or orange. 5–20 mm.
   Adults of this group occur on flowers and foliage, and fly to lights at night. They are not common. Adults feed on pollen and nectar, and larvae feed in moist decaying wood, especially conifers and driftwood.

FALSE TIGER BEETLES   Family Othniidae   Not illus.
   Identification: Somewhat similar to tiger beetles (p. 151), but antennae with a 3-segmented club and tarsi 5-5-4. Brownish, FW often mottled. 5–9 mm.
   Othniids occur on foliage, under bark, on cacti, and in rotting leaves. They are probably predaceous. One species has been reported from Virginia and 4 others from the western states; all are rare.

AEGIALITID BEETLES   Family Aegialitidae   Not illus.
   Identification: Subcylindrical, long-legged, black. Tarsi 5-5-4, last tarsal segment longer than others combined. FW meet imperfectly, exposing tip of abdomen. All coxae widely separated. 3–4 mm.
   These insects spend their entire life in rock cracks along the seacoast, below the high tidemark. The 3 N. American species occur along the Pacific Coast from California to Alaska and are very rare.

NARROW-WAISTED BARK BEETLES   Not illus.
Family Salpingidae
   Identification: Elongate to oval. Pronotum usually narrowed basally (hence the common name) and rounded or faintly mar-

gined laterally. Brownish to dull black. Tarsi 5-5-4. Antennae serrate or slightly clubbed. 2–15 mm.

Adults of this group occur on vegetation, in detritus, under the bark of conifers, and under stones. Some species have the head prolonged anteriorly into a snout. Adults and larvae are predaceous.

PEDILID BEETLES   Family Pedilidae

Identification: Similar to Anthicidae (p. 181), but body more elongate, head *narrowed behind eyes into a neck*. Pronotum oval or rounded. Black or brown, often with pale or red markings. Antennae long, threadlike or serrate. 4.5–15.0 mm.

Adult pedilids usually occur on flowers and foliage, and are attracted to lights at night. They are uncommon. Larvae live in decaying vegetable material, sometimes on the shores of streams, ponds, lakes, or the seashore. Most of our 57 species are western.

FIRE-COLORED BEETLES   See also Pl. 6
Family Pyrochroidae

Identification: Shape and color distinctive: elongate, narrow, elytra (FW) parallel-sided or slightly wider posteriorly, pronotum oval or somewhat square and much narrower than FW, head broad, as wide as pronotum; usually black, pronotum and sometimes head reddish or yellowish, or entire body reddish or yellowish; antennae serrate or *pectinate*, in some males nearly plumose. Tarsi *5-5-4.* 6–20 mm.

Adults of this small group are found on flowers and vegetation, are are not common. Larvae occur under the bark of logs and stumps, and are predaceous.

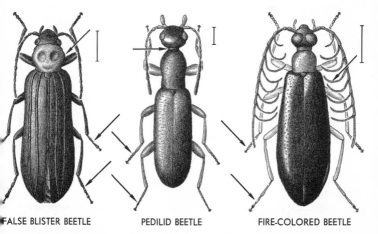

FALSE BLISTER BEETLE   PEDILID BEETLE   FIRE-COLORED BEETLE

HEMIPEPLID BEETLES Family Hemipeplidae **Not illus.**
Identification: Very elongate, slender, parallel-sided, distinctly flattened. Yellow to yellowish brown. 8–12 mm. Similar to Cucujidae (p. 176) but 3rd tarsal segment lobed and front coxal cavities closed behind.

This family is represented in the U.S. by 2 species, found in Florida, Georgia, and California. They are not common.

Superfamily Melooidea

Tarsi 5-5-4. Usually moderate-sized and soft-bodied.

BLISTER BEETLES Family Meloidae **See also Pl. 6**
Identification: Shape distinctive: usually elongate, slender (a few are oval or round), pronotum *narrower than FW*, head *broad, usually wider than pronotum.* Body soft, often leathery. FW loosely covering abdomen, rarely shortened. Antennae thread-like or beadlike, intermediate segments sometimes modified. Legs long, slender. Black or brown, sometimes brightly colored, often with light pubescence. 3–20 (usually 10–15) mm.

Blister beetles are common insects occurring on the flowers and foliage of various plants. The name "blister" beetles is based on the fact that the body contains cantharidin, a substance capable of blistering the skin. This chemical is extracted from the body of certain species and used medicinally. Adult blister beetles are plant feeders, and some are serious pests of potatoes, tomatoes, beets, clover, and other plants. They may completely defoliate a plant. Larvae are parasitic and generally beneficial; they usually feed on grasshopper eggs, but some feed on eggs or larvae of bees. Larvae that parasitize bees climb onto flowers and attach themselves to bees visiting the flowers. The bees then carry these larvae to their nest, where the larvae attack the bee eggs. Meloid larvae undergo hypermetamorphosis (in which the various larval instars are quite different in form): the 1st instar is long-legged and active, whereas following instars are grublike or maggotlike. Members of the genus *Meloe*, which are rather large and black or bluish, have very short, overlapping front wings (elytra); they are called oil beetles because they exude an oily substance from the joints of the legs when disturbed; this substance can raise blisters on one's skin.

WEDGE-SHAPED BEETLES Family Rhipiphoridae
Identification: Elongate, humpbacked, wedge-shaped, similar to Mordellidae but abdomen *blunt,* not pointed. Antennae *pectinate* or flabellate in ♂, serrate in ♀. FW entire or *short,* pointed. Usually black and orange. 4–15 mm.

Adults generally occur on flowers but are not common. Larvae are parasitic on wasps, bees, and cockroaches; they undergo hypermetamorphosis (see p. 41). Some females are larviform.

Superfamily Mordelloidea

Unique in shape, and in behavior when captured.

TUMBLING FLOWER BEETLES Family Mordellidae
Identification: Humpbacked, wedge-shaped. Head *bent down, situated ventrally*. Abdomen *pointed* and extending beyond FW. Usually blackish or gray, sometimes with light markings; generally pubescent. Antennae short, threadlike, serrate, or clubbed. Tarsi 5-5-4. 1.5–15.0 (usually 3–7) mm.

Mordellids are common on flowers and foliage, and when captured tumble about in a comical fashion. They are often difficult to catch, since they run rapidly or take flight when

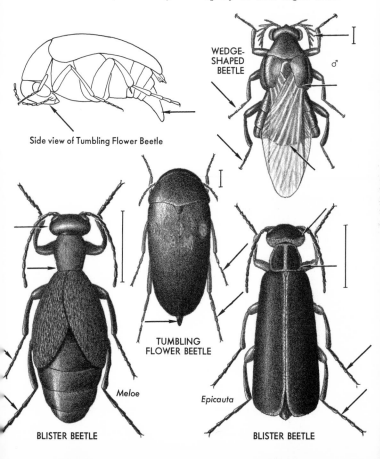

Side view of Tumbling Flower Beetle

WEDGE-SHAPED BEETLE ♂

TUMBLING FLOWER BEETLE

BLISTER BEETLE *Meloe*

Epicauta BLISTER BEETLE

alarmed. Larvae occur in rotten wood and plant pith; some are leaf and stem miners, and a few are predaceous.

Superfamily Tenebrionoidea

Tarsi 5-5-4. Front coxal cavities closed behind (except in Melandryidae). Mostly moderate in size.

DARKLING BEETLES   Family Tenebrionidae

Identification: Antennae usually 11-segmented, *threadlike, beadlike, or slightly clubbed.* Eyes nearly always notched. Tarsal claws simple. Generally dull black or brown, sometimes with red. 2–35 mm. A varied group usually recognizable by 5-5-4 tarsi, form of eyes, and antennae.

This is a large group whose members are common in a variety of habitats — under bark, in rotten wood, under logs, in fungi, on the ground in desert areas, and in termite and ant nests. Some are pests of stored products. Both adults and larvae are scavengers, feeding on decaying vegetation, fungi, seeds, and other types of organic materials; a few attack living plants.

Darkling beetles are variable in body form and often resemble beetles in other families. Members of the genus *Diaperis,* which inhabit fungi, are similar in appearance and coloration to ladybird beetles. Many species rather closely resemble ground beetles, though they are usually not as shiny. Some fungusinhabiting tenebrionids have the dorsal surface hard and warty. A species of this type is the Forked Fungus Beetle, *Bolitotherus cornutus* (Panzer), which is 10–12 mm. and common in woody bracket fungi; the pronotum of the male bears 2 hornlike protuberances.

A few are destructive to stored grain and flour. Members of the genus *Tenebrio* (black or dark brown and 13–17 mm.) are pests of stored grain; their larvae are called mealworms. Beetles in the genus *Tribolium* are brown and about 5 mm.; they are pests of flour and other stored products and are known as flour beetles.

Members of the genus *Eleodes* run about with the abdomen raised at an angle of about 45 degrees. They emit a foul-smelling black fluid when disturbed. About 100 species of *Eleodes* occur in the western states.

Darkling beetles are widely distributed but are most abundant in the western states; of the approximately 1400 N. American species, only about 150 occur in the East.

LONG-JOINTED BARK BEETLES   Family Lagriidae

Identification: Shape and antennae distinctive: *elongate, narrow,* FW widest apically, pronotum *narrower than FW,* head about as wide as pronotum; antennae threadlike, *last segment elongate.* Dark-colored, often slightly metallic. 6–15 mm.

These beetles occur on flowers, foliage, or under bark, and are generally uncommon. Larvae feed in decaying vegetation, in rotten wood, or under bark.

COMB-CLAWED BEETLES Family Alleculidae
Identification: Tarsal claws *pectinate*. Elongate-robust to elongate-narrow. Brownish to black, with silky pubescence. Antennae usually threadlike or serrate, rarely pectinate. 5–15 mm.

These beetles are common on flowers, under bark, and on vegetation, and probably feed on pollen. Larvae live under

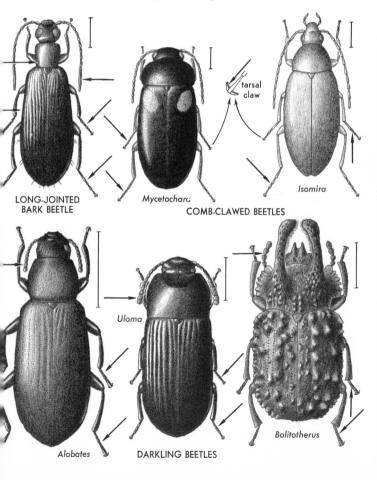

tarsal claw

LONG-JOINTED BARK BEETLE

Mycetochara

COMB-CLAWED BEETLES

Isomira

Uloma

Bolitotherus

Alobates

DARKLING BEETLES

bark, in rotting wood, in fungi, or in vegetable detritus and are
similar in appearance to wireworms.

FALSE DARKLING BEETLES Family Melandryidae
  Identification: *Elongate-oval.* Nearly always dark-colored.
Pronotum usually with *2 dents at base.* Front coxal cavities
open behind. 1st segment of hind tarsi *longer than any other
segment.* Antennae generally threadlike. 3–20 mm.
  Adults and larvae are found under bark, in dry wood, or in
dry fungi; some adults are found on flowers and foliage. Larvae
are carnivorous or plant-feeding. The most common eastern
melandryids (genus *Penthe*) are elongate-oval, black with black
pubescence, and 10–14 mm.

Superfamily Bostrichoidea

Tarsi *5-5-5.* Pronotum usually extending over and partly or
completely concealing head from above. Generally small.

SPIDER BEETLES Family Ptinidae
  Identification: Shape distinctive: spiderlike, FW elongate-oval,
pronotum *narrower than FW* and nearly or completely concealing head from above, legs long and slender. FW usually
dull and with erect pubescence, sometimes shiny and not
pubescent. Reddish brown to black. Antennae *long, threadlike.*
1–5 mm.
  Adults and larvae of this small family are found in various
dried animal and plant materials, such as animal carcasses,
animal droppings, dry wood, stored products, and in museum
specimens of plants and animals. Some species live in ant nests.
Spider beetles are not common.

DEATH-WATCH BEETLES Family Anobiidae
  Identification: Pronotum *hoodlike, usually enclosing head* and
concealing it from above. Antennae nearly always with last
3 segments *lengthened and expanded,* or simply lengthened, sometimes serrate or *pectinate,* rarely threadlike. Shape variable,
usually elongate and cylindrical, sometimes oval to nearly
spherical. Appendages often contractile. Hind coxae grooved
for reception of femora. Light brown to black. 1.1–9.0 mm.
  Nearly all anobiids feed exclusively on plant materials as
larvae and adults. Many bore into seasoned wood; some are
found indoors after having emerged from furniture, woodwork,
flooring, or timbers. Some species produce a ticking sound in
their burrows. Superstitious people, thinking this a portent of
death, have called these insects "death-watch" beetles. Some
live under bark, others in fungi, and some in seeds and galls.
Two species, the Drugstore Beetle, *Stegobium paniceum* (Linn.),
and the Tobacco Beetle, *Lasioderma serricorne* (Fabricius), are

serious pests of stored products. Both feed on a wide variety of materials of plant and animal origin, and are among the very few anobiids that feed on materials of animal origin.

Most anobiids are infrequently collected. The greatest number and variety, at least in the East, can be taken by sweeping or beating foliage in wooded areas where the overhead canopy is dense. Examine the catch closely or you will overlook them, since many draw in the appendages and play dead when disturbed.

BRANCH and TWIG BORERS Family Bostrichidae
Identification: Form distinctive: broadly to narrowly cylindrical, head bent down and appearing on ventral surface of prothorax, *nearly* or completely *concealed from above;* pronotum usually tuberculate or with *rasplike teeth anteriorly,* not hoodlike

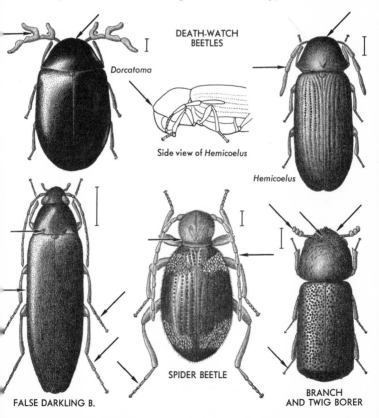

DEATH-WATCH BEETLES

Dorcatoma

Side view of *Hemicoelus*

Hemicoelus

FALSE DARKLING B.

SPIDER BEETLE

BRANCH AND TWIG BORER

or enclosing head. Antennal club *3-* or *4-segmented*, loose. 2–20 mm. (1 western species to 2 in.).

Bostrichids are wood borers, and attack living trees, dead twigs and branches, or dry seasoned timber. The adults of one unusual western species bore into the lead sheathing of telephone cables, allowing moisture to enter the cable and causing a short circuit; this insect, *Scobicia declivis* (LeConte), is called the Short-circuit Beetle (normally lives in wood and does not feed when it bores into cables). The giant of this family is the Palm Borer, *Dinapate wrighti* Horn, which occurs in California; it is about 2 in. long.

PSOID BEETLES Family Psoidae
Identification: Similar to Bostrichidae (p. 189), but head not bent down, *visible dorsally*. Mandibles large and strong. 6–28 mm.

These beetles occur in the West, where they bore into the heartwood or branches of various trees and shrubs. Some severely prune trees and are very destructive to orchards in Oregon and California.

POWDER-POST BEETLES Family Lyctidae
Identification: Form distinctive: *narrow, elongate*, flattened, head *visible dorsally*. Antennal club *2-segmented*, abrupt. Reddish brown to black. 1–7 mm.

The common name refers to their habit of boring into seasoned wood and reducing it to powder. Lyctids are very destructive to dried wood and wood products of various kinds, including woodwork, timbers, tool handles, gunstocks, and other manufactured materials.

Superfamily Scarabaeoidea

Terminal antennal segments extended laterally into a club of various types, usually lamellate, sometimes flabellate. Tarsi 5-5-5. Mostly moderate-sized to large.

STAG BEETLES Family Lucanidae
Identification: Elongate-robust. Antennae *elbowed*, club *3-* or *4-segmented*, segments of club not capable of being held together in a tight ball. Black to reddish brown. Mandibles of ♂ *very large*, sometimes branched. Pronotum without a median groove. FW usually smooth. 8–40 mm.

Most adult stag beetles feed on sap flows; larvae live in decaying logs and stumps and apparently feed on juices of rotting wood (larva of 1 species feeds in sod). The greatly developed, sometimes branched mandibles of the males of a few species give these beetles their common name. Adults of most species are

found on the ground in woods, others on sandy beaches. Adults
of a large reddish-brown eastern species frequently fly to lights
at night.

BESSBUGS Family Passalidae
Identification: Elongate-robust, parallel-sided, black and shiny.
Head with *a forward-directed horn.* Pronotum with a distinct
median groove, FW with *longitudinal grooves.* Antennae *not
elbowed,* segments of club *not capable of being held together in a
tight ball.* Pronotum and FW *distinctly separated at sides.*
30–40 mm.

Only 1 of the 3 U.S. species of bessbugs, *Popilius disjunctus*

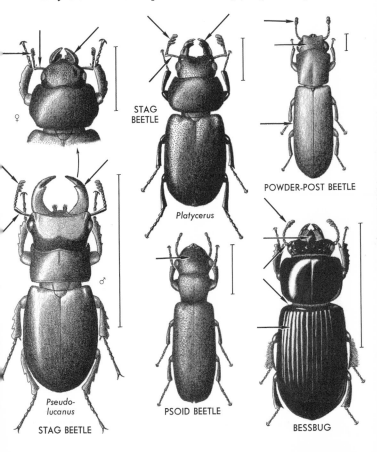

STAG BEETLE

Platycerus

POWDER-POST BEETLE

*Pseudo-
lucanus*

STAG BEETLE

PSOID BEETLE

BESSBUG

(Illiger), occurs in the East; the other 2 occur in s. Texas. The eastern species forms colonies in well-decayed logs and stumps and is fairly common. Both adults and larvae stridulate; the sounds produced probably serve as a means of communication. Bessbugs have a number of common names, including patent-leather beetles, betsy-beetles, and horned passalus beetles. Despite their size and strong mandibles, the passalids do not bite.

SCARAB BEETLES Family Scarabaeidae   **See also Pl. 7**
Identification: Oval or elongate, usually stout and heavy-bodied, varying greatly in form and size. Antennae 8- to 11-segmented, lamellate (rarely flabellate), segments of club *capable of being held tight together*. 2–50 mm.

This is one of the largest families of beetles, with nearly 1300 N. American species. Many are very important because of damage done by larvae or adults. There are 14 subfamilies in N. America, of which only the most important are discussed here.

Dung Beetles and Tumblebugs, Subfamily Scarabaeinae (see also Pl. 7). Hind legs situated closer to tip of abdomen than to middle legs; hind tibiae usually with *only 1 apical spur*. These beetles occur in or near dung, manure, and carrion. Tumblebugs (*Canthon* and *Deltochilum*) are dull black (some are green), about 20 mm. or less, without horns, and the hind tibiae are rather slender; a pair will form a mass of dung into a ball, roll the ball a distance, dig a hole, and bury it; then the female lays eggs in it. Males of some dung beetles (like *Phanaeus*) bear horns on both head and pronotum, or on either.

Aphodian Dung Beetles, Subfamily Aphodiinae. Members of this group have the hind legs closer to tip of the abdomen than to middle legs, and hind tibiae bear 2 apical spurs. They are usually smaller and more elongate than Scarabaeinae. Aphodiines are quite common in cow dung. Adults are generally black, sometimes with the front wings red or yellowish.

Earth-boring Dung Beetles, Subfamily Geotrupinae (not illus.). The body is very stout, convex, and shiny, and the antennae are 11-segmented. Adults and larvae are found in cow dung, horse manure, carrion, fungi, and under logs. The most common species (*Geotrupes*) are 14–20 mm. and black (often with a purplish luster) or brownish.

Subfamily Acanthocerinae (not illus.). Black, round, 5–6 mm., the middle and hind tibiae dilated and spiny. These beetles can bend head and prothorax downward and roll themselves into a ball. The 3 U.S. species, which are not common, occur from the eastern states to Texas. They are found under bark and in rotting logs and stumps.

Skin Beetles, Subfamily Troginae. These beetles are dull brownish, the dorsal surface is roughened or *tuberculate*, and the 2nd antennal segment rises before tip of the 1st. They are usually found in dry animal carcasses, where they feed on hide, fur, feathers, and dried tissues on the bones. They draw in their legs and play dead when disturbed, and because they are usually covered with debris are easily overlooked. Beneficial scavengers, they represent one of the last stages in the succession of organisms feeding on animal carcasses.

June or May Beetles, Chafers, and Others, Subfamily Melolonthinae. In this and the remaining subfamilies of scarabs the hind legs are situated at about midbody, closer to the middle legs than to tip of the abdomen. Melolonthines have the clypeus expanded laterally, usually concealing the mandibles

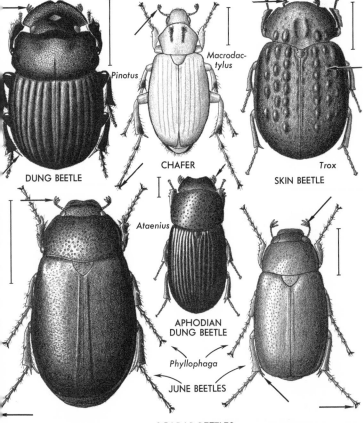

Pinotus

Macrodactylus

CHAFER

Trox

DUNG BEETLE

SKIN BEETLE

Ataenius

APHODIAN
DUNG BEETLE

Phyllophaga

JUNE BEETLES

SCARAB BEETLES

and labrum, and the tarsal claws are of *equal size and usually toothed or bifid*. The best-known members of this group are probably the June beetles, or Junebugs, which are common at lights in early summer. There are over 100 N. American species, most belonging to the genus *Phyllophaga*. June beetle larvae are white grubs that feed in the soil on roots of grasses and other plants; when abundant they cause serious damage to lawns, pastures, and various crops. Adults feed on flowers and foliage of various trees and shrubs and are capable of completely defoliating them.

Shining Leaf Chafers, Subfamily Rutelinae (see also Pl. 7). These beetles have tarsal claws, at least on hind legs, of *unequal size*, and there are 2 apical spurs on the hind tibiae. Adults are foliage and fruit feeders, and larvae usually feed on plant roots. One of the most serious pests in this group is the Japanese Beetle (Pl. 7), *Popillia japonica* Newman, accidentally introduced into the e. U.S. about 1916. It has since spread over much of the country and severely damages lawns, golf courses, pastures, shrubbery, and fruits. Larvae feed in the soil on roots of various plants; adults feed on foliage, fruits, and flowers of more than 200 kinds of plants.

Rhinoceros Beetles, Hercules Beetles, and Elephant Beetles, Subfamily Dynastinae. These beetles have tarsal claws *simple* (and usually equal in size), front coxae transverse, and the dorsal surface is more or less convex; males of many species bear horns on the head and/or pronotum. Many are 1 in. or more long, and a few are over 2 in. The group contains some of the largest N. American beetles. The largest eastern species is the Eastern Hercules Beetle (also called Unicorn Beetle), *Dynastes tityus* (Linn.), which is 2–2½ in. and greenish gray mottled or blotched with black; it is common in the Southeast, and ranges as far north as s. Ohio and Indiana. The Rhinoceros Beetle, *Xyloryctes jamaicensis* (Drury), is dark brown and slightly over 1 in.; males have a large horn on the head (females have only a small tubercle); it occurs in the East. A few small and widely distributed members of this group, without horns on either head or pronotum (such as *Ligyrus*), occasionally damage crops.

Flower Beetles and Others, Subfamily Cetoniinae (see also Pl. 7). These have tarsal claws simple and equal in size, front coxae conical, and the body flattened dorsally; the lateral margins of the elytra (FW) are often *narrowed behind the front corners*, and there are no horns. Our species are small to moderate-sized, but some African species (Goliath beetles) reach a length of 4 or 5 in. Adults of most species are pollen feeders, found on flowers; some feed on the juices of decaying wood and are found under bark. Larvae occur in the soil and often damage roots. Adults of the Green June Beetle, *Cotinis nitida* (Linn.), a dark green beetle about 1 in., feed on grapes, ripening fruit, foliage, and young corn; larvae, which have the habit of crawling on their back, feed in the soil on plant roots. This beetle is common in the southeastern states. Some of the smaller flower beetles (like *Trichiotinus*, 9–12 mm., and *Valgus*, 7.5 mm. or less) have the elytra truncate and not much longer than wide. Members of the genus *Cremastocheilus* (9–15 mm.) occur in ant nests.

Superfamily Cerambycoidea

Tarsi *apparently 4-4-4*, *actually 5-5-5* (4th segment very small and concealed in bilobed 3rd segment). These are plant feeders. Many of great economic importance.

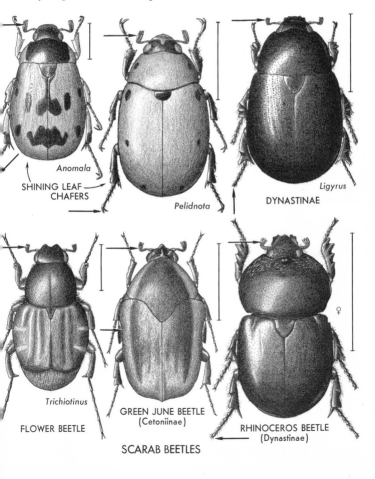

Anomala

SHINING LEAF CHAFERS

Pelidnota

Ligyrus

DYNASTINAE

Trichiotinus

FLOWER BEETLE

GREEN JUNE BEETLE
(Cetoniinae)

RHINOCEROS BEETLE
(Dynastinae)

SCARAB BEETLES

Plate 1

DAMSELFLIES AND DRAGONFLIES (Odonata)

At rest, damselflies hold their wings together above the body or diverging; dragonflies hold them horizontal.

NARROW-WINGED DAMSELFLIES, Family Coenagrionidae   p. 74
Wings *stalked at base* and held together above body at rest; 2 antenodal cross veins; M_3 rises behind nodus.
CIVIL BLUET, *Enallagma civile* (Hagen); N. America.
VIOLET DANCER, *Argia violacea* (Hagen); ne. U.S.
COMMON FORKTAIL, *Ischnura verticalis* (Say), ♀; e. N. America.

BROAD-WINGED DAMSELFLIES, Family Calopterygidae   p. 74
Wings *gradually narrowed at base* and held together above body at rest; wings usually with blackish or reddish areas; 10 or more antenodal cross veins.
BLACK-WINGED DAMSELFLY, *Calopteryx maculata* (Beauvais), ♂; e. N. America.

COMMON SKIMMERS, Family Libellulidae   p. 72
Dragonflies *without* a brace vein; anal loop in HW elongate, with a bisector, and usually *foot-shaped;* hind margin of compound eyes straight or nearly so.
ELISA SKIMMER, *Celithemis elisa* (Hagen); e. N. America.
COMMON AMBERWING, *Perithemis tenera* (Say), ♂; e. N. America.

DARNERS, Family Aeshnidae   p. 70
Dragonflies *with a brace vein*, and with compound eyes *in contact* for a considerable distance on dorsal side of head; ♀ with ovipositor well developed.
GREEN DARNER, *Anax junius* (Drury); N. America.
EASTERN BLUE DARNER, *Aeshna verticalis* Hagen; ne. U.S.

CLUBTAILS, Family Gomphidae   p. 70
Dragonflies *with a brace vein*, and with compound eyes *separated;* terminal abdominal segments sometimes *dilated;* ♀ without an ovipositor.
Gomphus vastus Walsh; e. U.S.

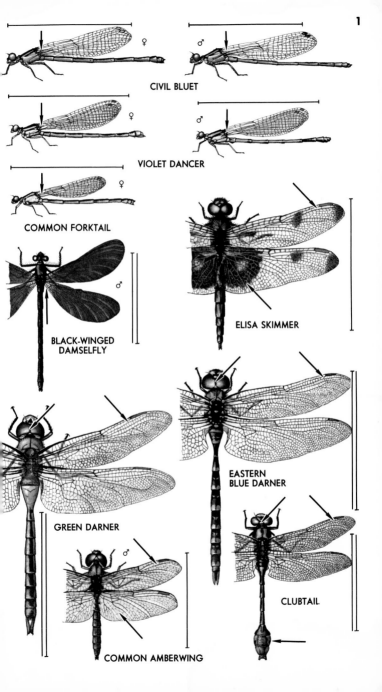

CIVIL BLUET

VIOLET DANCER

COMMON FORKTAIL

BLACK-WINGED
DAMSELFLY

ELISA SKIMMER

GREEN DARNER

EASTERN
BLUE DARNER

COMMON AMBERWING

CLUBTAIL

Plate 2

GRASSHOPPERS, CRICKETS, AND COCKROACHES
(Orthoptera)

Usually large insects; hind legs often (grasshoppers and crickets) enlarged; FW narrow, HW broad and at rest folded fanwise.

LONG-HORNED GRASSHOPPERS, Family Tettigoniidae   p. 80
Antennae *long and hairlike;* tarsi *4-segmented;* ovipositor sword-shaped.
BUSH KATYDIDS, Subfamily Phaneropterinae   p. 80
Usually green and over 1 in.; FW flat, shorter than HW; prosternal spines absent; vertex rounded.
Scudderia curvicauda (De Geer), ♂; e. N. America.
MEADOW GRASSHOPPERS, Subfamily Conocephalinae p. 82
Slender, greenish, seldom over 1 in.; prosternum usually with a pair of small spines; vertex short.
Conocephalus brevipennis (Scudder), ♂; e. N. America.

SHORT-HORNED GRASSHOPPERS, Family Acrididae   p. 78
Antennae relatively *short;* tarsi *3-segmented;* pronotum not prolonged backward over abdomen; wings usually well developed.
SPUR-THROATED GRASSHOPPERS,   p. 78
Subfamily Cyrtacanthacridinae
A spine or tubercle on prosternum.
Schistocerca americana (Drury); e. N. America.
BAND-WINGED GRASSHOPPERS,   p. 78
Subfamily Oedipodinae
HW usually *brightly colored;* a median longitudinal *keel on pronotum;* hind margin of pronotum *triangularly extended backward;* face vertical or nearly so.
Dissosteira pictipennis Brunner; Calif. to s. Oregon.

CRICKETS, Family Gryllidae   p. 82
Body somewhat flattened; antennae *long and hairlike;* tarsi *3-segmented;* ovipositor usually long and cylindrical.
BUSH CRICKETS, Subfamily Trigonidiinae   p. 84
2nd tarsal segment heart-shaped and flattened dorsoventrally; no teeth between tibial spines; ovipositor sword-shaped.
Phyllopalpus pulchellus (Uhler); N.Y. to Illinois and Florida.

COCKROACHES, Family Blattidae   p. 86
Body flattened and oval, head *concealed from above* by pronotum; antennae *long, hairlike;* tarsi *5-segmented.*
ORIENTAL COCKROACH, *Blatta orientalis* Linn.; N. America (introduced).

group, and many are common. One of the best known is the Locust Borer (Pl. 7), *Megacyllene robiniae* (Forster); adult about 20 mm. and black, with narrow transverse and oblique yellow bands. It is common on goldenrod in fall, and larvae are serious pests of living black locust.

Superfamily Chrysomeloidea

Tarsi as in Cerambycoidea (*apparently 4-4-4, actually 5-5-5*, 4th segment small and concealed). All of these beetles are plant feeders. Many are serious pests.

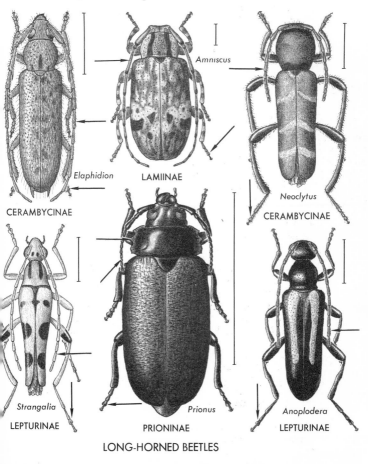

Amniscus

Elaphidion   LAMIINAE

CERAMBYCINAE

Neoclytus

CERAMBYCINAE

Strangalia   Prionus   Anoplodera

LEPTURINAE   PRIONINAE   LEPTURINAE

LONG-HORNED BEETLES

LEAF BEETLES Family Chrysomelidae **See also Pl. 8**
Identification: Antennae nearly always *less than half as long as body*. 1–20 mm., rarely over 12 mm. Body generally oval. Eyes usually not notched. Similar to Cerambycidae and Bruchidae; see pp. 196 and 200 for differences.

This is a very large family (nearly 1400 N. American species), and many species are quite common. Adults occur on flowers and foliage; larvae feed on foliage and roots. Many are serious pests of cultivated plants and a few act as vectors of plant diseases. Numerous subfamilies are recognized, but only the most important are discussed here.

Tortoise Beetles, Subfamily Cassidinae (see also Pl. 8). *Broadly oval* or nearly circular, often with body expanded and flattened, resembling a tiny turtle; the head is largely or *completely concealed from above*. Larvae are oval, flat, spiny, and bear a forked process at posterior end of the body to which are attached cast skins, excrement, and debris; this process is held over the body much like a parasol. A few tortoise beetles resemble ladybird beetles; they differ in the segmentation of tarsi (*apparently 4-4-4* in tortoise beetles, 3-3-3 in ladybirds). Some are very brilliantly colored in life with golden or silvery markings, but these colors often fade after death.

Leaf-mining Leaf Beetles, Subfamily Hispinae (see also Pl. 8). These are 4–7 mm., usually brownish, and the elytra (FW) *bear ridges* between which are rows of punctures; they are parallel-sided or slightly widened apically, and the pronotum is narrower than base of the elytra. Most larvae are leaf miners. One common species, the Locust Leaf Miner, *Xenochalepus dorsalis* (Thunberg), is a serious pest of black locust.

Case-bearing Leaf Beetles, Subfamilies Clytrinae, Cryptocephalinae (see also Pl. 8), and Chlamisinae. Members of these groups are small (usually 6 mm. or less), broadly cylindrical, with head buried in prothorax *nearly to eyes*, and last dorsal abdominal segment (pygidium) not covered by elytra. Clytrinae have smooth elytra, but serrate or pectinate antennae; Cryptocephalinae have smooth elytra, and antennae are *thread-like* or slightly clubbed; Chlamisinae have elytra tuberculate. These beetles are dark-colored, often with red, yellow, or orange markings. They play dead when disturbed. Larvae construct portable cases.

Subfamily Galerucinae. These beetles resemble the Criocerinae (p. 200), but are relatively soft-bodied, the pronotum is usually *margined laterally*, and the head is not narrowed posteriorly into a neck. The Spotted Cucumber Beetle, *Diabrotica undecimpunctata howardi* Barber, and the Striped Cucumber Beetle, *Acalymma vittatum* (Fabricius), feed on cucurbits and other plants. They damage plants by their feeding and act as vectors of cucurbit wilt.

Subfamily Eumolpinae (see also Pl. 8). These beetles are *oval* and convex. They resemble Chrysomelinae (p. 200), but differ in having front coxae rounded and 3rd tarsal segment *bilobed beneath*. Many are metallic or yellow and spotted. The Dogbane Beetle (Pl. 8), *Chrysochus auratus* (Fabricius), is very attractive — iridescent blue-green with a coppery tinge, 8–10 mm., occurs on dogbane and milkweed.

Long-horned Leaf Beetles, Subfamily Donaciinae. The donaciines are elongate, with *long antennae*, and resemble some

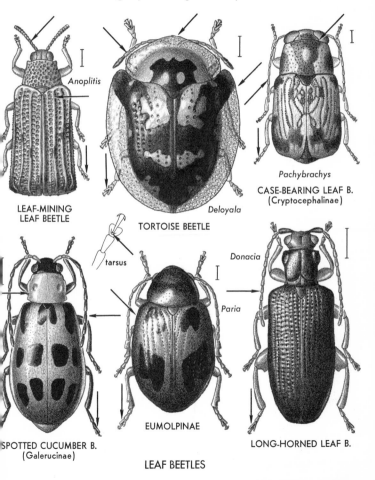

Anoplitis

Deloyala

Pachybrachys

CASE-BEARING LEAF B.
(Cryptocephalinae)

LEAF-MINING
LEAF BEETLE

TORTOISE BEETLE

tarsus

Donacia

Paria

SPOTTED CUCUMBER B.
(Galerucinae)

EUMOLPINAE

LONG-HORNED LEAF B.

LEAF BEETLES

of the cerambycids. They are mostly black or brown, usually with a metallic luster, and range from 5.5 to 12.0 mm. Larvae feed in submerged parts of aquatic plants; adults are found on flowers and foliage of water lilies and other aquatic plants, and are active, fast-flying, often difficult to capture.

Flea Beetles, Subfamily Alticinae. Flea beetles are mostly 2–5 mm., black or bluish (sometimes with light markings) and with *enlarged* hind femora; antennae are close together at the base and front coxae are usually conical. The common name refers to their jumping habits. Some flea beetles are important pests of various cultivated plants; larvae feed in roots of the host plant and adults feed on the leaves. Adult feeding produces holes in the leaves. A heavily infested plant looks as if tiny shot had been fired into the leaves.

Subfamily Criocerinae (see also Pl. 8). These have the pronotum rounded (its base narrower than base of FW, or elytra), the punctures of the elytra are in rows, and the head is prominent and narrowed posteriorly. The group is small, but contains some important crop pests: *Crioceris* (2 species) attacks asparagus, *Lema trilineata* (Olivier) attacks potatoes, and *Oulema melanopus* (Linn.), the Cereal Leaf Beetle, attacks grains.

Subfamily Chrysomelinae (see also Pl. 8). Most members of this group are *oval to nearly circular*, very convex, often brightly colored, and have the head sunk in the prothorax almost to the eyes; antennae are widely separated at base, and pronotum is margined laterally. Most species feed on various weeds and are of little economic importance. The best-known and most important species is the Colorado Potato Beetle, *Leptinotarsa decemlineata* (Say), a serious pest of potatoes; it is large, orange-yellow, and has longitudinal black stripes on the elytra.

SEED BEETLES Family Bruchidae

Identification: Shape distinctive: body oval or egg-shaped, broadest posteriorly; head concealed from above, prolonged into a short broad snout. Antennae *clubbed* or serrate, sometimes pectinate. Black or brown, often mottled or marked with patches of whitish or brownish pubescence. Elytra (FW) short, *exposing tip of abdomen*. 1–10 mm. Similar to Chrysomelidae (p. 198), although differing in body shape and in having a snout.

Seed beetles are usually found on foliage, or in stored peas, beans, or other seeds; larvae of most species feed inside seeds, and some seriously damage beans or peas. The Bean Weevil, *Acanthoscelides obtectus* (Say), attacks beans in storage or in the field and may completely destroy them; in a heavy infestation, as many as a dozen beetles may develop in a single bean. The Pea Weevil, *Bruchus pisorum* (Linn.), attacks peas in the field; larvae consume the central portion of the pea.

Superfamily Curculionoidea

Head prolonged into a more or less distinct snout. Tarsi 5-5-5, usually apparently 4-4-4.

PRIMITIVE WEEVILS Family Brentidae
  Identification: FW *elongate and parallel-sided.* Prothorax pear-shaped. Head with *a long or short straight beak.* Femora stout, toothed. Antennae threadlike or *beadlike.* Dark brown to blackish. FW with orange marks. 7–30 mm.

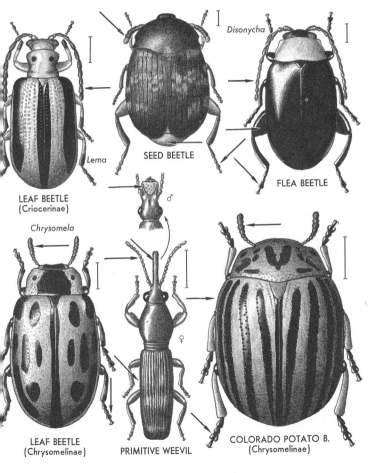

Disonycha

Lema

SEED BEETLE

FLEA BEETLE

LEAF BEETLE
(Criocerinae)

Chrysomela

♂

♀

LEAF BEETLE
(Chrysomelinae)

PRIMITIVE WEEVIL

COLORADO POTATO B.
(Chrysomelinae)

Adults of this group are found under bark and in worm-eaten wood, where they feed on fungi, the sap from tree wounds, or wood-eating insects. Larvae are wood borers.

FUNGUS WEEVILS Family Anthribidae
Identification: Robust, elongate to oval. Usually brownish and often mottled with patches of white, gray, straw-colored, brown, or black pubescence. Beak short, broad. Antennae *clubbed*, not elbowed. Pronotum often with sharp lateral margins posteriorly. 1–11 mm.

Adult anthribids are usually found on dead twigs and branches, under bark, or on fungi (generally woody fungi), and are not common. Most are good fliers and some jump. Larvae live in plant materials on which adults are found. The eastern species most often encountered is *Euparius marmoreus* (Olivier), which is 3.5–8.5 mm. and brown mottled with patches of white, black, ashy, and brown pubescence. Adults and larvae are found on polypore fungi.

SNOUT BEETLES Family Curculionidae   **See also Pl. 8**
Identification: Snout usually *well developed*. Antennae *clubbed and nearly always elbowed*. Palps small and rigid, often concealed within mouth. Labrum absent. 1–35 mm.

This is one of the largest families of insects (over 2500 N. American species), and its members are common. Practically all are plant feeders; large numbers are serious pests of cultivated plants. Many snout beetles chew holes in fruits, nuts, and other parts of the plant. Adults often bear pubescence or scales, and frequently play dead when disturbed. From N. America 42 subfamilies are recognized, only a few of which can be mentioned here.

Subfamily Cyladinae (Pl. 8). Antlike, 5–6 mm. Pronotum reddish, FW blue-black. Antennae not elbowed, last segment long, swollen. Our only representative of this group is the Sweetpotato Weevil (Pl. 8), *Cylas formicarius elegantulus* (Summers), a pest of sweet potatoes occurring in the South.

Subfamily Apioninae. Black or gray. 1.0–4.5 mm. Somewhat pear-shaped. Antennae *not elbowed*. Trochanters elongate. Larvae bore in seeds, stems, and other parts of various plants (chiefly legumes); adults usually occur on foliage.

Subfamily Baridinae (not illus.). Part of thoracic pleura (mesepimera) visible from above between prothorax and FW. This is the largest subfamily of snout beetles (about 500 N. American species). Several are important pests.

Broad-nosed Weevils, chiefly Subfamilies Leptopiinae, Brachyrhininae, and Thylacitinae (see also Pl. 8). Beak *short, quadrate*, often widened apically, usually with 1 or more longitudinal grooves. Mandibles large, with a small cusp that breaks off and leaves a scar. Antennal scrobe (groove in beak into which basal antennal segment fits) only vaguely defined. Most species are flightless because the elytra are grown together or the hind wings are reduced. White-fringed beetles (*Graphognathus*, Thylacitinae) are important pests in the Southeast, where they feed on many cultivated plants; they reproduce parthenogenetically, and no males are known.

Acorn and Nut Weevils, Subfamily Curculioninae. Snout *slender and very long*, as long as body or longer. Femora with a stout triangular tooth. Eyes often partly covered by prothorax.

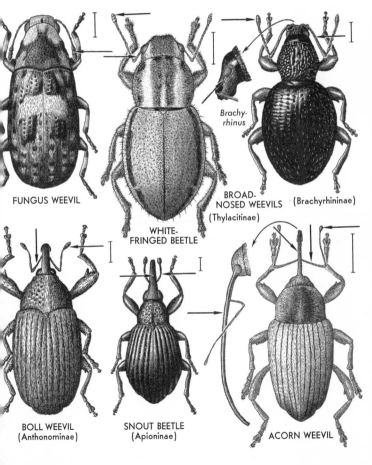

FUNGUS WEEVIL

WHITE-FRINGED BEETLE
(Thylacitinae)

Brachy-rhinus

BROAD-NOSED WEEVILS   (Brachyrhininae)

BOLL WEEVIL
(Anthonominae)

SNOUT BEETLE
(Apioninae)

ACORN WEEVIL

FW with narrow scales. Larvae develop in the fruit of various nut-producing trees.

Subfamily Anthonominae (see also p. 203). Antennae *elbowed and clubbed*, rising near apex of snout, the basal segment fitting into a well-defined scrobe (groove in beak into which basal antennal segment fits). Front coxae contiguous, located in about middle of prothorax. Snout *fairly long*, not fitting into a prosternal groove at rest. An important pest in this group is the Boll Weevil (illus., p. 203), *Anthonomus grandis* Boheman (about 5 mm., yellowish brown), which does much damage to cotton; adults feed on the seedpod (boll) and lay eggs in the feeding hole; larvae feed inside the bolls and eventually destroy them. This is a large subfamily, with about 200 N. American species.

Subfamily Cryptorhynchinae. Beak at rest fits into a groove in prosternum. Antennae *elbowed and clubbed*. Eyes oval and partly covered by prothorax when beak is in prosternal groove. FW usually wider than prothorax, giving the insect *a broad-shouldered appearance*. The Plum Curculio, *Conotrachelus nenuphar* (Herbst), is a common species and a serious pest of stone fruits; injury results from both adult and larval feeding.

Billbugs and Grain Weevils, Subfamily Rhynchophorinae. Antennae rise *near eyes,* the *basal segment* not fitting into the short scrobe (groove) and *extending past posterior margin of eye.* 6 antennal segments between basal segment and club; 1st segment of antennal club *enlarged and shining.* Pygidium (last dorsal abdominal segment) usually exposed. Members of this group are 3–31 mm. Some of our largest snout beetles belong to the group. Billbugs are large snout beetles that feed on grasses; larvae bore in stems and adults feed on foliage. Grain weevils (*Sitophilus*) are brownish and 3–4 mm.; they attack stored grain and are often serious pests.

PINHOLE BORERS   Family Platypodidae

Identification: *Very elongate-slender, parallel-sided.* Brownish. Tarsi long, slender, *1st segment long.* Head visible dorsally, as wide as or slightly wider than pronotum. 2–8 mm.

Pinhole borers attack trees, and their burrows extend deep into the heartwood; adults and larvae feed on a fungus in the burrows. These beetles usually attack weakened or unhealthy trees, and often bore into felled logs. Adults occasionally fly to lights. The group is small, with only 7 species in N. America.

BARK or ENGRAVER BEETLES and AMBROSIA BEETLES
Family Scolytidae

Identification: Elongate, cylindrical. Head visible dorsally or concealed, narrower than pronotum. Tarsi short, 1st segment not elongate. Antennae elbowed and *clubbed*. Brownish to black. 1–9 (mostly 1–3) mm.

Nearly all scolytids bore into bark or wood, both as larvae and as adults. Adults spend most of their lives in their burrows, leaving them only long enough to find a new host. Bark or engraver beetles burrow just under the bark; ambrosia beetles burrow into the heartwood and feed on fungi in the galleries. Bark beetles are very common and usually attack weakened, dying, dead, or recently cut trees; some attack living trees and since they often kill the tree are very serious pests, particularly in the West.

Bark, or engraver, beetles excavate patterns (galleries) under the bark, each species making a characteristic pattern. The adults

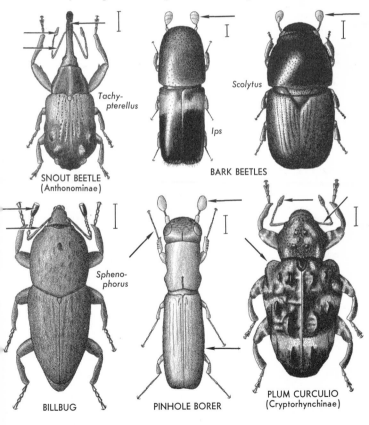

SNOUT BEETLE
(Anthonominae)

Tachy-pterellus

Ips

Scolytus

BARK BEETLES

BILLBUG

Spheno-phorus

PINHOLE BORER

PLUM CURCULIO
(Cryptorhynchinae)

come in first and excavate 1 or more brood galleries, along the sides of which they lay their eggs; when the larvae hatch they bore away from the brood gallery, their galleries increasing in size as they tunnel, thus forming the typical pattern under the bark. Each species attacks a particular species of tree (or 1 of several related species). The galleries permit the entrance of fungi, which often rot the bark. The Elm Bark Beetle, *Scolytus multistriatus* (Marsham), is the chief vector of Dutch elm disease — a disease that has killed thousands of elms in the e. U.S.

Twisted-winged Parasites:
Order Strepsiptera

Identification: *Minute* insects, 0.5–4.0 mm., the sexes quite different. ♂: blackish; FW *reduced to short clublike structures*, HW *large and fanlike*, with a few weak radiating veins; eyes bulging; antennae 4- to 7-segmented, *some segments with a long lateral process;* tarsi *2- to 5-segmented;* mouth parts chewing but usually reduced. ♀: wingless; usually lacking legs and antennae; mouth parts generally vestigial. Metamorphosis complete, with hypermetamorphosis (see p. 41).

Similar orders: Male strepsipterans are somewhat beetlelike, but can be recognized by the characteristic wings and antennae. Females are generally saclike and without appendages, and must usually be recognized by their location in a host insect.

Immature stages and habits: Strepsipterans are internal parasites of other insects. Adult males on emergence leave the host and fly about; females of most species never leave the host. Each female produces many (a few thousand) tiny larvae, which have well-developed legs and are very active; they leave the host and enter another host, where they molt to a legless stage. Most strepsipterans have bees or various hoppers (Homoptera) as hosts; a few attack insects in other orders. The host is injured but rarely killed; the sex organs may be damaged or the shape or color of the abdomen may be changed. Parasitized hosts often can be recognized by the body of the parasite protruding from between the abdominal segments. If such hosts are caged, male strepsipterans frequently can be reared from them. Adult males are very seldom encountered.

Importance: These insects are of no economic importance.

Classification: Four families, which are separated by the tarsal and antennal characters of males.

No. of species: World, 300; N. America, 60.

MENGEIDS Family Mengeidae   **Not illus.**
   Identification: Tarsi 5-segmented, with 2 claws. Antennae

7-segmented, 3rd and 4th segments with long lateral processes.

Only 1 member of this family, *Triozocera mexicana* Pierce, is known from the U.S.; the female of this species is unknown, but the male has been taken in Texas. Females of some European mengeids are free-living as adults, and are usually found under stones; these mengeids are parasites of bristletails (Thysanura, see p. 60).

STYLOPIDS Family Stylopidae
Identification: Tarsi *4-segmented*, without claws. Antennae 4- to 6-segmented, *only 3rd segment with a lateral process*

This family is the largest in the order, with about 40 species in N. America. Most stylopids are parasites of bees (chiefly Andrenidae and Halictidae); a few parasitize vespid or sphecid wasps.

HALICTOPHAGIDS Family Halictophagidae
Identification: Tarsi *3-segmented*, without claws. Antennae 7-segmented, *3rd to 5th segments with long lateral processes*, last segment elongate.

This family is small (14 N. American species) but widely distributed. Most species are parasites of leafhoppers, tree-hoppers, and spittlebugs; 1 species attacks planthoppers and pygmy mole crickets.

ELENCHIDS Family Elenchidae   **Not illus.**
Identification: Tarsi 2-segmented, without claws. Antennae 4-segmented, 3rd segment with a long lateral process.

The members of this small family are parasites of planthoppers (Fulgoroidea).

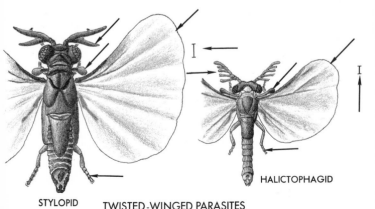

STYLOPID   TWISTED-WINGED PARASITES   HALICTOPHAGID

Scorpionflies and Their Allies:
Order Mecoptera

Identification: Small to medium-sized. Body usually slender and relatively soft. *Long-faced.* Mouth parts chewing, at end of a long snoutlike structure. 4 membranous wings (wings rarely absent or vestigial); long and narrow, HW about same size as FW, with rather generalized venation but with extra cross veins; wings often spotted or transversely banded. Legs usually long, slender, the tarsi *5-segmented*, with 1 or 2 claws. Antennae *threadlike, about half body length.* Metamorphosis complete.

Similar orders: (1) Neuroptera (p. 140): without a long-faced appearance; usually with numerous costal cross veins. (2) Diptera (p. 260): only 1 pair of wings. (3) Hymenoptera (p. 312): without a long-faced appearance; HW smaller than FW; wing venation different.

Immature stages: Eggs are generally laid on the ground, and larvae live in or on the surface of the ground or in moss. Larvae are usually caterpillarlike, with 8 pairs of short prolegs. They feed on dead insects and other organic materials.

Habits: Adults are usually found in areas of fairly dense vegetation; some are predaceous on other insects, others are omnivorous or are scavengers. The name "scorpionfly" is derived from the fact that the male genitalia of some species are large and conspicuous and carried curved upward over the back like the sting of a scorpion.

Importance: Scorpionflies are not of economic importance. They do not bite or sting.

Classification: Four families, separated chiefly by wing and leg characters.

No. of species: World, 400; N. America, 75.

SNOW SCORPIONFLIES Family Boreidae

Identification: Dark-colored, *2–5 mm.* Wings bristlelike or hooklike in ♂, *small and scalelike in* ♀. 10th abdominal segment of ♀ *prolonged posteriorly into an ovipositorlike structure* about half as long as abdomen (other ♀ Mecoptera lack such a structure and have abdomen tapering posteriorly). Tarsi with 2 claws.

Snow scorpionflies occur in and feed on mosses. Adults appear in winter or early spring, and are usually seen on the snow (hence the common name). The bristlelike or hooklike wings of the male are used in grasping the female at the time of mating. In N. America there are 15 species, 2 in the East and 13 in the West (California to Alaska). They are not often collected.

EARWIGFLIES Family Meropeidae
Identification: Ocelli absent (present in other Mecoptera).
Wings relatively broad, Rs and M with *5 or more branches*.
Tarsi with 2 claws.

This group is represented in N. America by a single rare
species, *Merope tuber* Newman, which occurs in the East Coast
states from Georgia to se. Canada. This insect is 10–12 mm.,
and the male has forcepslike terminal abdominal appendages
that resemble the cerci of earwigs (see illus., p. 99).

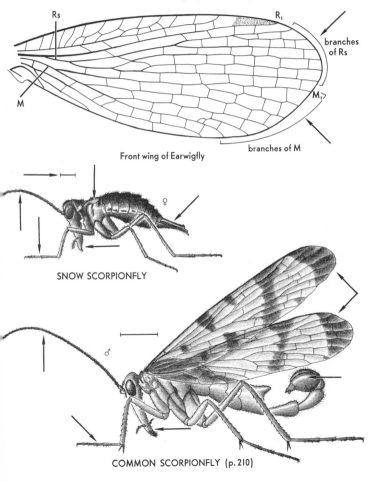

Front wing of Earwigfly

SNOW SCORPIONFLY

COMMON SCORPIONFLY (p. 210)

COMMON SCORPIONFLIES   See also p. 209
Family Panorpidae

Identification: Rs 5-branched (R_2 *forked*), M 4-branched. Tarsi *normal*, with 2 claws. ♂ genitalia *large and bulbous, usually curved upward* and forward like the sting of a scorpion.

Most of the 40-odd N. American panorpids are 15–20 mm., brownish, with dark spots or bands on wings. They are widely distributed and fairly common. Adults feed chiefly on dead or dying insects, sometimes on fruits or nectar.

HANGINGFLIES   Family Bittacidae

Identification: Rs and M 4-branched (R_2 *not forked*). Wings *narrower at base* than in Panorpidae. Tarsi with 1 claw; 5th segment *capable of being folded back on 4th.* ♂ genitalia enlarged but not bulbous.

Our 9 species of bittacids are widely distributed and often fairly common. Most are light brown and long-legged, about 20–25 mm., and often resemble large crane flies. Some have brownish areas on certain cross veins, and 1 species has blackish wing tips. This species holds its wings outstretched at rest; others fold the wings back over the abdomen. Bittacids spend most of their time hanging from vegetation by their front legs. They feed on various small insects which they capture with their raptorial hind feet. One California species is wingless.

Caddisflies: Order Trichoptera

Identification: Slender, elongate, mothlike insects. 1.5–25.0 mm. Antennae long and threadlike, usually as long as body or longer. 4 membranous wings (wings vestigial or absent in ♀ of a few species): HW a little shorter than FW, the wings (especially FW) hairy; wings *held rooflike over body at rest;* wing venation rather generalized, with M *usually 4-branched in FW* and 3-branched in HW, and Cu *3-branched;* wings generally with *a small spot* in fork of R_{4+5}. Mouth parts reduced, best described as "sponging," palps well developed. Legs relatively long and slender. Tarsi *5-segmented.* Metamorphosis complete, larvae aquatic.

Similar orders: Lepidoptera (p. 218): wings covered with scales; usually with a coiled proboscis; maxillary palps generally absent or vestigial; M in FW 3-branched; no spot in fork of R_{4+5}.

Immature stages: Larvae are caterpillarlike, with a pair of hooklike appendages at posterior end of the body, and usually with filamentous gills on the abdominal segments. They are fairly active insects, and some move backward more often (and faster) than forward. Many larvae construct portable cases of various small objects fastened together with a gluelike substance or with silk;

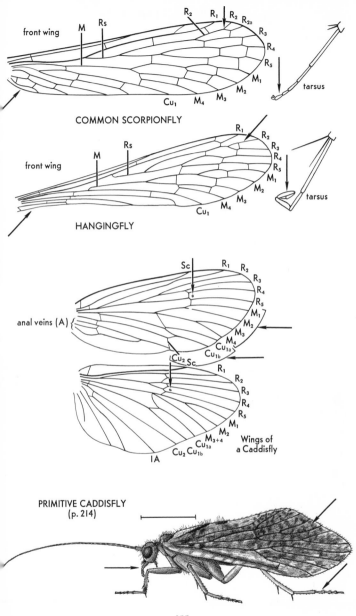

front wing

M Rs

R_2 R_1 R_2 R_{2a}
R_3
R_4
R_5
M_1

tarsus

Cu_1 M_4 M_3 M_2

COMMON SCORPIONFLY

R_1 R_2
R_3
R_4
R_5
M_1

M Rs

front wing

M_2

tarsus

Cu_1 M_4 M_3

HANGINGFLY

Sc R_1 R_2
R_3
R_4
R_5
M_1
anal veins (A) M_2
M_3
M_4
Cu_{1a}
Cu_{1b}

Cu_2 Sc R_1 R_2
R_3
R_4
R_5
M_1
M_2 Wings of
M_{3+4} a Caddisfly
Cu_{1a}
1A Cu_2 Cu_{1b}

PRIMITIVE CADDISFLY
(p. 214)

211

as the larva grows the case may be enlarged, or the larva may leave and construct a new and larger case. Larval cases vary considerably, both in shape and in the materials of which they are made; they may be slender or oval, straight or curved, and made of bits of leaves, twigs, sand grains, or small pebbles. Each species makes a characteristic type of case. Larvae of some species construct silken nets and feed on material caught in the nets. Most larvae feed on plant materials, but a few (which usually do not make cases) are predaceous. When a larva is full-grown it attaches its case to some object in the water, then closes the case and pupates inside. The pupa, which usually has well-developed mandibles, cuts or works its way out of the case, crawls out of the water onto a stone or other object, and undergoes its final molt to the adult. Emergence of some species occurs at surface of water.

Habits: Caddisflies are generally rather dull-colored insects, and their flight is jerky and erratic. They are largely nocturnal, spending the day resting in cool dark places; they are strongly attracted to lights at night. Eggs are laid in masses or strings, usually on stones or other objects in the water but occasionally on objects overhanging or near the water.

Importance: Caddisflies, particularly the immature stages, are an important item in the food of many freshwater fish.

Classification: The N. American species are arranged in 17 families; these families are not grouped into superfamilies or suborders.

No. of species: World, 4450; N. America, 975.

Identification of families of Trichoptera: The chief characters used in separating families of caddisflies are those of the ocelli, maxillary palps, thoracic warts, and tibial spurs. Ocelli may be present or absent. The maxillary palps are usually 5-segmented, and the segments may differ in size and shape; the palps sometimes differ in form or segmentation in the two sexes. Thoracic warts are wartlike swellings on the dorsal surface of the thorax; they vary in size, number, and location in different families. Mounting a caddisfly on a pin often damages or destroys these structures; they are more easily studied in specimens preserved in alcohol. The tibial spurs are large, usually brownish, movable structures; there may be 1 or 2 at the apex of the tibia, and 1 or 2 located proximad of the apex. The leg spines are small, usually black structures.

Identification of the families of Trichoptera may be facilitated by dividing them into the following 5 groups:

1. Ocelli present or absent; some hairs on the wings clubbed; very small (1.5–6.0 mm.): Hydroptilidae.
2. Ocelli present; no wing hairs clubbed: Philopotamidae, Rhyacophilidae, Phryganeidae, and Limnephilidae.
3. Ocelli absent; no wing hairs clubbed; terminal segment of maxillary palps much longer than the other segments, and with faint cross striations: Psychomyiidae and Hydropsychidae.

4. Ocelli absent; no wing hairs clubbed; terminal segment of maxillary palps not much longer than other segments, and without cross striations; middle tibiae with preapical spurs, and with or without a row of black spines: Molannidae, Calamoceratidae, Odontoceridae, Goeridae, Lepidostomata- tidae, and some Brachycentridae.

5. Similar to Group 4, but middle tibiae without preapical spurs and with a row of black spines: Leptoceridae, Helico- psychidae, Beraeidae, Sericostomatidae, and some Brachy- centridae.

MICRO-CADDISFLIES Family Hydroptilidae **See also p. 215**
Identification: Very small (1.5–6.0 mm.), usually with a salt-and-pepper coloration and relatively short antennae. Very hairy, with some wing hairs clubbed. Posterior portion of scutellum forms a flat triangular area with steep sides; meso-

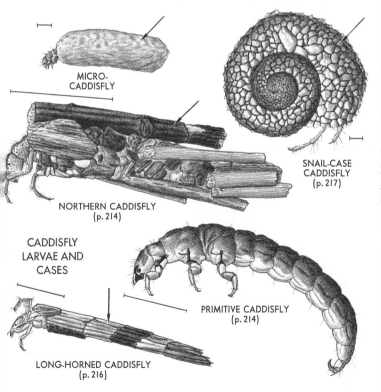

MICRO-
CADDISFLY

SNAIL-CASE
CADDISFLY
(p. 217)

NORTHERN CADDISFLY
(p. 214)

CADDISFLY
LARVAE AND
CASES

PRIMITIVE CADDISFLY
(p. 214)

LONG-HORNED CADDISFLY
(p. 216)

scutum and scutellum *without warts*. Ocelli present or absent. Front tibiae with 1 spur or none.

Members of this group are widely distributed and fairly common. Larvae occur in ponds and streams. *Cases made by the last instar are often purse-shaped*, with both ends open.

FINGER-NET CADDISFLIES   Family Philopotamidae
Identification: Usually brownish, with gray or blackish wings, and 6–9 mm. 5th segment of maxillary palps *2 or 3 times as long as 4th*.

Larvae live in rapid streams, where they construct finger-shaped nets attached to stones; they pupate in cases made of pebbles and attached to the underside of stones.

PRIMITIVE CADDISFLIES   See also pp. 211, 213
Family Rhyacophilidae
Identification: Fifth segment of maxillary palps *not much longer than 4th*, and 2nd segment about same length as 1st.

This is a large and widely distributed group. Adults are 3–13 mm. and usually brownish with mottled wings; antennae are relatively short. Larvae live in rapid streams; some make turtle-shaped cases of small pebbles, and others (which are predaceous) do not make cases.

LARGE CADDISFLIES   Family Phryganeidae
Identification: Maxillary palps 4-segmented in ♂ and 5-segmented in ♀, in ♀ with 2nd segment much longer than 1st and 5th segment not much longer than 4th. Ocelli *present*. Front tibiae with at least 2 spurs, middle tibiae with 4 spurs.

Adult phryganeids are 14–25 mm. and have the wings mottled with gray and brown. Larvae of most species live in marshes and ponds, and make long slender cases of spirally arranged strips of plant material.

NORTHERN CADDISFLIES   Family Limnephilidae   p. 213
Identification: Maxillary palps 3-segmented in ♂ and 5-segmented in ♀; palps of ♀ as in Phryganeidae. Front tibiae with 1 spur or none, middle tibiae with 2 or 3.

This is a large and widely distributed group, but most species are northern or western in distribution. Adults are 7–23 mm. and usually brownish with dark wing markings. Larvae occur chiefly in ponds and slow-moving streams, and *construct various types of cases*.

TRUMPET-NET and TUBE-MAKING CADDISFLIES
Family Psychomyiidae
Identification: Mesoscutum with *a pair of small warts*. 5th segment of maxillary palps with *faint cross striations*.

This is a large and widely distributed group of small caddis-

flies, mostly brownish and 4–11 mm. Larvae occur in a variety
of aquatic habitats. Some larvae construct a trumpet-shaped
net, usually in running water; others burrow into the sand at
the bottom of streams and cement the walls of the burrow to
form a fairly rigid tube.

NET-SPINNING CADDISFLIES Family Hydropsychidae
Identification: Mesoscutum *without warts*.

Adults of this group are found along streams. They are widely
distributed and fairly common. Larvae construct a cup-shaped
net, with the open side facing upstream, and spend most of their
time in a retreat near the net.

MOLANNIDS Family Molannidae
Identification: Middle femora with *a row of 6–10 spines*.

Our 5 species of molannids occur east of the Rocky Mts. from
s. Canada south to Oklahoma, Illinois, and Pennsylvania.
Adults are 10–15 mm. Larvae occur in streams with a sandy
bottom; their cases are cylindrical tubes of sand grains, with
lateral expansions.

CALAMOCERATIDS Family Calamoceratidae   p. 217
Identification: Scutellum small, rectangular, *without warts;*

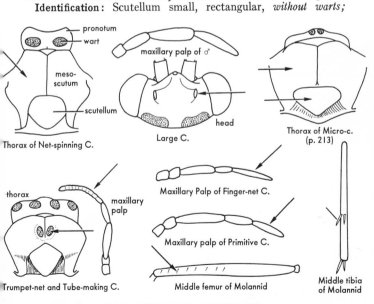

CHARACTERS OF CADDISFLIES

mesoscutal warts represented by *2 rows of small bristly spots* extending length of scutum. Maxillary palps 5- or 6-segmented.

Two of the 5 U.S. species of calamoceratids occur in the eastern states, and 3 occur in the West (Arizona, California, Alaska). They are relatively rare. The larva of 1 eastern species makes its case in a hollowed-out twig.

ODONTOCERIDS   Family Odontoceridae
Identification: Scutellum large and domelike, with *a single wart occupying most of sclerite*. Tibial spurs not hairy.

Ten rather rare species of odontocerids occur in N. America, 5 in the East and 5 in the West. The known larvae occur in riffles of streams and make cylindrical, slightly curved cases of sand grains.

GOERIDS   Family Goeridae   Not illus.
Identification: Scutellum with a single elongate wart occupying only central part of sclerite. Tibial spurs hairy. Maxillary palps 3-segmented in ♂ and 5-segmented in ♀.

This is a small group of rather rare caddisflies, most of them restricted to the East. Three N. American species have been reared; their larvae occur in streams and make cylindrical cases of sand grains and small pebbles, with 1 or 2 larger pebbles glued to each side.

LEPIDOSTOMATIDS   Family Lepidostomatidae
Identification: Scutellum with *a pair of warts*. Maxillary palps 1- or 3-segmented in ♂ and 5-segmented in ♀. Preapical tibial spurs long, hairy, located about middle of tibia.

This group is widely distributed but its members are not common. Larvae usually occur in streams or springs; their cases are often square in cross section. Males of some species have rather bizarre characters, such as peculiarly modified maxillary palps, leaflike legs, or widened wings.

BRACHYCENTRIDS   Family Brachycentridae
Identification: Scutellum with *a pair of warts*. Maxillary palps 3-segmented in ♂ and 5-segmented in ♀. Middle tibiae with or without apical spurs. Mesoscutum with a pair of small, widely separated warts.

Brachycentrids are 6–11 mm. and occur along streams. Larval cases are elongate, either round or square in cross section, and are made of sand or bits of vegetable material. Young larvae of some species live near shore, whereas older larvae move to midstream and attach their cases to stones.

LONG-HORNED CADDISFLIES   See also p. 213
Family Leptoceridae
Identification: Slender, pale-colored, 5–17 mm. Antennae *long,*

hairlike, often nearly twice as long as body. Pronotum with a pair of warts separated by *a deep notch*. Mesoscutal warts represented by *2 irregular rows of bristly spots*.

This group is widely distributed. Larvae occur in various types of aquatic habitats, and *make cases of different kinds*.

SNAIL-CASE CADDISFLIES   See also p. 213
Family Helicopsychidae

Identification: Costal margin of HW with *a row of tiny hooks in basal portion*, and somewhat angulate in middle. Mesoscutum and scutellum each with *a pair of small warts*.

Only 4 species in this group occur in N. America, but 1 is widely distributed. Adults are brownish or mottled and 5–7 mm. Larvae occur in clear, cool, slow-moving streams with a sandy bottom; their cases are *about ¼ in. wide and shaped like a snail shell*.

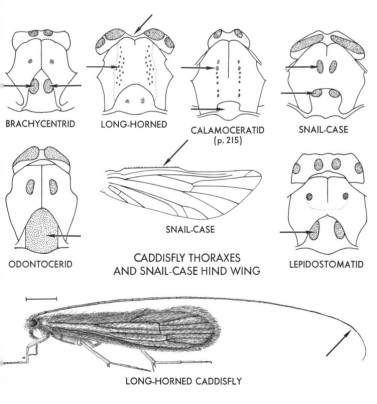

BRACHYCENTRID   LONG-HORNED   CALAMOCERATID (p. 215)   SNAIL-CASE

ODONTOCERID   SNAIL-CASE

CADDISFLY THORAXES AND SNAIL-CASE HIND WING   LEPIDOSTOMATID

LONG-HORNED CADDISFLY

BERAEIDS   Family Beraeidae   **Not illus.**
   Identification: Mesoscutum without warts. Apical spurs of
middle tibiae about half as long as basal tarsal segment.
   This group contains only 3 small (about 5 mm.), brownish,
and rather rare species, occurring in e. N. America. Their larvae
make cylindrical and slightly curved cases of sand grains.

SERICOSTOMATIDS   Family Sericostomatidae   **Not illus.**
   Identification: Mesoscutum with a median groove anteriorly
and a pair of small warts very close to this groove. Apical spurs
of middle tibiae not more than ⅓ length of basal tarsal segment.
FW with a long cross vein between R_1 and R_2.
   The 6 N. American species in this group occur in the mountains
of the eastern states, and in the West. One species is fairly
common along streams in arid parts of California and Arizona.
Larvae live in lakes and streams and make cylindrical cases of
sand grains.

Butterflies and Moths: Order Lepidoptera

Identification: With 4 membranous wings (rarely wingless), HW
a little smaller than FW, the wings *largely or entirely covered with
scales.* Mouth parts sucking, the proboscis *usually in the form of a
coiled tube.* Mandibles nearly always vestigial or lacking. Labial
palps usually *well developed and conspicuous;* maxillary palps
generally vestigial or lacking. Antennae *long, slender,* sometimes
plumose, always *knobbed apically in butterflies.* Metamorphosis
complete.
Similar orders: (1) Trichoptera (p. 210): few or no scales on wings;
no coiled proboscis; maxillary palps well developed; M in FW
usually 4-branched (3-branched in Lepidoptera). (2) Hymenoptera (p. 312): no scales on wings; mouth parts chewing, with
well-developed mandibles.
Immature stages: Lepidopterous larvae are commonly called
caterpillars. They are usually cylindrical, with a well-developed
head, *3 pairs of thoracic legs,* and 5 (sometimes fewer) *pairs of
abdominal prolegs.* The prolegs are short and fleshy and are provided with a number of tiny hooks (crochets); they are normally
present on 4 consecutive segments near the middle of the body
(abdominal segments 3–6) and on the last segment. Larvae lack
compound eyes but usually have *a group of small ocelli* on each
side of the head. Many caterpillars are ornamented with hairs or
spines, and although some look very ferocious most are quite
harmless to handle. A few give off an unpleasant odor when disturbed, and a few have body hairs that can sting or irritate the
skin. Lepidopterous larvae have the salivary glands modified

into silk glands; the silk is spun from the mouth and used principally in making cocoons or shelters. Many larvae pupate in silken cocoons; others make no cocoon. Most butterfly larvae make no cocoon, and their pupae are often called chrysalids (singular, chrysalis); chrysalids are often tuberculate or sculptured, and sometimes brightly colored; moth pupae are usually brownish and smooth. Most caterpillars are external feeders on foliage; a few live inside leaves as leaf miners, a few are gall makers, and a few bore into fruit, stems, and other parts of a plant. A very few caterpillars are predaceous on other insects.

Habits: Adult Lepidoptera feed principally on nectar and other liquid food, and many are common on flowers; a few do not feed as adults. Their flight is usually rather erratic but fairly fast. A few butterflies migrate long distances.

Importance: The larvae of many species are serious pests of cultivated plants; a few are pests of stored foods (grain, flour, and meal), and a few are pests of fabrics.

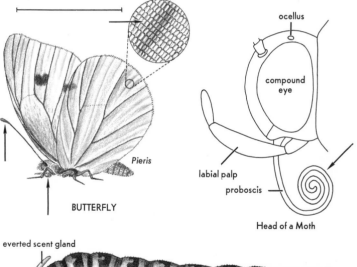

Pieris

BUTTERFLY

ocellus

compound eye

labial palp

proboscis

Head of a Moth

everted scent gland

ocelli

Papilio

thoracic legs

CATERPILLAR

prolegs

Classification: Two suborders, Frenatae and Jugatae, differing chiefly in wing venation and the way the front and hind wings are kept together; Rs in the hind wing is unbranched in frenates, branched in jugates; frenates generally have a frenulum (see opp.), and jugates have a *jugum* (a fingerlike lobe at base of front wing). The suborder Frenatae is divided into a series of superfamilies, which are arranged in 2 groups, Macrolepidoptera (p. 222) and Microlepidoptera (p. 240). Butterflies and skippers, making up the frenate superfamilies Papilionoidea and Hesperioidea, have knobbed antennae and lack a frenulum; moths (rest of order) have antennae of various sorts, usually threadlike or plumose (only rarely slightly clubbed), and they generally have a frenulum. **No. of species:** World, 112,000; N. America, 11,000.

Identification of Lepidoptera: The principal characters used in separating families of Lepidoptera are those of the wing venation; other characters include the presence or absence of a frenulum, the presence or absence of ocelli, and characters of the legs, mouth parts, and antennae. Many of these characters are difficult to see, and most beginners try to identify their specimens from pictures. This method may be satisfactory for butterflies if a good illustrated guide such as Klots's *A Field Guide to the Butterflies* is available, but not for most of the moths (which make up the bulk of the order). The identification of most Lepidoptera to family requires a knowledge of wing venation and other characters.

The wing venation in the Lepidoptera is relatively simple, and that of a generalized frenate is shown opposite. Veins indicated by dotted lines are atrophied or lost in many groups. Loss of the basal portion of M results in the formation of a large cell in the central basal part of the wing. This is the *discal cell*, and it provides a starting point in identifying the veins. Sc and the anal veins are always free of the discal cell in the front wing, and the branches of R, M, and Cu come off this cell. Ten veins come off the discal cell in the front wing (if all are present): R_1, R_2, R_3, R_4, R_5, M_1, M_2, M_3, Cu_1, and Cu_2. In the frenate hind wing the anal veins are always free of the discal cell; Sc may or may not be free of this cell; Sc and R_1 always fuse in the hind wing, and Rs is unbranched. The veins in the frenate hind wing (if all are present) are Sc $+ R_1$, Rs, M_1, M_2, M_3, Cu_1, and Cu_2, plus 3 anal veins behind the discal cell. The venational variations encountered involve the number of veins present, how they branch, and where particular veins rise. The *frenulum* (see opp.) is a bristle or group of bristles at the base of the front edge of the hind wing.

The wing venation in most Lepidoptera is obscured by scales, and it is often necessary to bleach or remove the scales to see the venation; if the scales are not too dense, the venation can sometimes be seen if there is a strong light behind the wing. A drop of alcohol on the wing often reveals the venation. When the alcohol evaporates the wing coloration is usually unchanged.

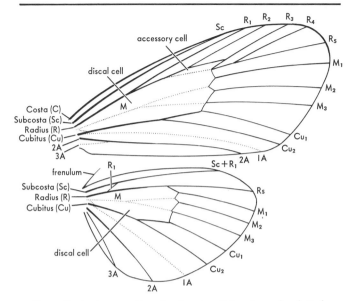

Generalized wing venation of a frenate. Veins shown by dotted lines are often weak or absent.

The best way to see the wing venation in a lepidopteran is to bleach the wings. The procedure for bleaching and mounting lepidopteran wings is as follows:

1. Carefully remove wings from one side of the body (include frenulum if one is present).
2. Dip wings in 95 percent alcohol for a few seconds.
3. Dip wings in a 10 percent solution of hydrochloric acid for a few seconds.
4. Place wings in Clorox; leave them there until color is removed (up to several minutes). If wings are slow in clearing, dip them in acid again and then return them to the Clorox.
5. Rinse wings in water to remove the Clorox.
6. Place wings on a slide (a 2 x 2-in. slide for most wings). This is done by floating wings in a dish and bringing the slide up from underneath. After wings are on the slide, center and orient them.
7. Allow wings to dry, then place another slide (of same size) on top of wings and bind slides together with binding tape. Place the slide label on the outside. The result is a permanent slide mount that can be studied under a microscope, or projected with a slide projector.

Frenate Lepidoptera: Suborder Frenatae

A frenulum present (see illus., p. 221), or humeral angle of HW more or less expanded; Rs in HW unbranched. This suborder includes the vast majority of species in the order.

Macrolepidoptera

Size variable but usually with a wingspread of 1 in. or more. FW more or less triangular, HW rounded. Fringe of hairs on anal margin of HW short. Generally only 1 anal vein (2A) in FW and 1 or 2 (2A, or 2A and 3A) in HW.

Butterflies: Superfamily Papilionoidea

Antennae *knobbed but never hooked at tip*, and close together at base. Some branches of R in FW stalked beyond discal cell, or fewer than 5 branches present. Wings generally large in proportion to body.

SWALLOWTAILS Family Papilionidae
Identification: FW with R *5-branched* and Cu *appearing 4-branched*. HW with *1 anal vein and with tail-like prolongations*. Front legs normal-sized, not reduced.

This group includes some of our largest and most strikingly colored butterflies, only a few of which can be mentioned here. The Tiger Swallowtail, *Papilio glaucus* Linn., one of our largest swallowtails, is brightly colored with yellow and black (some individuals have the wings almost entirely dark); its larva (illus., p. 219) feeds on various trees. The Black Swallowtail, *P. polyxenes asterius* Stoll, is black with 2 rows of yellow spots around wing margins; larva feeds on carrots, parsley, and related plants. The Zebra Swallowtail, *Graphium marcellus* (Cramer), is pale greenish with black stripes, and has rather long tails; larva feeds on papaw. The Spicebush Swallowtail, *P. troilus* Linn., is blackish with a row of small yellow spots along outer margin of the front wing and extensive blue-green areas in the hind wing; its larva feeds on spicebush and sassafras.

PARNASSIANS Family Parnassiidae
Identification: Similar to Papilionidae, but R in FW *4-branched* and HW *without tail-like prolongations*.

Parnassians are usually gray or white with dark markings. Most species have 2 small reddish eye spots in the hind wing. These butterflies have a wingspread of about 2 in., and are principally western in distribution.

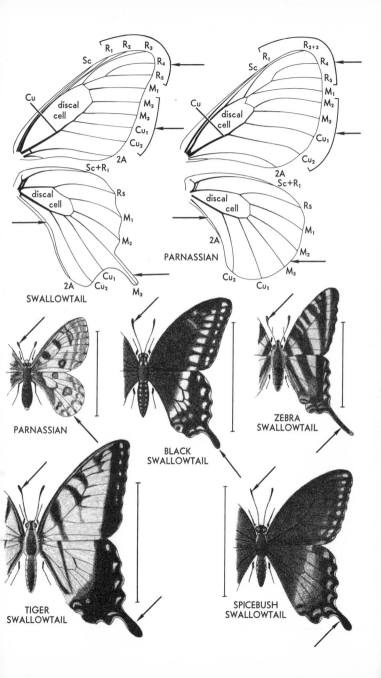

R_1 R_2 R_3 R_4 R_5
Sc
Cu
discal cell
M_1
M_2
M_3
Cu_1
Cu_2
2A

R_1 R_{2+3} R_4 R_5 M_1
Sc
Cu
discal cell
M_2
M_3
Cu_1
Cu_2
2A
$Sc+R_1$

$Sc+R_1$
discal cell
Rs
M_1
M_2
2A
Cu_1 Cu_2
M_3

SWALLOWTAIL

discal cell
Rs
M_1
2A
M_2
M_3
Cu_2 Cu_1

PARNASSIAN

PARNASSIAN

BLACK SWALLOWTAIL

ZEBRA SWALLOWTAIL

TIGER SWALLOWTAIL

SPICEBUSH SWALLOWTAIL

WHITES, SULFURS, and ORANGE-TIPS   See also Pl. 9
Family Pieridae

Identification: Small to medium-sized, usually white, yellow, or orange, marked with black. FW with *Cu appearing 3-branched*, R *3- or 4-branched* (5-branched in some orange-tips), and M_1 *stalked with a branch of R* for a distance beyond discal cell. HW with *2 anal veins*, and with or without a humeral vein. Front legs normal or slightly reduced, the tarsal claws forked.

Whites are white with black markings. Our most common species is the Cabbage Butterfly (see also p. 219), *Pieris rapae* (Linn.); its larva feeds on cabbage and related plants, and is a serious pest of cabbage. **Sulfurs** (Pl. 9) are yellow or orange, and our most common species have the wings bordered with black; some sulfurs are very common butterflies; larvae of the common species feed on clovers. **Orange-tips** are small white butterflies that have underside of the wings mottled with greenish, and tips of the front wings are often orange; they are relatively uncommon, and most species are western; larvae feed on shepherd's purse and related plants.

GOSSAMER-WINGED BUTTERFLIES   See also Pl. 9
Family Lycaenidae

Identification: Small, delicate, often brightly colored. Wing venation as in Pieridae, but FW with M_1 *not stalked with a branch of R* beyond discal cell (except in harvesters) and R never with more than 4 branches; HW *without a humeral vein and C not thickened*. Front legs of ♂ usually reduced; tarsal claws not forked.

This is a large group, many species being quite common. Larvae are somewhat sluglike, and many secrete a honeydewlike material that attracts ants; some live in ant nests. Adults are rapid fliers.

Harvesters, Subfamily Gerydinae. Differing from other lycaenids in having M_1 in FW *stalked with a branch of R* for a short distance beyond discal cell; R in FW *4-branched*. The single U.S. species in this group, *Feniseca tarquinius* (Fabricius), occurs in the East; it is a small yellowish-brown butterfly with border of the front wing and central basal portion of the hind wing dark brown. Larva feeds on aphids. This butterfly is not common but is most likely to be found near alders growing in swampy places.

Coppers, Subfamily Lycaeninae (Pl. 9). Brownish or reddish, often with a coppery tinge, and with black markings. R in FW 4-branched. Coppers are fast-flying butterflies that generally occur in meadows, marshes, and other open areas. Larvae feed on dock (*Rumex*).

Blues, Subfamily Plebeiinae. Small, delicate, with upper surface of wings usually largely or entirely blue. R in FW usually 4-branched. Females are generally darker than males;

some have little or no blue in the wings. Many larvae secrete a honeydewlike material, and some live in ant nests.

Hairstreaks, Subfamily Theclinae (not illus.). Dark brown or grayish, with delicate striping on underside of wings. Generally 2 or 3 hairlike tails on HW. R in FW 3-branched. Elfins (*Incisalia*) are small, brownish, and the hind wings lack tails and have a somewhat scalloped margin. Hairstreaks usually occur in

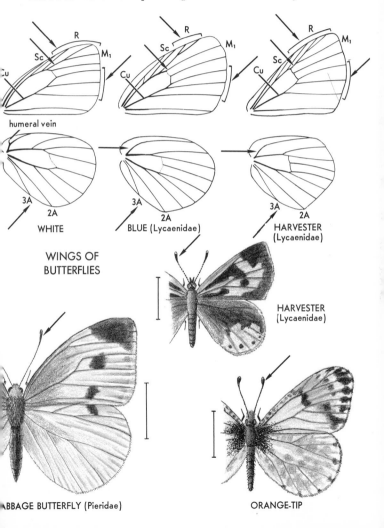

WINGS OF
BUTTERFLIES

WHITE

BLUE (Lycaenidae)

HARVESTER (Lycaenidae)

HARVESTER (Lycaenidae)

CABBAGE BUTTERFLY (Pieridae)

ORANGE-TIP

meadows, along roadsides, and in other open areas; they are often found on flowers.

METALMARKS Family Riodinidae
Identification: Small dark-colored butterflies. R in FW *4-branched*. HW with *a short humeral vein* and C *thickened out to humeral angle of wing*.

This group is chiefly tropical, and most of our species occur in the South and Southwest; 3 eastern species range north to Ohio but are rare in the North. They are brownish, with narrow lines or spots on wings; most have a wingspread of 1 in. or less; larvae feed on various weeds.

BRUSH-FOOTED BUTTERFLIES   See also Pl. 9
Family Nymphalidae
Identification: Variable in size and color. Front legs *greatly reduced*. FW relatively broad and triangular, with R *5-branched*, Cu appearing *3-branched*, and 3A *lacking*. HW with *2 anal veins*, humeral vein *straight* or bent toward wing tip, and discal cell *open or closed by a weak vein*. No veins greatly swollen at base.

This is the largest family of Papilionoidea, and includes many common species; only a few can be mentioned here. Fritillaries (*Speyeria* and *Boloria*) are medium-sized to large, brownish, with numerous black spots or narrow bands on the wings, and usually with silvery spots on underside of the hind wings; larvae feed on violets. Crescent-spots (*Phyciodes*) are small and brownish, with numerous black markings on the wings; larvae feed chiefly on asters. Anglewings (*Polygonia*) are small to medium-sized, brownish, with dark markings on the wings; wing margins are irregular, and underside of the wings resembles a dead leaf; larvae feed mainly on nettles and elm. The Mourningcloak (Pl. 9), *Nymphalis antiopa* (Linn.), is common and widely distributed; its wings are blackish, margined with yellow; larva is gregarious and feeds on willow and elm. The Red Admiral (Pl. 9), *Vanessa atalanta* (Linn.), is common and widely distributed; its larva feeds on nettles. The Viceroy (Pl. 9), *Limenitis archippus* (Cramer), looks much like a Monarch but is somewhat smaller and has a black line across the hind wing; its larva feeds on willow and poplar. Mimicry like that of the Monarch and Viceroy occurs in many butterflies and is believed to offer 1 species (Viceroy in this case) some protection from predators. Body fluids of the Monarch are apparently distasteful to predators, so they avoid it; the Viceroy's body fluids are not distasteful, but its resemblance to the Monarch may cause predators to avoid it.

NYMPHS, SATYRS, and ARCTICS   See also Pl. 9
Family Satyridae
Identification: Small to medium-sized butterflies, usually gray-

ish or brownish and often with eye spots in the wings. Venation as in Nymphalidae, but some veins (*especially Sc*) *greatly swollen at base.* Front legs much reduced.

One of the most common and strikingly marked species in this group is the Wood Nymph (see also Pl. 9), *Cercyonis pegala* (Fabricius), a medium-sized, dark brown butterfly having a broad yellowish band across the front wings with 2 small eye spots. Wood satyrs (*Euptychia*) are small grayish butterflies, about 1 in. in wingspread, with small black eye spots in the wings. The Pearly Eye, *Lethe portlandica* Fabricius, is a woodland species that often alights on tree trunks; it is brownish, with a row of black spots along outer edge of the hind wings. Arctics (*Oeneis*) occur chiefly in the arctic region and on mountaintops; 1 species, *O. jutta* Hübner, may be found in sphagnum bogs in New England. Satyrid larvae feed on grasses.

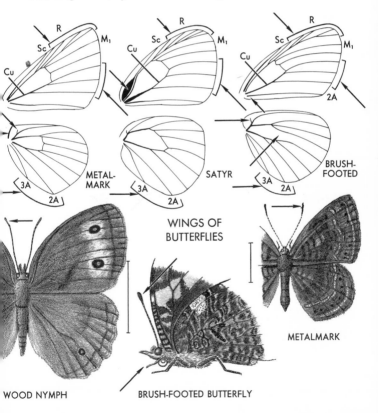

WINGS OF BUTTERFLIES

METAL-MARK

SATYR

BRUSH-FOOTED

METALMARK

WOOD NYMPH

BRUSH-FOOTED BUTTERFLY

SNOUT BUTTERFLIES   Family Libytheidae   **Not illus.**
  Identification: Similar to Nymphalidae (p. 226), but labial palps
  longer than thorax, thickly hairy, and projecting forward.
   Our only species in this group has distinctively shaped front
wings and a wingspread of about 1½ in. It occurs throughout
the East and Southwest, but is uncommon in the Northeast.
Larva feeds on hackberry.

HELICONIANS   Family Heliconiidae
  Identification: Similar to Nymphalidae (p. 226), but FW narrow,
  elongate, and HW humeral vein *bent toward base of wing*.
   Our few species of heliconians occur in the South. One of the
most strikingly colored is the Zebra Butterfly, *Heliconius
charitonius* (Linn.), which is black with yellow stripes. Its larva
feeds on passion flowers.

MILKWEED BUTTERFLIES   Family Danaidae   **Pl. 9**
  Identification: Large brownish butterflies, usually marked with
  black. Similar to Nymphalidae (p. 226) but 3A present in FW,
  discal cell in HW closed by a well-developed vein, and antennae
  without scales.
   Our most common danaid is the Monarch (Pl. 9), *Danaus
plexippus* (Linn.), which occurs throughout the U.S. and s.
Canada. The Viceroy (Nymphalidae) is very similar, but is
slightly smaller and has a black line across the hind wing. The
Monarch is one of the few butterflies in this country that
migrate; it migrates south in fall, often in immense aggregations,
and reappears in the North the following spring. The Monarchs
appearing in the North are usually not the same individuals that
migrated south the season before, but their offspring; the insect
reproduces on its wintering ground or after a short northward
flight in spring. Larvae of danaids feed on milkweed.

Skippers: Superfamily Hesperioidea

Antennae *clubbed and usually also hooked at tip*, and widely separated at base. R in FW *5-branched*, all branches coming off discal
cell. Relatively stout-bodied. Strong fliers. Larvae generally
pupate in a cocoon formed of leaves and silk.

COMMON SKIPPERS   Family Hesperiidae
  Identification: Head about as wide as or wider than thorax.
  Hind tibiae usually with 2 pairs of spurs. Wingspread generally
  less than 30 mm. Widely distributed.
   This is a large group and many species are quite common.
The front and hind wings at rest are often held at a slightly
different angle. Larvae feed on leaves, and usually live in a
shelter formed of a rolled-up leaf or several leaves tied together;
they are smooth-bodied, with a small and necklike prothorax.

GIANT SKIPPERS Family Megathymidae   **Not illus.**
Identification: Head narrower than thorax. Antennae not hooked at tip, but with a large club. Hind tibiae with only 1 pair of spurs. Wingspread 40 mm. or more.

Giant skippers are fast-flying insects that hold their wings vertical at rest. They occur in the South and West. Larvae bore in stems and roots of yucca and related plants. Larvae are

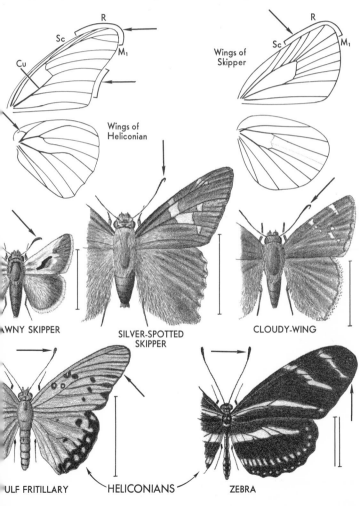

R
Sc
Cu
M₁
Wings of Heliconian

Wings of Skipper
R
Sc
M₁

TAWNY SKIPPER

SILVER-SPOTTED SKIPPER

CLOUDY-WING

GULF FRITILLARY   HELICONIANS   ZEBRA

edible, and in Mexico are considered a delicacy; they are cooked by frying in deep fat, and are canned and sold under the name "Gusanos de Maguey."

Macro-Moths: Macrolepidoptera, in part

Antennae threadlike or plumose. Frenulum usually present. 1A nearly always lacking in FW and HW. Fringe on anal margin of HW short. Tibial spurs short. Wings never lanceolate. Wingspread usually over 20 mm. The 21 families of macro-moths may be divided into 3 groups: (1) Sphingidae — fairly distinct in appearance and venation; (2) Dioptidae through Zanolidae — Cu in FW appears 3-branched; and (3) Ctenuchidae through Drepanidae — Cu in FW appears 4-branched.

Macro-Moths, Group 1

SPHINX or HAWK MOTHS   See also Pl. 10
Family Sphingidae
   Identification: Medium-sized to large, *heavy-bodied*, with wings relatively small. Antennae *thickened, somewhat spindle-shaped apically.* Sc and Rs in HW parallel to end of discal cell and beyond, connected by *an oblique cross vein* about opposite middle of discal cell. Frenulum *present but sometimes small.*
   Sphinx moths are strong fliers, with a very rapid wingbeat. They feed on flowers, much like hummingbirds. Most species feed at dusk or at night; a few feed during the day. Some species have large areas of the wings devoid of scales and resemble bumble bees. Larvae of most species have a soft spinelike process near the posterior end of the body and are often called hornworms; some are pests of tomatoes, tobacco, and other plants. They usually pupate in the ground.

Macro-Moths, Group 2

Cu in FW appears 3-branched. The families in this group may be divided into 4 groups on the basis of venation in anterior part of hind wing.
   1. Sc + R_1 and Rs diverging at base of wing: Dioptidae, Saturniidae, Citheroniidae, Lacosomidae, Epiplemidae.
   2. Sc rather abruptly angled into humeral angle of wing, often connected to humeral angle by a cross vein; beyond this bend Sc and R are either fused or are closely parallel for a short distance along anterior side of discal cell: Geometridae, Manidiidae.
   3. Sc and R approximately parallel along basal half of discal cell, then connected by a distinct cross vein, diverging beyond the cross vein: Bombycidae.
   4. Sc + R_1 and Rs close and parallel along at least basal half of anterior side of discal cell, often farther, then diverging: Thyatiridae, Notodontidae, Zanolidae.

Arctiidae are discussed under Group 3 of the Macro-Moths because Cu in the front wing appears 4-branched in most of them; in the Lithosiinae, which have Cu in the front wing appearing 3-branched, Sc and Rs in the hind wing are fused to beyond the middle of the discal cell, then they diverge.

OAK MOTHS Family Dioptidae   **Not illus.**
Identification: Slender, pale brown moths. Wingspread 25–35 mm. Frenulum well developed. M_3 and Cu_1 in FW and HW stalked for a short distance beyond discal cell.

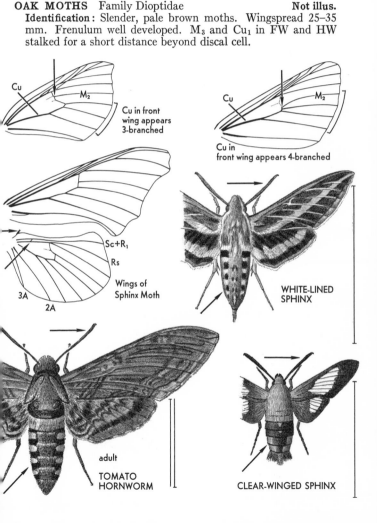

Cu in front wing appears 3-branched

Cu in front wing appears 4-branched

Sc+R_1
Rs
Wings of Sphinx Moth
3A
2A

WHITE-LINED SPHINX

adult
TOMATO HORNWORM

CLEAR-WINGED SPHINX

A single species of oak moth occurs in California. Its larva feeds on various oaks (and occasionally other trees), and sometimes does considerable damage.

GIANT SILKWORM MOTHS   See also Pl. 10
Family Saturniidae

Identification: Medium-sized to large moths, with broad wings. Frenulum small or *vestigial.* Humeral angle of HW *not noticeably expanded;* HW with *only 1 anal vein.* Wings usually with eye spots. Discal cell in FW *generally open.*

This group includes our largest moths, some of which have a wingspread of about 6 in.; many are brightly colored. The antennae are somewhat plumose, especially in males. Mouth parts are reduced, and adults do not feed. Larvae are large caterpillars and many have tubercles or spines on the body; they pupate in silken cocoons. Our largest saturniid is the Cecropia Moth (Pl. 10), *Hyalophora cecropia* (Linn.), with a wingspread of 5 or 6 in. The Luna Moth (Pl. 10), *Actias luna* (Linn.), is light green, with a long tail on each hind wing. The Polyphemus Moth (Pl. 10), *Antheraea polyphemus* (Cramer), is large, yellowish brown, with a round windowlike spot near the center of each wing. The Io Moth (Pl. 10), *Automeris io* (Fabricius), has a wingspread of about 2–2½ in.; males are bright yellow, with a large eye spot in each hind wing; females are similar but have dark brown front wings. The larva of the Io is a spiny green caterpillar with a narrow lateral stripe of red above and white below; the stinging spines make handling an Io larva like handling nettles.

ROYAL MOTHS   Family Citheroniidae   See also Pl. 10

Identification: Medium-sized to large, usually yellowish or brownish. Frenulum *absent.* Humeral angle of HW *considerably expanded.* Venation as in Saturniidae, but *with 2 anal veins in HW* and discal cells *closed.* Usually no eye spot in wings. Antennae plumose only in basal half.

Royal moth larvae usually have horns or spines on the anterior segments. They feed on various trees and pupate in the ground. The largest species in this group is the Regal Moth (Pl. 10), *Citheronia regalis* (Fabricius), which has a wingspread of 5 or 6 in.; its larva feeds chiefly on walnut and hickory. The Imperial Moth, *Eacles imperialis* (Drury), is large, yellow, marked with pinkish purple; its larva feeds on various trees. Most of the moths in the genus *Anisota* are brownish, with a wingspread of about 1½ in.; they resemble tent caterpillar moths (Lasiocampidae) but have Cu in the front wing appearing 3-branched and there are no humeral veins in the hind wing.

SACK-BEARERS   Family Lacosomidae

Identification: Medium-sized, stout-bodied moths, usually yel-

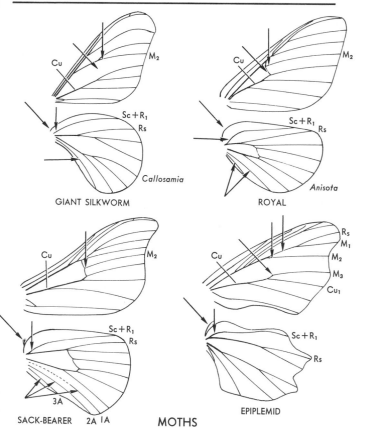

GIANT SILKWORM   ROYAL

SACK-BEARER   MOTHS   EPIPLEMID

lowish or brownish with dark lines or spots. Frenulum *small* or
vestigial; *2 (rarely 3) anal veins in HW*. Sc and Rs in HW not
connected by a cross vein.

Larvae of these moths construct portable cases of leaves.
Three species (none common) occur in the U.S. — 2 in the East
and 1 in Arizona. One eastern species has apex of the front
wing somewhat sickle-shaped, and the other has distal margin
of the front wing toothed or scalloped.

EPIPLEMID MOTHS   Family Epiplemidae
Identification: Grayish or yellowish, with a wingspread of about
20 mm. Frenulum *well developed*. M₁ and R₅ in FW *stalked*.
M₃ and Cu₁ *not stalked*.

Only 5 species of epiplemids occur in the U.S. They are relatively rare.

GEOMETER MOTHS   Family Geometridae   **See also Pl. 10**
Identification: Small to medium-sized, usually slender-bodied. Sc in HW with *a rather abrupt angle basally,* and often connected to humeral angle of wing by a cross vein. Antennae not dilated apically, or if so then eyes are bare.

This is a large group, with some 1200 N. American species, occurring almost everywhere. Larvae are small slender caterpillars with only 2 or 3 pairs of prolegs; they move in a looping fashion, and are called measuringworms or inchworms. The moths usually hold wings outstretched at rest rather than back over the body. Females of a few species (like cankerworms) are wingless. Larvae feed on many different plants; some tree feeders occasionally damage orchard and shade trees.

MANIDIID MOTHS   Family Manidiidae   **Not illus.**
Identification: Similar to Geometridae, but antennae dilated apically and eyes hairy.

A single rare species in this group occurs in Arizona.

SILKWORM MOTHS   Family Bombycidae
Identification: Heavy-bodied white moths. Wingspread 35–40 mm. Sc and R in HW *connected by a cross vein* opposite middle of discal cell, then diverging. Frenulum *very small.*

Silkworm moths are not native to N. America, but 1 species, *Bombyx mori* (Linn.), which is the source of natural silk, is sometimes reared here. This insect, the larva of which feeds on mulberry, is not a wild species in this country.

THYATIRID MOTHS   Family Thyatiridae   **Not illus.**
Identification: Similar to Noctuidae (p. 238), but Cu in FW appears 3-branched, and Sc + R_1 and Rs in HW are approximately parallel along anterior side of discal cell. Differ from Notodontidae in that Cu in HW appears 4-branched (3-branched in Notodontidae), and Rs and M_1 in HW are not stalked.

Moths are medium-sized, and usually brownish with wavy or zigzag lines on the front wings. They are not common.

PROMINENTS   Family Notodontidae   **See also Pl. 11**
Identification: Medium-sized, usually brownish moths. Sc + R_1 and Rs in HW *close together and parallel* along discal cell; Rs and M_1 in HW *stalked a short distance* beyond discal cell.

Larvae of these moths are usually gregarious. When disturbed they often freeze with ends of the body elevated. Larvae of most species feed on trees and shrubs, and some attack orchard trees. Most larvae are striped. Notodontids are fairly common moths.

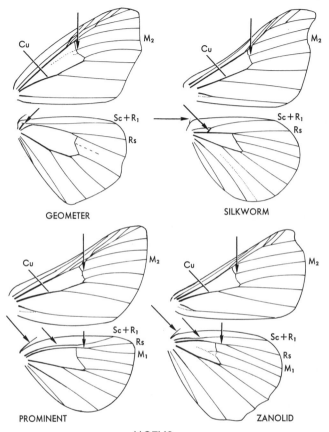

GEOMETER

SILKWORM

PROMINENT

ZANOLID

MOTHS

ZANOLID MOTHS Family Zanolidae
  Identification: Similar to Notodontidae, but Sc + R₁ and Rs in HW *diverge about middle* of discal cell. Proboscis lacking. FW with 1 or 2 small clear spots near tip. Tarsal claws without a blunt tooth near base.
  This group is represented in the U.S. by 3 species of *Apatelodes*, which have a wingspread of $1\frac{1}{2}$–2 in., and are gray with window-like spots near tip of the front wings. One species has the distal margin of the wings somewhat toothed. Larvae feed on various trees and shrubs.

Macro-Moths, Group 3

Cu in FW appears 4-branched (except in a few Arctiidae). Frenulum well developed except in Lasiocampidae and Drepanidae.

TENT CATERPILLARS and LAPPET MOTHS See also Pl. 11
Family Lasiocampidae
  Identification: Medium-sized, stout-bodied, rather hairy moths. HW *without a frenulum* but with humeral angle *expanded* and with *humeral veins*. Cu_2 in FW rises *in basal* $\frac{1}{2}$ *or* $\frac{1}{3}$ of discal cell. Antennae somewhat plumose.
  A common eastern species in this group is the Eastern Tent Caterpillar (Pl. 11), *Malacosoma americanum* (Fabricius). Its larvae are gregarious and construct a silken tent, usually in the fork of a branch, and use it as a shelter. These larvae feed on apple, cherry, and related trees, and may completely defoliate a tree. Overwintering eggs hatch early in the season, and larvae become full-grown by late May or early June. Larvae spin silken cocoons in various protected places and moths appear about 3 weeks later. A similar species, the Forest Tent Caterpillar, *Malacosoma disstria* Hübner, does not construct a tent. Larva of *M. americanum* has a yellow stripe down the back; that of *M. disstria* has a dorsal row of keyhole-shaped spots. Adults of both species have a wingspread of about 1–1½ in. (females are slightly larger than males) and are yellowish brown with 2 narrow light lines across front wings; adults of *M. americanum* are somewhat darker than those of *M. disstria*. Lappet moths (*Tolype*), about the same size as tent caterpillar moths, are bluish gray with white markings; their larvae feed on various trees. *Gloveria arizonensis* Packard, a common southwestern species, is dark gray, with a wingspread of about 2½ in.

HOOK-TIP MOTHS Family Drepanidae **See also Pl. 11**
  Identification: Small, brownish, slender-bodied. Apex of FW usually *sickle-shaped*. HW with Sc + R_1 and Rs *separated along anterior side* of discal cell. Frenulum small or *absent*.
  These moths have a wingspread of about 1 in. or less, and can usually be recognized by the sickle-shaped apex of the front wing. The 6 U.S. species are not common.

CTENUCHID MOTHS Family Ctenuchidae **See also Pl. 11**
  Identification: Sc + R_1 in HW *absent*.
  Ctenuchids are common moths that are active during the day and feed on flowers. Larvae are quite hairy, and cocoons are formed principally of larval body hairs; most larvae feed on grasses. Scape moths (*Cisseps*) have narrow wings and are slate-colored, the central part of the hind wings being lighter.

The Virginia Ctenucha (Pl. 11), *Ctenucha virginica* (Charpentier), is larger and broader-winged; its wings are blackish, with a narrow white margin along rear edge of the hind wings, and the body is metallic blue; larva is a hairy yellowish caterpillar. The Lichen Moth, *Lycomorpha pholus* (Drury), is small, narrowwinged, and blackish, with the base of the wings yellow; adults occur commonly on goldenrod and larvae feed on lichens.

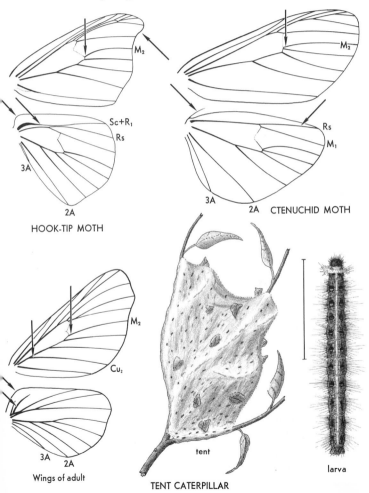

HOOK-TIP MOTH

CTENUCHID MOTH

Wings of adult

TENT CATERPILLAR

larva

TIGER MOTHS   Family Arctiidae   **See also Pl. 11**
Identification: Small to medium-sized, usually light-colored, often brightly spotted or banded. Cu in HW appears 4-branched; Sc and R in HW usually *fused to about middle* of discal cell, or for a short distance beyond basal areole, and Sc swollen at base. Ocelli present (except in Lithosiinae). If Cu appears 3-branched (some Lithosiinae), Sc and R in HW are fused to middle of discal cell or beyond, and M_2 and M_3 in FW are absent. Noctuids are very similar but generally dark-colored, the palps usually longer (extending beyond middle of face), and Sc and R in HW fuse for only a short distance beyond the basal areole.

This is a large group, many species of which are common moths. Larvae are usually very hairy, and some are called woollybears; most of them feed on grasses but a few feed on trees and shrubs. Adults are generally heavy-bodied and hold wings rooflike over the body at rest; many are beautifully colored and some are largely white. Larvae of the Fall Webworm, *Hyphantria cunea* (Drury), often seriously damage trees and shrubs; they spin silk over the foliage, skeletonizing the leaves as they feed, and may form a web over foliage of entire branches; adults are small white moths.

NOLID MOTHS   Family Nolidae   **Not illus.**
Identification: Wing venation as in Arctiidae. FW with tufts of raised scales. Ocelli absent.

This is a small group and its members are not common. Most nolids have a wingspread of 1 in. or less. Some larvae feed on lichens, others feed on various trees; larva of the Sorghum Webworm, *Celama sorghiella* (Riley), feeds on sorghum.

NOCTUID MOTHS   Family Noctuidae   **See also Pl. 11**
Identification: Sc and R in HW *fused for a short distance* beyond a small basal areole, then separating; Cu in HW appears 3- or 4-branched (M_2 in HW *often weak or absent*). Ocelli nearly always present. Antennae slender and threadlike, never plumose. Palps extend to middle of face or beyond.

This is the largest family in the order, with some 2700 N. American species, and many are common moths. Most are nocturnal. Noctuids vary considerably in size and color but most have a wingspread of 20–40 mm. and are dark-colored. The wings at rest may be held flat or rooflike over the body. Underwings (*Catocala*), most of which have a wingspread of $1\frac{1}{2}$–$2\frac{1}{2}$ in., are strikingly colored; the front wings are generally a mottled brownish or gray, but the hind wings have concentric bands of red, yellow, or orange. Noctuid larvae are smooth and dull-colored and most have 5 pairs of prolegs; a few, called loopers, have only 3 pairs, and move like inchworms. Larvae of some species (cutworms) feed on roots and shoots of various plants and often cut off the stem just above the ground. Larva of the Corn Earworm, *Heliothis zea* (Boddie), feeds on the growing ears of corn, and also burrows into tomatoes and the bolls (seedpods) of cotton. Larvae of other species bore into stems and fruits.

FORESTER MOTHS Family Agaristidae **Pl. 12**
Identification: Black, with 2 whitish or yellowish spots in each wing. Wingspread about 1 in. Venation as in Noctuidae. Antennae swollen apically. Frenulum well developed.

The Eight-spotted Forester (Pl. 12), *Alypia octomaculata* (Fabricius), is a common and widely distributed species; larva feeds on grape and Virginia creeper. Most of the other 27 U.S. species occur in the West or in the Gulf states.

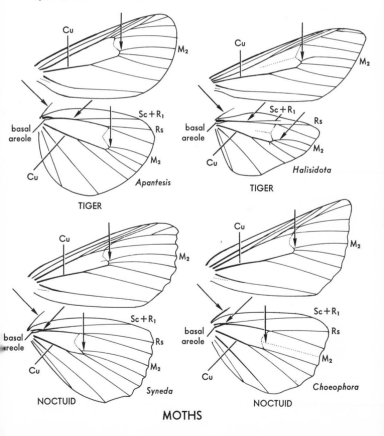

MOTHS

PERICOPID MOTHS Family Pericopidae **Not illus.**

Identification: Medium-sized, black or bluish with extensive light areas in wings. 2 large rounded prominences on dorsal surface of 1st abdominal segment, separated by about ⅓ width of abdomen. Venation as in Noctuidae (p. 238).

Most of the 6 U.S. species of pericopids occur in the West. *Composia fidelissima* Herrich-Schäffer, which is found in s. Florida, is dark blue marked with red and white.

TUSSOCK MOTHS and Others **See also Pl. 12**
Family Liparidae

Identification: Similar to Noctuidae (p. 238), but with *a much larger basal areole* in HW and without ocelli. Rs and M₁ in HW *sometimes stalked*. Antennae of ♂ plumose.

Tussock moth larvae are very distinctive caterpillars. They have a pair of pencil-like hair tufts at the anterior end, a single similar tuft at the posterior end, and 4 short thick hair tufts on the back. Adult male tussock moths are grayish brown, with broad wings and a wingspread of 20–25 mm.; females are wingless. The Gypsy Moth (Pl. 12), *Porthetria dispar* (Linn.), a species introduced from Europe, is most common in the East; its larva often does a great deal of damage to forest trees. Male Gypsy Moths are brownish, with plumose antennae, and are good fliers; females, white with black markings, do not fly.

Microlepidoptera

Size variable but usually with a wingspread of 20 mm. or less. Wing shape variable, sometimes relatively broad, sometimes narrow and pointed apically. Tibial spurs generally long. Many, especially narrow-winged forms, with a fringe of long hairs on anal margin of HW. Wing venation variable but broad-winged forms usually with 2 anal veins in FW and 3 in HW. This is a large group making up about half of the order; identification of many is often difficult. The families of Microlepidoptera are discussed below in 3 groups:

1. With a distinctive wing shape or scaling (p. 240).
2. Wings *relatively broad* and more or less rounded apically, FW *somewhat triangular*, HW *usually as broad as or broader* than FW, and with 3 anal veins (p. 242).
3. Wings *narrow and more or less pointed apically*, HW *usually narrower* than FW and with anal area reduced; a long fringe on anal margin of HW (p. 252).

A few families of Microlepidoptera contain species that fall into 2 of the above groups, but in most families all species in the family can be placed in just 1 of these groups.

Microlepidoptera, Group 1

Wings with distinctive shape or scaling: lobed (Pterophoridae and

Alucitidae), distal margin of HW excavated behind tip, with tip produced (Gelechiidae), or wings with extensive areas devoid of scales (Aegeriidae).

PLUME MOTHS Family Pterophoridae
  Identification: Small, slender, long-legged, brownish or gray. Wings at rest held horizontal, at right angles to body. FW with 2–4 apical lobes, *HW with 3*.

Plume moths are common insects, easily recognized by the wing position at rest and the lobed wings; the lobes of the hind wing, with their long fringe, are somewhat plumelike. Plume moth larvae are chiefly leaf rollers or stem borers, and some occasionally damage cultivated plants. The Grape Plume Moth, *Pterophorus periscelidactylus* Fitch, is a pest of grape.

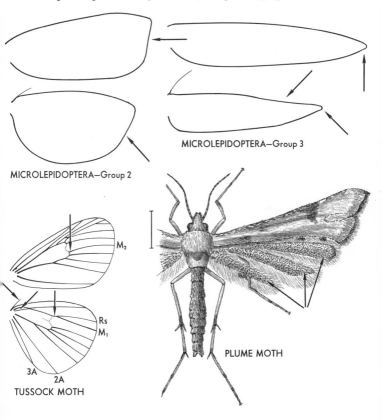

MICROLEPIDOPTERA–Group 3

MICROLEPIDOPTERA–Group 2

M_2

Rs
M_1

3A
2A
TUSSOCK MOTH

PLUME MOTH

MANY-PLUME MOTHS Family Alucitidae   **Not illus.**
  Identification: Similar to Pterophoridae, but each wing divided into 6 plumelike lobes.

  A single rare species of many-plume moth occurs in the northeastern states. It has a wingspread of about 12 mm.

GELECHIID MOTHS Family Gelechiidae
  Identification: Small to minute moths. FW narrowly rounded or *pointed at apex.* HW somewhat trapezoidal, the apex *usually prolonged* and margin behind apex *concave.* Head smooth-scaled. Palps long and upcurved, *3rd segment long and tapering.* If HW is narrow and pointed apically, then R_5 in FW is stalked with R_4 and extends to costal margin of wing.

  This is one of the largest families of Microlepidoptera, with some 600 N. American species. Many are common moths. Larvae vary considerably in habits; some are leaf rollers or leaf tiers, some are leaf miners, a few are gall makers, and 1 species attacks stored grain. Larvae of *Gnorimoschema* live in stem galls on goldenrod; the galls are elongate, spindle-shaped, and thin-walled. Larva of the Angoumois Grain Moth, *Sitotroga cerealella* (Olivier), feeds in the kernels of corn and other grains and often causes serious damage to grain in storage. Larva of the Pink Bollworm, *Pectinophora gossypiella* (Saunders), attacks the bolls of cotton.

CLEAR-WINGED MOTHS Family Aegeriidae **See also Pl. 12**
  Identification: Wasplike moths, with extensive areas in wings (especially HW) devoid of scales. FW *long, narrow,* rounded apically, HW broader; posterior margin of FW and costal margin of HW with a series of interlocking spines.

  Aegeriids are day-flying and often brightly colored; many strongly resemble wasps. The sexes usually differ in color, and the male often has more clear area in the wings than the female. Larvae bore in roots, stems, and trunks of various plants and trees. Some species are serious pests of garden crops, orchard trees, or forest trees.

Microlepidoptera, Group 2

Size variable, but wingspread usually 20 mm. or more. Similar to macro-moths (pp. 230 ff.), but HW generally with *3 anal veins* and FW with *1A often preserved,* at least near wing margin; HW usually as wide as or wider than FW; FW more or less triangular, apically rounded or somewhat square-tipped; tibial spurs usually long.

CARPENTER and LEOPARD MOTHS   **See also Pl. 12**
Family Cossidae
  Identification: Medium-sized, heavy-bodied moths. Wings

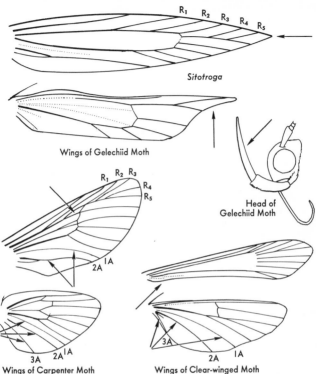

R_1 R_2 R_3 R_4 R_5

Sitotroga

Wings of Gelechiid Moth

R_1 R_2 R_3 R_4 R_5

Head of
Gelechiid Moth

2A 1A

3A 2A 1A
Wings of Carpenter Moth

3A 2A 1A
Wings of Clear-winged Moth

usually spotted or mottled; *2 complete anal veins* in FW; FW
with *an accessory cell*, and some branches of R stalked. Abdomen
extends beyond HW.

Cossid larvae are wood-boring, and sometimes seriously
damage trees. Adults of the Carpenterworm (Pl. 12), *Prionoxystus robiniae* (Peck), a common species of carpenter moth,
have a wingspread of about 2 in. The Leopard Moth, *Zeuzera pyrina* (Linn.), is slightly smaller and whitish, with black spots
on the wings.

DALCERID MOTHS Family Dalceridae   **Not illus.**
  Identification: Superficially resemble some megalopygids (p.
244), but venation as in the Cossidae.
  Two rare species of dalcerids occur in Arizona. They are
orange-yellow without dark markings, and have a wingspread
of about 1 in.

SLUG CATERPILLARS Family Limacodidae **See also Pl. 12**
Identification: Small to medium-sized, stout-bodied, with broad rounded wings. Mostly brownish, marked with green, silver, or some other color. FW has *2 complete anal veins;* 3A in FW short, meeting 2A near base of wing; M_2 in FW rises *closer to M_3 than to M_1.* Sc and R in HW *separate at base, fused for a short distance* near middle of discal cell. No accessory cell in FW.

Limacodid larvae are rather fleshy, with short thoracic legs and no prolegs; they move about a little like slugs. Some larvae have stinging hairs. A common species of this type is the Saddleback Caterpillar, *Sibine stimulea* (Clemens), which feeds on various trees.

FLANNEL MOTHS Family Megalopygidae
Identification: Stout-bodied, very hairy, generally brownish or cream-colored, with a wingspread of 25–35 mm. Sc and R in HW *fused to middle of discal cell or beyond.* Some branches of R in FW stalked beyond discal cell. M_2 in FW *rises near M_3.*

Larvae of these moths are stout and hairy, with some of the hairs forming a crest down middle of the back; some body hairs are stinging. This is a small group and its members are not common.

PLANTHOPPER PARASITES Family Epipyropidae **Not illus.**
Identification: Small, with broad wings and plumose antennae. FW with an accessory cell; no branches of R stalked.

Larvae of these moths live, probably as parasites, on the bodies of planthoppers (Fulgoroidea). Two very rare species occur in the U.S.

SMOKY MOTHS Family Pyromorphidae
Identification: Small gray or black moths, with wings thinly scaled. HW with 2 or *3 anal veins* (if with 2, then 2 complete anal veins in FW), and Sc and R *fused to near end of discal cell.* All branches of R in FW rise from discal cell, or R_3 and R_4 *short-stalked.*

The more common smoky moths resemble scape moths (Ctenuchidae, p. 236), but can be recognized by the wing venation. Larvae of most species feed on grape or Virginia creeper.

WINDOW-WINGED MOTHS Family Thyrididae
Identification: Small, dark-colored, with light translucent spots in wings. M_2 in FW *rises near M_3;* all branches of R and M in FW rise from the usually *open discal cell* (R_3 and R_4 are stalked in 1 genus in the Gulf states).

The front wings of these moths are somewhat triangular, the hind wings are rounded or irregularly scalloped. The group is small and its members are not common.

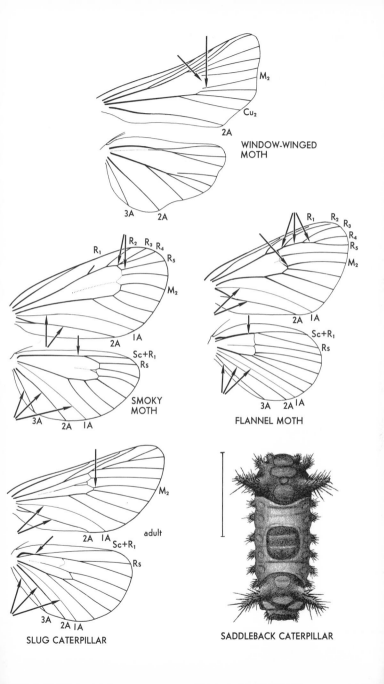

WINDOW-WINGED MOTH

M_2
Cu_2
2A

3A 2A

SMOKY MOTH

R_1 R_2 R_3 R_4
R_5
M_2
1A
2A 1A

$Sc+R_1$
Rs

3A 2A 1A

FLANNEL MOTH

R_1 R_2 R_3
R_4
R_5
M_2
2A 1A

$Sc+R_1$
Rs

3A 2A 1A

SLUG CATERPILLAR

M_2
2A 1A adult
$Sc+R_1$
Rs

3A 2A 1A

SADDLEBACK CATERPILLAR

PYRALID MOTHS Family Pyralidae **See also Pl. 12**
Identification: Small moths. FW usually elongate-triangular, HW broad and rounded. M_2 in FW rises *near* M_3. $Sc + R_1$ and Rs in HW *fused* or very close together for a distance beyond discal cell, then separating. Palps often large and projecting forward.

This is the largest family of Microlepidoptera, with over 1100 N. American species. Its members occur almost everywhere and many are very common. Larvae vary in habits: many feed on foliage in the early instars and bore into stems in later instars; many feed about roots of grasses and other plants; a few feed on stored grain or meal, and a few are aquatic. Many are pests of cultivated plants. One of the most important pest species is the European Corn Borer (Pl. 12), *Ostrinia nubilalis* (Hübner). Members of the genus *Crambus*, often called closewings, are common in meadows; they are whitish or pale yellowish brown, and the wings are held close about the body. A species in this group that feeds on cactus has been introduced into Australia, where it helps control the prickly pear cactus.

BAGWORM MOTHS Family Psychidae
Identification: Small, mostly stout-bodied moths. ♀ usually wingless and with or without legs, antennae, and eyes. Mouth parts vestigial. Most ♂ (Psychinae) with wings thinly scaled or almost devoid of scales, HW with 2 anal veins, FW with 1A and 2A *fused at tip* or connected by a cross vein, and HW *about as wide as long*. Species with more elongate wings and 3 anal veins in HW can be distinguished from other similar Microlepidoptera by the vestigial mouth parts.

Psychid larvae construct portable bags, or cases, of bits of leaves and twigs, and eventually pupate in this bag. Wingless females lay their eggs in the bag, and usually never leave it until the eggs are laid. The Evergreen Bagworm, *Thyridopteryx ephemeraeformis* (Haworth), is a common species with wingless females; larva feeds on cedars, and the male is black with almost clear wings. Other species are somewhat smoky in color and have the wings thinly scaled.

BURROWING WEBWORMS Family Acrolophidae
Identification: Noctuidlike moths with a wingspread of 12 mm. or more. Eyes usually hairy. 1st segment of labial palps *as large as 2nd or larger*, the palps upturned and in ♂ reaching back over thorax. Wing venation complete, no veins stalked.

Larvae of these moths live in the ground and feed on roots of grasses. They usually construct a tubular web leading from the surface down into the ground, and retreat into this tube when disturbed. These insects are sometimes destructive to young corn plants.

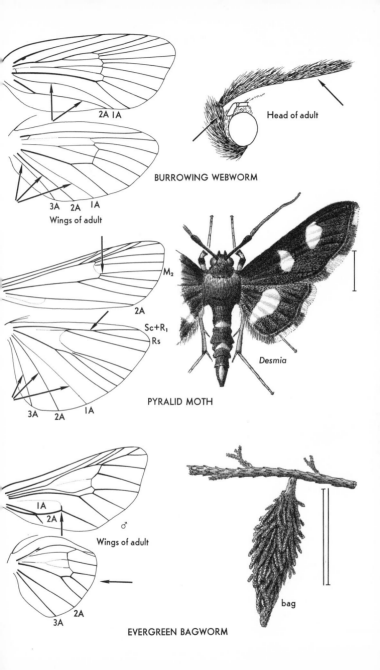

BURROWING WEBWORM

Head of adult

Wings of adult

3A 2A 1A

2A 1A

PYRALID MOTH

M₂

2A

Sc+R₁

Rs

3A 2A 1A

Desmia

EVERGREEN BAGWORM

Wings of adult

♂

1A

2A

3A 2A

bag

OLETHREUTID MOTHS   Family Olethreutidae
Identification: Small brownish or gray moths, FW *rather square-tipped*. Cu_2 in FW rises *in basal $\frac{3}{4}$ of discal cell*. FW with R_4 and R_5 separate, or M_2, M_3, and Cu_1 strongly converge distally. Upper side of Cu in HW usually with a fringe of long hairs.

This is a large family, with over 700 N. American species. Many are serious pests of cultivated plants; the larvae usually bore into the stems or fruits of the plant. One of the most important pests in this group is the Codling Moth, *Carpocapsa pomonella* (Linn.), which attacks apple and other fruits; a small caterpillar found inside an apple is very probably the larva of this moth.

TORTRICID MOTHS   Family Tortricidae   See also Pl. 12
Identification: Similar to Olethreutidae, but Cu in HW lacking fringe of long hairs, R_4 and R_5 in FW usually stalked or fused, and M_2, M_3, and Cu_1 in FW parallel or divergent.

Most tortricid larvae are leaf rollers or leaf tiers. Some tie a number of leaves together with silk and feed inside the shelter so formed. An important pest of the group is the Spruce Budworm, *Choristoneura fumiferana* (Clemens), which may defoliate and kill spruce or other evergreens; this species is important in n. New England and the Maritime Provinces of Canada. Tortricids are common moths.

PHALONIID MOTHS   Family Phaloniidae   Not illus.
Identification: Small moths, HW broad and rounded. Cu_2 in FW rises in distal $\frac{1}{4}$ of discal cell. 1A absent in FW. R_5 in FW usually not stalked with R_4, and extends to outer margin of wing. M_1 in HW usually stalked with Rs. 3rd segment of labial palps short, blunt, the palps beaklike.

Some phaloniid larvae tie leaves together to form a shelter. They are mostly seed or stem borers and are uncommon.

CARPOSINID MOTHS   Family Carposinidae   Not illus.
Identification: Small moths. HW with only 1 branch of M. 1A completely lacking in FW.

This is a small, relatively rare group. The larva of 1 species bores into the fruit of currants.

OECOPHORID MOTHS   Family Oecophoridae
Identification: Small, somewhat flattened. Wings relatively broad, rounded apically, HW as wide as FW or nearly so. Cu_2 in FW rises *in distal $\frac{1}{4}$ of discal cell*, R_4 and R_5 in FW *stalked;* Rs and M_1 in HW *not stalked*. Head usually smooth-scaled. Palps long, upcurved, usually extending beyond vertex.

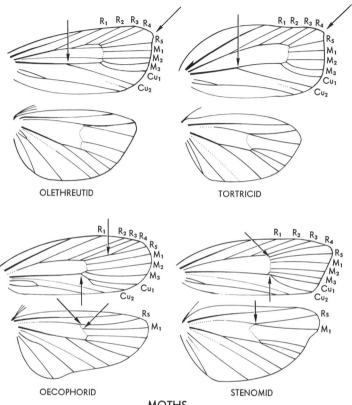

OLETHREUTID

TORTRICID

OECOPHORID

STENOMID

MOTHS

Oecophorids are fairly common, usually brownish moths. *Depressaria heracliana* (Linn.) attacks wild carrot, parsley, and related plants; the larva ties up the flower heads with silk and feeds inside them, then burrows into the stem.

STENOMID MOTHS Family Stenomidae
Identification: Cu₂ in FW rises *at end of discal cell.* Rs and M₁ in HW *stalked;* R₄ and R₅ in FW *usually not stalked*, or if stalked then R₅ extends to outer margin of wing. Head smooth-scaled.

Stenomid larvae usually feed in webs on leaves of oak. The moths are relatively large and plain-colored, whitish or gray, sometimes with dark markings. This group is small (24 N. American species), its members not common.

ETHMIID MOTHS Family Ethmiidae **Not illus.**
Identification: Similar to Oecophoridae (p. 248), but M_2 in HW rises closer to M_1 than to M_3.

Most ethmiids have the front wings marked with black and white. Larvae live in webs and feed chiefly on bindweed.

GLYPHIPTERYGID MOTHS Family Glyphipterygidae
Identification: Small, FW rather square-tipped. Ocelli *large and conspicuous*. Head *smooth-scaled*. Cu_2 in FW rises in *distal* ¼ *of discal cell*. Rs and M_1 in HW *separated at origin*. R_5 in FW free or stalked with R_4, *extending to* apex or *outer margin* of wing. 2A in HW *forked at base*.

About 50 species occur in N. America but they are not common. Larvae of most species are leaf tiers.

ERMINE MOTHS Family Yponomeutidae **See also Pl. 12**
Identification: Small moths, FW usually brightly patterned. Head smooth-scaled. Cu_2 in FW rises *in distal* ¼ *of discal cell*. Rs and M_1 in HW *separated at their origin*. R_4 and R_5 in FW *separate*, R_5 extending to apex or outer margin of wing. M_1 and M_2 in HW *not stalked* (except in *Argyresthia*, which has the wings pointed apically).

Ermine moths are so called because some species (*Yponomeuta*) have the front wings white with black spots; other species are differently colored, but most have the front wings brightly patterned. Larvae of most species feed in webs spun over the leaves; a few are leaf miners, and some bore into fruit. Ermine moths are fairly common.

CLOTHES MOTHS and Others Family Tineidae
Identification: Wings usually somewhat rounded apically, the HW about as wide as FW, sometimes narrowly rounded or *pointed apically* and HW narrower than FW. Maxillary palps usually present, folded at rest. Head rough-scaled or bristly. Antennae with a whorl of erect scales on each segment.

Most of the more than 130 species of N. American tineids are small and plain-colored. Many larvae are scavengers or feed on fungi, and some feed on fabrics; relatively few feed on foliage. Many larvae are casemakers. Three species in this group that feed on clothes and various woolen materials are often called clothes moths. The Webbing Clothes Moth, *Tineola bisselliella* (Hummel), is straw-colored and has a wingspread of 12–16 mm.; larva does not form cases. The Casemaking Clothes Moth, *Tinea pellionella* (Linn.), is about the same size but is more brownish and has 3 small dark spots in each front wing; its larva is a casemaker. The Carpet Moth, *Trichophaga tapetzella* (Linn.), is 12–14 mm. in wingspread and base of the front wings

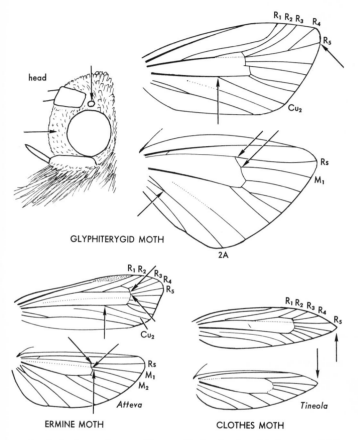

GLYPHITERYGID MOTH

ERMINE MOTH   CLOTHES MOTH

is dark; larva forms silken galleries in the fabrics on which
it feeds.

YUCCA MOTHS and Others Family Incurvariidae   **p. 253**
  Identification: Small moths. Wing surface with minute spines
  under the scales. Wings narrowly rounded apically, HW about
  as wide as FW. Venation usually complete, with R_4 and R_5 in
  FW generally *stalked*, and R_5 *extending to costal margin* of wing.
  Maxillary palps usually *well developed*, *folded*, the folded part
  ½ to ⅔ as long as width of head (sometimes vestigial or short
  and not folded).

Subfamily Incurvariinae (not illus.). The maxillary palps are folded, the folded part about half as long as width of head. Most are black or metallic bluish. Larva of the Maple Leaf Cutter, *Paraclemensia acerifoliella* (Fitch), is a leaf miner when young and a casemaker when older; cases of older larvae are made from 2 circular pieces of the leaf and are somewhat turtle-like. The members of this group are not common.

Yucca Moths, Subfamily Prodoxinae. These are similar to the Incurvariinae but white. Yucca moths in the genus *Tegeticula* pollinate the yucca; the female lays her eggs in the ovary of a yucca flower, and the larvae feed on the seeds; after ovipositing, the female thrusts a mass of yucca pollen into the stigma of the flower in which the eggs are laid. Pollen is collected by means of long curled tentacles on the maxillae. Yucca moths in the genus *Prodoxus* lack maxillary tentacles and do not pollinate yucca, but their larvae feed on its flower stem and the fleshy part of the fruit.

Fairy Moths, Subfamily Adelinae (not illus.). These moths have antennae at least as long as the front wings (in males to several times as long). Larvae usually live in flowers or seeds, and pupate inside 2 oval pieces of a leaf. There are about a dozen N. American species, and they are not common.

Microlepidoptera, Group 3

Small to minute, wingspread 3–20 mm. Wings narrow and more or less pointed apically; HW usually narrower than FW, with anal area reduced and with a long fringe on anal margin of wing.

Separation of families in this group will be a problem for the beginner. It is based principally on wing venation, mouth parts, head scaling, and occasionally other characters. Wing venation often is difficult to make out, even after the wings are cleared. Maxillary palps are vestigial or absent in most of these moths but in a few are well developed and at rest held in a folded position on either side of the proboscis. Labial palps are usually well developed, the basal segment small and the other 2 elongate; they curve up in front of the head, often to middle of the face or beyond. Some of these moths have an eye cap: the basal antennal segment is enlarged and concave beneath and fits over the eye when the antenna is depressed. The head is smooth-scaled in most moths in this group, but in some is rather bristly, especially on the vertex.

OPOSTEGID MOTHS   Family Opostegidae   **Not illus.**
  Identification: Small to minute. Antennae with an eye cap. Maxillary palps small and folded. Venation greatly reduced, FW with only 3 or 4 unbranched veins.

Only 6 species of opostegids occur in N. America, and they are not common. Larvae are leaf miners.

NEPTICULID MOTHS Family Nepticulidae   **Not illus.**
Identification: Minute moths. Antennae with an eye cap.
Maxillary palps well developed, long, folded. FW with branched
veins.

Some nepticulids have a wingspread of only a few mm. They
are fairly common, but because of their small size are often overlooked. Larvae are mostly leaf miners, but a few form galls on
the twigs or leaf petioles of various trees.

LYONETIID MOTHS Family Lyonetiidae
Identification: Small to very small moths. Antennae with *an
eye cap.* Vertex usually *rough and bristly.* Labial palps *very
short* and drooping. Ocelli absent.

Some species in this fairly large group are quite common.
Larvae are leaf miners, or live in webs between leaves. The
largest genus is *Bucculatrix*, the larvae of which form whitish,
longitudinally ribbed cocoons attached to twigs.

LEAF BLOTCH MINERS Family Gracilariidae   **p. 255**
Identification: Small to minute moths. Antennae with or without an eye cap. Maxillary palps usually absent; if present, small
and projecting forward. Scaling on vertex rough or smooth.

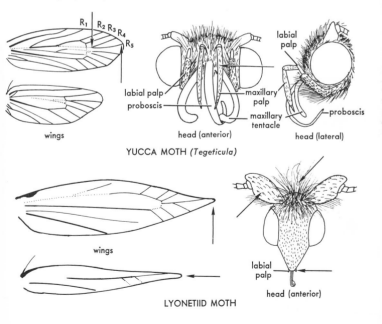

YUCCA MOTH *(Tegeticula)*

LYONETIID MOTH

HW usually *without a discal cell*, and costal margin *humped slightly near base*. FW generally without an accessory cell, but if one is present (*Parornix*) it is less than $\frac{1}{3}$ as long as discal cell and there are 5 veins extending from discal cell to costal margin of wing. Venation of FW usually reduced, with 8 or fewer veins extending from discal cell to wing margin, *not more than 4 of which normally extend to costal margin*.

This is a large group, with over 200 N. American species. Larvae are leaf miners, and usually make blotch mines. Larvae of *Phyllocnistis* make narrow winding mines containing a dark central line of excrement; *P. populiella* Chambers is a common species attacking aspens and poplars.

OINOPHILID MOTHS   Family Oinophilidae   **Not illus.**
Identification: Very small, strongly flattened moths. Head smooth-scaled. R_5 in FW, when present, extends to costal margin of wing.

Our single oinophilid occurs in Mississippi and Louisiana. It is brownish gray, with a wingspread of about 9 mm. Larvae feed on fungi and decaying plant materials.

DIAMONDBACK MOTHS   Family Plutellidae
Identification: Small moths with wings *narrowly rounded at apex* and HW about as wide as FW. Rs and M_1 in HW stalked or *very close together in basal $\frac{1}{3}$ of their length*. Head smooth-scaled. R_4 and R_5 in FW *not stalked*.

The front wings of these moths are often brightly patterned; light marks along costal margin of the wing in some species form diamond-shaped spots when the wings are folded over the abdomen. Larvae of most species are leaf miners or leaf tiers; a few are pests of garden plants.

DOUGLASIID MOTHS   Family Douglasiidae
Identification: Small moths. HW *without a discal cell*, R vein near middle of wing *with a branch to costal margin* at about $\frac{2}{3}$ the wing length; R_5 in FW, when present, *free from R_4 but stalked with M_1*. Ocelli very large.

Only 4 species of douglasiids occur in N. America. Larvae are leaf miners.

CASEBEARERS   Family Coleophoridae
Identification: Small to minute moths. Discal cell of FW *oblique*, its apex *much closer to hind margin* of wing than to costal margin. R_2 in FW rises *about halfway between R_1 and R_3*, but not at apex of discal cell. Front tibiae slender, without a movable pad on inner surface.

About 100 species of casebearers occur in N. America, and some are fairly common. Young larvae are usually leaf miners, but older larvae construct portable cases of bits of leaves and excrement; older larvae feed by protruding the head from end of the case and eating holes in leaves of the host plant. The Pistol Casebearer, *Coleophora malivorella* Riley, and the Cigar Casebearer, *C. serratella* (Linn.), are pests of apple and other fruit trees; the common names refer to the shape of the cases.

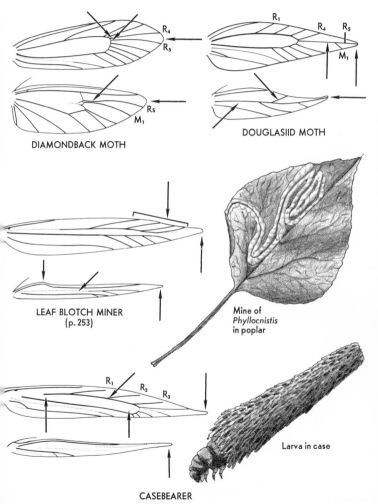

DIAMONDBACK MOTH

DOUGLASIID MOTH

LEAF BLOTCH MINER
(p. 253)

Mine of
Phyllocnistis
in poplar

Larva in case

CASEBEARER

COSMOPTERYGID MOTHS   Family Cosmopterygidae

Identification: Head smooth-scaled. R_1 in FW usually rises *about middle of discal cell* or slightly beyond, and R_2 rises *before apex of cell,* usually a little more than halfway between R_1 and R_3. R_4 and R_5 in FW *stalked* or fused. Discal cell in FW variable in position, but if oblique (as in Coleophoridae) front tibiae have a well-developed pad on inner surface at about half their length.

Cosmopterygids are small moths that vary somewhat in wing shape and venation and in color; a few have apex of the front wing elongated. Larvae of most species are leaf miners; 1 species feeds in the bolls of cotton.

BLASTOBASID MOTHS   Family Blastobasidae

Identification: Small moths. FW with *a stigmalike thickening* between C and R_1. R_2 in FW rises at or *near apex of discal cell.* R_4 and R_5 in FW *long-stalked.*

About 100 species of blastobasids occur in N. America, but they are not common. Some larvae are scavengers; the larva of 1 species feeds inside acorns that have been hollowed out by acorn weevils.

SHIELD BEARERS   Family Heliozelidae   Not illus.

Identification: Small moths. Head smooth-scaled. Palps short and drooping. Discal cell absent in HW, sometimes (*Coptodisca*) also absent in FW.

Larvae of most shield bearers are leaf miners and when ready to pupate cut out an oval section of the leaf and make it into a pupal case that is attached to another part of the host plant. Most species attack trees.

HELIODINID MOTHS   Family Heliodinidae

Identification: Very small moths. Head smooth-scaled. Venation variable, FW sometimes (*Cycloplasis*) with only 3 or 4 veins, usually with a well-developed discal cell and 8–10 veins extending from cell to wing margin and R_1 rising *about middle of cell. At least 3 veins* rise from apex of discal cell in FW. HW *without a forked vein* at apex.

These moths rest with the hind or middle legs outstretched or elevated above the wings. Larvae vary in habits: some are leaf miners, some are external feeders on foliage, and 1 species is an internal parasite of oak scales (Kermidae).

EPERMENIID MOTHS   Family Epermeniidae   Not illus.

Identification: Small moths. FW with 10 veins from discal cell to wing margin, 4 of them to costal margin. Head smooth-scaled. R_1 in FW rises before middle of discal cell. Rs in HW ends at or before apex of wing. Ocelli absent.

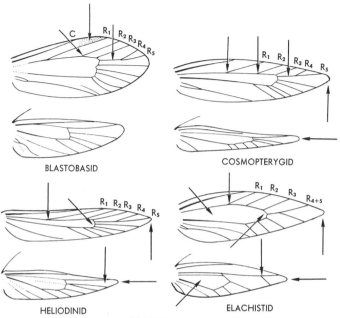

BLASTOBASID

COSMOPTERYGID

HELIODINID

ELACHISTID

MOTHS

This is a small and uncommon group. The moths are yellowish, grayish, or brownish.

SCYTHRID MOTHS   Family Scythridae   **Not illus.**
Identification: Small moths. FW with 9 veins extending from discal cell to wing margin, 4 of them to costal margin. R_1 in FW rises about ⅔ the length of discal cell. Forked vein at tip of HW.

This is a small group, and not common. Larvae are leaf folders or leaf tiers.

ELACHISTID MOTHS   Family Elachistidae
Identification: Mostly dark brown or gray, with silvery spots or bands. Head smooth-scaled. Discal cell *present* in both FW and HW. FW with only 8 or 9 veins extending from discal cell to wing margin, 4 or fewer of them to costal margin, and *only 1 or 2 veins* rising from apex of discal cell. R_1 in FW rises *about middle of discal cell.* HW with *a forked vein at apex.*

Larvae are leaf miners in grasses and sedges. Elachistids are not common.

TISCHERIID MOTHS Family Tischeriidae
Identification: Face smooth-scaled, but vertex with rough bristly hair. Labial palps small. Costal margin of FW somewhat arched and apex *prolonged* to a sharp point. FW with *5 veins* extending from discal cell to costal wing margin, and with an accessory cell at least half as long as the discal cell.

Larvae of most tischeriids make blotch mines in oak leaves. The Apple Leaf Trumpet Miner, *Tischeria malifoliella* Clemens, is a common pest in the East; its larva makes a trumpet-shaped mine. Other species mine in leaves of blackberry or raspberry.

Jugate Moths: Suborder Jugatae

Venation in FW and HW similar, Rs in HW with *as many branches as in FW*. No frenulum, the wings on each side united by a jugum (a fingerlike lobe at base of FW). This is a small group, with about 30 N. American species. Most are quite rare.

ERIOCRANIID MOTHS Family Eriocraniidae **Not illus.**
Identification: Wingspread 12 mm. or less. Maxillary palps well developed, 5-segmented. Mandibles vestigial. Middle tibiae with 1 spur. Sc in FW forked near its tip.

Eriocraniids are somewhat similar to clothes moths. Larvae are leaf miners, usually attacking trees. Larva of *Mnemonica auricyanea* Walsingham makes blotch mines in oak and chestnut, and pupates in the soil. None of our 5 N. American species is common.

MANDIBULATE MOTHS Family Micropterygidae
Identification: Similar to Eriocraniidae, but with functional mandibles, middle tibiae without spurs, and Sc in FW *forked near its middle*.

These moths differ from all other Lepidoptera in having functional mandibles. They feed chiefly on pollen. Larvae whose habits are known feed on mosses and liverworts. Only 3 species of mandibulate moths occur in N. America, and they are quite rare.

GHOST MOTHS or SWIFTS Family Hepialidae
Identification: Wingspread 1–3 in. Maxillary palps well developed. *No tibial spurs.*

Ghost moths are relatively uncommon, but are the jugates most likely to be encountered. The name "swift" refers to the very fast flight of most of these moths. Some of the larger species are similar to sphinx moths. Larvae bore in the roots of various trees; *Sthenopis argenteomaculatus* Harris attacks alder and *S. thule* Strecker bores in willow.

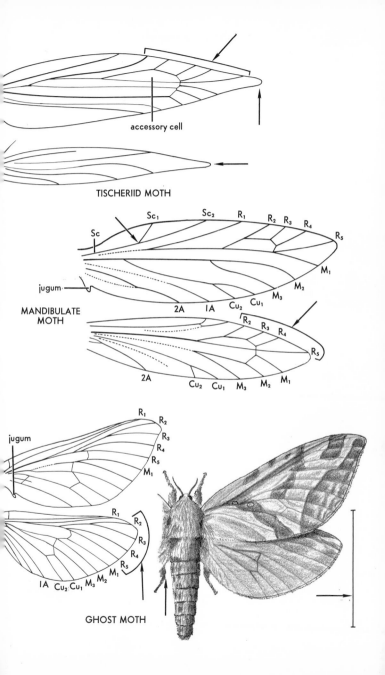

TISCHERIID MOTH

accessory cell

MANDIBULATE MOTH

Sc   Sc₁   Sc₂   R₁   R₂ R₃ R₄   R₅

jugum   2A   1A   Cu₂   Cu₁   M₃   M₂   M₁

R₂ R₃ R₄   R₅

2A   Cu₂   Cu₁   M₃   M₂   M₁

GHOST MOTH

jugum   R₁   R₂   R₃   R₄   R₅   M₁

R₁   R₂   R₃   R₄   R₅   M₁

1A   Cu₂ Cu₁ M₃ M₂ M₁

Flies: Order Diptera

Identification: *One pair* of membranous wings, borne by meso-thorax (wings rarely reduced or lacking). HW reduced to small knobbed structures (halteres). Antennae *variable, often short, inconspicuous, and 3-segmented.* Compound eyes large, sometimes meeting on dorsal side of head. Mouth parts *sucking* (rarely vestigial), maxillary palps well developed, labial palps lacking. Tarsi nearly always *5-segmented.* Relatively soft-bodied. Meta-morphosis complete.

Similar orders: Most insects in other orders likely to be confused with Diptera have 2 pairs of wings. The few with 1 pair (certain grasshoppers, beetles, mayflies, and others) generally do not resemble flies. Male scale insects resemble midges, but have 1-segmented tarsi and 1 or 2 long stylelike processes at end of the abdomen.

Immature stages: Larvae are usually legless and wormlike, and often lack a well-developed head; they are commonly called maggots. They live in water, soil, decaying materials, or in plant or animal tissues. Many are aquatic and occur in a variety of aquatic habitats. The plant-feeding species generally live in the roots, fruit, leaves, or other parts of the plant. Many are parasitic, living in the bodies of other animals.

Habits: Flies occur in many different habitats; each species is usually found near the habitat of its larvae. Adults often occur on flowers. Many are bloodsucking, and are to be found on or near the animals on which they feed.

Importance: Flies constitute one of the larger orders of insects and are abundant in individuals as well as species; they occur almost everywhere. They are an important food of many larger animals. Many species are parasitic or predaceous on other insects and are of value in keeping noxious species under control; others are of value as scavengers. Large numbers are a nuisance because they bite; some are important as vectors of disease. Many attack and damage cultivated plants; a few of these serve as vectors of plant diseases.

Classification: Three suborders — Nematocera, Brachycera, and Cyclorrhapha — differing principally in wing venation and an-tennal structure. Wing venation provides useful characters for separating families throughout the order; the venational termin-ology usually used is that of Comstock, but many terms of an older terminology, particularly those referring to cells, are frequently used; these 2 terminologies are illustrated opposite. Other char-acters used in separating families of Diptera are discussed in the accounts of the groups in which they are used.

No. of species: World, 86,000; N. America, 16,130.

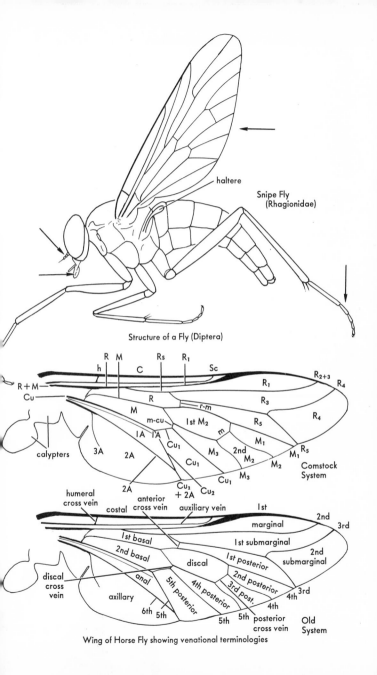

haltere

Snipe Fly
(Rhagionidae)

Structure of a Fly (Diptera)

Comstock System

h R M Rs R₁ Sc
C
R + M
Cu
R₁ R₂₊₃ R₄
R₃
M R r-m R₅ R₄
m-cu 1st M₂ m R₅
1A 1A M₃ M₁
3A Cu₁ 2nd M₁ R₅
2A M₃ M₂ M₂
Cu₁ M₂
Cu₂ Cu₁ M₃
2A + 2A Cu₂
calypters

Old System

humeral 1st
cross vein costal anterior auxiliary vein
cross vein marginal 2nd
1st basal 3rd
2nd basal 1st submarginal
discal 1st posterior 2nd
submarginal
discal 2nd 3rd
cross anal 5th posterior 4th posterior post. 4th
vein axillary 3rd post. 4th
6th 5th 5th posterior 5th
5th cross vein

Wing of Horse Fly showing venational terminologies

Suborder Nematocera

Antennae apparently with 6 or more segments (3rd subdivided), plumose in some males. Wing venation varies from complete (with R 5-branched) to greatly reduced. R_{2+3} often forked (never forked in other suborders). Mostly slender, soft-bodied, midgelike, with relatively long legs and antennae. Larvae usually aquatic or living in moist soil, the nonaquatic larvae generally being gall makers.

CRANE FLIES   Family Tipulidae
Identification: Mosquitolike, with *very long legs*. Mesonotum with a *V-shaped suture*. Ocelli *absent*. R with 4 or fewer branches. *2 anal veins reach wing margin.*

This is a large group, with nearly 1500 N. American species. Many of its members are very common flies. Most species are 10–25 mm. and brownish or gray; a few have dark markings on the wings. Larvae live in water or in moist soil, and generally feed on decaying plant material. Adults are most common near water or where there is abundant vegetation. Crane flies do not bite.

WINTER CRANE FLIES   Family Trichoceridae
Identification: Similar to Tipulidae, but *with ocelli*.

These crane flies are most likely to be seen in early spring or on mild days in winter. They are not common. Larvae live in decaying plant materials.

PRIMITIVE CRANE FLIES   Family Tanyderidae
Identification: Similar to Tipulidae, but R *5-branched*. M_3 cell with *a cross vein*. Anal angle of wing *well developed*.

This group contains 4 N. American species, 1 in the East and 3 in the West, none of them common. The eastern species occurs from Quebec to Florida; it is 7–10 mm., and grayish brown with brown crossbands on the wings; it generally occurs in dense vegetation near streams, and the larvae live in wet sand along stream shores.

PHANTOM CRANE FLIES   Family Ptychopteridae
Identification: Similar to Tipulidae, but wings with *only 1 anal vein reaching margin* and *without a closed discal cell*.

Our most common ptychopterid is *Bittacomorpha clavipes* (Fabricius), which has legs banded with black and white and the basal tarsal segment swollen; it often flies with the legs extended. Other species lack leg bands and do not have a swollen basal tarsal segment. Larvae live in decaying plant materials and adults occur in swampy areas.

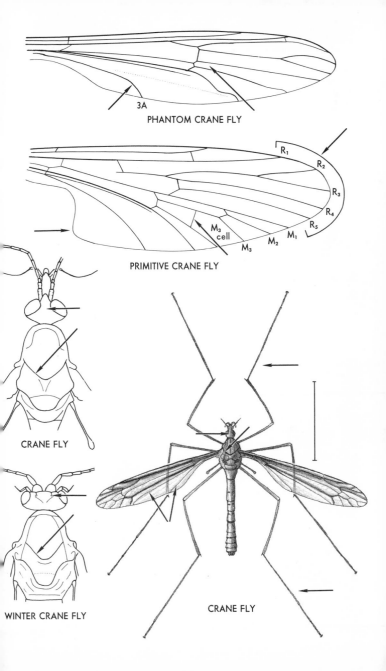

PHANTOM CRANE FLY

3A

PRIMITIVE CRANE FLY

R_1
R_2
R_3
R_4
R_5
M_1
M_2
M_3
M_3 cell

CRANE FLY

WINTER CRANE FLY

CRANE FLY

MOTH and SAND FLIES   Family Psychodidae
Identification: Small, *very hairy* flies, mostly 5 mm. or less.
Wings usually broad, *pointed apically*, and at rest are held roof-
like over body (moth flies) or together above body (sand flies).
R *5-branched.*

Moth flies occur near drains and sewers, often in considerable
numbers; larvae live in places where there are decaying materials.
Sand flies (subfamily Phlebotominae) occur near water; larvae
live in moist soil. Moth flies are common and widely distributed,
and do not bite; sand flies occur in the South and the tropics,
and they bite. Sand flies serve as vectors of several diseases —
pappataci fever, kala-azar, oriental sore, espundia, and oroya
fever or verruga peruana — in S. America and other tropical
areas of the world.

NET-WINGED MIDGES   Family Blephariceridae
Identification: Mosquitolike in size, with long legs and resembling crane flies but without a V-shaped suture on mesonotum. Anal angle of wing *projects*. Wings sometimes with a network of fine lines between the veins. Ocelli present.

These flies occur along swift-moving streams, in which the
larvae live. They are relatively rare.

NYMPHOMYIID FLIES   Family Nymphomyiidae   **Not illus.**
Identification: Wings vestigial. Antennae 5-segmented, 3rd
segment large and club-shaped. Head elongate. Mouth parts
vestigial. Legs long and slender and widely separated.

One species in this group has been reported from rapid streams
in New Brunswick. Larvae are assumed to be aquatic.

MOUNTAIN MIDGES   Family Deuterophlebiidae   **Not illus.**
Identification: Wings broad (broadest in basal $\frac{1}{4}$), pubescent,
almost veinless but with a fanlike development of folds. Antennae very long, at least 3 times as long as body. Ocelli and
mouth parts lacking.

Four species of mountain midges have been reported from the
West (Colorado to California), where the larvae occur in swift-
flowing mountain streams.

DIXID MIDGES   Family Dixidae
Identification: Similar to mosquitoes (p. 266) but wings lacking
scales and body bare (not scaly).

Dixid midges are common and widely distributed insects.
Larvae occur in pools and ponds, and adults are usually found
near these habitats. Larvae are slender and wormlike, and feed
on surface of the water; the body is generally bent into a U, and
the larvae move by alternately straightening and bending the
body. Adults are blackish and 5–6 mm. They do not bite.

PHANTOM MIDGES Family Chaoboridae

Identification: Similar to mosquitoes (p. 266) but wing scales mostly confined to margin and *proboscis short*.

These insects are quite common, and generally occur near pools and ponds in which the larvae live. The common name of the group is derived from the appearance of some larvae, which

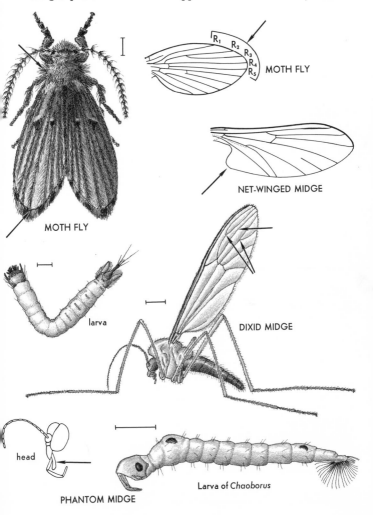

MOTH FLY

MOTH FLY

NET-WINGED MIDGE

larva

DIXID MIDGE

head

PHANTOM MIDGE

Larva of *Chaoborus*

are nearly transparent; these larvae are predaceous, capturing prey with their antennae. Adults do not bite.

MOSQUITOES Family Culicidae

Identification: Wings long, narrow, with *scales along veins and wing margin.* Distal part of wing with *an unforked vein between 2 forked veins.* Proboscis *long.* Ocelli absent.

Mosquitoes are common, widely distributed, and well-known insects. Males have very plumose antennae and do not bite; females, which have only a few short hairs on the antennae, do bite and are often serious pests. Mosquitoes serve as vectors of several important diseases: malaria, yellow fever, dengue, filariasis, and encephalitis; these diseases are chiefly tropical but some may occur in this country.

This family is divided into 3 subfamilies, Anophelinae, Culicinae, and Toxorhynchitinae. Anophelinae have palps long in both sexes (clubbed in ♂) and the scutellum rounded; they rest with the body and proboscis in an almost straight line, at an angle to the substrate (some appear almost to "stand on their heads"). Culicinae have palps of the female short and those of the male usually long, and the scutellum 3-lobed; they rest with the proboscis bent down and the body more or less parallel to the substrate. Toxorhynchitinae are large mosquitoes, with the scutellum rounded and palps of the female short; the basal part of the proboscis is stout, the apical part is slender and decurved. Anophelinae are represented in N. America by 1 genus, *Anopheles,* most species of which have patches of light and dark scales on the wings. Most of our mosquitoes (*Culex, Aedes, Psorophora,* and others) belong to the Culicinae. Toxorhynchitinae are represented by 1 genus, *Toxorhynchites,* and are not very common.

Mosquito larvae are aquatic and occur in ponds, pools, various containers of water, and in tree holes containing water. Larvae breathe at the surface; larvae of Toxorhynchitinae and Culicinae have *a breathing tube* at the posterior end of the body; larvae of *Anopheles lack a breathing tube,* and spend most of their time at the surface. Most larvae feed on organic debris; a few are predaceous. Pupae are aquatic and generally very active. Eggs are usually laid on surface of the water, either singly or in rafts. A few lay eggs near water, and the eggs hatch when flooded.

SOLITARY MIDGES Family Thaumaleidae   **Not illus.**

Identification: Bare, reddish-yellow or brownish flies, about 8 mm. Venation reduced, and only 7 veins reach wing margin (R 2-branched, M unbranched). Ocelli absent. Antennae short, about as long as head, the 2 basal segments enlarged.

This group includes 5 rare N. American species, 2 in the East (Quebec to N. Carolina) and 3 in the West (British Columbia

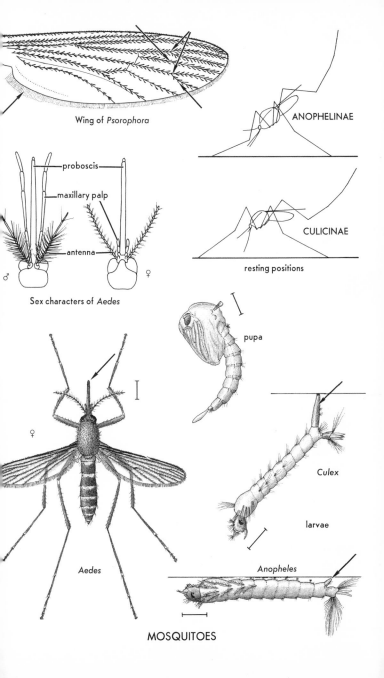

Wing of *Psorophora*

ANOPHELINAE

CULICINAE

resting positions

proboscis

maxillary palp

antenna

♂   ♀

Sex characters of *Aedes*

pupa

♀

Aedes

Culex

larvae

Anopheles

MOSQUITOES

and Idaho). Larvae occur on rocks in streams, and adults are usually found on vegetation near streams.

PUNKIES or BITING MIDGES Family Ceratopogonidae
Identification: Minute flies, generally *less than 3 mm.* Ocelli absent. Radial branches prominent. Thickened part of C usually ends ½ or ¾ way to wing tip; M with 2 branches. Front tarsi *not lengthened.*

Many punkies bite man and may be very annoying. A few live as ectoparasites on the bodies of other insects and a few are predaceous. Larvae are mostly slender and snakelike, aquatic or semiaquatic.

MIDGES Family Chironomidae
Identification: Ocelli absent. Thickened part of C ends near wing tip. M unbranched. Front tarsi usually *lengthened.* Wings long and narrow. ♂ antennae generally *plumose.*

Midges are very common insects, found almost everywhere and often in considerable numbers. Larvae of most species are aquatic, and many live in tubes constructed of debris; some larvae are red. Adults are generally soft-bodied, with long legs and antennae and a short proboscis; they do not bite. Midges frequently occur in large swarms, particularly near ponds and lakes.

BLACK FLIES Family Simuliidae
Identification: Generally 4 mm. or less, stocky in build, and somewhat *humpbacked.* Antennae *short.* Ocelli absent. Wings *broad at base,* narrowing distally, anterior veins *heavy* and remaining veins weak. Usually gray.

Female black flies are vicious biters and are serious pests in many parts of the country. Larvae live in streams, often in large numbers, where they attach to objects in the water. Black flies are widely distributed; adults appear chiefly in late spring and early summer. In parts of the tropics these insects serve as the vector of onchocerciasis, a disease caused by a roundworm that sometimes also causes blindness.

WOOD GNATS Family Anisopodidae
Identification: Mosquitolike in appearance, 4–6 mm. Ocelli present. Thickened section of C ends *near wing tip.* A discal cell and 5 posterior cells usually *present* (Anisopodinae); if a discal cell is lacking (Mycetobiinae) the base of M is *lacking,* the 2 basal cells *coalesce,* and Rs forks *opposite the r-m cross vein.*

The most common wood gnats (Anisopodinae) have faint spots on the wings, and usually occur in moist places where there is abundant vegetation; larvae occur in decaying materials. Wood gnats are often attracted to sap, and the larvae of some species live in fermenting sap.

PACHYNEURID GNATS Family Pachyneuridae
Identification: Similar to Anisopodidae, but Rs 3-branched; R_2
resembles *a cross vein* and extends from R_{2+3} to about the end
of R_1.

There are 2 rather rare species of pachyneurids in the U.S.,
1 in the East and 1 in the West. The eastern species, *Axymyia
furcata* McAtee, occurs from Massachusetts to Virginia. It is

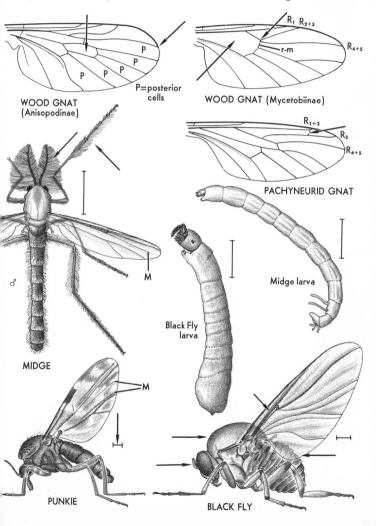

WOOD GNAT
(Anisopodinae)

P=posterior
cells

WOOD GNAT (Mycetobiinae)

R_1 R_{2+3}

r-m

R_{4+5}

R_{1+2}

R_3

R_{4+5}

PACHYNEURID GNAT

Midge larva

Black Fly
larva

♂

M

MIDGE

M

PUNKIE

BLACK FLY

dark brown, about 5–6 mm., and has been taken in low vegetation bordering mountain streams.

MARCH FLIES   Family Bibionidae

Identification: Small to medium-sized, stout-bodied, and usually black. Ocelli present. Antennae short, rising low on face. Thickened section of C ends near wing tip. Anal angle of wing usually *well developed*. Pulvilli (pads beneath tarsal claws) present. Tibiae with *apical spurs*.

March flies are common insects usually found on flowers. Larvae feed on roots and in decaying vegetation. Adults are most common in spring and early summer; some species are abundant in March (hence the common name).

FUNGUS GNATS   Family Mycetophilidae

Identification: Slender, long-legged, mosquitolike, with *elongated coxae*. Ocelli present. Thickened section of C ends near wing tip. Rs *simple* or 2-branched; if 2-branched the fork is beyond r-m, or r-m is obliterated by the fusion of Rs and M. Eyes do not meet above antennae. Pulvilli (see above) absent or minute.

This is a large group whose members are common in areas where there is an abundance of decaying vegetation or fungi. Most species are between 5 and 10 mm. and have relatively long antennae. Larvae live in fungi, decaying vegetation, or moist soil.

DARK-WINGED FUNGUS GNATS   Family Sciaridae

Identification: Similar to Mycetophilidae, but eyes meet *above bases of antennae*. R-m cross vein *appears as a basal continuation of Rs*, the base of Rs resembling a cross vein.

Sciarids are common insects usually found in moist shady places. Most species are 5 mm. or less, and dark-colored. Larvae feed in fungi, decaying vegetation, or on plant roots; a few species are pests in mushroom cellars.

MINUTE BLACK SCAVENGER FLIES   Family Scatopsidae

Identification: Black or dark brown, 3 mm. or less, rather stocky in build, with short antennae. Veins in anterior part of wing heavy, remaining veins weak. Rs *not forked*. Palps 1-segmented.

Scatopsid larvae occur in decaying material and excrement, and adults are usually found around such materials; adults often enter houses, where they are generally seen on windows. These flies are fairly common.

HYPEROSCELIDID GNATS   Not illus.

Family Hyperoscelididae

Identification: Similar to Scatopsidae, but Rs forked and the palps 3- or 4-segmented.

A single rare species in this group has been recorded from Quebec, Alaska, and Washington. Its larva is unknown.

GALL GNATS. Family Cecidomyiidae

Identification: Minute flies, rarely over 3 mm., usually slender, with long legs and antennae. Venation reduced, with 7 or fewer veins reaching wing margin. Ocelli present or absent.

This is a large and widely distributed group whose members occur in a variety of situations. Larvae of most species are gall makers; some are plant feeders but do not form a gall, some occur in decaying materials, and several are parasitic or predaceous. A few species are important crop pests. The Hessian

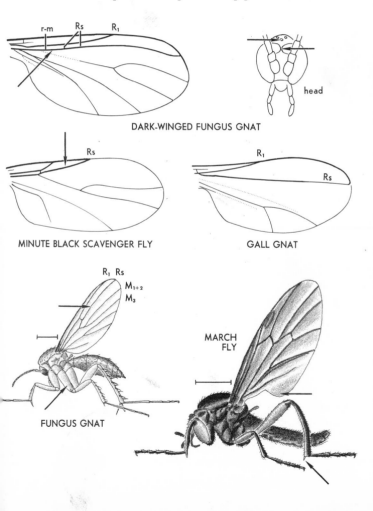

DARK-WINGED FUNGUS GNAT

MINUTE BLACK SCAVENGER FLY

GALL GNAT

FUNGUS GNAT

MARCH FLY

Fly, *Mayetiola destructor* (Say), is a serious pest of wheat, and other species attack clovers.

Suborder Brachycera

Five or fewer (usually 3) antennal segments, the 3rd *sometimes annulated* (subdivided by rings), sometimes with a terminal style (illus., p. 275), only rarely with an arista (see opp.). Rs usually 3-branched (R_{4+5} forked). No frontal suture. Anal cell generally *longer than 2nd basal cell*, and in most cases closed near wing margin. Mostly medium-sized to large, relatively robust flies.

The families in this suborder may be divided into 3 groups on the basis of form of 3rd antennal segment and number of pads on last tarsal segment:

1. 3rd antennal segment annulated or subdivided; tarsi with 3 pads: Xylophagidae, Xylomyidae, Stratiomyidae, Tabanidae, and Pelecorhynchidae.
2. 3rd antennal segment not annulated; tarsi with 3 pads: Rhagionidae, Nemestrinidae, and Acroceridae.
3. 3rd antennal segment not annulated; tarsi with 2 pads or none: the remaining families (Hilarimorphidae through Dolichopodidae).

XYLOPHAGID FLIES   Family Xylophagidae

Identification: Third antennal segment *elongate*. M_3 cell *open* (except in *Rachicerus*, in which the antennae appear many-segmented). Calypters (illus., p. 275) small or vestigial. At least middle tibiae with apical spurs.

Xylophagids are not common; the ones most often seen are in the genera *Xylophagus* and *Coenomyia*. *Xylophagus* flies are slender and ichneumonlike, generally 10–13 mm., with eyes bare, the scutellum lacking spinelike protuberances, and the posterior cells usually longer than wide. *Coenomyia* flies are robust, 14–25 mm., with eyes pubescent, the scutellum bearing 2 spinelike protuberances and the posterior cells about as long as wide. Other xylophagids are 2–9 mm. and rare. Larvae occur in decaying wood or in the soil.

XYLOMYID FLIES   Family Xylomyidae

Identification: Similar to Xylophagidae (most resemble *Xylophagus*), but with the M_3 cell *closed*.

These flies are not very common, but those most likely to be encountered are slender, ichneumonlike, and 10 mm. or less. Larvae occur in decaying wood or under bark.

SOLDIER FLIES   Family Stratiomyidae

Identification: Third antennal segment rounded or *elongate*. Branches of R crowded toward anterior part of wing, with R_5 *ending in front of wing tip*.

Members of this group vary in appearance. The most common species are 10–15 mm. and wasplike, with the 3rd antennal segment elongate. Others are brownish or metallic blue-black, often less than 10 mm., and some have the 3rd antennal segment rather rounded, with a long style or an arista. Adults are usually found on flowers. Larvae occur in a variety of situations: some are aquatic, some live in decaying materials, and some are found in other situations.

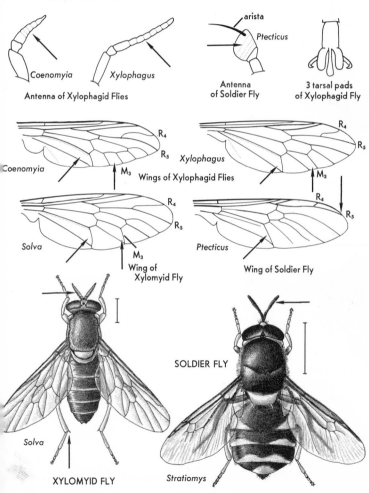

Coenomyia

Xylophagus

Antenna of Xylophagid Flies

arista

Ptecticus

Antenna of Soldier Fly

3 tarsal pads of Xylophagid Fly

Coenomyia — R₄ R₅ M₃

Xylophagus — R₄ R₅ M₃

Wings of Xylophagid Flies

Solva — R₄ R₅ M₃

Wing of Xylomyid Fly

Ptecticus — R₄ R₅

Wing of Soldier Fly

SOLDIER FLY

Solva

XYLOMYID FLY

Stratiomys

HORSE and DEER FLIES Family Tabanidae   See also Pl. 13
  Identification: Third antennal segment *elongate*. Calypters large. R₄ and R₅ *divergent, enclosing wing tip.*

Tabanids are relatively stout-bodied, medium-sized to large (mostly 10–25 mm.), and many are very common. Females are bloodsucking, and are often serious pests of man and animals. Males, much less often seen, feed on flowers. The eyes meet dorsally in the male and are separated in the female; the eyes are brightly colored or iridescent in many species. Larvae of most species are aquatic. Adults are often abundant near swamps or ponds where the larvae occur, but are strong fliers and may range many miles from their breeding places. Deer flies (*Chrysops*) are smaller than most other tabanids (House Fly size or slightly larger), black or brownish, and usually have dark spots on the wings; the 3rd antennal segment lacks a basal toothlike process, and there are apical spurs on the hind tibiae. The larger horse flies, most of which are in the genus *Tabanus*, are usually gray or blackish, generally without dark spots on the wings (some species have entirely dark wings); the 3rd antennal segment has *a basal toothlike process* and there are no apical spurs on the hind tibiae. Some species of *Tabanus*, commonly called greenheads, have bright green eyes in life.

PELECORHYNCHID FLIES   Not illus.
Family Pelecorhynchidae
  Identification: Similar to Tabanidae, but 2A somewhat S-shaped (straight or gently curved in Tabanidae), anal cell open (closed in Tabanidae), and eyes densely hairy (usually bare in Tabanidae).

The only U.S. member of this family is *Bequaertomyia jonesi* (Cresson), which occurs in the Pacific Coast states. This fly is 13–15 mm., black, with wings smoky and antennae and palps orange.

SNIPE FLIES Family Rhagionidae   See also p. 261
  Identification: Third antennal segment *more or less rounded* and bearing a long slender terminal style. Calypters small or vestigial. Venation *normal.*

Snipe flies are mostly 8–15 mm., with the abdomen somewhat tapering posteriorly, the legs long, and the head more or less rounded; some species have spots on the wings. Most are black or gray; some are black with a yellow mesonotum. Snipe flies are common, and generally occur in wooded areas or areas of fairly dense vegetation. Eastern species in this group do not bite, but some western species do. Larvae generally occur in decaying vegetation; some are aquatic.

TANGLE-VEINED FLIES Family Nemestrinidae
  Identification: Venation peculiar, with most branches of M

ending in front of wing tip. 3rd antennal segment short, rounded, and with a long slender terminal style. Tibiae without apical spurs.

Nemestrinids are medium-sized, stout-bodied flies that do quite a bit of hovering and are fast fliers. They are quite rare but are most likely to be found in weedy fields where the vegetation is high.

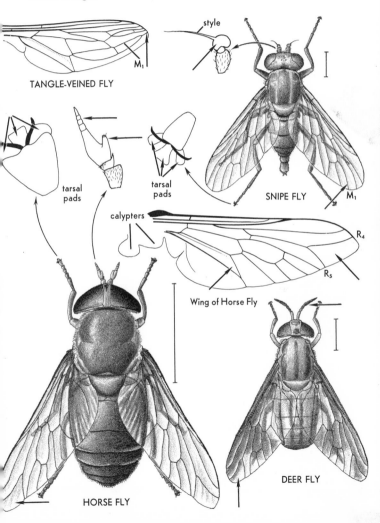

TANGLE-VEINED FLY

M_1

style

SNIPE FLY

M_1

tarsal pads

tarsal pads

calypters

Wing of Horse Fly

R_4

R_5

HORSE FLY

DEER FLY

SMALL-HEADED FLIES Family Acroceridae
Identification: Appearance distinctive: head *very small* and attached low on thorax, the body appearing *humpbacked;* calypters very large. Venation often *reduced*.

Acrocerids are medium-sized to small and are rather rare. Some species have a long slender proboscis. Larvae are parasites of spiders.

HILARIMORPHID FLIES Family Hilarimorphidae **Not illus.**
Identification: Third antennal segment oval, with a short 2-segmented style. Tibiae without apical spurs. 4 posterior cells and no closed discal cell.

Three very rare species are known from the U.S. They have been taken from New England to the West Coast.

STILETTO FLIES Family Therevidae
Identification: Medium-sized, usually grayish flies, with abdomen *somewhat tapering*. 3rd antennal segment *slightly elongated*, often with a short terminal style. *5 posterior cells*, the 4th *sometimes closed*.

Therevids resemble some robber flies (Asilidae), but differ in having the vertex flat or slightly convex (hollowed out in robber flies). They are relatively uncommon, and are usually found in open areas. Larvae occur in soil or decaying materials and are predaceous.

FLOWER-LOVING FLIES Family Apioceridae **Not illus.**
Identification: Similar to Therevidae but larger, and M_1 curves forward and ends in front of wing tip.

This is a small group of rare flies occurring in arid regions of the West and usually found on flowers.

WINDOW FLIES Family Scenopinidae
Identification: Moderately robust flies somewhat smaller than a House Fly, and usually grayish or blackish. 3 posterior cells. M_{1+2} ends *in front of wing tip*.

Window flies are so named because some are occasionally found on windows. They are relatively rare. Larvae usually occur in decaying wood or fungi; most are predaceous, and feed on a variety of insects.

ROBBER FLIES Family Asilidae **See also Pl. 13**
Identification: Top of head *hollowed out* between eyes; *3 ocelli*. 3rd antennal segment usually *elongate*, often bearing a short terminal style. Body varies from very hairy to nearly bare, but face usually *bearded*.

Robber flies are common insects, 5–30 mm., with legs and thorax relatively large. Most are relatively bare, with a long abdomen that tapers posteriorly; some are robust and hairy, and resemble bumble bees; some have a *very long and slender* abdomen, and resemble damselflies. They occur in a variety of habitats and are predaceous, often attacking insects larger than themselves. Larger species can inflict a painful bite if handled carelessly. Larvae occur chiefly in soil or decaying wood, and some are predaceous on larvae of other insects.

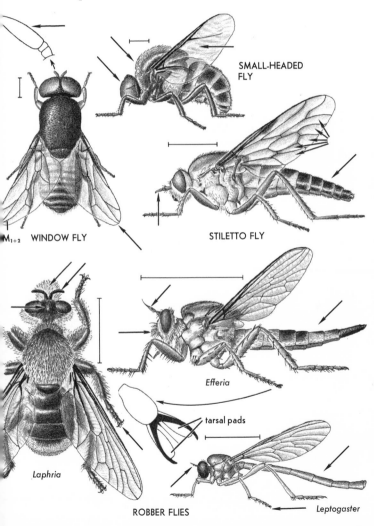

SMALL-HEADED FLY

STILETTO FLY

M_{1+2} WINDOW FLY

Efferia

tarsal pads

Laphria

ROBBER FLIES

Leptogaster

MYDAS FLIES   Family Mydidae   **See also Pl. 13**
   Identification: Large flies, about 1 in. Elongate, bare, blackish, some with 2nd abdominal segment yellowish or orange. Antennae long, 4-segmented, last segment *somewhat swollen. 1 ocellus* or none. Top of head somewhat hollowed out between eyes. M₁ ends at or *in front of wing tip.*

   Members of this small group are not very common. Adults are predaceous. Larvae occur in decaying wood or in soil.

BEE FLIES   Family Bombyliidae   **See also Pl. 13**
   Identification: Usually stout-bodied and hairy. 3rd antennal segment *variable in shape.* M₁ ends *behind wing tip.* 3 or 4 posterior cells. Discal cell present. Anal cell *open* or closed near wing margin.

   Bee flies are mostly medium to large, and are usually found on flowers or resting on the ground in open areas. The wings at rest are held outstretched. Some have patterned wings, and some have a very long proboscis (but do not bite). Larvae are parasites of other insects.

DANCE FLIES   Family Empididae
   Identification: Third antennal segment usually rounded, with *a long terminal style.* Rs 2- or 3-branched. Anal cell often shorter than 2nd basal cell, rarely absent. R-m cross vein located *beyond basal ¼ of wing.* ♂ genitalia not folded forward under abdomen.

   Members of this large group vary somewhat in appearance and wing venation. Most are small (some minute) and have *a stout thorax* and a tapering abdomen. Many resemble small muscoids but lack a frontal suture. Empidids are common flies occurring in many different situations; some occur in swarms, flying with an up-and-down or circular movement (hence the common name). Most are predaceous but many occur on flowers. Larvae live in the soil, decaying vegetation, under bark, in decaying wood, and in water.

LONG-LEGGED FLIES   **See also Pl. 13**
Family Dolichopodidae
   Identification: Small to medium-sized, and usually metallic green or coppery. Rs 2-branched, *slightly swollen at the fork.* R-m cross vein in basal ¼ of wing or absent. Anal cell *small,* sometimes absent. ♂ genitalia often *large and folded forward* under abdomen. Antennae usually *aristate.*

   Dolichopodids are very common, occurring in many different situations but most frequently in marshy places and meadows. Males often have very large genitalia, and sometimes have the legs peculiarly ornamented. Most adults are predaceous on

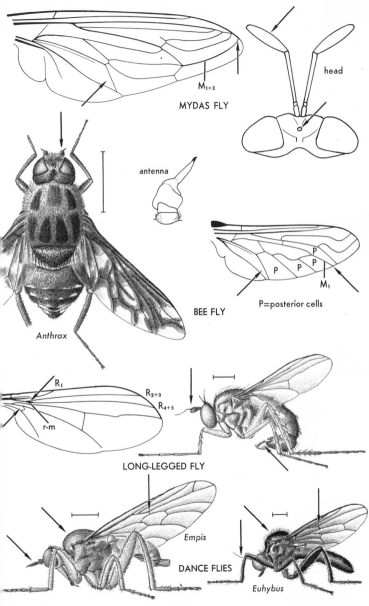

MYDAS FLY

M_{1+2}

head

antenna

BEE FLY

P

P

P

P

M_1

P=posterior cells

Anthrax

R_1

R_{2+3}

R_{4+5}

r-m

LONG-LEGGED FLY

Empis

DANCE FLIES

Euhybus

smaller insects. Larvae occur in wet soil, under bark, in decaying vegetation, and in water.

Suborder Cyclorrhapha

Antennae 3-segmented, aristate. Rs 2-branched. Frontal suture absent (Aschiza) or present (Schizophora).

Division Aschiza

Without a frontal suture.

SPEAR-WINGED FLIES   Family Lonchopteridae
   Identification: Slender, yellowish to brownish, 2–5 mm. Wings *pointed at apex* and without cross veins except at base.
   These flies are generally found in moist shady or grassy places, and are fairly common. Larvae occur in decaying vegetation. This family is a small one. Our 4 species belong to the genus *Lonchoptera*.

HUMPBACKED FLIES   Family Phoridae
   Identification: Small to minute, usually dark-colored, with distinctive appearance and wing venation: appear *humpbacked* and wings have *strong veins in costal area*, the remaining veins being *weaker and oblique*. Hind femora *flattened*. Antennae very short, the 2 basal segments very small and 3rd segment globular and bearing a long arista (bristle).
   Humpbacked flies are quite common. They occur in a variety of habitats but probably most often where there is decaying vegetation. Larvae vary in habits; some live in decaying materials or in fungi, some are parasites of other insects, and some live in the nests of ants and termites.

FLAT-FOOTED FLIES   Family Platypezidae
   Identification: Small black or brown flies with the hind tibiae and tarsi *dilated*. Anal cell *longer than 2nd basal cell*, and *pointed apically*.
   Platypezids are rather uncommon flies usually found in wooded areas. Adults of some species are attracted to smoke. Larvae live in fungi.

BIG-HEADED FLIES   Family Pipunculidae
   Identification: Head *very large*, hemispherical, and consisting almost entirely of eyes. Wings somewhat narrowed basally. Anal cell *long*, closed near wing margin.
   Members of this group are small and not very common. They are usually found in meadows or along the edges of woods. Larvae are parasites of various Homoptera, chiefly leafhoppers and planthoppers.

SYRPHID FLIES Family Syrphidae   **See also Pl. 13**
Identification: A spurious vein usually *present between R and M*. R_5 cell (and usually also M_2 cell) *closed*. Anal cell *long*, closed near wing margin. Proboscis short and fleshy.

Many members of this large group are very common flies. Syrphids occur in many habitats, usually on flowers. All are good fliers, and often do a great deal of hovering. Adults vary greatly in size, color, and appearance; many are brightly colored with yellow, brown, and black; others are uniformly black or

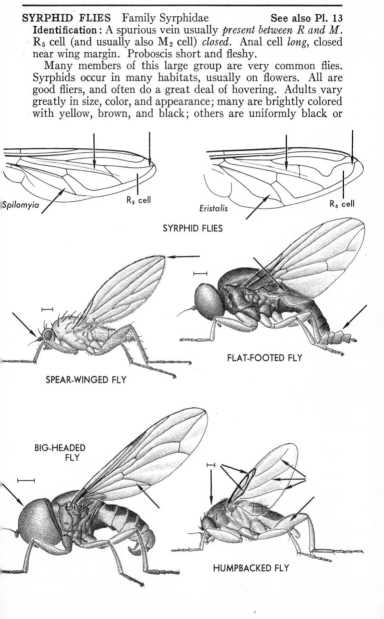

Spilomyia R_5 cell   *Eristalis* R_5 cell

SYRPHID FLIES

FLAT-FOOTED FLY

SPEAR-WINGED FLY

BIG-HEADED FLY

HUMPBACKED FLY

brown. Some species are relatively bare and strongly resemble wasps; others are quite hairy, and resemble bees. The resemblance of many syrphids to various Hymenoptera is often very striking, and it may require a second look to determine that they are flies and not Hymenoptera. Syrphids do not bite or sting. Larvae also vary in appearance and habits; many are predaceous on aphids, many are scavengers (living in dung, carrion, decaying vegetation, or in highly polluted aquatic habitats), and some live in ant nests. Aphid-feeding larvae are maggotlike and usually greenish; some larvae living in polluted aquatic habitats have the posterior end extended as a long tail-like structure and are called rat-tailed maggots; larvae living in ant nests are oval and very flat.

THICK-HEADED FLIES Family Conopidae

Identification: Venation as in Syrphidae, but lacking a spurious vein. Proboscis *long, slender*, and often folding. Abdomen usually *narrowed at base*.

Thick-headed flies are usually medium-sized and brownish; many resemble small thread-waisted wasps. The head is slightly wider than the thorax and the antennae are generally *long*. Adults are commonly found on flowers. Larvae are parasites of adult bees and wasps.

Muscoid Flies: Division Schizophora

A frontal suture present.

Adult flies in the suborder Cyclorrhapha emerge from the puparium through a circular opening at the anterior end. This opening is made with a saclike structure called the *ptilinum*, which is everted from the head of the fly. After emergence the ptilinum is withdrawn into the head, and in the Schizophora the break in the head wall through which the ptilinum was everted is marked by a suture called the *frontal suture*. This suture is in the form of an inverted U or V, with its apex just above the base of the antennae, and the 2 arms extending downward toward the cheeks.

Muscoid flies have *aristate antennae*, numerous bristles on the head and body, and most of them are rather stout-bodied. Muscoids are usually small; many are very small. This group makes up about ⅓ of the order, and its members occur almost everywhere, often in considerable numbers. Because of their small size and the large number of species and families, their identification can be difficult.

The principal characters used in separating families of muscoid flies are those of the bristles and wing venation. The characteristic bristles and areas of the head are shown opposite and those of the thorax are shown on p. 287. The chief venational characters used are the size and shape of various cells, the development of Sc, and the presence of breaks in the costa. Sc may be complete (extending to costa) or incomplete (not extending to costa, fading out distally or fusing with R_1). Costal breaks are points on the costa where the sclerotization is weak or the vein appears to be broken; they are best seen with transmitted light.

The muscoid flies are divided into 2 groups, the acalyptrates (Section Acalyptratae) and calyptrates (Section Calyptratae, p. 302), chiefly on the basis of the development of the calypters and the *structure of the 2nd antennal segment*.

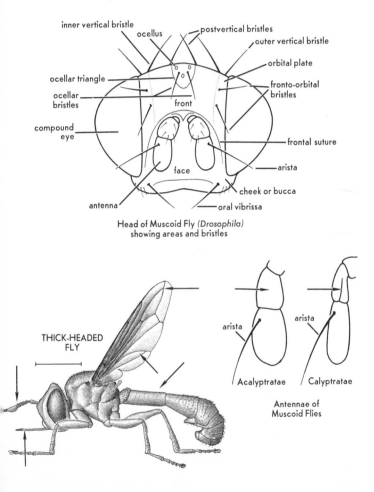

Head of Muscoid Fly *(Drosophila)*
showing areas and bristles

THICK-HEADED FLY

Acalyptratae / Calyptratae

Antennae of
Muscoid Flies

Acalyptrate Muscoids: Section Acalyptratae

Calypters absent or vestigial. Second antennal segment *without a longitudinal suture* (except in some Psilidae); see p. 283.

This Section includes a large number of families, many of which are difficult to separate. The key below should be of value in separating these families. See illustrations on pp. 283 and 287 for technical characters.

1.	Coxae widely separated; wingless ectoparasites of the Honey Bee	**Braulidae (p. 295)**
1'.	Coxae close together; not ectoparasitic in habit; wings nearly alway present	2
2(1').	Sc complete or nearly so	3
2'.	Sc incomplete	17
3(2).	Posterior spiracle of thorax with at least 1 bristle; palps vestigial; head spherical; abdomen elongate and usually narrowed at base	**Sepsidae (p. 290)**
3'.	Without this combination of characters	4
4(3').	Dorsum of thorax flattened; legs and abdomen very bristly; seashore species	**Coelopidae (p. 290)**
4'.	Without this combination of characters	5
5(4').	Oral vibrissae present	6
5'.	Oral vibrissae lacking	8
6(5).	2nd basal and discal cells confluent **Aulacigastridae (p. 294); Curtonotidae (p. 302)**	
6'.	2nd basal and discal cells separated	7
7(6').	Costa broken only near humeral cross vein; eyes with microscopic pubescence	**Acartophthalmidae (p. 294)**
7'.	Without this combination of characters **Piophilidae, Neottiophilidae (p. 292); Thyreophoridae, Lonchaeidae (p. 294); Clusiidae (p. 295); Trixoscelididae, Heleomyzidae, Chryomyidae (p. 296)**	
8(5').	Costa broken near humeral cross vein	**Acartophthalmidae (p. 294)**
8'.	Costa entire, broken near end of R_1, or broken near humeral cross vein and near end of R_1	9
9(8').	R_5 cell narrowed distally; legs long and slender **Micropezidae, Tanypezidae, Neriidae (p. 286)**	
9'.	R_5 cell not narrowed distally, or legs not particularly long and slender	10
10(9').	Eyes prominently bulging, vertex sunken; femora enlarged	**Ropalomeridae, Rhinotoridae (p. 286)**
10'.	Without this combination of characters	11
11(10').	Tibiae with preapical bristles	12
11'.	Tibiae without preapical bristles	13
12(11).	Postvertical bristles converging; 2A short, not reaching wing margin	**Lauxaniidae (p. 292)**
12'.	Postvertical bristles parallel, diverging, or absent; 2A reaching wing margin, at least as a fold **Sciomyzidae, Dryomyzidae (p. 290); Helcomyzidae (p. 291)**	
13(11').	Ocelli absent; medium-sized to large flies, wings usually patterned	**Pyrgotidae (p. 288)**

13'.   Ocelli present; size and wing color variable   14

14(13'). Anal cell with an acute distal projection posteriorly; wings usually patterned   **Otitidae, Tephritidae (p. 288)**

14'.   Anal cell truncate or rounded apically, without an acute distal projection posteriorly   15

15(14'). Head extended on each side into a lateral process bearing eye, with antennae widely separated on eye stalks; scutellum with 2 tubercles   **Diopsidae (p. 286)**

15'.   Without this combination of characters   16

16(15'). Costa broken near end of Sc or R_1
    Tephritidae, Richardiidae (p. 288);
    Lonchaeidae, Pallopteridae (p. 294); Canaceidae (p. 298)

16'.   Costa not broken near end of Sc or R_1
    Platystomatidae, Otitidae (p. 288);
    Chamaemyiidae (p. 292)

17(2'). Basal segment of hind tarsi short and swollen, shorter than 2nd segment   **Sphaeroceridae (p. 296)**

17'.   Basal segment of hind tarsi not swollen, and usually longer than 2nd segment   18

18(17'). R_{2+3} ending in C just beyond R_1 **Asteiidae (p. 296)**

18'. R_{2+3} longer, ending beyond middle of wing   19

19(18'). 3rd antennal segment large, reaching lower edge of head, with arista absent or represented by only a small apical tubercle   **Cryptochetidae (p. 297)**

19'.   Without this combination of characters   20

20(19'). Costa broken once or twice, at least near end of R_1 21

20'.   Costa not broken   **Neriidae (p. 286);**
    Periscelididae, Chamaemyiidae (p. 292)

21(20). Costa broken once, near end of R_1 22

21'.   Costa broken twice, near end of R_1 and near humeral cross vein   26

22(21). Anal cell lacking; ocellar triangle usually large and distinct   **Chloropidae (p. 298)**

22'.   Anal cell present or ocellar triangle small   23

23(22'). Sternopleural bristles present   24

23'.   No sternopleural bristles   **Psilidae (p. 290);**
    Canaceidae (p. 298)

24(23). Eyes prominently bulging, vertex sunken; front femora thickened   **Rhinotoridae (p. 286)**

24'.   Without this combination of characters   25

25(24'). Postvertical bristles converging   **Trixoscelididae (p. 296);**
    Tethinidae, Anthomyzidae (p. 298)

25'.   Postvertical bristles diverging or absent
    Opomyzidae (p. 298); Agromyzidae, Odiniidae (p. 300)

26(21'). Antennae retractile into deep grooves, face receding; eyes small and round   **Thyreophoridae (p. 294)**

26'.   Without this combination of characters   27

27(26'). Anal cell absent; oral vibrissae absent; postvertical bristles diverging   **Ephydridae (p. 300)**

27'.   Anal cell and oral vibrissae usually present; postvertical bristles parallel or converging (rarely absent)
    Milichiidae, Drosophilidae (p. 300);
    Curtonotidae, Diastatidae, Camillidae (p. 302)

STILT-LEGGED FLIES Family Micropezidae

Identification: Medium-sized, slender, usually black. Legs *long and stiltlike*. Sc complete. Oral vibrissae absent. R_5 cell *narrowed* or closed apically. Anal cell usually *long and pointed*. Arista dorsal.

These flies are relatively uncommon, and are generally found in moist places. Larvae occur in dung.

TANYPEZID FLIES Family Tanypezidae **Not illus.**

Identification: Similar to Micropezidae, but head in profile higher than long and anal cell rounded apically.

Two rare species of tanypezids occur in the East, and are usually found in moist woods. Larvae are unknown.

CACTUS FLIES Family Neriidae

Identification: Similar to Micropezidae, but with the antennae *long and projecting forward*, and the arista *apical*. Grayish flies with brown markings.

Two species of cactus flies occur on or near decaying cacti from Texas to California. Larvae live in decaying cacti.

ROPALOMERID FLIES Family Ropalomeridae **Not illus.**

Identification: Medium-sized and usually brownish or grayish. Sc complete. Oral vibrissae lacking. Eyes prominently bulging, the vertex sunken. Femora enlarged. R_1 ends far beyond Sc. R_5 cell narrowed distally. Posterior thoracic spiracle with a group of bristles. Palps broad.

Our only species, *Rhytidops floridensis* (Aldrich), occurs about fresh exudates of palm trees in Florida.

RHINOTORID FLIES Family Rhinotoridae **Not illus.**

Identification: Similar to Ropalomeridae, but R_1 ends close to Sc, the R_5 cell is not narrowed distally, the posterior thoracic spiracle is without a group of bristles, and the palps are narrow.

The single U.S. species in this family has been taken at banana-baited traps in New Mexico and Arizona. Its larva is unknown.

STALK-EYED FLIES Family Diopsidae

Identification: Small blackish flies. Sc complete. Oral vibrissae lacking. Head *slightly extended on each side* into a short stalklike process bearing the eye, the antennae *widely separated*. Scutellum with 2 tubercles. Front femora swollen.

This group is represented in N. America by a single rare species, *Sphyracephala brevicornis* (Say), which occurs from Quebec to Colorado and N. Carolina. Larva breeds in decaying vegetation. Adults are sometimes found on skunk cabbage. Some tropical species in this group have long and slender eye stalks.

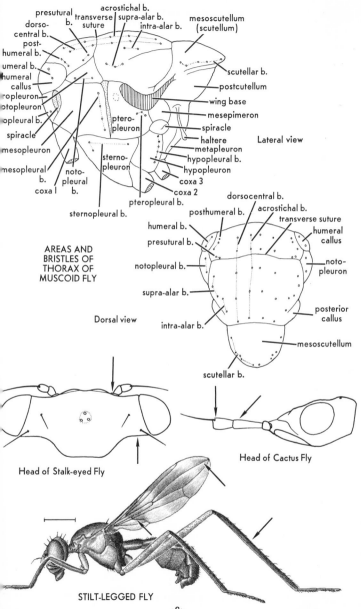

acrostichal b.
presutural b.
transverse suture
supra-alar b.
intra-alar b.
mesoscutellum (scutellum)
dorso-central b.
post-humeral b.
umeral b.
humeral callus
ropleuron
otopleuron
opleural b.
spiracle
mesopleuron
mesopleural b.
notopleural b.
coxa I
scutellar b.
postcutellum
wing base
mesepimeron
spiracle
haltere
metapleuron
hypopleural b.
hypopleuron
coxa 3
coxa 2
pteropleural b.
sternopleuron
pteropleuron
sternopleural b.

Lateral view

AREAS AND BRISTLES OF THORAX OF MUSCOID FLY

Dorsal view

dorsocentral b.
acrostichal b.
transverse suture
humeral callus
notopleuron
posterior callus
mesoscutellum
posthumeral b.
humeral b.
presutural b.
notopleural b.
supra-alar b.
intra-alar b.
scutellar b.

Head of Stalk-eyed Fly

Head of Cactus Fly

STILT-LEGGED FLY

287

PICTURE-WINGED FLIES   See also Pl. 14
Family Otitidae

Identification: Small to medium-sized, usually blackish and shiny. Wings often *banded or patterned*. Sc *complete, only slightly curved at tip*. Anal cell generally with *an acute distal projection posteriorly* (if anal cell is rounded apically, then costa is not broken, postvertical bristles are parallel or convergent, sternopleural bristles are usually present, and anterior side of anal cell is usually less than ¼ as long as posterior side of discal cell). Oral vibrissae lacking. Without well-developed bristles on anterior half of front. Tibiae usually without preapical bristles.

These flies are common in moist places, and are sometimes quite abundant. Habits of the larvae vary — some are plant feeders (a few of these are pests of cultivated plants) and some occur in decaying materials.

PLATYSTOMATID FLIES   Family Platystomatidae

Identification: Similar to Otitidae, but anal cell always *rounded apically*, its anterior side more than ¼ as long as posterior side of discal cell. R_1 with bristles. Sternopleural bristles lacking; propleural bristles weak or lacking. Costa not broken near end of Sc.

This is a much smaller group than the Otitidae but some species are fairly common. The wings are usually marked with narrow dark bands, and the costa is not broken.

RICHARDIID FLIES   Family Richardiidae   **Not illus.**

Identification: Similar to Otitidae, but anal cell rounded or truncate apically, never with a pointed distal projection posteriorly. Costa broken near end of Sc.

These flies are uncommon in our area but are common in the tropics. Larvae occur in decaying vegetation.

PYRGOTID FLIES   Family Pyrgotidae

Identification: Medium-sized to large flies. Head *large and rounded*. Ocelli *lacking*. Wings usually spotted or patterned. Sc complete. Oral vibrissae lacking.

Members of this group are mostly nocturnal, and often are attracted to lights; they are not common. Larvae are parasites of June beetles.

FRUIT FLIES   Family Tephritidae   **See also Pl. 14**

Identification: Small to medium-sized, often brightly colored. Wings usually *spotted or banded*. Apex of Sc *bent abruptly forward* at almost a right angle, and usually not quite reaching costa. Anal cell often with *an acute distal projection posteriorly*. Anterior half of front with 1 or more erect bristles.

Many species in this large group are quite common, and are

usually found on flowers or vegetation. Most species have
attractively patterned wings; the wings may be banded or
spotted, and the spotting sometimes forms intricate patterns.
Some species move their wings slowly up and down while resting.
Larvae are plant feeders, and a few are pests of fruits. Larva
of *Rhagoletis pomonella* (Walsh) tunnels in the fruit of apple, and
is called an Apple Maggot (Pl. 14). The Mediterranean Fruit
Fly, *Ceratitis capitata* (Wiedemann), is a serious pest of citrus.

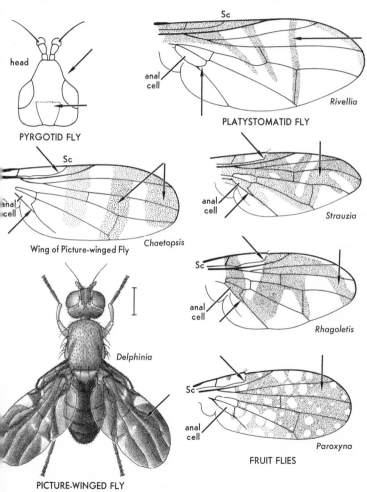

head

PYRGOTID FLY

Sc

anal
cell

Rivellia

PLATYSTOMATID FLY

Sc

anal
cell

Wing of Picture-winged Fly

Chaetopsis

anal
cell

Strauzia

Sc

anal
cell

Rhagoletis

Sc

anal
cell

Paroxyna

FRUIT FLIES

Delphinia

PICTURE-WINGED FLY

Species of *Eurosta* form round, thick-walled stem galls on golden-rod. Many species breed in the flower heads of Compositae.

RUST FLIES Family Psilidae
Identification: Small to medium-sized, usually slender and brownish, with relatively long antennae. Species with a longitudinal suture on 2nd antennal segment have *3rd antennal segment very long*, longer than arista. Species without this suture on antennae have Sc incomplete, costa broken near end of R₁, no sternopleural bristles, and no oral vibrissae.

Rust flies are fairly common insects. Larvae are plant feeders, and some species are pests of garden crops.

SEAWEED FLIES Family Coelopidae
Identification: Small to medium-sized, brown to blackish. Dorsum of thorax *somewhat flattened*, and body and legs *very bristly*. Sc complete.

Seaweed flies occur along the seashore, often in large numbers; larvae live in seaweed washed up on the shore. Adults occur around this seaweed, or on flowers and vegetation near the shore.

BLACK SCAVENGER FLIES Family Sepsidae
Identification: Small, usually shining black or purple flies, with head *rounded* and abdomen usually *narrowed at base*. Palps vestigial. Posterior spiracle of thorax with at least 1 bristle. Sc complete. Oral vibrissae lacking.

Larvae of these flies live in manure and similar materials, and adults are usually found around such materials. Sepsids are common flies and are often abundant around manure piles.

MARSH FLIES Family Sciomyzidae   See also Pl. 14
Identification: Small to medium-sized, usually yellowish or brownish, often with *spotted* or patterned wings. Sc *complete*. R₁ usually ends *at middle of wing*. Oral vibrissae *absent*. Postverticals *slightly divergent*. Preapical tibial bristles present. Antennae generally *project forward*, often long. Femora with bristles, and middle femur usually with a characteristic bristle near middle of anterior surface.

Marsh flies are common insects that occur in marshy areas near ponds and streams. Larvae feed on aquatic snails, usually as predators.

DRYOMYZID FLIES Family Dryomyzidae
Identification: Yellowish or brownish, similar to Sciomyzidae but antennae usually not projecting, R₁ ending *beyond middle of wing*, and femoral bristles not developed. 3rd antennal segment longer than wide, more or less flattened laterally.

Dryomyzids are small to medium-sized and often have brownish spots on the cross veins. They occur in moist woods and along the seashore but are not common. Larval stages are unknown.

HELCOMYZID FLIES Family Helcomyzidae   **Not illus.**
Identification: Similar to Dryomyzidae but blackish and 3rd antennal segment spherical.

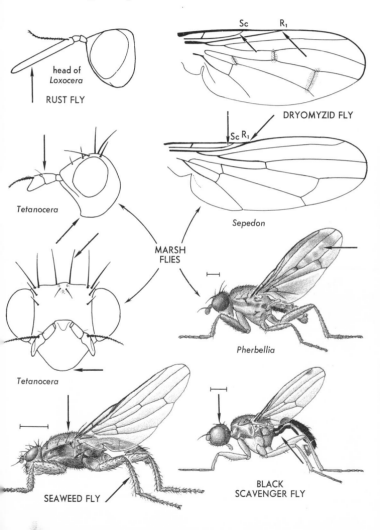

head of
Loxocera
RUST FLY

Sc   R₁

DRYOMYZID FLY

Sc R₁

Tetanocera

Sepedon

MARSH
FLIES

Tetanocera

Pherbellia

SEAWEED FLY

BLACK
SCAVENGER FLY

Helcomyzids are uncommon flies occurring along the Pacific Coast from Oregon to Alaska. Larvae develop in rotting seaweed.

LAUXANIID FLIES Family Lauxaniidae   **See also Pl. 14**
Identification: Small, usually rather stout-bodied flies, often with spots on the wings. Sc *complete.* 2A *short, not reaching wing margin.* Oral vibrissae *absent.* Postvertical bristles *converge.* Tibiae with *preapical bristles.*

Lauxaniids are common flies that usually occur in wooded areas or in places where the vegetation is fairly dense. Larvae breed in decaying vegetable matter and occur in leaf litter, bird nests, and similar situations.

CHAMAEMYIID FLIES Family Chamaemyiidae
Identification: Very small flies, usually grayish with *black spots on abdomen.* Sc variable, complete or incomplete. Costa not broken. Postvertical bristles *converge.* Tibiae without preapical bristles. Oral vibrissae *absent.* Arista bare or pubescent.

These flies are usually *less than 4 mm.* and are relatively common. Larvae of some species are predaceous on aphids and mealybugs.

PERISCELIDID FLIES Family Periscelididae   **Not illus.**
Identification: Small flies, similar to Chamaemyiidae but postvertical bristles diverging, Sc incomplete, and arista plumose.

The 3 U.S. species are widely distributed but rare. Adults may occur at fresh sap flows on trees.

SKIPPER FLIES Family Piophilidae
Identification: Small flies, usually *less than 5 mm.*, black or bluish, and rather metallic. Sc complete. 2A does not reach wing margin. Oral vibrissae *present.* Postvertical bristles *diverge.* 2nd basal and discal cells separated. *2 or fewer pairs* of fronto-orbital bristles; 2 sternopleural bristles. Arista rises near base of 3rd antennal segment.

Larvae of skipper flies live in decaying animal materials, and some occasionally are pests in meats and cheese. Piophilids are called skipper flies because the larvae can jump. Adults are fairly common.

NEOTTIOPHILID FLIES Family Neottiophilidae   **Not illus.**
Identification: Similar to Piophilidae, but with 4 or 5 sternopleural bristles, vein 2A reaching wing margin, and costa spiny.

This family contains only 2 species, both European, but 1 has been recorded in n. Quebec. Nothing is known of the habits of this species; the larva of the other (European) is a bloodsucking ectoparasite of nestling birds.

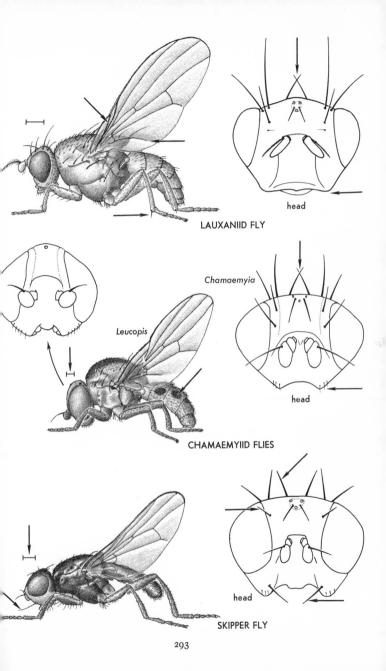

LAUXANIID FLY

head

Chamaemyia

Leucopis

CHAMAEMYIID FLIES

head

SKIPPER FLY

head

293

THYREOPHORID FLIES   Family Thyreophoridae   **Not illus.**
Identification: Sc incomplete. Costa broken near tip of R_1 and near humeral cross vein. Antennae retractile into deep grooves below bases of antennae, the face receding. Postvertical bristles diverge. Oral vibrissae present.

This group is represented in the U.S. by 2 rare species occurring in California and Arizona.

PALLOPTERID FLIES   Family Pallopteridae   **Not illus.**
Identification: Small, usually pale-colored flies with patterned wings. Sc complete. Costa broken near end of Sc. Anal cell rounded apically. Oral vibrissae absent. Tibiae lack preapical bristles. Head in profile rounded, eyes round. 3rd antennal segment oval. Postvertical bristles parallel.

Pallopterids are rare flies usually found in moist shady places. Our 9 species are widely distributed.

LONCHAEID FLIES   Family Lonchaeidae
Identification: Small, shiny black flies. Abdomen in dorsal view somewhat rounded but pointed apically. Oral vibrissae absent. Sc complete. Costa broken near end of Sc. 2A usually *wavy*. Tibiae without preapical bristles. Head in profile hemispherical, the eyes *large and oval*. 3rd antennal segment *elongate*. Postvertical bristles diverge.

Lonchaeids are fairly common flies that occur in shady places. Larvae are found in live, injured, or dead plant tissue, often along with other insects attacking the plant.

ACARTOPHTHALMID FLIES   **Not illus.**
Family Acartophthalmidae
Identification: Sc complete. Costa broken near humeral cross vein. Oral vibrissae weakly developed. Eyes slightly pubescent. Postvertical bristles widely separated and diverging.

Adults of this small group are quite rare but have been taken on rotting fungi and carrion from Massachusetts to Oregon and Alaska. *Acartophthalmus nigrinus* (Zetterstedt), a widely distributed species, is about 2 mm., blackish, with the front coxae and halteres yellowish.

AULACIGASTRID FLIES   **Not illus.**
Family Aulacigastridae
Identification: Sc complete or nearly so. Costa broken near humeral cross vein and near end of R_1. 2nd basal and discal cells confluent. Oral vibrissae present. Postvertical bristles lacking. Arista pubescent.

This family is represented in the U.S. by a single species, *Aulacigaster leucopeza* Meigen, a small black fly that occurs from the east coast to Kansas and Texas. It is fairly common and usually found in sap flows.

BEE LICE   Family Braulidae   **Not illus.**
 Identification: Wingless, 1.5 mm. Coxae widely separated. Abdominal segmentation somewhat obscure. Mesonotum short, resembling abdominal segments. No scutellum.

Braulids are represented in this country by a single very rare species, *Braula coeca* Nitzsch, which is an ectoparasite of the Honey Bee.

CLUSIID FLIES   Family Clusiidae
 Identification: Sc complete. Oral vibrissae *present*. 2nd basal and discal cells separated. Postvertical bristles diverging or *absent*. *2–4 pairs* of fronto-orbital bristles. Arista rises near apex of 3rd antennal segment. 2nd antennal segment often with *an angular projection on outer side*.

Clusiids are small flies, mostly 3–4 mm., that often have brownish or smoky wings. The body color varies but many

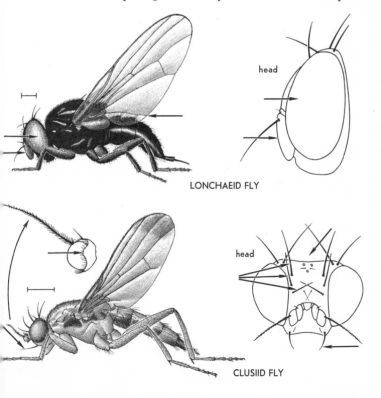

LONCHAEID FLY

head

CLUSIID FLY

head

species have the thorax black dorsally and yellowish laterally. Larvae occur in decaying wood. These flies are not very common.

TRIXOSCELIDID FLIES Family Trixoscelididae
Identification: Sc usually complete. Oral vibrissae *present*. 2nd basal and discal cells separated. Postvertical bristles *converge*. Tibiae with *preapical bristles*. Costa *spiny*. Orbital plates *long*, extending nearly to antennae.

Trixoscelidids are very small flies, generally *2–3 mm.*, most of which occur in the West; only 2 rather rare species occur in the East, 1 in Florida and 1 in Maryland. Some species occur in grassy areas and woodlands; others, including many western species, live in desert areas. Larvae of 1 eastern species inhabit bird nests.

HELEOMYZID FLIES Family Heleomyzidae
Identification: Similar in general appearance to Sciomyzidae (p. 290), but antennae *smaller* and not projecting forward, oral vibrissae *present*, and postvertical bristles *converging*. Costa usually *spiny*. Orbital plates *short*, not reaching antennae.

Heleomyzids are fairly common flies usually found in areas of abundant vegetation. Most are brownish and some have spots on the wings. Larvae occur in fungi, bird nests, mammal burrows, and in other places where there are decaying materials.

CHYROMYID FLIES Family Chyromyidae   **Not illus.**
Identification: Small yellow flies with golden eyes. Sc complete. Oral vibrissae weakly developed. 2nd basal and discal cells separated. Tibiae without preapical bristles. Postvertical bristles converge.

Adults of this small but widely distributed group usually occur on vegetation. Larvae probably are scavengers.

SMALL DUNG FLIES Family Sphaeroceridae
Identification: Very small and blackish or brownish. Sc *incomplete*. Basal segment of hind tarsi *somewhat swollen* and *shorter than 2nd segment*.

Sphaerocerids usually occur near manure or other refuse, and are very common. Larvae live in dung and various decaying materials.

ASTEIID FLIES Family Asteiidae
Identification: Mostly 2 mm. or less, and usually light-colored. *Sc incomplete*. R_{2+3} ends in costa *just beyond end of R_1*. Postvertical bristles diverge.

The group is a small one, its members relatively rare. Immature stages are unknown.

CRYPTOCHETID FLIES
Not illus.

Family Cryptochetidae

Identification: Sc incomplete. 3rd antennal segment large, extends almost to lower edge of head. Arista absent, but a short spine or tubercle at apex of 3rd antennal segment. Eyes large, vertically elongate.

One species of cryptochetid, *Cryptochetum iceryae* (Williston),

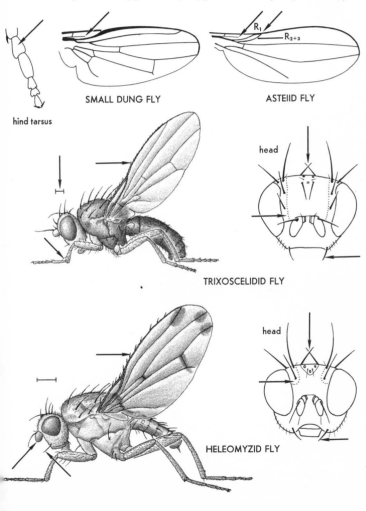

hind tarsus

SMALL DUNG FLY

ASTEIID FLY

TRIXOSCELIDID FLY

head

HELEOMYZID FLY

head

occurs in California, where it has been introduced from Australia; its larva is parasitic on scale insects in the family Margarodidae. This insect is about 1.5 mm., stout-bodied, with head and thorax dark metallic blue and abdomen metallic green.

FRIT FLIES Family Chloropidae
Identification: *Small to very small flies.* Color variable, some species blackish or grayish, some brightly colored with black and yellow. Sc incomplete. Costa *broken near end of* R_1. Anal cell *lacking.* Ocellar triangle usually *large*, shining. Postvertical bristles *converging*, parallel, or absent.

This is a large group, and many of its members are common flies. They occur in a variety of habitats but are most common in grassy areas. Larvae of many species live in grass stems; a few live in decaying materials. Adults of a few species (called eye gnats) are attracted to the eyes or to sores.

BEACH FLIES Family Canaceidae **Not illus.**
Identification: Sc incomplete. Costa broken near end of R_1. Anal cell present. Ocellar triangle large and shining, reaching to near base of antennae. Oral vibrissae present.

Canaceids are small flies, 3.5 mm. or less, occurring along the seashore, chiefly in the intertidal zone, and they are not common. Larvae feed on algae.

TETHINID FLIES Family Tethinidae
Identification: Sc incomplete. Costa broken near end of R_1. Anal cell present. Sternopleural bristles present. Postvertical bristles *converge*. Oral vibrissae *present*. All fronto-orbital bristles *directed outward*. At least some dorsocentral bristles in anterior part of mesonotum.

This family is represented in the U.S. by 22 relatively uncommon species, most of which occur along the seashore; the inland species usually inhabit alkaline areas. The majority of the seashore species are found along the Pacific Coast. Larvae are unknown.

ANTHOMYZID FLIES Family Anthomyzidae
Identification: Similar to Tethinidae, but with *at least 1 pair of fronto-orbital bristles bent upward* and with no dorsocentral bristles in anterior part of mesonotum.

Anthomyzids are *small*, somewhat elongate flies that occur in grass and low vegetation, especially in marshy areas. They are widely distributed and fairly common.

OPOMYZID FLIES Family Opomyzidae
Identification: Similar to Anthomyzidae and Tethinidae, but postvertical bristles *absent* or diverging. Oral vibrissae present or *absent*. More stout-bodied than Anthomyzidae.

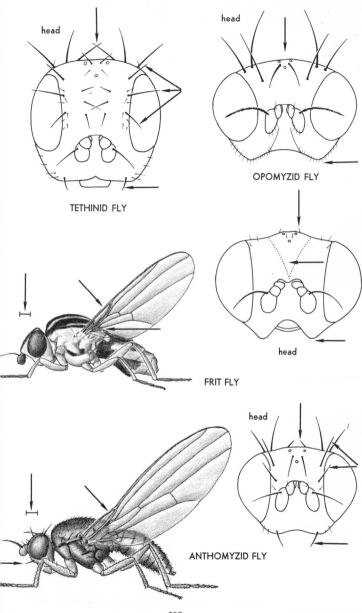

head

TETHINID FLY

head

OPOMYZID FLY

FRIT FLY

head

head

ANTHOMYZID FLY

299

These are rare flies, small to minute, usually dark-colored, and generally found in grassy places. Most of the 13 N. American species occur in Canada and w. U.S.

LEAF MINER FLIES Family Agromyzidae
Identification: *Small* to very small flies, usually blackish or yellowish. Sc incomplete or fused with R_1. Costa *broken near end of R_1*. Anal cell *present*. Sternopleural bristles present. Postvertical bristles *diverge*. Oral vibrissae *present*. No preapical tibial bristles. 6 abdominal segments.

Leaf miner flies are common insects usually occurring on vegetation. Larvae are mostly leaf miners and generally make a narrow winding mine; some feed in stems and seeds.

ODINIID FLIES Family Odiniidae   **Not illus.**
Identification: Similar to Agromyzidae, but with preapical tibial bristles and 5 abdominal segments.

Adults of this small group occur around rotting logs and sap flows but are uncommon. Larvae are scavengers.

SHORE FLIES Family Ephydridae
Identification: Most species blackish and relatively small; some very small. Sc incomplete. Costa *broken near end of R_1* and *near humeral cross vein*. Anal cell *absent*. Face usually *somewhat bulging*. Oral vibrissae absent. Postvertical bristles diverging (sometimes small and difficult to see).

Shore flies are common insects often occurring in large numbers along the shores of ponds and streams and along the seashore. Larvae are usually aquatic. Larvae of the seashore species live in brackish water and adults often cluster in large numbers on the surface of pools just above the high tidemark.

MILICHIID FLIES Family Milichiidae
Identification: Very small flies, usually blackish. Sc *incomplete*. Costa *broken near end of R_1* and *near humeral cross vein*. Anal cell *present*. Postvertical bristles *converging* or parallel. Oral vibrissae *weakly developed*. At least 1 pair of fronto-orbital bristles *bent inward*.

Milichiids are fairly common in grassy areas. Larvae are scavengers.

POMACE FLIES Family Drosophilidae   **See also p. 283**
Identification: Usually yellowish or brownish, *3–4 mm*. Sc incomplete. Costa *broken near end of R_1* and *near humeral cross vein;* not spiny. Anal cell *present*. Postvertical bristles *converge*. Oral vibrissae *well developed*. Arista *plumose*. Sternopleural bristle present; no mesopleural bristles.

Pomace flies are very common, and are usually found near

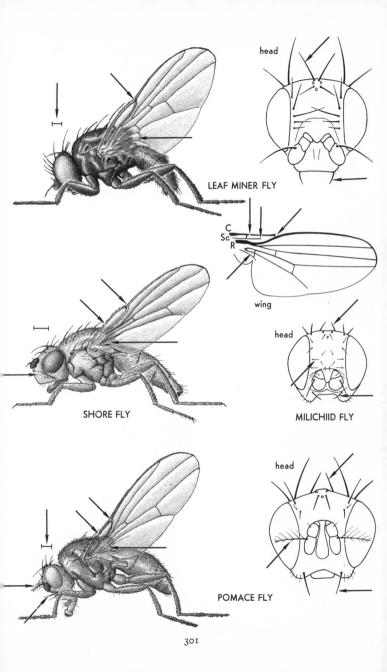

LEAF MINER FLY

wing

C
Sc
R

head

SHORE FLY

MILICHIID FLY

head

POMACE FLY

head

301

decaying vegetation or fruit. Larvae of most species breed in decaying fruit or fungi. Species of *Drosophila* have been used extensively in studies of heredity.

CAMILLID FLIES Family Camillidae **Not illus.**
Identification: Similar to Drosophilidae, but body metallic, no sternopleural bristles, and mesopleura bristly.

A single species in this group has been recorded in Ontario. Its immature stages are unknown.

DIASTATID FLIES Family Diastatidae
Identification: Similar to Drosophilidae, but costa *spiny* and mesopleura with bristles. Arista *short-plumose*. Fronto-orbital bristles close to eyes, the downward-bent pair positioned *above the upward-bent pair*.

These flies are similar to the Drosophilidae, but little is known of their habits. The U.S. has 6 species.

CURTONOTID FLIES Family Curtonotidae
Identification: Similar to Diastatidae, but arista *long-plumose*, fronto-orbital bristles remote from eyes, the downward-bent pair positioned *below upward-bent pair* and *no cross vein* separating 2nd basal and discal cells.

Curtonotids are represented in the U.S. by 1 species, *Curtonotum helvum* Loew, occurring in the East. It is found in high grass in moist places and its larva is unknown.

Calyptrate Muscoids: Section Calyptratae

Calypters usually well developed. Second antennal segment *with a longitudinal suture* (except in Gasterophilidae); see p. 283.

This is a large group that contains many common and well-known flies. The 11 families of calyptrates may be divided into 4 groups to aid identification:

1. Body somewhat leathery and flattened dorsoventrally; coxae separated; abdominal segmentation usually indistinct; often wingless; ectoparasites of birds and mammals: Hippoboscidae, Streblidae, and Nycteribiidae (louse and bat flies).

2. Mouth opening small, mouth parts vestigial or lacking; robust, hairy, beelike: Gasterophilidae, Cuterebridae, and Oestridae (bot and warble flies).

3. R_5 cell usually parallel-sided, only rarely narrowed distally; hypopleura usually without bristles (if hypopleural bristles are present, there are no pteropleural bristles or the proboscis is slender, rigid, and piercing): Anthomyiidae and Muscidae.

4. R_5 cell narrowed or closed distally; hypopleura and pteropleura with bristles; proboscis not slender and piercing: Tachinidae, Calliphoridae, and Sarcophagidae.

LOUSE FLIES Family Hippoboscidae
Identification: *Winged or wingless;* wings when present, with *strong veins anteriorly* and weak veins posteriorly. Palps slender, elongate, and forming a sheath for the proboscis. Eyes well developed.

Winged louse flies are usually found on birds. A common wingless species in this group is the Sheep Ked, *Melophagus*

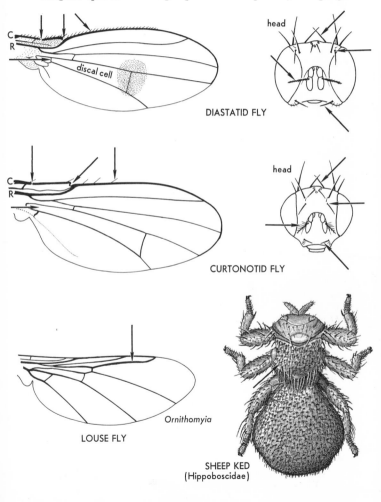

DIASTATID FLY

CURTONOTID FLY

LOUSE FLY

Ornithomyia

SHEEP KED
(Hippoboscidae)

ovinus (Linn.), about 6 mm. and reddish brown; it is an ecto-parasite of sheep.

BAT FLIES   Not illus.
Families Streblidae and Nycteribiidae
    Identification: Streblidae: winged or wingless, wings when present uniformly veined; head with a fleshy movable neck, and not folding back into a groove on mesonotum; palps broad and extending leaflike in front of head; eyes small or vestigial. Nycteribiidae: wingless, somewhat spiderlike in appearance; head small and narrow and at rest folding back into a groove on mesonotum.
    Members of these 2 families are ectoparasites of bats, and are seldom encountered.

HORSE BOT FLIES Family Gasterophilidae
    Identification: Beelike flies resembling the Honey Bee. 2nd antennal segment without a longitudinal suture. R_5 cell *widened distally.*
    Larvae of these flies develop in the stomach or intestine of horses, and when full grown pass out with the feces and pupate in the ground. Eggs are usually laid on the lips or jaws of the horse, and either burrow through the skin into the mouth, or get into the mouth when licked by the horse. These insects are rather serious pests of horses. Adults are not common, but are generally found in the vicinity of horse barns and pastures.

ROBUST BOT FLIES Family Cuterebridae
    Identification: Scutellum extends *beyond metanotum.* Post-scutellum *not developed.* R_5 cell narrowed or closed distally. Large robust flies resembling bumble bees.
    Larvae mostly are parasites of rabbits and rodents, usually developing just under the skin. Adults are rare.

BOT and WARBLE FLIES Family Oestridae
    Identification: Scutellum *very short.* Postscutellum usually *well developed.* R_5 cell narrowed or closed distally.
    Oestrid larvae are parasites of various animals, including some domestic animals. Ox warbles (*Hypoderma*) parasitize cattle; larvae develop in boil-like swellings just under the skin, usually on the back of the animal; adults are very annoying to cattle though they do not bite. The Sheep Bot Fly, *Oestrus ovis* Linn., is a parasite of sheep; its larva develops in the nostrils of the sheep. Adult bot and warble flies are not very common; they are most likely to be found in the vicinity of their hosts.

ANTHOMYIID FLIES Family Anthomyiidae
    Identification: R_5 cell *parallel-sided.* Hypopleura *without bristles.* 2A *reaches wing margin,* at least as a fold. Often *only 1*

sternopleural bristle, or fine erect hairs on undersurface of scutellum.

This is a large group that includes many common flies. Most are similar to a House Fly in general appearance and vary from being smaller to larger than a House Fly. Larval habits vary: many are plant feeders, and some of these are serious pests of

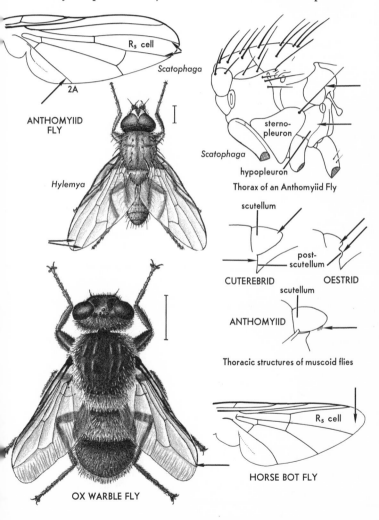

ANTHOMYIID FLY

Scatophaga

Hylemya

R₅ cell

2A

sterno-pleuron

Scatophaga

hypopleuron

Thorax of an Anthomyiid Fly

scutellum

post-scutellum

CUTEREBRID

OESTRID

scutellum

ANTHOMYIID

Thoracic structures of muscoid flies

R₅ cell

HORSE BOT FLY

OX WARBLE FLY

cultivated plants; many are scavengers, living in excrement or decaying materials; some are aquatic.

MUSCID FLIES   Family Muscidae   **See also Pl. 14**
Identification: Similar to Anthomyiidae, but 2A *short* and *not reaching wing margin*, undersurface of scutellum usually without fine hairs, and generally more than 1 sternopleural bristle. R_5 cell *parallel-sided or narrowed distally*.

This group includes many common flies, some of which are important pests. Most of them resemble the House Fly. The House Fly (Pl. 14), *Musca domestica* Linn., is a common household pest that breeds in various sorts of filth; it may serve as a vector of several diseases (typhoid fever, dysentery, cholera, and others); it has a short fleshy proboscis (and does not bite), and the R_5 cell is narrowed distally. The Little House Fly, *Fannia canicularis* (Linn.), is often a nuisance in houses and around poultry yards; adults can be recognized by the form of 3A (bends toward wing tip distally); its larva breeds in filth. The Stable Fly, *Stomoxys calcitrans* (Linn.), is very similar to the House Fly, but has a slender proboscis and it bites; it breeds in decaying vegetation.

TACHINID FLIES   Family Tachinidae   **See also Pl. 14**
Identification: R_5 cell *narrowed* or closed *distally*. Postscutellum *developed*. Hypopleura with *bristles*. Arista usually bare.

This is one of the largest families of Diptera, and its members are to be found almost everywhere. Most tachinids resemble the House Fly but many are larger; some are hairy and beelike. Tachinids can usually be distinguished from other calyptrates by the bare arista; some have the arista plumose, and can be recognized as tachinids by the well-developed postscutellum. Larvae are parasites of other insects, and many are of value in keeping noxious species under control.

BLOW FLIES   Family Calliphoridae   **See also Pl. 14**
Identification: Similar to Tachinidae, but postscutellum not developed. Arista plumose. Body often metallic. Usually *2 notopleural bristles*, and hindmost posthumeral bristle located *lateral to presutural bristle*.

This is a large group of flies, and its members are often common and abundant. Most species are as large as the House Fly and some are larger. Many are metallic bluish or green. Larvae are generally scavengers, living in carrion, dung, and similar materials; most maggots one finds in the body of a dead animal are blow fly larvae. Larvae usually feed on dead tissue, but a few, such as the Screw-worm, *Cochliomyia hominivorax* (Coquerel), may attack living tissue (in an animal's nostrils or in wounds).

FLESH FLIES Family Sarcophagidae   See also Pl. 14

Identification: Similar to Calliphoridae, but arista plumose only in basal half, body generally blackish with gray thoracic stripes (never metallic), usually *4 notopleural bristles*, and hindmost posthumeral bristle located even with or *toward midline from presutural bristle.*

Flesh flies are fairly common and usually resemble the House Fly. Larvae of most species are scavengers, feeding in the same sorts of materials as blow fly larvae; a few are parasites of other insects, a few develop in skin sores of vertebrates, and some feed on the insects stored in the nests of various wasps.

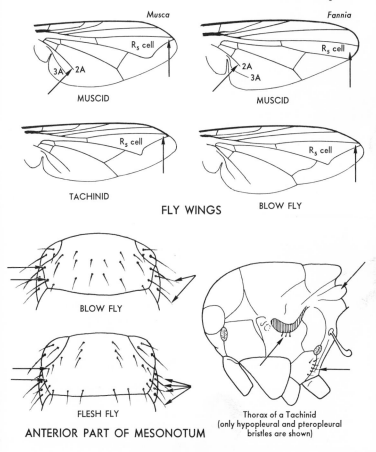

Musca

R₅ cell

3A 2A

MUSCID

Fannia

R₅ cell

2A
3A

MUSCID

R₅ cell

TACHINID

R₅ cell

BLOW FLY

FLY WINGS

BLOW FLY

FLESH FLY

ANTERIOR PART OF MESONOTUM

Thorax of a Tachinid
(only hypopleural and pteropleural
bristles are shown)

Fleas: Order Siphonaptera

Identification: Small wingless insects, generally less than 5 mm. and usually living as ectoparasites on birds or mammals. Body laterally flattened, rather bristly, and heavily sclerotized. Antennae short, 3-segmented, usually fitting into grooves on head. Ocelli lacking. Compound eyes present or absent. Legs relatively long, coxae *large*, tarsi *5-segmented*. Mouth parts sucking, the palps well developed. Metamorphosis complete. Usually jumping insects.

Similar orders: (1, 2) Mallophaga and Anoplura (pp. 106, 108): dorsoventrally flattened; legs short, tarsi 1- or 2-segmented; not jumping insects.

Immature stages: Larvae are slender, whitish, and legless, with a well-developed head and 2 small hooks on posterior end of body; they are usually found in dirt or debris, often in nest of the host. Larvae feed on various organic materials and pupate in silken cocoons.

Habits: Fleas are active insects that generally move freely over body of the host and from one host to another; some may spend considerable time off the host. Eggs are laid on the host or in dirt of the host nest; if laid on the host they eventually fall off, and larvae develop off the host. Adults feed on blood of the host. Many species (including those attacking man) are not very specific in their choice of a host and may feed on various animals.

Importance: Many fleas are annoying pests because of their bloodsucking habits. A few act as vectors of disease (bubonic plague and endemic typhus) and a few burrow into the skin of man or animals.

Classification: There are differences of opinion regarding the number and arrangement of the families of fleas; we follow an arrangement in which the fleas are grouped in 7 families. Families are separated principally by head and abdominal characters and on the character of various bristles. Some of these characters are difficult to see unless the specimen is mounted on a microscope slide.

No. of species: World, 1100; N. America, 238.

COMMON FLEAS   Family Pulicidae

Identification: Abdominal *terga 2–6 with a single row of bristles*. Compound eyes *well developed*. Genal comb (row of strong bristles on lower front border of head) present or absent.

This is a large group, and many of its members are fairly common; the fleas most often attacking man and domestic animals, and those most important as disease vectors, belong to this family. Many are not very specific in their selection of a host,

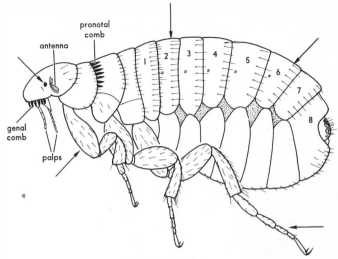

DOG FLEA (Pulicidae)

and though they may be named from their principal host they often attack man and other animals indiscriminately. Many are worldwide in distribution. The Cat and Dog Fleas, *Cteno-cephalides felis* (Bouché) and *C. canis* (Curtis), often occur in houses where these animals are kept and may attack man; the Dog Flea serves as the intermediate host of a dog tapeworm. Cat and Dog Fleas possess both genal and pronotal combs (pronotal comb is a row of strong spines on posterior margin of pronotum). The Human Flea, *Pulex irritans* Linn., and the Rat Flea, *Xenopsylla cheopis* (Rothschild), lack genal and pronotal combs; both attack man and other animals.

The most important flea-borne disease is bubonic plague, transmitted chiefly by the Rat Flea; this is primarily a rodent disease but occasionally occurs in man, sometimes in epidemic form. Plague infection usually occurs at the time of biting, but may also result from the ingestion of an infected flea or by scratching its feces into the skin.

BAT FLEAS   Family Ischnopsyllidae   **p. 311**
Identification: Parasites of bats. Genal comb *present and con-sisting of 2* or *3 broad lobes* on each side. Head elongated. Eyes absent or vestigial. Some or all of abdominal terga 2–6 with 2 rows of bristles.

This is a small group whose members are not often seen.

STICKTIGHT and CHIGOE FLEAS Family Tungidae

Identification: The 3 thoracic terga together *shorter* than the 1st abdominal tergum.

The most common species in this group is the Sticktight Flea, *Echidnophaga gallinacea* (Westwood), an important pest of poultry; it also attacks other birds and mammals. Adults usually occur on head of the host, often in dense masses, and remain attached for long periods. This insect is more common in the southern states. Another member of this family occasionally occurring in the southern states is the Chigoe, *Tunga penetrans* (Linn.); females burrow into the skin of man and other animals, usually on the feet. Males and newly emerged females of the Chigoe live much like other fleas, and feed on various hosts; the females burrow into the skin of man and other animals after mating. Once under the skin, the female's abdomen becomes greatly distended, and the surrounding tissues of the host swell to form a boil-like sore.

RODENT FLEAS Family Dolichopsyllidae

Identification: Some or all of abdominal terga 2–6 *with 2 rows of bristles* (if these terga bear only 1 row of bristles, eyes are absent or vestigial and there is no genal comb). Genal comb usually *absent*, but if present consists of 3 or more narrow lobes on each side. Pronotal comb *present*. *No suture* on dorsal surface of head between antennae.

This is a large group whose members are chiefly parasites of rodents; a few attack birds, and one of these is sometimes a pest of poultry. Some fleas in this family act as vectors of bubonic plague but they generally transmit the plague from one rodent to another and are not important as a vector of plague to man.

RAT AND MOUSE FLEAS Family Hystrichopsyllidae

Identification: Similar to Dolichopsyllidae, but usually with *a suture* on dorsal surface of head between antennae, *a genal comb*, and *2 or 3 rows of bristles* on anterior part of head.

This is a small family whose members are parasites of rats, mice, and shrews.

MALACOPSYLLID FLEAS Family Malacopsyllidae

Identification: Some or all of abdominal terga 2–6 with 2 rows of bristles. Pronotal and genal combs absent. Clypeal tubercle (in middle of front part of head) *well developed* and *somewhat pointed*. 1 long bristle on each side of next to last abdominal segment.

This group is represented in the U.S. by 2 species of *Rhopalopsyllus*, which are parasites of opossums and rats. They occur from Georgia and Florida to Texas.

CARNIVORE FLEAS Family Vermipsyllidae
Identification: Similar to Malacopsyllidae, but with clypeal
tubercle small and rounded or *lacking*, and without long bristles
near end of abdomen. Parasites of carnivores.

This is a small group whose members are parasites of bears,
wolves, and other large carnivores. They resemble some Pulicidae
in lacking genal and pronotal combs, but have 2 rows of bristles
on most abdominal terga. They occur in the West.

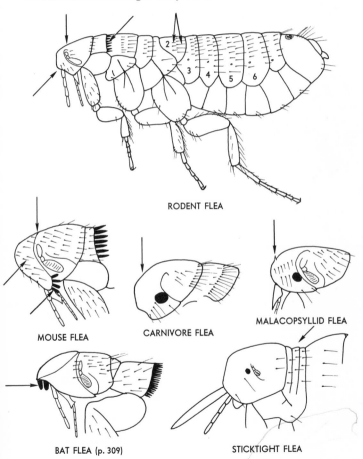

RODENT FLEA

MOUSE FLEA

CARNIVORE FLEA

MALACOPSYLLID FLEA

BAT FLEA (p. 309)

STICKTIGHT FLEA

Sawflies, Ichneumons, Chalcids, Ants, Wasps, and Bees: Order Hymenoptera

Identification: Wings, when present, 4 in number, membranous; FW a little larger than HW; wings with relatively few veins, venation in some minute forms nearly lacking. Antennae usually fairly long, generally with 10 or more segments. ♀ with well-developed ovipositor, which is sometimes longer than the body, and is sometimes modified into a sting. Tarsi 5-segmented (except in a few minute forms). Mouth parts chewing, sometimes with the maxillae and labium modified into a tonguelike sucking structure. Metamorphosis complete.

Similar orders: (1) Diptera (p. 260): only 2 wings; antennae often 3-segmented; mouth parts sucking; softer-bodied. (2) Lepidoptera (p. 218): wings covered with scales, at least in part; usually with a coiled proboscis. (3, 4) Ephemeroptera and Odonata (pp. 65, 68): antennae very short; wings with a more extensive venation.

Immature stages: Larvae caterpillarlike (Symphyta) or maggotlike with a well-developed head (Apocrita). Larvae of Symphyta resemble those of Lepidoptera, but usually have 6 or more pairs of prolegs that lack crochets, and 1 pair of large ocelli. Many larvae are plant feeders, feeding on or in foliage, stems, fruits, and other parts of the plant; many live as parasites in or on bodies of other insects; others live in nests constructed by the adults and feed on material put in nest by the adults. Pupation occurs in a cocoon, in special cells, or (in many parasitic species) in the host.

Habits: Adults are found in many habitats; most occur on flowers or vegetation, but some live on the ground or in debris, and many nest in the ground. Species whose larvae are plant feeders usually lay their eggs in or on the food plant; parasitic species generally lay their eggs on or in the host. Many Hymenoptera construct a nest of some sort and lay their eggs in this nest. Ovipositor of some species is modified into a sting, which is often used to paralyze prey and is an effective means of defense.

Importance: Some Hymenoptera, especially bees, are important plant pollinators. The Honey Bee provides us with useful products (honey and wax). Many parasitic and predaceous species aid in keeping noxious insects under control. Some plant-feeding species are serious pests of cultivated plants.

Classification: Two suborders, Symphyta and Apocrita, which differ in body shape and wing venation. Each suborder is divided into superfamilies.

No. of species: World, 105,000; N. America, 16,300.

Characters used in identification: Principal characters used in separating families of Hymenoptera are those of wing venation, legs, antennae, pronotum, certain sutures on the thorax, and the

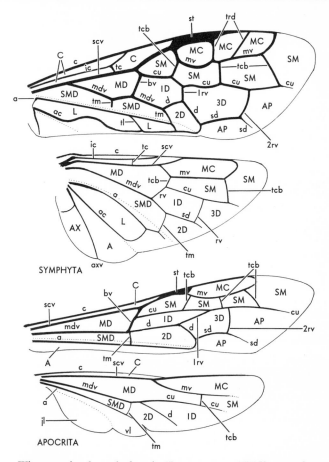

Wing venational terminology in Hymenoptera. VEINS: *a*, anal; *ac*, accessory; *axv*, axillary; *bv*, basal; *c*, costal; *cu*, cubital; *d*, discoidal; *ic*, intercostal; *mdv*, median; *mv*, marginal; *rv*, recurrent; *scv*, subcostal; *sd*, subdiscoidal; *st*, stigma; *tc*, transverse costal; *tcb*, transverse cubitals; *tl*, transverse lanceolate; *tm*, transverse median; *trd*, transverse marginal. CELLS: *A*, anal; *AP*, apical; *AX*, axillary; *C*, costal; *D*, discoidal; *L*, lanceolate; *MC*, marginal; *MD*, median; *SM*, submarginal; *SMD*, submedian. The basal cells in the hind wing of Symphyta are *MD*, *SMD*, and *L*, and those in Apocrita are *MD* and *SMD*. Lobes in the hind wing: *jl*, jugal; *vl*, vannal.

ovipositor. Not all entomologists agree on how the standard venational terminology (p. 35) should be applied in this order, so we use an older terminology, which is shown on p. 313. Numbers of cells mentioned in descriptions of Hymenoptera refer to the number of *closed* cells, unless otherwise indicated. Leg characters involve the number of trochanter segments (1 or 2), spurs at apex of the tibia, and occasionally other features. Antennae may vary in shape, number of segments, or in location on the face. Shape of the pronotum is useful in distinguishing superfamilies of Apocrita and some families of Symphyta, and the character of various thoracic sutures is used to separate families in a few superfamilies. Ovipositor in many cases rises anterior to apex of the abdomen and cannot be withdrawn into body (Hymenoptera with such an ovipositor generally do not sting); the ovipositor in others issues from the apex of the abdomen, and is withdrawn when not in use (most Hymenoptera with this type of ovipositor can sting).

Sawflies, Horntails, and Wood Wasps: Suborder Symphyta

Base of abdomen broadly joined to thorax. FW with 1–3 marginal cells and nearly always with an accessory vein. HW with 3 basal cells. Trochanters 2-segmented. Larvae plant feeders (except Orussidae). ♀ nonstinging.

The sawflies in the first 7 families below (Tenthredinidae through Diprionidae), and the Orussidae, have *2 apical spurs* on the front tibiae; other families have only 1. Sawflies commonly occur on flowers or are found in association with their food plants.

COMMON SAWFLIES   See also Pl. 15
Family Tenthredinidae
    Identification: Antennae *threadlike*, usually *9-segmented*, the segments similar. FW with 1 or *2 marginal cells*, and without an intercostal vein.
    This is the largest family of sawflies, with about 800 N. American species; it contains most of the species the general collector will encounter. These sawflies are 5–20 mm.; some are black, some brownish, and some are brightly patterned. They are usually found on flowers or vegetation. Larvae of most species are external feeders on foliage; a few are leaf miners and a few are gall makers. Some members of this group cause considerable damage to cultivated plants and forest trees.

XYELID SAWFLIES   Family Xyelidae
    Identification: Usually brownish and less than 10 mm. 3rd antennal segment *very long*, often longer than the remaining segments combined. FW with *an intercostal vein* and *3* (rarely 2) *marginal cells*.

Xyelids are uncommon. Larvae are external feeders on elm, hickory, and staminate flowers of pine or bore in new pine shoots.

WEB-SPINNING and LEAF-ROLLING SAWFLIES
Family Pamphiliidae
Identification: Relatively stout-bodied, 15 mm. or less, and usually brightly colored. Antennae long and slender, with *13 or more similar segments*. FW with *an intercostal vein, 2 marginal cells*, and 2 transverse median veins.

Pamphiliids are not common. Larvae roll up leaves, tie them with silk, and feed inside the shelter so formed; they feed on various trees and shrubs.

PERGID SAWFLIES   Family Pergidae   **Not illus.**
Identification: Small sawflies, usually less than 10 mm. Antennae 6-segmented and threadlike.

Pergids occur from the eastern states west to Arizona, but are uncommon. Larvae feed on foliage of oak and hickory.

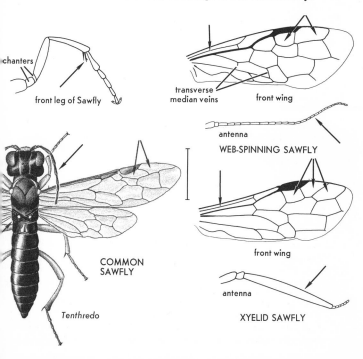

chanters

front leg of Sawfly

transverse median veins

front wing

antenna

WEB-SPINNING SAWFLY

COMMON SAWFLY

Tenthredo

front wing

antenna

XYELID SAWFLY

ARGID SAWFLIES Family Argidae
Identification: Relatively stout-bodied, and 15 mm. or less. Antennae 3-segmented, the *3rd segment very long* (U-shaped in many males).

Larvae of most species feed on various trees and shrubs.

CIMBICID SAWFLIES Family Cimbicidae   See also Pl. 15
Identification: Our largest sawflies, 18–25 mm. Look somewhat like bumble bees (but are not hairy) or hornets. Antennae with 7 or fewer segments and *slightly clubbed*.

Cimbicids do not sting but can inflict a strong pinch with the mandibles. Most larvae feed on willow and elm; these are greenish yellow, with black spiracles and a black stripe down the back; the body is often in a spiral position; when disturbed they may eject a fluid from glands above the spiracles.

CONIFER SAWFLIES Family Diprionidae
Identification: *Stout-bodied.* Antennae with *13 or more segments*, usually serrate in ♀ and *pectinate in ♂*.

Most diprionids are 12 mm. or less, and their larvae feed on conifers. They are scarce in the Midwest but common in most areas where conifers are abundant.

HORNTAILS Family Siricidae   See also Pl. 15
Identification: Large insects (mostly 25–35 mm.), usually brownish or black, and some species have dark wings. Pronotum in dorsal view *wider than long* and *shorter along midline than laterally*. Apex of abdomen with a dorsally located spear or spine (♀ with 2 long slender structures at apex of abdomen, lower one the ovipositor).

This and the remaining families of Symphyta (except Orussidae) have a *single apical spur* on the front tibiae. Larvae are wood-boring, and attack both deciduous trees and conifers.

CEDAR WOOD WASPS Family Syntexidae
Identification: Pronotum in dorsal view *trapezoidal, about twice as wide as long*. FW with a costal cell.

Our only syntexid, *Syntexis libocedrii* Rohwer, occurs in n. California and s. Oregon. It is black and about 8 mm., and its larva bores in the wood of the incense cedar.

WOOD WASPS Family Xiphydriidae
Identification: Blackish and 20–25 mm. Pronotum in dorsal view *U-shaped, much longer laterally than along midline*. FW with *a costal cell* and *a transverse costal vein*.

Larvae bore in the dead and decaying wood of deciduous trees.

PARASITIC WOOD WASPS Family Orussidae
Identification: FW with *only 1 submarginal cell*. Antennae rise below eyes, just above mouth. 8–14 mm.

This is a small and relatively rare group. Adults resemble horntails but are much smaller; larvae are parasites of metallic wood-boring beetles (Buprestidae).

STEM SAWFLIES Family Cephidae
Identification: Pronotum in dorsal view *trapezoidal, about as long as wide.* Costal cell in FW lacking or *very narrow.* Abdomen somewhat flattened laterally.

Cephids are usually black and 9–13 mm. Larvae bore in the stems of various grasses and shrubs.

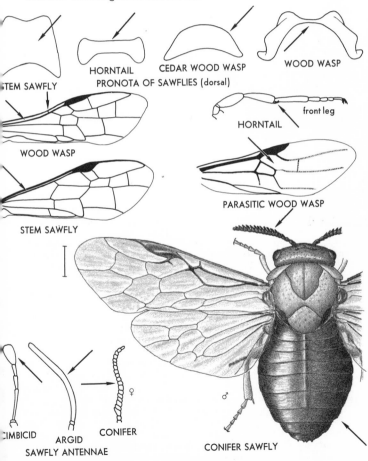

STEM SAWFLY

HORNTAIL   CEDAR WOOD WASP   WOOD WASP
PRONOTA OF SAWFLIES (dorsal)

WOOD WASP

front leg

HORNTAIL

PARASITIC WOOD WASP

STEM SAWFLY

CIMBICID   ARGID   CONIFER   ♀
SAWFLY ANTENNAE

♂

CONIFER SAWFLY

Parasitic Hymenoptera, Ants, Wasps, and Bees: Suborder Apocrita

Base of abdomen constricted, sometimes distinctly stalked. Thorax contains a 4th segment, the *propodeum* (actually the basal abdominal segment, fused to thorax). Wings without an accessory vein and HW with not more than 2 basal cells; venation in some minute forms greatly reduced, almost lacking.

Many Apocrita larvae live as parasites in or on bodies of other insects or spiders, and many are plant feeders. Parasitic forms generally lay their eggs on, in, or near body of the host; many have a long ovipositor with which they reach hosts in cocoons or other seemingly protected situations; a few lay their eggs on vegetation, and the newly hatched larvae remain on the vegetation until they can attach to a host passing by. From 1 to many parasites may develop in a single host individual (depending on species of parasite); the host is nearly always killed by the parasite, but usually not until the parasite has completed its larval development. Many parasitic Apocrita are very valuable insects, since they aid in the control of noxious species.

This suborder is divided into 11 superfamilies, adults of which can usually be separated by the character of the pronotum, antennae, and ovipositor, the number of trochanter segments, and the wing venation. Pronotum in profile may appear (a) more or less triangular and extending nearly to the *tegulae* (small scalelike structures overlying bases of front wings), (b) more or less squarish and not extending to the tegulae, or (c) short and collarlike, with a small rounded lobe on each side that does not reach the tegulae. Antennae vary in number of segments they contain and in whether or not they are elbowed; the 1st segment of an elbowed antenna is much longer than any other segment, and in nonelbowed antennae is comparatively short. The distinction between "elbowed" and "not elbowed" is occasionally not very sharp. The terminal antennal segments are usually slender, but are sometimes swollen to form a club and are pectinate in a few Chalcidoidea. The ovipositor in some groups (a) rises anterior to apex of the abdomen (on the ventral side) and is more or less permanently extruded, and usually cannot be withdrawn into abdomen. In other groups (b) the ovipositor issues from apex of abdomen and is withdrawn when not in use. Apocrita with an ovipositor of the 1st type (a) usually do not sting; those with an ovipositor of the 2nd type (b) usually do. Trochanters may be 1- or 2-segmented. Venation varies from almost no veins to a maximum of 10 closed cells in front wing (see p. 313). If there are at least 6 closed cells in the front wing the venation may be described as "normal"; if there are fewer, it may be described as "reduced."

Larvae of Ichneumonoidea, Evanioidea, Pelecinoidea, Bethy-

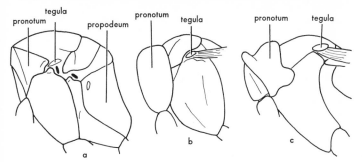

Forms of the pronotum in Apocrita

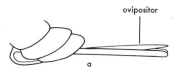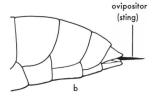

Forms of the ovipositor in Apocrita

Characters of the Superfamilies of Apocrita

Character	Ichneumonoidea	Chalcidoidea	Cynipoidea	Evanioidea	Pelecinoidea	Proctotrupoidea	Bethyloidea	Scolioidea	Vespoidea	Sphecoidea	Apoidea
Pronotum[1]	a	b	a	a	a	a	a,b	a,b	a	c	c
Ovipositor[1]	a	a[4]	a	a	b	b	b	b	b	b	b
Sting	no[4]	no	no	no	no	no	yes[4]	yes[4]	yes	yes	yes[4]
No. of hind trochanter segments	2	2	1[4]	2	1	1-2	1[4]	1	1	1	1
Antennae[2]	T	E	T	T	T	E,T	T[4]	T[4]	T	T	T
No. of antennal segments	16+[4]	5-13	13-16	13-14	14	7-15	10+	12-13	12-13	12-13	12-13
Venation[3]	N[4]	R	R	N	R	N,R	N,R	N[4]	N	N	N

[1] Letters refer to the types illustrated above.
[2] E, elbowed; T, not elbowed (usually threadlike).
[3] N, normal; R, reduced.
[4] Exceptions occur.

loidea, most Scolioidea, most Chalcidoidea, and a few Cynipoidea
are parasites of other insects or spiders; adults of these generally
seek out and oviposit in or on a host, then go on seeking other
hosts; they do not make a nest. Adults of Vespoidea and Sphecoidea generally build a nest, or cells of some sort, then go out and
capture prey (other insects or spiders) with which they provision
the nest or cells; after doing this they go their way, leaving the
young to fend for themselves (except in the social wasps). There is
no sharp line of distinction between these 2 methods of operation,
and in the family Pompilidae one may find a range in habits from
one extreme to the other. Bees (Apoidea) resemble Vespoidea and
Sphecoidea in building and provisioning nests or cells, but provision them with nectar and pollen. Social wasps and bees do not
provision the nest, but feed the young as they grow. Ants, which
are also social, generally construct a nest and feed the young as
they grow. The food of young ants may be plant or animal material, depending on the species. Some wasps (certain Sphecidae and
Chrysididae) and cuckoo bees are *inquilines:* they build no nest
and collect no food for their young, but lay their eggs in nests of
other wasps or bees, where their young feed on the food with which
these nests are provisioned. The term "cuckoo" is derived from
the European Cuckoo (and our cowbirds), which lays its eggs in
the nests of other birds.

Apocrita that are plant-feeding in the larval stage include bees,
gall wasps (Cynipinae), and some Chalcidoidea. Gall wasp larvae
live in and feed on plant galls; the plant-feeding chalcid larvae
feed in various ways on plants (a few feed in galls).

Superfamily Ichneumonoidea

Pronotum in profile more or less triangular, and extending to
tegulae or nearly so. Antennae *threadlike,* usually with *16 or more
segments.* Hind trochanters *2-segmented.* Ovipositor rises in front
of apex of abdomen, not capable of being withdrawn, often long,
sometimes longer than body. Venation usually normal. FW *without a costal cell* (except in Stephanidae).

This is one of the largest superfamilies in the order, and its
members are to be found almost everywhere. The known larvae
are parasites of other insects or spiders.

BRACONIDS Family Braconidae   **See also Pl. 15**
   Identification: Most are brownish or black, not brightly colored.
1 recurrent vein (see p. 313) or none, the 2nd recurrent vein
absent. 2–15 mm. 1st submarginal and 1st discoidal cells either
coalesce or are separated by base of cubital vein.

This is a large and widely distributed group found almost
everywhere. Larvae are parasites of a great variety of insects,
and many are important agents in the control of noxious insects.

Some species pupate in silken cocoons on the outside of the body of the host.

STEPHANIDS Family Stephanidae   **Not illus.**
Identification: Costal cell present. Head spherical on long neck and bearing a crown of teeth. 5–19 mm. Gasteruptiids and aulacids (p. 334) are similar but do not have a crown of teeth, and abdomen is attached to propodeum high above hind coxae.

This is a small group of very rare insects. Larvae are parasites of wood-boring beetles.

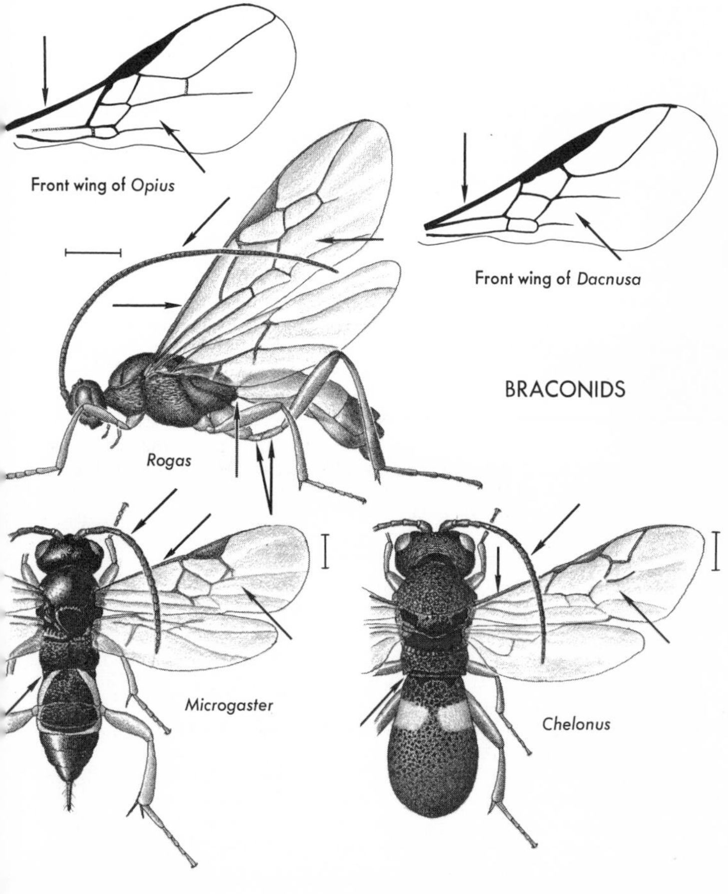

Front wing of *Opius*

Front wing of *Dacnusa*

BRACONIDS

Rogas

Microgaster

Chelonus

ICHNEUMONS   Family Ichneumonidae   **See also Pl. 15**
Identification: Slender, wasplike, 3–40 mm. *2 recurrent veins.*
2nd submarginal cell *small* or lacking. Base of cubital vein
lacking, 1st submarginal and 1st discoidal cells fused. Antennae
with 16 or more segments and usually *at least half as long as body.*
Braconids have only 1 recurrent vein or none; gasteruptiids and
aulacids (p. 334) have head set out on a slender neck, the
abdomen attached high above hind coxae, and FW with a costal
cell; wasps (Scolioidea, Vespoidea, and Sphecoidea, pp. 340, 346,
348) are usually stouter-bodied, with shorter antennae (that
nearly always have 13 or fewer segments), 1 trochanter segment,
a costal cell, and the cubital vein complete; trigonalids (p. 340),
which have long many-segmented antennae, have a costal cell
and a complete cubital vein.

This is the largest family of insects, with over 3000 N. American species. They are common insects, found almost everywhere.
They vary greatly in size and color: many are uniformly colored,
from yellowish to black, and many are brightly patterned with
black and brown or black and yellow; many have middle
segments of antennae yellowish or whitish. Most species have
a long ovipositor.

Most ichneumons do not sting, though they generally try to
do so when handled. The few that will sting are usually large,
yellowish brown, and have a laterally flattened abdomen. These
ichneumons have a short, sharp ovipositor capable of piercing
the skin. They must be able to move the abdomen in order to
sting, and if grasped by the abdomen are quite harmless.

The family Ichneumonidae is divided into a number of subfamilies, many of which are further divided into tribes. Each
subfamily or tribe is often parasitic on a particular group of
insects. Many ichneumons are of value in the control of noxious
insects.

Chalcids: Superfamily Chalcidoidea

Pronotum in profile *somewhat squarish* and not quite reaching
tegulae. Antennae *elbowed* and usually short, with 5–13 segments.
At least 1 pair of trochanters 2-segmented. Ovipositor generally
short, occasionally as long as body, and usually rising in front of
apex of abdomen. Wing venation *greatly reduced.* Mostly 5 mm.
or less. Small Proctotrupoidea (p. 335) with elbowed antennae
and a similarly reduced venation have the pronotum more triangular and the ovipositor apical.

This is a large group occurring almost everywhere. Most
chalcids are black, blue-black, or greenish, and many are metallic.
Wings are usually held flat over abdomen at rest; a few are wingless or have wings greatly reduced. Most larvae are parasites of
other insects and some are hyperparasites; many are plant feeders.

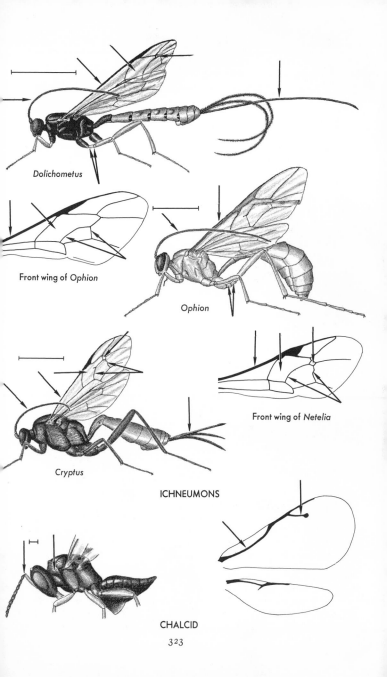

Dolichometus

Front wing of *Ophion*

Ophion

Cryptus

Front wing of *Netelia*

ICHNEUMONS

CHALCID

323

The small size of most chalcids is likely to make their identification difficult; the key below is designed to aid the beginner in separating the families of chalcids.

1.   HW very narrow, almost linear   **Mymaridae (p. 324)**
1'.   HW elongate-oval, not linear   2
2(1'). Tarsi 3-segmented   **Trichogrammatidae (p. 324)**
2'.   Tarsi 4- or 5-segmented   3
3(2'). Tarsi 4-segmented; apical spur of front tibiae small and
         straight   **Eulophidae (p. 324)**
3'.   Tarsi 5-segmented; apical spur of front tibiae large and
         curved   4
4(3'). Head of ♀ oblong, with a deep longitudinal groove above;
         ♂ wingless; front and hind legs stout, middle legs
         slender   **Agaonidae (p. 328)**
4'.   Without this combination of characters   5
5(4'). Mesopleura convex; apical spur of middle tibiae large
         and stout   **Tanaostigmatidae, Thysanidae,
         Eupelmidae, Encyrtidae, Eutrichosomatidae (p. 326)**
5'.   Mesopleura with a broad shallow groove; apical spur of
         middle tibiae small   6
6(5'). Mandibles sickle-shaped; thorax strongly arched, the
         pronotum usually not visible from above; scutellum
         large; abdomen laterally flattened   **Eucharitidae (p. 326)**
6'.   Without this combination of characters   7
7(6'). Hind femora greatly enlarged and usually toothed be-
         neath   **Chalcedectidae, some Torymidae,
         Leucospididae, Chalcididae (p. 328)**
7'.   Hind femora slender, not greatly enlarged   8
8(7'). Hind coxae considerably larger than front coxae
                                  Torymidae, Ormyridae (p. 328)
8'.   Hind coxae little if any larger than front coxae
         Pteromalidae, Perilampidae, Eurytomidae (p. 330)

FAIRYFLIES Family Mymaridae
   Identification: HW *very narrow, almost linear*.
   Fairyflies are minute insects, mostly less than 1 mm. (smallest is only 0.21 mm.), usually blackish, with relatively long legs and antennae. Larvae are egg parasites.

TRICHOGRAMMATIDS Family Trichogrammatidae
   Identification: Minute insects, 1 mm. or less, and rather stocky in build. Tarsi *3-segmented*. Tiny hairs of wings usually *in rows*.
   Larvae are parasites of insect eggs, and some are of value in controlling insect pests.

EULOPHIDS Family Eulophidae
   Identification: 1–3 mm. and varying in shape and color; most are black, a few brilliantly metallic. Tarsi *4-segmented*. Apical spur of front tibiae *small*, straight. Axillae *extend forward beyond tegulae*. ♂ antennae often pectinate.

This is a large, fairly common group of about 600 N. American species. Larvae are parasites of various other insects: Eulophinae are parasites of leaf miners; Tetrastichinae are egg parasites or attack larvae and pupae of Coleoptera, Lepidoptera, and Diptera; Entedontinae are chiefly parasites of small larvae in cases or leaf mines; Aphelininae are parasites of aphids, scale insects, and whiteflies; Elachertinae and Elasminae are parasites of caterpillars, the latter as hyperparasites attacking braconids and ichneumons in the caterpillars.

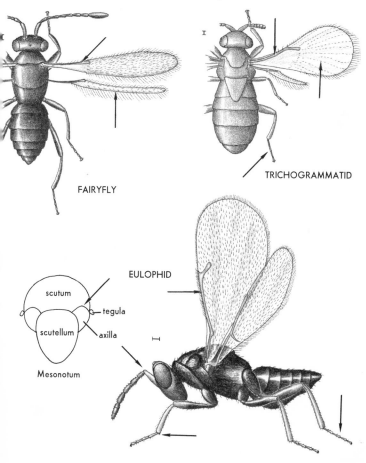

FAIRYFLY

TRICHOGRAMMATID

EULOPHID

scutum

tegula

scutellum

axilla

Mesonotum

ENCYRTIDS   Family Encyrtidae
Identification: 1–2 mm. and usually black or brown; some are
wingless. *Mesopleura* and *mesonotum convex*. Parapsidal sutures
indistinct or *lacking*. Marginal vein *very short*. Scutellum *not
much wider than long*. Apical spur of front tibiae *large and
curved*, of middle tibiae large and stout.

The encyrtids are a large and widely distributed group.
Larvae of most species are parasites of scale insects and whiteflies. Many species are polyembryonic, with 10 to over 1000
young developing from a single egg.

THYSANIDS   Family Thysanidae   **Not illus.**
Identification: Similar to Encyrtidae but marginal vein as long
as submarginal, and scutellum much wider than long.

Thysanids are small and stout-bodied. Larvae are mostly
hyperparasites, attacking parasites of scale insects and other
Homoptera. The group is small and rare.

EUPELMIDS   Family Eupelmidae
Identification: Similar to Encyrtidae but marginal vein *long*,
mesonotum flattened or *concave*, and parapsidal sutures usually
distinct and nearly straight.

Eupelmids are black or brown and usually over 2 mm. Some
species have the wings greatly reduced. Larvae are parasites
of various insects and spiders. Eupelmids are fairly common,
but generally not as common as encyrtids.

TANAOSTIGMATIDS   Family Tanaostigmatidae   **Not illus.**
Identification: Similar to Eupelmidae but mesonotum slightly
convex, parapsidal sutures complete and curved laterally,
scapulae short. 1st antennal segment of ♀ somewhat dilated
or flattened laterally; terminal antennal segments of ♂ with
4 branches.

Four rare species have been reported from Florida, Arizona,
and California. Most larvae are gall makers.

EUTRICHOSOMATIDS   **Not illus.**
Family Eutrichosomatidae
Identification: Similar to Tanaostigmatidae but 1st antennal
segment of ♀ slender and terminal antennal segments of ♂
without branches.

This group is represented in the U.S. by 2 rare species of
Eutrichosoma, 1 occurring in Georgia and Texas and 1 from
Maryland west to New Mexico, Idaho, and Montana. Larvae
are parasites of snout beetles.

EUCHARITIDS   Family Eucharitidae
Identification: Shape characteristic: head *short*, thorax *hump-*

backed, pronotum usually not visible from above, scutellum often *extending backward* over base of abdomen, and abdomen *stalked and attached low on thorax*.

This is a small group of rather uncommon insects, usually black, with interesting habits. Larvae are parasites of ant pupae; eggs are laid in large numbers on vegetation and the larvae on hatching attach themselves to a passing ant that carries them

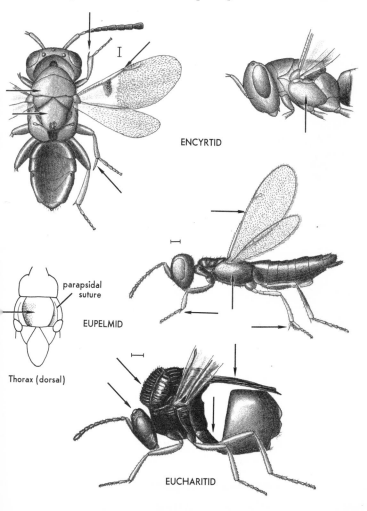

ENCYRTID

EUPELMID

parapsidal
suture

Thorax (dorsal)

EUCHARITID

to its nest, where the eucharitid larvae leave the ant and attack the ant pupae.

CHALCIDIDS Family Chalcididae

Identification: Generally uniformly dark-colored. Hind femora *greatly swollen*, toothed beneath. Hind coxae *considerably larger* than front coxae, long and cylindrical. Ovipositor usually short. Wings not folded longitudinally at rest.

Chalcidids are mostly 2–7 mm., and are relatively common. Larvae are parasites of a variety of insects.

CHALCEDECTIDS Family Chalcedectidae   **Not illus.**

Identification: Hind femora greatly swollen. Hind coxae little if any larger than front coxae.

Four rare species have been reported from the s. U.S. Larvae are parasites of Buprestidae.

LEUCOSPIDIDS Family Leucospididae

Identification: Similar to Chalcididae but larger (8–12 mm.). Brightly colored with black and yellow. Somewhat hump-backed in appearance. Wings folded longitudinally at rest. Ovipositor *curves upward and forward* along dorsal side of abdomen.

These are a small group of uncommon insects resembling small yellowjackets. They are usually found on flowers. Larvae are parasites of various wasps and bees.

TORYMIDS Family Torymidae

Identification: Elongate, usually metallic green, and mostly 2–4 mm. Hind coxae *much larger* than front coxae. Ovipositor *as long as body or longer*. Hind femora *slender*, or if greatly swollen hind coxae are triangular in cross section. Parapsidal sutures *present*. Abdomen smooth, shiny.

Larvae of some species are parasites of various caterpillars, gall insects, or insect eggs; larvae of others feed on seeds.

ORMYRIDS Family Ormyridae   **Not illus.**

Identification: Similar to Torymidae but parapsidal sutures indistinct or absent, ovipositor short and often hidden, and abdomen usually with rows of deep punctures.

This is a small group of rather rare chalcids. Larvae are parasites of gall insects.

FIG WASPS Family Agaonidae

Identification: Black. Head of ♀ somewhat oblong, with *a deep dorsal longitudinal groove*. ♀ winged, ♂ wingless. Front and hind legs *stout*, middle legs slender.

This group is represented in the U.S. by 2 species, 1 occurring

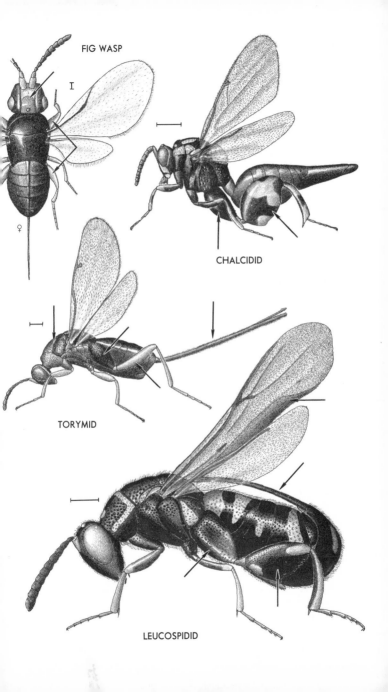

FIG WASP

♀

CHALCID

TORYMID

LEUCOSPIDID

in Florida and 1 in California and Arizona. Fig wasps pollinate certain varieties of figs.

PTEROMALIDS Family Pteromalidae

Identification: Tarsi *5-segmented*. Apical spur of front tibiae *large and curved*. Mesopleura slightly concave, or with *a broad shallow groove*. Front and hind coxae about same size. Hind femora not enlarged. Pronotum in dorsal view *somewhat conical, narrowed toward front*.

Pteromalids are common insects, and most of the chalcids encountered by the general collector will probably belong to this family. They are mostly 2–4 mm., and are usually black or metallic green. Larvae are parasites of a variety of insects, and many species are important agents in the control of crop pests.

EURYTOMIDS or SEED CHALCIDS Family Eurytomidae

Identification: Similar to Pteromalidae but pronotum in dorsal view *squarish*, not particularly narrowed anteriorly. Usually dull black, not shiny. Thorax rough or pitted. Abdomen of ♀ rounded or oval. Often somewhat hairy.

Eurytomids are fairly common chalcids. Some larvae are parasites of other insects and some feed on plants; a few are parasites as young and plant feeders when older. Plant-feeding species attack seeds and stems or are gall makers.

PERILAMPIDS Family Perilampidae

Identification: Relatively large chalcids; most are 6–8 mm. and metallic blue or blue-black. Thorax *stout, pitted* with punctures. Pronotum in dorsal view *transversely linear*. Abdomen *small*, in profile *triangular, shining*. Perilampids strongly resemble cuckoo wasps (Chrysididae; p. 338), but have a differently shaped abdomen and a more reduced wing venation.

Larvae are mostly hyperparasites, attacking the Diptera and Hymenoptera that are parasitic in caterpillars.

Gall Wasps and Others: Superfamily Cynipoidea

Pronotum in lateral view (see p. 333) *more or less triangular*, extending to tegulae or nearly so. Antennae *threadlike, 13- to 16-segmented*. Trochanters usually 1-segmented. Ovipositor rises anterior to apex of abdomen. Wing venation *reduced*. (For additional characters see p. 319.) The most distinctive features of the Cynipoidea are the wing venation and the threadlike antennae.

Most members of this group are black and 2–8 mm.; many have the abdomen shiny and often laterally flattened. More than 800 species of Cynipoidea occur in the U.S. The vast majority are gall wasps (Cynipinae) and the rest, as far as known, are parasites of other insects.

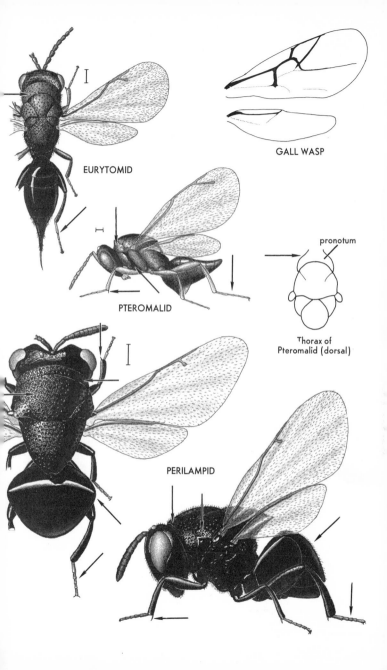

EURYTOMID

GALL WASP

PTEROMALID

pronotum

Thorax of
Pteromalid (dorsal)

PERILAMPID

IBALIIDS Family Ibaliidae

Identification: Usually black and yellowish brown, the abdomen banded. Length 7–16 mm.; abdomen elongate and laterally flattened. 1st segment of hind tarsi *twice as long* as other segments combined; 2nd segment with *a long apical process* extending to tip of 4th segment. FW usually with brownish spots in middle and at apex.

This is a small and rare group. Larvae are parasites of horntails (Siricidae).

LIOPTERIDS Family Liopteridae   **Not illus.**

Identification: Abdomen stalked and attached far above base of hind coxae. Propodeum with a median furrow.

Three rare species occur in Texas, Idaho, and California. Their larval stages are unknown.

FIGITIDS Family Figitidae

Identification: A small group of shining black insects, mostly 3–6 mm. Anacharitinae: abdomen *distinctly stalked*, attached near base of hind coxae. Aspiceratinae: 2nd abdominal tergum (1st tergum forms stalk, and 2nd is 1st tergum in swollen part of abdomen) *somewhat shovel-shaped*, in lateral view *narrow dorsoventrally*, shorter than 3rd along middorsal line. Figitinae: 2nd abdominal tergum *not particularly shovel-shaped, wider dorsoventrally* in side view, and about as long as 3rd along middorsal line.

Figitids are not common. Larvae are parasites of pupae of various Diptera (Aspiceratinae and Figitinae) or lacewings (Anacharitinae).

CYNIPIDS Family Cynipidae

Identification: Eucoilinae: 4–6 mm., shining black, scutellum with *a dorsal O-shaped elevation*. Charipinae (not illus.): 2 mm. or less; thorax smooth. Cynipinae: usually over 2 mm. (mostly 6–8 mm.), the thorax rather rough, the abdomen *oval and shining*.

Eucoilinae and Charipinae are parasitic in the larval stage, Eucoilinae on pupae of Diptera and Charipinae on the braconids that parasitize aphids. These cynipids are more common than the figitids.

The vast majority of Cynipoidea the general collector will encounter will be Cynipinae (gall wasps), many of which are common insects. They either are gall makers or live in galls formed by another organism; each gall maker forms a characteristic gall on a particular part of a particular plant. The galls are much more often seen, and are usually more distinctive, than the gall wasps themselves. Many gall wasps form galls on oak leaves.

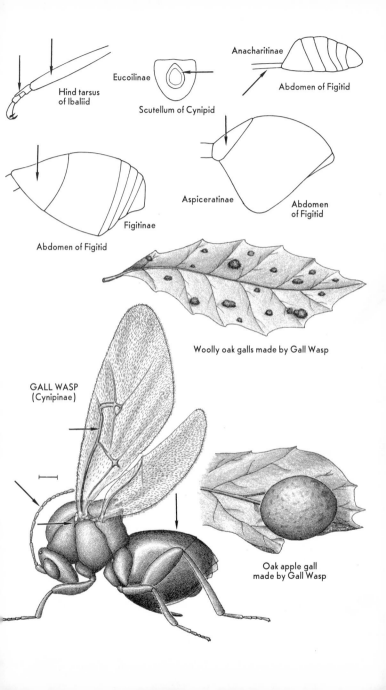

Hind tarsus
of Ibaliid

Eucoilinae

Scutellum of Cynipid

Anacharitinae

Abdomen of Figitid

Figitinae

Abdomen of Figitid

Aspiceratinae

Abdomen
of Figitid

Woolly oak galls made by Gall Wasp

GALL WASP
(Cynipinae)

Oak apple gall
made by Gall Wasp

Superfamily Evanioidea

Abdomen attached high above hind coxae. Antennae threadlike, 13- or 14-segmented. Trochanters *2-segmented*. Venation fairly complete. FW with *a costal cell*. (For additional characters see p. 319.)

ENSIGN WASPS Family Evaniidae
Identification: Black, somewhat spiderlike in appearance, and 6–10 mm.; the small abdomen is carried like a flag (hence the common name). Characteristic appearance: thorax stout, abdomen *small* and attached by *a slender stalk high above hind coxae*. Ovipositor very short, not protruding.

Larvae are parasitic in the egg capsules of cockroaches, and adults are likely to be found in places where cockroaches occur.

GASTERUPTIIDS Family Gasteruptiidae
Identification: Similar to Ichneumonidae (p. 322) but head set out *on a slender neck*, abdomen attached *high above hind coxae*, antennae *short*, and FW with *a costal cell*, only *1 recurrent vein*, and cubital vein complete. Ovipositor long, often as long as body. Black, 13–20 mm.

Adults are fairly common, and are usually found on flowers. Larvae are parasites of solitary wasps and bees.

AULACIDS Family Aulacidae
Identification: Similar to Gasteruptiidae but antennae longer and FW with *2 recurrent veins*. Black, or black with a reddish abdomen, and wings often banded or spotted.

Aulacid larvae parasitize various wood-boring insects, and adults are generally found around logs in which the hosts occur. These insects are moderately common.

Superfamily Pelecinoidea

Female about 2 in., shining black, with wings short and abdomen *very long and slender*. ♂ about 1 in., abdomen club-shaped. (For additional characters, see p. 319.)

PELECINIDS Family Pelecinidae
Identification: By the characters of the superfamily.

This group is represented in the U.S. by a single species, *Pelecinus polyturator* (Drury), which occurs in the eastern part of the country. Females, which are very distinctive in appearance, are fairly common but males are very rare. Larvae are parasites of white grubs.

Superfamily Proctotrupoidea

Trochanters 1- or 2-segmented; if 2-segmented 2nd segment is often poorly defined. Small, often minute, usually shining black. (For additional characters see p. 319.) Differ from Chalcidoidea and Bethyloidea (pp. 322, 338) in form of the pronotum, and from most Bethyloidea in lacking a jugal lobe in hind wing. Differ from Cynipoidea (p. 330) in location of the ovipositor. All known larvae are parasites of other insects.

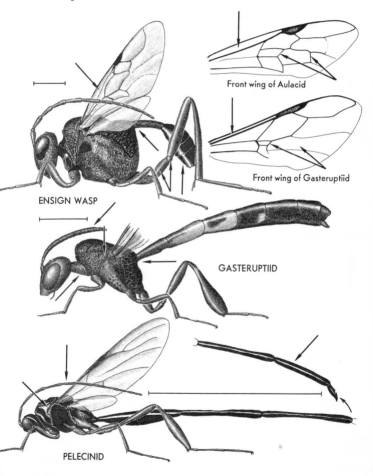

Front wing of Aulacid

Front wing of Gasteruptiid

ENSIGN WASP

GASTERUPTIID

PELECINID

HELORIDS Family Heloridae   **Not illus.**
Identification: Antennae 15-segmented, and rising at middle of
face. Venation normal. 1st discoidal cell in FW triangular.
4 mm.

One very rare but widely distributed species of helorid occurs
in the U.S. Its larva is a parasite of lacewings.

VANHORNIIDS Family Vanhorniidae
Identification: Mandibles with *tips directed outward*, and not
meeting when closed. Abdomen somewhat elongate, the 1st
segment occupying most of abdomen. Antennae 13-segmented.
Trochanters 1-segmented.

Our only species is very rare and occurs in the Northeast.
It is 6–8 mm., black, with a somewhat reduced wing venation.
Larvae parasitize the larvae of Eucnemidae.

ROPRONIIDS Family Roproniidae
Identification: Appearance: about 10 mm., thorax moderately
robust and black, abdomen small, somewhat triangular, laterally
flattened, with a long petiole, and brownish. Venation normal,
1st discoidal cell in FW *irregularly 6-sided*. Antennae 14-seg-
mented, rising at middle of face. Trochanters 1-segmented or
indistinctly 2-segmented.

Three very rare species occur in the U.S., 2 in the East and
1 in California and Oregon. Larvae parasitize sawflies.

PROCTOTRUPIDS Family Proctotrupidae
Identification: Characteristic venation: FW with a costal cell,
a *large stigma*, and a *very small marginal cell*. Antennae *13-
segmented, threadlike*, and rising *at middle of face*. Abdomen
spindle-shaped, with a short cylindrical petiole. Trochanters
1-segmented.

Proctotrupids are moderately common insects that vary from
about 3 to 10 mm.; the abdomen is often brownish. Little is
known of the larval stages, but some are known to parasitize
beetles.

CERAPHRONIDS Family Ceraphronidae
Identification: Chalcidlike, but pronotum in lateral view triangular and extending to tegulae. Antennae *elbowed*, 9- to
11-segmented, and rise low on face. Venation reduced. HW
without a distinct jugal lobe. Trochanters 2-segmented. Abdomen
rounded laterally.

This is a large group of small black insects, mostly less than
4 mm.; a few are wingless. Larvae are parasites of a variety of
insects.

DIAPRIIDS Family Diapriidae
Identification: Small to minute, black and shining, fairly common. Antennae *11- to 15-segmented, threadlike*, and rising on

a shelflike protuberance in middle of face. Trochanters 2-segmented. Venation reduced, sometimes (Diapriinae) nearly absent. HW without a jugal lobe.

Larvae of most species are parasites of fungus gnats and other Diptera, and adults are usually found in wooded areas where there is decaying vegetation and fungi. Two of the 4 sub-

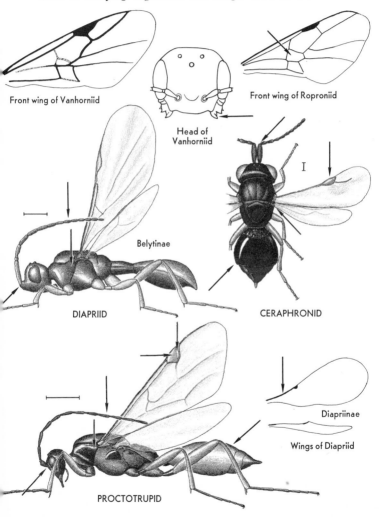

Front wing of Vanhorniid

Head of Vanhorniid

Front wing of Roproniid

Belytinae

DIAPRIID

CERAPHRONID

PROCTOTRUPID

Diapriinae

Wings of Diapriid

families are common; the Diapriinae are minute, with the venation *greatly reduced* (no closed cell in hind wing); the Belytinae are larger (5–7 mm.), with slightly more venation (a closed cell in hind wing).

SCELIONIDS Family Scelionidae

Identification: Minute insects, usually 2 mm. or less; black (rarely brown). Antennae *elbowed, rising low on face,* generally 11- or 12-segmented (occasionally 7- or 8-segmented and clubbed, the club unsegmented). Abdomen *flattened,* the lateral margins *sharp.* Venation *greatly reduced,* chalcidlike. HW without a jugal lobe.

This is a large, fairly common group. Larvae are chiefly egg parasites. Some females, which parasitize the eggs of grasshoppers or mantids, attach to the abdomen of a grasshopper or mantid and ride around on it until it lays its eggs; then the scelionid gets off and oviposits in the eggs of the host.

PLATYGASTERIDS Family Platygasteridae

Identification: Similar to Scelionidae but antennae 9- or 10-segmented, if clubbed the club segmented. Abdomen more or less flattened, less so than in Scelionidae.

Platygasterids are minute insects, shining black, with *almost no wing venation.* Some species have a peculiarly shaped abdomen. Females of the genus *Inostemma* have *a long handlelike process* extending from the base of the abdomen forward over the thorax (this process serves as a receptacle for the long ovipositor when it is withdrawn into the body). Most larvae are parasites of gall gnats (Cecidomyiidae); some parasitize mealybugs or whiteflies.

Superfamily Bethyloidea

Pronotum in lateral view variable, sometimes triangular, sometimes quadrate. Antennae generally 10- to 13-segmented and *threadlike.* Trochanters *1-segmented* (except Trigonalidae). Ovipositor issues from apex of abdomen. Venation usually *reduced.* HW of forms with reduced venation has *a jugal lobe.* Larvae, as far as known, parasites of other insects.

CUCKOO WASPS Family Chrysididae   See also Pl. 15

Identification: Body metallic blue or green, usually with coarse sculpturing. Abdomen with 4 or fewer segments, concave beneath, the last tergum often toothed apically. Hind wing with *a distinct lobe* at base and *without closed cells.*

Cuckoo wasps are about 6–12 mm. and have a brilliant metallic coloring; they are common insects. Some of them resemble perilampids (p. 330) and certain halictid bees (p. 356); they have more venation than a perilampid and not as much as a

halictid. When disturbed they commonly curl up into a ball.
They do not sting. Larvae are parasites or inquilines in nests of
other wasps or bees.

BETHYLIDS Family Bethylidae
  Identification: Small to medium-sized, usually black. Head
  somewhat elongated. Antennae *12- or 13-segmented, slightly*

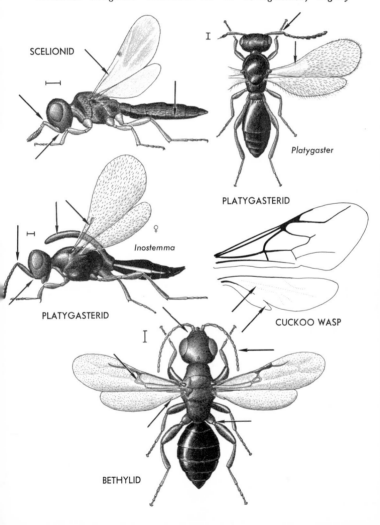

SCELIONID

Platygaster

PLATYGASTERID

Inostemma ♀

PLATYGASTERID

CUCKOO WASP

BETHYLID

elbowed. HW with a *jugal lobe.* Venation *reduced.* Abdomen
6- or 7-segmented.

Bethylids are generally 8 mm. or less and are seldom encountered. Larvae are parasites of other insect larvae, especially
Coleoptera and Lepidoptera. A few bethylids will sting. Females of many species are wingless and antlike.

DRYINIDS Family Dryinidae
Identification: Small black insects with a *reduced* wing venation.
Antennae *10-segmented, rising low on face,* and *not distinctly
elbowed.* HW *with a jugal lobe.* Front tarsi of ♀ often *pincerlike.*
Dryinids are relatively uncommon insects whose larvae are
parasites of planthoppers, leafhoppers, or treehoppers. Most
are 5–8 mm. Some species are polyembryonic, with 40 to 60
young developing from a single egg.

TRIGONALIDS Family Trigonalidae
Identification: Stout-bodied, wasplike; usually brightly colored
and 10–12 mm. Antennae *long, with 16 or more segments.*
Trochanters 2-segmented, 2nd segment sometimes indistinct.
Venation complete. FW *with a costal cell.* HW *without a jugal
lobe.* Differ from wasps (Scolioidea, Vespoidea, Sphecoidea) in
the long many-segmented antennae and from ichneumons by the
costal cell in FW.
Trigonalids are relatively rare. Larvae parasitize vespid
larvae or caterpillar parasites. Eggs are laid on foliage and
hatch when eaten (with the foliage) by a caterpillar. The
trigonalid larvae then attack a parasite in the caterpillar, or, if
the caterpillar is eaten by a vespid and later regurgitated and
fed to its larva, attack the vespid larva.

SCLEROGIBBIDS Family Sclerogibbidae   **Not illus.**
Identification: Similar to Bethylidae (p. 339) but antennae of
♂ with 23 segments and rising low on face. ♂ winged, ♀ wingless. FW with a small marginal cell and 1 submarginal cell.
HW with a closed cell.
One very rare species, known only from the male, has been
taken in Arizona. The larva of this species is unknown, but
sclerogibbids occurring elsewhere are known to parasitize webspinners (Embioptera).

Ants and Parasitic Wasps:
Superfamily Scolioidea

Pronotum in lateral view variable, more or less squarish to triangular, extending nearly to tegulae. Antennae 12- or 13-seg-
mented (with fewer segments in some ants), distinctly elbowed only
in ants. Ovipositor issues from apex of abdomen. Venation usually
fairly complete.

The term "wasp" is used in this book (with a few exceptions) for members of the superfamilies Scolioidea (other than ants), Vespoidea, and Sphecoidea. Wasps are Hymenoptera in which the females usually sting, antennae are generally 13-segmented in the male and 12-segmented in the female, trochanters are 1-segmented, and larvae usually feed on animal food. Vespoid and sphecoid wasps (pp. 346, 348) generally build a nest, capture prey and provision the nest with it, and thus might be described as predaceous. Scolioid wasps are parasitic, their behavior like that of the parasitic members of the preceding superfamilies; they oviposit in or on the body of a host, then oviposit in other hosts, and make no further provision for their young. Bees (Apoidea, p. 354) differ from wasps in that the young are fed plant rather than animal food.

Scolioid wasps differ from Sphecoidea in the form of the pronotum (see illus., p. 319); Vespidae differ from Scolioidea in having the 1st discoidal cell of the front wings very long and in folding their wings longitudinally at rest; Pompilidae (p. 346) differ from scolioid wasps in having long legs and a transverse suture on the mesopleura. Females of many scolioid wasps are wingless and antlike; females of vespoid and sphecoid wasps have well-developed wings.

RHOPALOSOMATID WASPS   Not illus.
Family Rhopalosomatidae
   Identification: Slender, brownish, 6–25 mm. Antennae long, each segment with 2 apical spines. FW (species with normal wings) with transverse median vein considerably beyond base of basal vein (wings very short in 1 species).

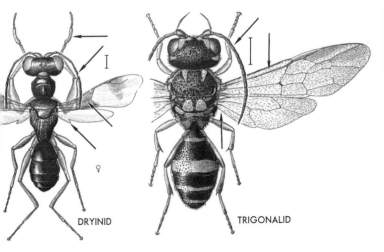

DRYINID   TRIGONALID

Two very rare species occur in the East. The larger has normal wings and resembles ichneumons in the genus *Ophion*, but the abdomen is not laterally flattened, the antennae contain only 12 or 13 segments, the trochanters are 1-segmented, and there is only 1 recurrent vein in the front wing. The smaller species (about 6 mm.) has very short and padlike wings. Larvae are parasites of crickets.

SIEROLOMORPHID WASPS   Not illus.
Family Sierolomorphidae

Identification: Shining black wasps, 4.5–6.0 mm. No jugal lobe in HW.

These wasps are widely distributed but are quite rare. Their immature stages are unknown.

TIPHIID WASPS   Family Tiphiidae   See also Pl. 15

Identification: Mesosternum with *2 posterior lobes*, or abdominal segments separated by rather strong constrictions.

Five of the 6 subfamilies of Tiphiidae occurring in the U.S. deserve special mention. The Tiphiinae, Myzininae, and Brachycistidinae have 2 posterior lobes on the mesosternum, the ♂ has an upcurved spine at end of the abdomen, and the ♀ is usually winged; the mesosternum of Methochinae and Myrmosinae lacks lobes (or has a pair of small toothlike projections posteriorly), the ♂ sometimes has an upcurved spine at the end of the abdomen, the abdominal segments are separated by fairly strong constrictions, and the ♀ is wingless.

Subfamily Tiphiinae. Black, *short-legged*, and generally *10–20 mm*. Middle tibiae with 1 apical spur. These wasps are fairly common and widely distributed; their larvae parasitize white grubs.

Subfamily Myzininae (Pl. 15). Black and yellow, longer-legged, and generally over 20 mm. Middle tibiae with 2 apical spurs. These wasps are also fairly common and widely distributed, and most species parasitize various beetle larvae.

Subfamily Brachycistidinae (not illus.). Brownish. Middle tibiae with 1 apical spur. ♀ wingless. These wasps are restricted to the western states and are mostly nocturnal.

Subfamily Methochinae. Thorax of ♀ divided into *3 parts*. ♂ with a spine at end of abdomen. ♂ 15 mm. or less, ♀ much smaller. Black or brownish. This is a small but widely distributed though not common group. Larvae parasitize tiger beetles.

Subfamily Myrmosinae. Similar to Methochinae but thorax of ♀ divided into 2 parts and ♂ without a spine at end of abdomen. This is a larger group than the Methochinae and somewhat more common. Larvae are parasites of various bees and wasps.

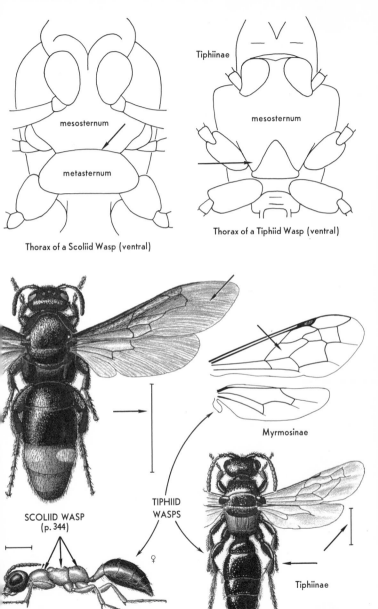

mesosternum

metasternum

Thorax of a Scoliid Wasp (ventral)

Tiphiinae

mesosternum

Thorax of a Tiphiid Wasp (ventral)

Myrmosinae

SCOLIID WASP
(p. 344)

TIPHIID
WASPS

♀

Methochinae

Tiphiinae

SCOLIID WASPS Family Scoliidae p. 343
Identification: *Large,* robust, hairy wasps, *mostly 20–30 mm.;* dark-colored, often with light markings. Mesosternum and metasternum form a large plate divided by *a transverse suture.* Hind coxae well separated. Wing membrane beyond closed cells with *numerous longitudinal wrinkles.*

Scoliid wasps are usually found on flowers. Larvae are parasites of white grubs.

VELVET ANTS Family Mutillidae See also Pl. 15
Identification: *Very hairy wasps,* often brightly colored. 6–20 mm. ♂ winged, ♀ wingless.

Mutillids are wasps that resemble ants but are quite hairy. Females inflict a very painful sting. Larvae are mostly parasites of larvae of ground-nesting bees and wasps; a few parasitize insects in other orders.

SAPYGID WASPS Family Sapygidae Not illus.
Identification: Slender, 15 mm. or less; black, marked with yellow. Eyes deeply notched. Differ from Myzininae (Tiphiidae) in being smaller and in lacking mesosternal lobes. Differ from mutillids in having the body bare.

This is a small but widely distributed and quite rare group. Larvae are parasites of leafcutting bees (Megachilidae).

ANTS Family Formicidae
Identification: First abdominal segment (or 1st 2 abdominal segments) *nodelike* or with a dorsal hump, differing from remaining segments. Antennae 6- to 13-segmented, and *strongly elbowed* (at least in ♀), the 1st segment quite long. Social insects, with different castes; queens and males usually winged, the workers wingless. Venation of winged forms normal or slightly reduced.

This is a large and widely distributed group occurring almost everywhere, often in considerable numbers. Ant colonies vary greatly in size, from a dozen or so up to many thousands of individuals. Most species nest in the ground but many nest in various natural cavities. Each colony usually consists of 1 or more queens (larger than other individuals and do all the egg laying), workers (larger colonies may contain 2 or more types of workers), and males; a few ants have no worker caste. Males and queens are produced at certain seasons, and mating usually occurs in a mating flight; males are generally much smaller than queens. After mating, the queen sheds its wings and either starts a new colony or enters an established colony.

Ants vary in habits: some are carnivorous, some are scavengers, and some are plant feeders. Most ants will bite when disturbed and many will sting; a few can eject a foul-smelling

Jugal lobe in HW *half as long* as submedian cell or longer. 6–7 mm. This is a small and rare group occurring in the Southwest. They nest in the ground and at least some species provision the nest with weevil larvae.

Potter Wasps, Subfamily Eumeninae. Most are 10–20 mm. and black with yellow or white markings. Middle tibiae with *1 apical spur.* Mandibles *elongate,* knifelike. This is a large and widely distributed group, and many species are very common.

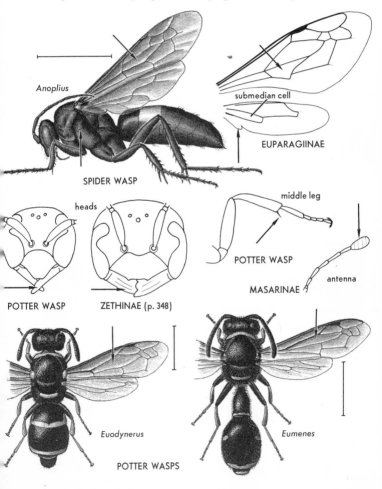

Anoplius

submedian cell

EUPARAGIINAE

SPIDER WASP

heads

POTTER WASP ZETHINAE (p. 348)

middle leg

POTTER WASP

MASARINAE antenna

Euodynerus Eumenes

POTTER WASPS

Some species make nests of mud, others nest in burrows or in natural cavities. Nests are usually provisioned with caterpillars.

Subfamily Zethinae (see illus., p. 347). Similar to Eumeninae but mandibles *short and broad*. About 1 in., black, thorax narrowed in front of wings and narrower than head, and abdomen stalked. Zethinae occur in the South and are not common.

Yellowjackets and Hornets, Subfamily Vespinae. Middle tibiae with 2 apical spurs. HW *without a jugal lobe*. Clypeus *broadly truncate* and *slightly notched at apex*. Yellowjackets (see also Pl. 16) have the abdomen banded with black and yellow; hornets are largely black, with yellowish-white markings on the face, thorax, and end of abdomen. These wasps build nests of a papery material and the tiers of cells are surrounded by an outer covering; some species nest in the ground and others nest above ground in various protected situations. The nest is begun by the queen (the only individual to overwinter). Her nest is an inch or two in diameter with a single tier of cells; as workers are produced the nest is enlarged, and by the end of the summer the nest may contain several tiers of cells and be several inches to a foot in diameter. Females of these wasps inflict a very painful sting.

Paper Wasps, Subfamily Polistinae. Somewhat brownish and *long-legged*. Middle tibiae with 2 apical spurs. HW with *a small jugal lobe*. Clypeus usually *pointed at apex*. 1st abdominal segment *conical*, not stalklike. These wasps are common and widely distributed. The nest consists of a single more or less circular tier of cells, attached by a short stalk to the underside of some surface (eaves of a building, ceiling of a porch, or similar surface); there is no outer covering as in nests of Vespinae.

Subfamily Polybiinae. Similar to Polistinae but 1st abdominal segment *slender and stalklike*. These wasps occur in the Gulf states and in the West, and most make nests similar to those of the Polistinae.

Sphecoid Wasps: Superfamily Sphecoidea

Pronotum usually short and collarlike, with a small rounded lobe on each side that does not reach the tegulae. Venation complete or nearly so. Body hairs simple. 1st segment of hind tarsi slender. Bees (Apoidea, p. 354) have a similarly shaped pronotum, but have most body hairs branched, and usually have the 1st segment of the hind tarsi enlarged and flattened. Sphecoid wasps are solitary, and adults are usually found on flowers; they nest in the ground, in natural cavities, or make mud nests, and each provisions its nest with characteristic prey.

AMPULICID WASPS Family Ampulicidae
Identification: Black and 10–15 mm. Prothorax *narrowed*

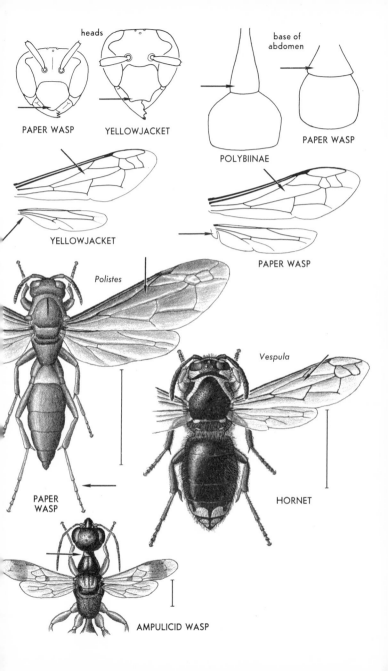

heads

PAPER WASP YELLOWJACKET

base of abdomen

POLYBIINAE PAPER WASP

YELLOWJACKET

PAPER WASP

Polistes

Vespula

PAPER WASP

HORNET

AMPULICID WASP

toward the front and somewhat *necklike*. Mesosternum with a forked process posteriorly. Parapsidal sutures distinct.

Ampulicids are rather rare. Nests are built in various protected situations, and are provisioned with immature cockroaches.

SPHECID WASPS Family Sphecidae   **See also Pl. 16**
Identification: Pronotum short and collarlike. Mesosternum without a forked process posteriorly. Parapsidal sutures indistinct or absent.

This large family contains many common wasps. There are 9 subfamilies, differing in appearance and habits, in N. America.

Astatine Wasps, Subfamily Astatinae. Dark-colored, mostly about 15 mm. Eyes large, often meeting dorsally in male. Middle tibiae with 2 apical spurs. HW with vannal lobe large and jugal lobe small. Marginal cell in FW *truncate apically,* marginal vein continuing a short way beyond end of cell. 3 submarginal cells in FW. Astatinae nest in the ground and provision their nests with bugs; they are not common.

Sand-loving Wasps, Subfamily Larrinae. Most species are brownish and 10–20 mm. Middle tibiae with *1 apical spur.* FW with 3 submarginal cells, 3rd often *oblique,* and marginal vein usually continuing a way beyond tip of marginal cell. Mandibles generally notched on outer margin. Lateral ocelli often distorted, not round. These wasps nest in sandy areas and provision their nests with grasshoppers or crickets.

Organ-pipe Mud-daubers, Subfamily Trypoxyloninae. Slender, black. FW with *1 submarginal cell,* and marginal cell *pointed apically.* Inner margins of eyes *notched.* Some make tubular nests of mud, and others nest in natural cavities; all provision their nests with spiders.

Aphid Wasps, Subfamily Pemphredoninae. Usually black, 8–15 mm. Middle tibiae with 1 apical spur. Marginal cell in FW *pointed apically.* Abdomen sometimes with a slender basal stalk. Pemphredonini have 2 (rarely 1) submarginal cells in the front wing, and the antennae rise *very low on the face;* some nest in the ground, others in twigs, and they provision with aphids or thrips. Psenini have 3 submarginal cells in the front wing, and antennae rise *near middle of the face;* they nest in natural cavities or in the ground, and provision their nests with hoppers (Homoptera).

Thread-waisted Wasps, Subfamily Sphecinae. Abdomen *stalked at base.* HW with *a large vannal lobe.* Middle tibiae with 2 apical spurs. Mostly 20–30 mm. Common wasps, grouped in 3 tribes. (1) Ammobiini: blackish or brownish, wings clear or dark. 2 or more basal teeth on front tarsal claws, *only 1 recurrent vein* meets 2nd submarginal cell, and discoidal vein in HW rises at anterior end of transverse median vein. They nest in

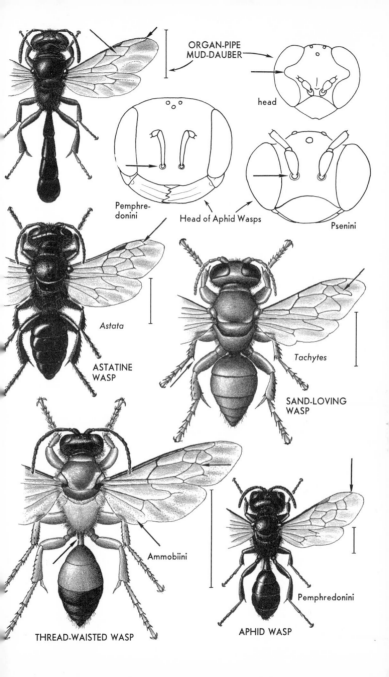

ORGAN-PIPE MUD-DAUBER

head

Pemphredonini

Head of Aphid Wasps

Psenini

Astata

ASTATINE WASP

Tachytes

SAND-LOVING WASP

Ammobiini

THREAD-WAISTED WASP

Pemphredonini

APHID WASP

the ground and provision with grasshoppers. (2) Sphecini (see illus., p. 353): most are slender, and black with base of abdomen orange (*Sphex*, Pl. 16); *no teeth* on front tarsal claws, *both recurrent veins* meet 2nd submarginal cell, discoidal vein in HW rises *distinctly beyond anterior end* of transverse median vein, and abdominal petiole usually is 2-segmented; they nest in the ground and provision with caterpillars. (3) Sceliphronini: *1 tooth* on front tarsal claws, *both recurrent veins* meet 2nd submarginal cell (except *Chlorion*, blackish with blackish wings), and HW venation as in Ammobiini; most are mud-daubers, making nests of mud and provisioning them with spiders; some of these (*Sceliphron*, Pl. 16) are brownish with yellow markings and clear wings, others (*Chalybion*) are blue-black with blackish wings.

Subfamily Nyssoninae. FW with 3 submarginal cells. 1 or 2 (usually 2) apical spurs on middle tibiae. Rather diverse in appearance and habits. Three of the 5 tribes in this subfamily are fairly common. (1) Gorytini (2 apical spurs on middle tibiae, 2nd submarginal cell *squarish*, propodeum rounded, thorax smooth) are mostly 10–15 mm., and black with yellow markings. The largest species in this tribe is the Cicada Killer, *Sphecius speciosus* (Drury), which is about 30 mm.; it nests in the ground and provisions its nest with cicadas. Most Gorytini nest in the ground, and provision their nests with various Homoptera. (2) Bembicini, or sand wasps (see also Pl. 16), are mostly 20–25 mm., and often have pale greenish markings; labrum is *relatively long and triangular*. Sand wasps nest in sandy areas, usually in colonies; their nests are sometimes not completely provisioned, and the young are fed as they grow. (3) Nyssonini (2nd submarginal cell *triangular*, thorax coarsely punctate, and propodeum angled or spined) are inquilines, laying their eggs in nests of other wasps. The remaining tribes in this subfamily (not illus.), which are much less common, are the (4) Stizini (basal vein far toward wing base from stigma) and (5) Alyssonini (2nd submarginal cell triangular, and apex of hind femur produced into a process extending over base of tibia).

Subfamily Mellininae (not illus.). Similar to Nyssoninae, but no recurrent veins meet 2nd submarginal cell. Nest in the ground and provision with flies. A small group, widely distributed but uncommon.

Subfamily Philanthinae. Medium-sized, mostly 12–18 mm., black with yellow markings. 1 apical spur on middle tibiae. 3 submarginal cells. A constriction between 1st and 2nd abdominal segments. Nest in ground. Philanthini have 2nd submarginal cell *squarish* and clypeus *extended upward;* most provision their nest with bees. Cercerini have 2nd submarginal cell *triangular*, and provision their nests with various types of beetles (chiefly snout beetles).

Subfamily Crabroninae. This group includes 2 tribes of ground-nesting wasps, the Crabronini (square-headed wasps) and Oxybelini (spiny digger wasps); Crabronini are quite common but Oxybelini are rather rare. Most Crabronini are black with yellow markings, and 8–20 mm.; head and eyes are large, antennae rise *very low on face*, there is *only 1 submarginal cell* in the front wing, and apex of marginal cell is *truncate*. Different species use different types of prey in provisioning their nests.

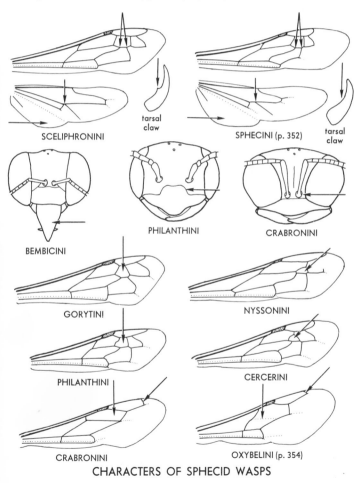

SCELIPHRONINI

tarsal claw

SPHECINI (p. 352)

tarsal claw

BEMBICINI

PHILANTHINI

CRABRONINI

GORYTINI

NYSSONINI

PHILANTHINI

CERCERINI

CRABRONINI

OXYBELINI (p. 354)

CHARACTERS OF SPHECID WASPS

Oxybelini are 10 mm. or less, stout-bodied, and dark-colored; the propodeum bears a long spine, or forked process, and the base of the cubital vein in the front wing is *weak* or absent; they nest in sandy areas and provision their nests with flies.

Bees: Superfamily Apoidea

Pronotum short, collarlike, with *a rounded lobe on each side that does not reach tegulae*. Body usually quite hairy, the body hairs branched or plumose. 1st segment of hind tarsi generally *enlarged and flattened*.

This is a large group, with more than 3300 N. American species; its members are to be found almost everywhere, particularly on flowers. Most species are solitary, nesting in the ground or in various natural cavities; the bumble bees and the Honey Bee are social. The cuckoo bees make no nest but lay their eggs in nests of other bees.

Bees are very valuable insects, largely because of the role they play in the pollination of plants; they are the most important insect pollinators. Insect-pollinated plants include most of our fruits, many vegetables, and important field crops such as clover, cotton, and tobacco.

Most pollen-collecting bees carry the pollen on their hind tibiae; the pollen-carrying surface of the tibia is usually bare and shiny and bordered with long hairs. Pollen sticks to the bee's body hairs when the bee visits a flower and is periodically combed off and placed on the hind tibiae. The 1st segment of the hind tarsi in most pollen-collecting bees is enlarged and flattened and bears a brush of hairs. Some bees do not have the hind legs so modified, and the leafcutting bees (Megachilidae) carry pollen on a brush of hairs on the ventral side of the abdomen.

The groups of bees are distinguished chiefly by characters of wings and tongue; the tongue characters are sometimes difficult to see, because the tongue when not in use is folded up tight against the ventral side of the head. The parts of the tongue in a large carpenter bee (*Xylocopa*) are shown opposite. To facilitate identification, the families of bees may be arranged in 3 groups:

1. Jugal lobe of HW as long as or longer than submedian cell; tongue (galeae and glossa) short; segments of labial palps usually similar and cylindrical; maxillary palps well developed: Colletidae, Andrenidae, and Halictidae.

2. Jugal lobe of HW shorter than submedian cell; tongue (galeae and glossa), labial palps, and maxillary palps as in Group 1: Melittidae (rare bees).

3. Jugal lobe of HW shorter than submedian cell, or lacking; tongue (galeae and glossa) long and usually slender; first 2 segments of labial palps long and flattened; maxillary palps well developed or vestigial: Megachilidae and Apidae.

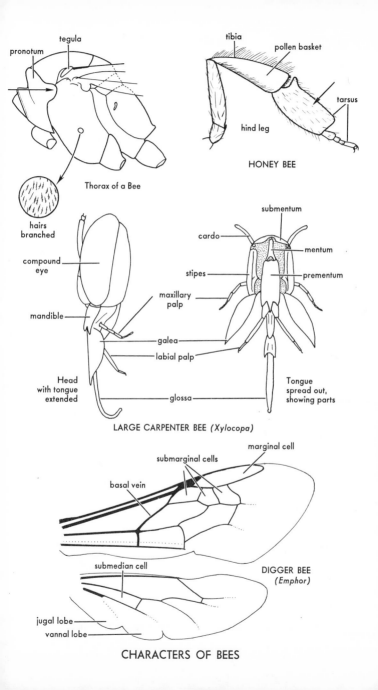

CHARACTERS OF BEES

YELLOW-FACED and PLASTERER BEES Family Colletidae
   Identification: Jugal lobe in HW *longer* than submedian cell.
   Basal vein straight or nearly so. *2* (Hylaeinae) *or 3* (Colletinae)
   submarginal cells. 1 subantennal suture below each antennal
   socket. Glossa short, bilobed or truncate.
      Yellow-faced Bees, Subfamily Hylaeinae. Slender black bees,
   10 mm. or less, usually with *whitish or yellowish areas* on face.
   2 submarginal cells. Body relatively bare. These bees lack a
   pollen-collecting apparatus on the hind legs, and resemble small
   wasps; they can be recognized as bees by the branched body
   hairs. They are quite common, and nest in the ground or in
   various natural cavities. Our species belong to the genus
   Hylaeus.
      Plasterer Bees, Subfamily Colletinae. More robust and hairy
   than Hylaeinae. Brownish, the abdomen banded with pale
   hairs. *3 submarginal cells.* 2nd recurrent vein somewhat
   S-shaped. These bees are much less common than the Hylaeinae.
   They nest in the ground and line their galleries with a thin
   transparent film (hence the common name).

ANDRENID BEES Family Andrenidae
   Identification: Jugal lobe in HW *longer* than submedian cell.
   2 subantennal sutures below each antennal socket. Basal vein
   straight or nearly so. 2 or 3 submarginal cells. Glossa short but
   pointed. Nest in burrows in the ground, often in colonies,
   usually in areas of sparse vegetation.
      Subfamily Andreninae. Most are dark brown to brownish
   black, 20 mm. or less. Marginal cell *pointed,* its apex on costal
   margin of wing. Usually *3 submarginal cells.* This is a large and
   widely distributed group, and many species are quite common.
   Nests usually consist of a vertical tunnel in the ground, with
   lateral tunnels branching off this vertical tunnel.
      Subfamily Panurginae. Most are reddish brown, 10 mm. or
   less. Marginal cell *truncate. 2 submarginal cells.* Stigma large.
   These bees are much less common than the Andreninae but are
   widely distributed.
      Subfamily Oxaeinae (not illus.). Similar to Panurginae but
   with 3 submarginal cells, and stigma very small. This small
   group is restricted to the southwestern states.

HALICTID BEES Family Halictidae   **See also Pl. 16**
   Identification: Similar to Andrenidae but with *only 1 subantennal suture* below each antennal socket, and basal vein
   strongly *arched.*
      These resemble the andrenids in nesting habits: sometimes
   large numbers nest close together, often so close that different
   bees may use the same passageway to the outside. Halictids
   vary from about 5 to 15 mm.; many are quite small. Most of

them are black or dark-colored, but some are partly or entirely brownish or metallic green. Some of the smaller halictids are attracted to perspiration, and are called sweat bees. The family contains 3 subfamilies: most of our species belong to the Halictinae (3 submarginal cells, 1st longer than 3rd); Nomiinae have

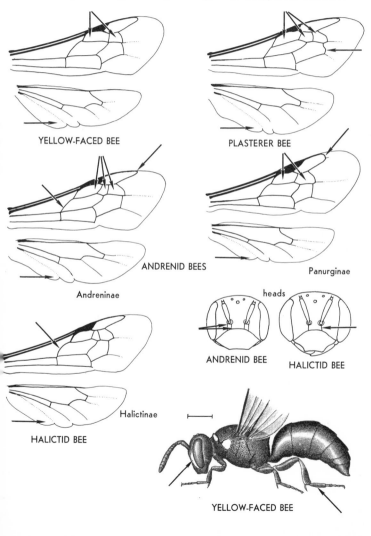

YELLOW-FACED BEE

PLASTERER BEE

ANDRENID BEES

Andreninae

Panurginae

heads

ANDRENID BEE

HALICTID BEE

Halictinae

HALICTID BEE

YELLOW-FACED BEE

3 submarginal cells, with 1st about same size as 3rd; and Dufoureinae have only 2 submarginal cells.

MELITTID BEES Family Melittidae   **Not illus.**
Identification: By the characters of Group 2 (p. 354).
Melittids are small, dark-colored, and rather rare; their nesting habits are similar to those of the Andrenidae.

LEAFCUTTING BEES Family Megachilidae
Identification: Most are stout-bodied, dark-colored, and 10–20 mm. Jugal lobe of HW *shorter* than submedian cell. FW with *2 nearly equal-sized submarginal cells.* Pollen carried on *underside* of abdomen (except in inquiline species). Subantennal sutures rise on *outer margins* of antennal sockets. First 2 segments of labial palps elongate and flattened. Maxillary palps vestigial. Glossa long and slender.
Many leafcutting bees are very common. They usually nest in the ground or in some natural cavity, with cell partitions of mud, resin, or leaf pulp. A few are inquilines.

DIGGER BEES, CARPENTER BEES, BUMBLE BEES,
HONEY BEES, and Others. Family Apidae   **See also Pl. 16**
Identification: Jugal lobe in HW *shorter than submedian cell* (rarely absent). Usually 3 submarginal cells. First 2 segments of labial palps elongate and flattened. Maxillary palps well developed or vestigial. Glossa long and slender.
This is a large group that varies in size, appearance, and habits. The family contains 3 subfamilies, Anthophorinae, Xylocopinae, and Apinae. Apinae include bumble bees and the Honey Bee, which are social; bees in the other 2 subfamilies are solitary. Each subfamily is further divided into tribes. Only more common groups in the family are mentioned here.
Digger Bees (Subfamily Anthophorinae, chiefly the tribes Anthophorini, Eucerini, and Emphorini). Robust and hairy, usually brownish, mostly 10–20 mm.; they nest in the ground. These differ from bumble bees and large carpenter bees in having 2nd submarginal cell *shorter than the 1st* (along posterior side); they differ from cuckoo bees in the Anthophorinae and from small carpenter bees in being much more hairy; and differ from the Honey Bee in having eyes bare and in having 2 *apical spurs* on the hind tibiae.
Cuckoo Bees (Subfamily Anthophorinae, chiefly the tribes Nomadini and Epeolini). Do not construct a nest but lay their eggs in nests of other bees. They are relatively bare, and wasplike in appearance; hind legs *do not have* a pollen-collecting apparatus. Nomadini are reddish or brownish, about 8–10 mm., and have *a very small rounded jugal lobe* in hind wing. Epeolini are larger, usually black, with whitish or yellowish markings.

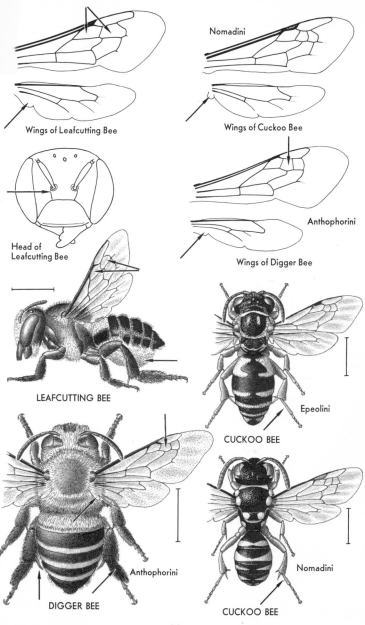

Nomadini

Wings of Leafcutting Bee

Wings of Cuckoo Bee

Head of
Leafcutting Bee

Anthophorini

Wings of Digger Bee

LEAFCUTTING BEE

Epeolini

CUCKOO BEE

Anthophorini

DIGGER BEE

Nomadini

CUCKOO BEE

Large Carpenter Bees (*Xylocopa*, Subfamily Xylocopinae); see also Pl. 16. Large, robust, and blackish; resemble bumble bees. They differ from bumble bees in having 2nd submarginal cell *triangular*, dorsal surface of abdomen bare and shining, mandibles immediately below the compound eyes, and in having a *small rounded jugal lobe* in hind wing. Most of them are about 1 in. They nest in cavities excavated in wood (sometimes in buildings).

Small Carpenter Bees (*Ceratina*, Subfamily Xylocopinae). These are *6–10 mm.*, relatively robust, not very hairy, and dark bluish green. Basal vein is *distinctly arched* and they may be confused with halictids, but the *much shorter jugal lobe* in hind wing distinguishes them. Small carpenter bees nest in galleries that they excavate in the pith of stems of various bushes.

Bumble Bees (Subfamily Apinae, Tribe Bombini); see also Pl. 16. Common and well-known insects; robust, hairy, generally 15–25 mm., and black with yellow (rarely orange) markings. 2nd submarginal cell is *more or less rectangular* and about as long as the 1st, dorsal surface of abdomen is hairy, there is a distinct space between base of the compound eye and base of the mandible (most other bees have mandibles attached very close to the eyes), and hind wings *lack a jugal lobe*. Most bumble bees nest in or on the ground, often in a deserted mouse nest. *Psithyrus* species are inquilines, laying their eggs in nests of other bumble bees. Bumble bees are social, and their colonies contain 3 castes: queens, drones (males), and workers (*Psithyrus* has no worker caste). Colonies are generally annual, the queens overwintering and starting new colonies in the spring. Queens are usually much larger than workers and drones. Bees in the genus *Psithyrus* do not collect pollen, and their hind tibiae are rounded, dull, and hairy; other bumble bees (which do collect pollen) have the hind tibiae bare, smooth, and shiny.

Honey Bee (*Apis mellifera* Linn., Subfamily Apinae, Tribe Apini). Only 1 species occurs in N. America, though there are several strains or races that differ slightly in color and other characters. Honey Bees are very common, widely distributed, and well-known insects. They differ from other bees in having the eyes *hairy, no apical spurs* on the hind tibiae, and they have a characteristic venation (marginal cell in front wing *narrow and parallel-sided*, 3rd submarginal cell *oblique*). Most Honey Bees nest in man-made hives; escaped swarms usually nest in hollow trees. Colonies contain 3 castes: workers (the most abundant individuals and ones most often seen), drones (a little larger, with eyes meeting dorsally), and the queen (abdomen longer than in workers). Honey Bees are extremely valuable insects, not only because of the honey and beeswax they produce, but because of their pollinating activities; their pollinating services are 15 to 20 times as valuable as their honey and wax.

It is often possible to increase greatly the yields of such crops as orchard fruits and clover seed by introducing hives of Honey Bees into orchards or clover fields when the crop is in bloom. The normal yield of red clover seed, for example (about 1 bushel per acre), can be increased to 4 or more bushels per acre with a dense Honey Bee population in the clover fields.

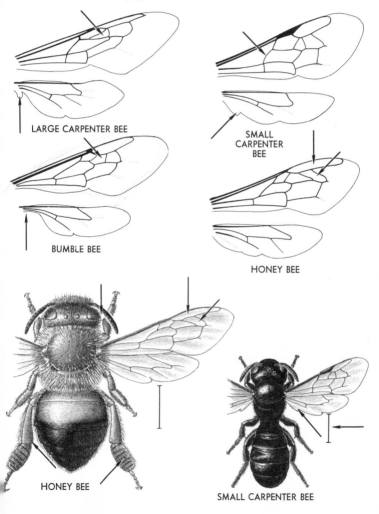

LARGE CARPENTER BEE

SMALL CARPENTER BEE

BUMBLE BEE

HONEY BEE

HONEY BEE

SMALL CARPENTER BEE

Honey Bees have an interesting "language": a worker that discovers a flower with a good flow of nectar can come back to the hive and "tell" the other workers what direction the flower is from the hive, how far away it is, and what kind of flower it is. Information on the direction and distance of the flower from the hive is communicated by means of a peculiar dance performed by the bee inside the hive. Information on the kind of flower involved is communicated by odor of the flower on the body of the bee or in its honey.

Glossary

THE DEFINITIONS given below are specific to use in this book; elsewhere some terms may have additional meanings. Page numbers refer to illustrations except when preceded by *see;* here the references are to definitions given in the text or to text in conjunction with illustrations shown opposite. Terms consisting of two or more words are generally listed under the most significant word.

Abdomen. The hindmost of the 3 main body divisions.

Acrostichal bristles. Two longitudinal rows of bristles along midline of mesonotum (Diptera, p. 287).

Anal. The posterior basal part (e.g., of wing); pertaining to last abdominal segment (which bears the anus). *Anal lobe,* a lobe in posterior part of wing. *Anal loop,* a group of cells in basal part of hind wing (Odonata, p. 73).

Annulate. With ringlike subdivisions (annulate 3rd antennal segment of certain Diptera, p. 273).

Anteapical. Just before the apex.

Antenna (pl., **antennae**). Feelerlike appendages located on head above mouth parts (p. 30). *Antennal club,* the enlarged terminal segments of a clubbed antenna. *Antennal scrobe,* a groove in the beak into which the base of the antenna fits (snout beetles). *Elbowed antennae,* with 1st segment elongated and the remaining segments coming off 1st at an angle (as in ants, p. 345). *Flabellate antennae,* with tonguelike processes on the terminal segments (as in Coleoptera). *Lamellate antennae,* with terminal segments expanded to one side and flattened or platelike.

Antenodal. Between base of wing and nodus (as in Odonata).

Antepygidial. Just in front of last abdominal segment (pygidium).

Anterior. Front; in front of.

Anterolateral. In front and to one side.

Anus. The posterior opening of the alimentary tract.

Apical. At the end, tip, or outermost part.

Arculus. A basal cross vein between R and Cu (Odonata, p. 71).

Areole. *See* Basal areole.

Arista. A large bristle on dorsal side of 3rd antennal segment (Diptera, p. 273). *Aristate,* with an arista.

Atrophied. Rudimentary, reduced in size.

Attenuated. Slender, gradually tapering toward the end.

Axilla (pl., **axillae**). A small sclerite on dorsal side of thorax, usually anterolateral to scutellum (Hymenoptera, p. 325).

Basal. At the base, or point of attachment. *Basad,* toward the base. *Basal areole*, the cell at base of hind wing between Sc and R (Lepidoptera, p. 239).

Beak. The proboscis, or protruding mouth part structures of a sucking insect (p. 32).

Bucca (pl., **buccae**). An area on head below compound eye (Diptera, p. 283).

Calypter. One of 2 small lobes at base of wing on posterior side (Diptera, p. 261).

Carapace. A hard dorsal covering formed by fusion of certain sclerites, in Crustacea.

Carina (pl., **carinae**). A keel or ridge.

Caudal. Pertaining to the tail or posterior part of body.

Cell. A space in the wing partly or completely surrounded by veins. *Accessory cell*, a closed cell in front wing of Lepidoptera, on anterior side of discal cell (p. 221). *Anal cell*, one in anal area of wing (Diptera, p. 261). *Apical cell*, 1 or more cells near wing tip (Hymenoptera, p. 313, *AP*). *Basal anal cell*, an anal cell near base of wing (Plecoptera, p. 95). *Basal cells*, the R and M cells in Diptera (p. 261); cells *MD*, *SMD*, and *L* in hind wing of Hymenoptera (p. 313). *Closed cell*, one bordered by veins and not extending to wing margin. *Discal cell*, one near central or basal part of wing (Diptera, p. 261, and Lepidoptera, p. 221). *Discoidal cell*, one near middle of wing (Hymenoptera, p. 313, *1D, 2D, 3D*). *Lanceolate cell*, one in anal area of wing (Hymenoptera, p. 313, *L*). *Marginal cell*, one bordering front margin near tip of wing (Diptera, p. 261, and Hymenoptera, p. 313, *MC*). *Median cell*, one in basal portion of wing (Hymenoptera, p. 313, *MD*). *Open cell*, one extending to wing margin. *Posterior cells*, those bordering rear edge of wing between R and Cu₂ (Diptera, p. 261). *Submarginal cell*, 1 or more cells just behind marginal cell (Diptera, p. 261, and Hymenoptera, p. 313, *SM*). *Submedian cell*, the cell in basal part of wing just behind median cell (Hymenoptera, p. 313, *SMD*).

Cephalothorax. A body region consisting of head and thoracic segments, in Crustacea and Chelicerata.

Cercus (pl., **cerci**). One of a pair of dorsally located appendages at posterior end of abdomen (p. 30).

Chelicera (pl., **chelicerae**). The anterior, usually fanglike, pair of appendages in arachnids.

Chrysalis (pl., **chrysalids** or **chrysalides**). The pupa of a butterfly (*see* p. 219).

Claval suture. The suture in the front wing of Hemiptera and Homoptera between the clavus and corium (p. 113).

Clavate. Clubbed, or enlarged toward tip.

Clavus. The portion of the front wing in Hemiptera and Homoptera behind the claval suture (p. 113).

Clubbed. With the tip enlarged or swollen.

Clypeus. A sclerite on face between frons and labrum (p. 30).

Cocoon. A case of silk in which the pupa is formed.

Collophore. A small tubular structure on ventral side of 1st abdominal segment, in Collembola.

Compound eye. An eye composed of many individual elements, each of which is marked externally by a facet; the facets are usually more or less hexagonal in shape (p. 30, *eye*).

Compressed. Flattened from side to side.

Corium. The basal, usually thickened, part of front wing (Hemiptera, p. 113).

Cornicle. One of a pair of elongate processes located dorsally near apex of abdomen (aphids, p. 135).

Costa. A longitudinal vein, usually forming front margin of wing (p. 35). *Costal area of wing,* that part just behind front margin. *Costal break,* a point on costa where the vein appears broken or weakened. *Costal margin of wing,* the front margin.

Coxa. The basal leg segment (p. 34). *Closed coxal cavities* (front, Coleoptera), bounded posteriorly by a prothoracic sclerite. *Open coxal cavities* (front, Coleoptera), bounded posteriorly by a mesothoracic sclerite.

Crochets. Tiny hooks on the prolegs of a caterpillar.

Cross vein. A vein connecting adjacent longitudinal veins. *Antenodal cross veins,* those just behind front edge of wing between base and nodus, extending from C to R (Odonata, p. 71). *Discal cross vein,* one just behind discal cell (Diptera, p. 261). *Humeral cross vein,* one in basal part of wing between C and Sc (p. 35, *h*). *Medial cross vein,* one connecting 2 branches of M (p. 35, *m*). *Mediocubital cross vein,* one connecting M and Cu (p. 35, *m-cu*). *Radial cross vein,* one just behind R_1 (p. 35, *r*). *Sectorial cross vein,* one connecting 2 branches of Rs (p. 35, *s*).

Cubital intercalaries. Longitudinal veins in distal part of wing between Cu_1 and Cu_2 (Ephemeroptera, p. 67).

Cubitus. The longitudinal vein just behind M (p. 35).

Cuneus. A more or less triangular apical piece of the corium, set off from rest of corium (Hemiptera, p. 113).

Deflexed. Bent downward.

Dentate. Toothed, or with toothlike projections.

Denticulate. With tiny toothlike projections.

Depressed. Flattened (from top to bottom).

Distal. Near or pertaining to that part farthest from body. *Distad,* toward the end farthest from body or base.

Dorsal. Pertaining to the back or upper side; top or uppermost. *Dorsad,* toward the top or back.

Dorsocentral bristles. A longitudinal row of bristles on mesonotum, just toward side from acrostichal bristles (Diptera, p. 287).

Dorsolateral. Above and to one side.

Ecdysis (pl., **ecdyses**). Molting, or shedding of exoskeleton.

Ectoparasite. A parasite living on the outside of its host.

Elytron (pl., **elytra**). A thickened, horny, or leathery front wing, in Coleoptera, Dermaptera, and some Homoptera.

Emarginate. Notched.

Emergence. The process of the adult leaving the pupal case or the last nymphal skin.

Endoparasite. A parasite living inside its host.

Entire. With a smooth outline, without teeth or notches.

Epimeron (pl., **epimera**). The thoracic sclerite just behind a pleural suture (p. 34).

Epiproct. A process or appendage just above anus, appearing to rise from 10th abdominal segment (p. 30).

Episternum (pl., **episterna**). The thoracic sclerite just in front of a pleural suture (p. 34).

Epistomal suture. The suture on face between frons and clypeus (p. 31).

Exoskeleton. A skeleton, or supporting structure, on outside of body.

Eye cap. An enlarged basal segment of the antenna that overhangs or caps the compound eye (Microlepidoptera, p. 253, head of Lyonetiidae).

Femur (pl., **femora**). The leg segment between trochanter and tibia (p. 34).

File. A filelike ridge on ventral side of front wing, part of sound-producing mechanism in certain Orthoptera (p. 77).

Filiform. Hairlike or threadlike.

Fontanelle. *See* p. 89.

Frenulum. A bristle or group of bristles at humeral angle of hind wing (Lepidoptera, p. 221).

Frons. An area on face, between frontal and epistomal sutures and including median ocellus (p. 30). *Frontal suture*, one of 2 sutures on each side of frons (p. 30); a suture in the form of an inverted U or V, with its apex just above base of antennae (Diptera, p. 283). *Fronto-orbital bristles*, bristles on upper front part of head next to compound eyes (Diptera, p. 283).

Furcula. The forked "tail" of springtails (*see* p. 62).

Gena (pl., **genae**). The area on head below compound eye (p. 30). *Genal comb*, a row of strong spines on lower front border of head (Siphonaptera, p. 309).

Genitalia. *See* p. 36.

Glabrous. Smooth, without hairs.

Globose or globular. Spherical or nearly so.

Glossa (pl., **glossae**). One of a pair of lobes at apex of labium, between the paraglossae (bees, p. 355).

Grub. *See* scarabaeiform larvae, p. 39.

Gula. A sclerite on underside of head in Coleoptera. *Gular sutures*, longitudinal sutures on underside of head, bordering gula.

Haltere. A small knobbed structure on each side of metathorax, representing the hind wings (Diptera, p. 261).

Homonyms. *See* p. 45.

Honeydew. *See* p. 130.

Humeral. Pertaining to the shoulder; pertaining to front basal part of the wing. *Humeral angle*, the basal front angle of the wing. *Humeral bristles*, bristles on humeral callus (Diptera, p. 287). *Humeral callus*, a rounded area on outer front portions of thoracic notum (Diptera, p. 287). *Humeral vein*, a branch of Sc extending into humeral angle of wing (p. 225).

Hyaline. Transparent and colorless, like glass.

Hypermetamorphosis. *See* p. 41.

Hyperparasite. A parasite whose host is another parasite.

Hypopharynx. A median mouth-part structure just in front of labium.

Hypopleuron (pl., **hypopleura**). A sclerite on thorax just above hind coxae, in Diptera (p. 287). *Hypopleural bristles*, a row of bristles on hypopleuron (p. 287).

Inquiline. An animal that lives in nest of another species.

Instar. The stage of an insect between successive molts.

Integument. The outer covering of the body.

Interstitial. Of trochanters: distal margin of trochanter at a right angle to long axis of leg. Of 2 veins: the ends of the veins meeting.

Intra-alar bristles. A row of bristles on mesonotum above wing bases (Diptera, p. 287).

Jugal lobe. A lobe at base of hind wing, on rear side (Hymenoptera, p. 313, *jl*).

Jugum. A fingerlike lobe at base of front wing on rear side (Hepialidae, p. 259).

Labium. The lower lip, or hindmost mouth-part structure (p. 30).

Labrum. The upper lip, situated in front of mandibles and below clypeus (p. 30).

Lacinia (pl., **laciniae**). The jawlike inner lobe of a maxilla (p. 30).

Lanceolate (wings). Narrow and tapering to a point at tip.

Larva (pl., **larvae**). The immature stage, between egg and pupa of an insect with complete metamorphosis (*see* pp. 38–41).

Lateral. On or pertaining to the right or left side. *Laterad*, toward the side, away from the midline.

Maggot. A legless larva without a well-developed head.

Mandible. A jaw (p. 30).

Margined. With a sharp lateral edge.

Maxilla (pl., **maxillae**). One of the paired mouth parts just behind the mandibles (p. 30).

Media. The longitudinal vein between R and Cu (p. 35).

Membrane. The part of wing surface between veins; thin tip part of the wing (Hemiptera, p. 113). *Membranous*, thin and more or less transparent (wings); thin and not hardened (body wall).

Mes-, meso-. Prefixes for names of mesothoracic structures (*see* p. 33).

Mesal. On or near the midline of the body. *Mesad*, toward the midline of the body.

Met-, meta-. Prefixes for names of metathoracic structures (*see* p. 33).

Millimeter. 0.001 meter, or 0.03937 in. (about 1/25 in.).

Nasutus (pl., **nasuti**). A termite caste having the head narrowed in front into a snout (p. 91).

Nodus. A strong cross vein near middle of front border of wing (Odonata, p. 71).

Notopleuron (pl., **notopleura**). An area on dorsolateral surface of thorax, at end of transverse suture, in Diptera (p. 287). *Notopleural bristles*, a group of bristles on notopleuron (p. 287).

Notum (pl., **nota**). The dorsal surface of a thoracic segment.

Nymph. Young of an insect with simple metamorphosis.

Occiput. The upper surface of head between occipital and postoccipital sutures (p. 30). *Occipital suture*, a suture on hind part of head, between vertex and occiput dorsally and between genae and postgenae laterally (p. 30).

Ocellus (pl., **ocelli**). A simple eye (p. 30). *Ocellar bristles*, a pair of bristles near ocelli (Diptera, p. 283). *Ocellar triangle*, a slightly raised triangular area in which the ocelli are located (Diptera, p. 283).

Oral. Pertaining to the mouth. *Oral vibrissae*, a pair of stout bristles at lower edge of face (Diptera, p. 283).

Orbital plate. An area on head next to compound eye (Diptera, p. 283).

Oviparous. Egg-laying.

Oviposit. To lay eggs.

Ovipositor. The egg-laying apparatus (p. 30).

Paedogenesis. *See* p. 150.

Palp. A feelerlike structure borne by the maxillae or labium (p. 30).

Paraproct. One of a pair of lobes located below and on each side of the anus (p. 30).

Parapsidal sutures. A pair of longitudinal sutures on mesonotum (Hymenoptera, p. 327).

Parasite. An animal that lives in or on the body of another animal (its host), at least during part of its life cycle.

Parthenogenesis. *See* p. 38.

Patella. A leg segment between the femur and tibia (chelicerate arthropods).

Pectinate. Bearing processes like the teeth of a comb.

Pedipalps. The pair of appendages (usually feelerlike) just behind the chelicerae (in chelicerate arthropods).

Petiole. A stalk or stem; basal stalk of abdomen in Hymenoptera. *Petiolate*, attached by a stalk or stem. *Petiolate abdomen*, with the basal segment slender and cylindrical, as in Anacharitinae (p. 333).

Pleural. Pertaining to lateral areas of body.

Plumose. Feathery, or bearing many long hairs.

Polyembryony. *See* p. 38.

Posterior. Hind or rear.

Posthumeral bristle. A bristle on outer front surface of thorax, just behind humeral callus (Diptera, p. 287).

Postscutellum. An area just below or behind scutellum (Diptera, p. 287).

Postvertical bristles. A pair of bristles behind ocellar triangle (Diptera, p. 283).

Preapical. Located just before the apex.

Predaceous. Feeding on other animals that are usually smaller or less powerful.

Presutural bristles. Bristles just in front of lateral ends of transverse suture (Diptera, p. 287).

Pro-. A prefix for names of prothoracic structures (*see* p. 33).

Proboscis. The beak (which *see*).

Pronotal comb. A row of strong spines on rear margin of pronotum (Siphonaptera, p. 309).

Propleural bristles. Bristles on propleuron (Diptera, p. 287).

Propodeum. A dorsal area on thorax behind metanotum, actually the 1st abdominal segment, in apocritous Hymenoptera (p. 319).

Proximal. Near body, or the base of an appendage. *Proximad*, toward the base, or the portion nearest body.

Pteropleuron (pl., pteropleura). An area on side of thorax, just below wing base (Diptera, p. 287). *Pteropleural bristles*, a group of bristles on pteropleuron (p. 287).

Ptilinum. *See* p. 282.

Pubescent. Covered with short fine hairs.

Pulvillus (pl., pulvilli). A pad or lobe beneath each tarsal claw (as in Diptera).

Puncture. A tiny pit or depression.

Pupa (pl., pupae). The stage between larva and adult in insects with complete metamorphosis (*see* p. 39).

Pygidium. The last dorsal segment of the abdomen.

Quadrate. Four-sided; square or rectangular.

Radial sector. The posterior of the 2 main branches of the radius (p. 35, *Rs*).

Radius. The longitudinal vein between Sc and M (p. 35).

Recurved. Curved upward or backward.

Reticulate. With a network of ridges or lines.

Scape. The basal segment of an antenna.

Scapula (pl., **scapulae**). An area on mesonotum just toward side from parapsidal suture (Hymenoptera).

Sclerite. A hardened body wall plate, usually bordered by sutures or membranous areas. *Sclerotized*, hardened.

Scraper. The sharpened angle of front wing of a cricket or long-horned grasshopper, a part of the sound-producing mechanism (p. 77).

Scutellum. A dorsal thoracic sclerite (p. 34); in Coleoptera, Hemiptera, and Homoptera the mesoscutellum, a more or less triangular sclerite behind pronotum.

Segment. A subdivision of the body or an appendage, between joints or articulations.

Sensoria (sing., **sensorium**). *See* p. 111.

Sessile. Attached, and not capable of moving from place to place; attached without a stem (petiole).

Seta (pl., **setae**). A bristle. *Setaceous*, bristlelike. *Setate*, with bristles.

Sigmoid. S-shaped.

Simple. Unmodified; not forked, toothed, branched, or divided.

Species. *See* p. 43.

Spindle-shaped. Elongate, cylindrical, tapering at ends.

Spiracle. An external opening of the tracheal system (p. 30). *Spiracular bristle*, one adjacent to a spiracle (Diptera).

Spur. A spine that is usually movable.

Stalked. With a stalk or stemlike base; (of veins) fused together at base.

Sternopleuron (pl., **sternopleura**). A sclerite on side of thorax, just above middle leg (Diptera, p. 287). *Sternopleural bristles*, bristles on sternopleuron (p. 287).

Stigma. A dark spot formed by a thickening of the wing membrane, located in distal part of wing along front edge (Odonata, p. 71, and Hymenoptera, p. 313, *st*).

Striate. With narrow grooves or suturelike lines.

Stridulate. To produce a noise by rubbing 2 surfaces or structures together.

Style. A slender elongate process at apex of antennae (as in snipe flies, p. 275).

Stylus (pl., **styli**). A short, slender, fingerlike process.

Subantennal suture. A suture on face extending downward from base of antenna.

Subapical. Located just before apex.

Subcosta. The longitudinal vein between C and R (p. 35).

Subgenal suture. A horizontal suture on head below gena (p. 30).

Subgenital plate. A platelike structure underlying the genitalia.

Subimago. *See* p. 66.

Subspecies. *See* pp. 43–44.

Supra-alar bristles. A group of bristles on mesonotum just above wing base (Diptera, p. 287).

Suture. A linelike groove in the body wall.

Synonyms. *See* p. 45.

Tarsus (pl., **tarsi**). The part of the leg beyond the tibia, usually consisting of 2–5 subdivisions (p. 34). *Tarsal claw*, a claw at apex of tarsus.

Tegmen (pl., **tegmina**). The thickened front wing of an orthopteran.

Tegula (pl., **tegulae**). A scalelike structure overlying base of front wing (Hymenoptera, p. 319).

Tergum (pl., **terga**). The dorsal surface of an abdominal segment.

Terminal. At the end; at posterior end (of abdomen).

Thorax. The body region behind head which bears legs and wings.

Tibia (pl., **tibiae**). The leg segment between femur and tarsus (p. 34). *Tibial spur*, a large spur or spine on tibia, usually at apex of tibia.

Trachea (pl., **tracheae**). *See* p. 36.

Transverse. Across, or at right angles to longitudinal axis. *Transverse suture*, a suture across mesonotum (Diptera, p. 287).

Triangle. A triangular cell or group of cells in central basal part of wing (Odonata, pp. 71 and 73).

Trochanter. The small leg segment between coxa and femur (p. 34).

Trochantin. A small sclerite in thoracic wall adjacent to base of coxa (as in Coleoptera).

Truncate. Cut off square at end.

Tuberculate. With small rounded protuberances.

Vannal lobe. A lobe in anal area of hind wing, just before end of anal vein (Hymenoptera, p. 313, *vl*).

Vein. A thickened line in wing. *Accessory vein*, the hindmost vein in anal area of front wing (Hymenoptera, p. 313, *ac*). *Anal veins*, longitudinal veins behind Cu (p. 35). *Basal vein*, a more or less transverse vein near middle of front wing (Hymenoptera, p. 313, *bv*). *Brace vein*, a slanting cross vein behind basal end of stigma (Odonata, p. 71). *Humeral vein*, a branch of Sc extending into humeral angle of wing (as in Neuroptera and Lepidoptera). *Intercostal vein*, a longitudinal vein in costal cell (Hymenoptera,

p. 313, *ic*). *Marginal vein*, one on or just inside wing margin; the vein forming posterior side of marginal cell (Hymenoptera, (p. 313, *mv*). *Recurrent vein*, 1 of 2 transverse veins just behind cubital vein (Hymenoptera, p. 313, *rv*). *Spurious vein*, a veinlike thickening between R and M (Syrphidae, p. 281). *Subdiscal* (or *subdiscoidal*) *vein*, the vein along rear side of 3rd discoidal cell (Hymenoptera, p. 313, *sd*). *Submarginal vein*, one just behind front margin of wing (as in Chalcidoidea). *Transverse costal vein*, a cross vein in costal cell (Hymenoptera, p. 313, *tc*). *Transverse cubital vein*, a cross vein between marginal and cubital veins (Hymenoptera, p. 313, *tcb*). *Transverse median vein*, a cross vein between median or discoidal and anal veins (Hymenoptera, p. 313, *tm*).

Ventral. Lower or underneath; pertaining to the underside. *Ventrad*, toward the underside, downward.

Vertex. Top of head, between compound eyes and in front of occipital suture (p. 30).

Vestigial. Small, poorly developed, nonfunctional.

Viviparous. Giving birth to live young, not egg-laying.

References

THE FOLLOWING LIST is designed for those who seek information beyond that given in this book. Although not intended to be complete, it includes some of the more important references under each heading, and the bibliography in each publication will lead to additional literature.

GENERAL

Borror, Donald J., and Dwight M. DeLong. 1970 (3rd ed.). An introduction to the study of insects. New York: Holt, Rinehart and Winston.

Brues, Charles T., Axel L. Melander, and Frank M. Carpenter. 1954. Classification of insects. Bull. Mus. Comp. Zool., Harvard Univ., 73:vi + 1–917.

Jaques, Harry E. 1947 (2nd ed.). How to know the insects. Dubuque, Ia.: Wm. C. Brown Co.

Lutz, Frank E. 1935. Field book of insects. New York: Putnam.

Swain, Ralph B. 1948. The insect guide. New York: Doubleday.

SPECIFIC GROUPS

ARTHROPODS OTHER THAN INSECTS

Baker, Edward W., John H. Camin, Frederick Cunliffe, Tyler A. Woolley, and Conrad E. Yunker. 1958. Guide to the families of mites. Contrib. No. 3, Inst. Acarology, Univ. Maryland.

Comstock, John H., and Willis J. Gertsch. 1940. The spider book. New York: Doubleday.

Kaston, Benjamin J., and Elizabeth Kaston. 1953. How to know the spiders. Dubuque, Ia.: Wm. C. Brown Co.

Miner, Roy W. 1950. Field book of seashore life. New York: Putnam.

(*See also* references under "Aquatic Insects," below.)

AQUATIC INSECTS

Morgan, Ann H. 1930. Field book of ponds and streams. New York: Putnam.

Pennak, Robert W. 1953. Fresh-water invertebrates of the United States. New York: Ronald Press.

Usinger, Robert L. (ed.). 1956. Aquatic insects of California, with keys to North American genera and California species. Berkeley: Univ. California Press.

PROTURA, THYSANURA, AND COLLEMBOLA

Maynard, Elliott A. 1951. A monograph of the Collembola or springtail insects of New York State. Ithaca, N.Y.: Comstock.

Scott, Harold G. 1961. Collembola: pictorial keys to the nearctic genera. Annals Entomol. Soc. Amer., 54:104–113.

Tuxen, S. L. 1964. The Protura. A revision of the species of the world with keys for determination. Paris: Hermann.

EPHEMEROPTERA

Burks, Barnard D. 1953. The mayflies, or Ephemeroptera, of Illinois. Bull. Ill. Natural Hist. Surv., 26: 1–216.

Needham, James G., Jay R. Traver, and Tin-Chi Hsu. 1935. The biology of mayflies. Ithaca, N.Y.: Comstock.

(*See also* references under "Aquatic Insects," p. 373.)

ODONATA

Corbet, Philip S. 1963. A biology of dragonflies. Chicago: Quadrangle Books.

Needham, James G., and Hortense B. Heywood. 1929. A handbook of the dragonflies of North America. Springfield, Ill.: Charles C. Thomas.

Needham, James G., and Minter J. Westfall, Jr. 1955. A manual of the dragonflies of North America (Anisoptera). Los Angeles: Univ. California Press.

Walker, Edmund M. 1953–58. The Odonata of Canada and Alaska. Vol. 1 (1953): General; The Zygoptera — damselflies. Vol. 2 (1958): The Anisoptera — 4 families. Toronto: Univ. Toronto Press.

(*See also* references under "Aquatic Insects," p. 373.)

ORTHOPTERA AND DERMAPTERA

Alexander, Richard D., and Donald J. Borror. 1956. The songs of insects. Boston: Houghton Mifflin (since 1966). A 12-inch LP in the Sounds of Nature series.

Blatchley, Willis S. 1920. Orthoptera of northeastern America. Indianapolis, Ind.: Nature Publishing Co.

Hebard, Morgan. 1934. The Dermaptera and Orthoptera of Illinois. Bull. Ill. Natural Hist. Surv., 20:iv + 125–179.

ISOPTERA

Banks, Nathan, and Thomas E. Snyder. 1920. A revision of the nearctic termites. Bull. No. 108, U.S. Natl. Museum.

Snyder, Thomas E. 1954. Order Isoptera — the termites of the United States and Canada. New York: Natl. Pest Control Assn.

——. 1965. Our native termites. Smiths. Inst. Rept. for 1964, pp. 497–506.

PLECOPTERA

Frison, Theodore H. 1935. The stoneflies, or Plecoptera, of Illinois. Bull. Ill. Natural Hist. Surv., 20:281–471.

——. 1942. Studies of North American Plecoptera, with special reference to the fauna of Illinois. Bull. Ill. Natural Hist. Surv., 22:231–355.

Needham, James G., and Peter W. Claassen. 1925. A monograph of the Plecoptera or stoneflies of America north of Mexico. Publ. No. 2, Thomas Say Foundation.

(*See also* references under "Aquatic Insects," p. 373.)

EMBIOPTERA, ZORAPTERA, AND PSOCOPTERA

Gurney, Ashley B. 1938. A synopsis of the order Zoraptera, with notes on the biology of *Zorotypus hubbardi* Caudell. Proc. Entomol. Soc. Wash., 40:57–87.

Pearman, J. V. 1936. The taxonomy of the Psocoptera; preliminary sketch. Proc. Roy. Entomol. Soc. London, Ser. B, 5:58–62.

Ross, Edward S. 1944. A revision of the Embioptera, or webspinners, of the New World. Proc. U.S. Natl. Museum, 94:401–504.

MALLOPHAGA AND ANOPLURA

Ewing, Henry E. 1929. A manual of external parasites. Springfield, Ill.: Charles C. Thomas.

Ferris, Gordon F. 1951. The sucking lice. Mem. No. 1, Pacific Coast Entomol. Soc.

THYSANOPTERA

Stannard, Lewis J., Jr. 1957. The phylogeny and classification of the North American genera of the suborder Tubulifera (Thysanoptera). Ill. Biol. Monog. No. 25.

———. 1968. The thrips, or Thysanoptera, of Illinois. Bull. Ill. Natural Hist. Surv., 29:vi + 215–552.

HEMIPTERA

Blatchley, Willis S. 1926. Heteroptera or true bugs of eastern North America, with special reference to the faunas of Indiana and Florida. Indianapolis, Ind.: Nature Publishing Co.

(*See also* references under "Aquatic Insects," p. 373.)

HOMOPTERA

DeLong, Dwight M. 1948. The leafhoppers, or Cicadellidae, of Illinois (Eurymelinae — Balcluthinae). Bull. Ill. Natural Hist. Surv., 24:91–376.

Ferris, Gordon F. 1937–53 (6 v.). Atlas of the scale insects of North America. Stanford Univ., Calif.: Stanford Univ. Press.

Hottes, Frederick C., and Theodore H. Frison. 1931. The plant lice, or Aphididae, of Illinois. Bull. Ill. Natural Hist. Surv., 19:121–447.

Metcalf, Zeno P. 1923. Fulgoridae of eastern North America. Jour. Elisha Mitchell Sci. Soc., 38:139–230.

NEUROPTERA

Carpenter, Frank M. 1940. A revision of nearctic Hemerobiidae, Berothidae, Sisyridae, Polystoechotidae, and Dilaridae (Neuroptera). Proc. Amer. Acad. Arts Sci., 74:193–280.

Parfin, Sophy I., and Ashley B. Gurney. 1956. The spongillaflies, with special reference to those of the western hemisphere (Sisyridae, Neuroptera). Proc. U.S. Natl. Museum, 105:421–529.

(*See also* references under "Aquatic Insects," p. 373.)

COLEOPTERA AND STREPSIPTERA

Arnett, Ross H., Jr. 1968. The beetles of the United States (a manual for identification). Ann Arbor, Mich.: The Amer. Entomol. Inst.

Blatchley, Willis S. 1910. An illustrated and descriptive catalogue of the Coleoptera or beetles (exclusive of the Rhynchophora) known to occur in Indiana. Indianapolis, Ind.: Nature Publishing Co.

——, and Charles W. Leng. 1916. Rhynchophora or weevils of northeastern North America. Indianapolis, Ind.: Nature Publishing Co.

Bohart, Richard M. 1941. A revision of the Strepsiptera with special reference to the species of North America. Calif. Univ. Pub. Entomol., 7:91–160.

Dillon, Elizabeth S., and Lawrence S. Dillon. 1961. A manual of common beetles of eastern North America. Evanston, Ill.: Row, Peterson & Co.

Edwards, J. Gordon. 1949. Coleoptera or beetles east of the Great Plains. Ann Arbor, Mich.: Edwards.

Jaques, Harry E. 1951. How to know the beetles. Dubuque, Ia.: Wm. C. Brown Co.

(*See also* references under "Aquatic Insects," p. 373.)

MECOPTERA AND TRICHOPTERA

Carpenter, Frank M. 1931. Revision of nearctic Mecoptera. Bull. Mus. Comp. Zool., Harvard Univ., 72:205–277.

Ross, Herbert H. 1944. The caddis flies or Trichoptera of Illinois. Bull. Ill. Natural Hist. Surv. 23:1–326.

LEPIDOPTERA

Forbes, William T. M. 1923–54. Lepidoptera of New York and neighboring states. Cornell Univ. Agric. Expt. Sta. Mem. 68 (1923), 274 (1948), and 329 (1954).

Holland, William J. 1949. The butterfly book. New York: Doubleday.

——. 1968. The moth book. New York: Dover.

Klots, Alexander B. 1951. A field guide to the butterflies. Boston: Houghton Mifflin.

DIPTERA

Curran, Charles H. 1965 (2nd rev. ed.). The families and genera of North American Diptera. Woodhaven, N.Y.: Henry Tripp.

Stone, Alan, et al. 1965. A catalogue of the Diptera of America north of Mexico. U.S.D.A. Agric. Handbook No. 276.

(*See also* references under "Aquatic Insects," p. 373.)

SIPHONAPTERA

Ewing, Henry E., and Irving Fox. 1943. The fleas of North America. U.S.D.A. Misc. Pub. No. 500.

Holland, George P. 1949. The Siphonaptera of Canada. Tech. Bull. No. 70, Canada Dept. Agric.

HYMENOPTERA

Muesebeck, Carl F. W., et al. 1951. Hymenoptera of America north of Mexico; synoptic catalogue. U.S.D.A. Agric. Monog. No. 2. First Supplement, 1958; Second Supplement, 1967, by Karl V. Krombein et al.

Index

THIS INDEX includes the names of insects and other animals and of insect-borne diseases mentioned in this *Field Guide;* the location of accounts of various subjects may be found in the Contents, and in some cases in the Glossary. Numbers in **boldface** refer to illustrations. Where two or more page references to the text occur, the asterisk after a number indicates the main text description. The index also includes synonyms, other spellings, and groups sometimes recognized as distinct but not mentioned in this book.

$\mathcal{U}$
U'
u
U_1
U_2

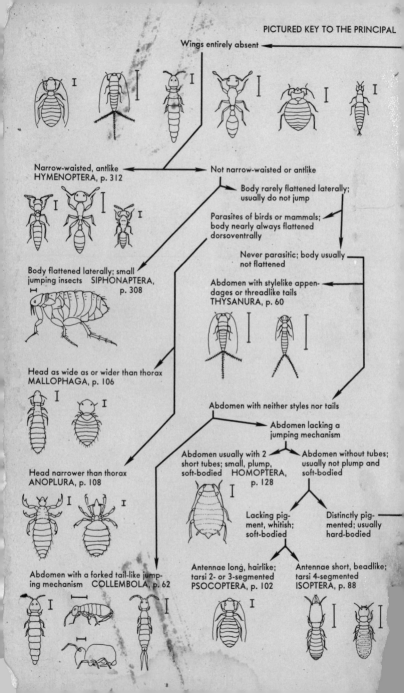

Wings entirely absent

Narrow-waisted, antlike
HYMENOPTERA, p. 312

Not narrow-waisted or antlike

Body rarely flattened laterally;
usually do not jump

Parasites of birds or mammals;
body nearly always flattened
dorsoventrally

Body flattened laterally; small
jumping insects SIPHONAPTERA,
p. 308

Never parasitic; body usually
not flattened

Abdomen with stylelike appendages or threadlike tails
THYSANURA, p. 60

Head as wide as or wider than thorax
MALLOPHAGA, p. 106

Abdomen with neither styles nor tails

Abdomen lacking a
jumping mechanism

Head narrower than thorax
ANOPLURA, p. 108

Abdomen usually with 2
short tubes; small, plump,
soft-bodied HOMOPTERA,
p. 128

Abdomen without tubes;
usually not plump and
soft-bodied

Lacking pig-
ment, whitish;
soft-bodied

Distinctly pig-
mented; usually
hard-bodied

Abdomen with a forked tail-like jumping mechanism COLLEMBOLA, p. 62

Antennae long, hairlike;
tarsi 2- or 3-segmented
PSOCOPTERA, p. 102

Antennae short, beadlike;
tarsi 4-segmented
ISOPTERA, p. 88